Reviews & Praise for Tatae's Promise

This moving and suspenseful book tells the story of Hinda Mondlak, who escaped from Auschwitz with her sister. Based on hours of her taped testimony, it describes in rich detail every phase of the persecutions she endured—Nazi occupation, the village ghetto, the death journey to Auschwitz, beatings, illness, starvation, escape, and then a harrowing flight from Russian troops. Saved occasionally through the unexpected kindness of others and always by her own courage, Hinda is vividly alive in this reweaving of her memories. A memorable story of resilience and enduring love.
—**Betty Sue Flowers, PhD,** Professor Emeritus UT-Austin, former Director, Johnson Presidential Library, and editor, *Joseph Campbell and the Power of Myth*

Hinda Mondlak's story is nothing short of extraordinary. To survive the selections in Auschwitz, followed by more than two years of brutal incarceration in this infamous factory of death, and then to… successfully escape…is a testament to the truly remarkable spirt of Hinda Mondlak.
—**Eli Rubenstein,** Religious Leader, Congregation Habonim Toronto National Director, March of the Living; Canada Director, International March of the Living; Appointed to the "Order of Canada" by The Governor General of Canada

The challenge you will have, as I did as I read it, is putting the book down. I just had to know what was going to happen next! Sherry Maysonave and Moises Goldman weave the stories of four main characters, each a separate piece of cloth, into a warm, beautiful quilt that seemed unthinkable to construct. Each story comes to life from the combination of the recorded oral history of the main character, Hinda Mondlak, and the engaging writing style of the authors.

As a student of the Holocaust and one who interviewed Holocaust survivors for Steven Spielberg's Survivors of the Shoah History Foundation, I thought I had heard it all. Now, I know I was wrong. This is not your ordinary Holocaust story. Do yourself a favor. Find out for yourself.
—**Mike O'Krent,** Founder and CEO, LifeStories Alive, LLC, Holocaust Survivors Interviewer for Steven Spielberg's Survivors of the Shoah History Foundation

The book is a testament to the resilience of the human spirit and the power of love — and the will to live to heal even the deepest wounds. Hinda's charismatic and relatable figure will resonate with readers from all backgrounds as she relentlessly struggles to preserve her faith and fulfill her father's promise: You will live; You will tell.

—Philip Klein, DMD, Chairman and President of the Board, Viva Learning, LLC

The book is written in an extraordinary and sensitive way. Salomon Mondlak, father of Hinda, asked Hinda to promise him that she would be both mother and father to her younger sisters... He promised her that she would survive and tell about the family's tragic fate.

During all my life, I was exposed to the Holocaust horrors with ongoing descriptions and testimonials. Every year, Israel honors Holocaust Memorial Day with a shutdown. The media tunes up to listen to testimonies of survivors. Every year each testimony is carefully selected and transmitted. I expose myself to them year after year. **BUT NOTHING compares to Hinda's testimony in this book.**

—Victor Yagoda, Deputy Director General, United Israel Appeal of Canada, Israel Office, Retired

In this great book, *Tatae's Promise,* Hinda Mondlak has three goals that she must accomplish, at all costs, and she does it with tremendous determination and resilience... she was one of only 200 people, out of millions, who successfully escaped Auschwitz.

Hinda understands... that if she does not fulfill her father's wish, she not only would fail him, but she would also fail humankind, by depriving all of us of knowing the terrible reality and incredible persecution that she endured because one fellow human can cause such on another fellow human for no reason other than they believe that there are superior and inferior races, and that handicapped people don't have the right to live.

This book should be read by anyone who wants to grasp the unfathomable suffering that Hitler and his followers intentionally caused; but most importantly, it should be read by the people who, in spite of massive evidence, still have the audacity to deny that the Holocaust occurred.

—Dr. Arturo Constantiner Sourasky, Board of Governors, Tel Aviv University and Tel-Aviv Sourasky Medical Center

A page turner, this book would not let me go. I could not put it down. I've read many Holocaust survival stories, and none can rival Tatae's Promise. It is engaging and beautifully written, even amidst the horror. At times, I was aghast and heartbroken, but, in the end, I felt incredibly inspired.
—**Carla Meaux,** Retired Insurance Executive

Tatae's Promise **grips your soul from page one,** telling the harrowing true-life story of the Mondlak family's unimaginable suffering under the depraved Nazi regime… This stark and riveting account of young Hinda Mondlak's unyielding determination to survive and ultimately escape Auschwitz with her younger sister… is by turns gut-wrenching, heartbreaking, and inspiring.

It's relevance today is more than historical as my recent visit to Rwanda's genocide museum makes poignantly clear. More than three-quarters of a century after Hinda's escape, millions of living people suffer under the repugnant brutalities of dictatorships, wars, ethnic cleansing, and hate-mongering. We must not avert our eyes from inhumanity, and we must never shrink from our obligation to tell.
—**John E. Shephard, Jr.,** Retired Senior Executive, Northrop Grumman and ITT-Exelis, U.S. Army Gulf War Veteran

How does one live by the fifth commandment and honor one's mother? This accounting…brings Hinda Mondlak's life to each of us as an offering of love. This recounting is at turns, tender, defiant, staggering, and hopeful… What sacrifices do our parents make for us so that we can live? Let us not forget, so we can know our parents as heroes. *Tatae's Promise* **is a tribute that penetrates our heart deeply.** Let us learn this story and teach it to our own children.
—**Neil F. Blumofe,** Senior Rabbi, Congregation Agudas Achim, Austin, Texas

This powerful, page-turning book is the story about man's capacity for evil and the triumph of the human spirit to endure and survive. Based on the true lives of Goldman's parents and their journeys through the ghettos of Poland and the Nazi concentration camps of Auschwitz and Buchenwald, *Tatae's Promise* is their gripping story of faith, family and tenacity which guides them through the inhumanity of the camps, their daring escape, and their paths to freedom."
—**Wheeler Chapman,** President, Chapman Financial Group

The exploration of one's roots offers the opportunity to not only identify relatives, but to understand the context in which they lived. We are gratified to see researchers such as Dr. Moises Goldman recording their family stories [*Tatae's Promise*] that can be accessible for future generations, and which can serve as a **template for other Jewish genealogists** to follow.
—Jack Kliger, President & CEO, and **Mr. Avraham Groll,** Vice President of JewishGen, Museum of Jewish Heritage—A Living Memorial to the Holocaust

Life takes many turns. A young Jewish girl… about to turn 16 years old, lived a happy family life before the war… This historical fiction story is told in such a manner that the reader just can't put the book down. I spent many evenings reading until 2 a.m. **Truly a remarkable read. A 10 on a scale of 1-10!**
—Lois Reiswig, President Maui Arts League, Retired IBM Executive

A masterpiece. The detailed information captured about the characters, especially Hinda, makes her, the other characters, and events very Real and Believable. We can never learn too much about the impact on the millions of lives systematically Murdered during the Holocaust.
—Wade Monroe, Retired Committee Member, Austin Jewish Foundation, Shalon Austin; Retired CFO, Trilogy Software

Based on the true story of a
young woman's escape from Auschwitz

TATAE'S PROMISE

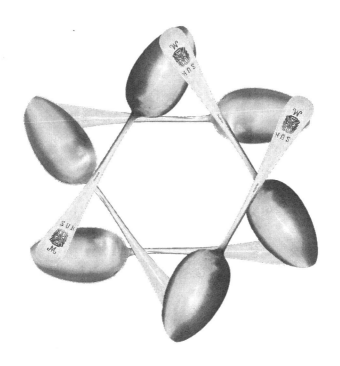

SHERRY | MOISES J
MAYSONAVE | GOLDMAN

DartFrog Blue

Book Cover Design by Larry Jolly, founder, Jolly Designs
Book Interior Design by Rebecca Finkel, F + P Graphic Design

DartFrog Blue
PO Box 867 | Manchester, VT 05254
DartFrog Blue is a division of DartFrog Books
DartFrogBooks.com

Hardcover ISBN: 978-1-959096-94-8
Hardcover dust jacket ISBN: 978-1-959096-95-5
Paperback ISBN: 978-1-959096-96-2
Ebook ISBN: 978-1-959096-97-9

LCCN: 2023942942

Printed in the United States of America

In memoriam,
I dedicate this book to my mother, Hinda:
My best friend and my guiding light, FOREVER.
— Moises J. Goldman, Ph.D.

With great love, I dedicate this book
to Hinda Mondlak Goldman:
An amazing woman, whom I admire.
Thank you for whispering in my ear the past four years.
— Sherry Maysonave

Preface

On May 5, 1985, my mother, Hinda Mondlak Goldman, who survived years of heinous abuse at the Auschwitz concentration camp, died in my arms. Coincidentally, on that same day, United States President Ronald Reagan and German Chancellor Helmut Kohl appeared at the Bergen-Belsen concentration camp in Germany. In his speech,* President Reagan said:

"Chancellor Kohl and honored guest [sic], this painful walk into the past has done much more than remind us of the war that consumed the European Continent. What we have seen makes unforgettably clear that no one of the rest of us can fully understand the enormity of the feelings carried by the victims of these camps. The survivors carry a memory beyond anything that we can comprehend. The awful evil started by one man, an evil that victimized all the world with its destruction, was uniquely destructive of the millions forced into the grim abyss of these camps. Here lie people—Jews—whose death was inflicted for no reason other than their very existence.... For year after year, until that man and his evil were destroyed, hell yawned forth its awful contents. People were brought here for no other purpose but to suffer and die—to go unfed when hungry, uncared for when sick, tortured when the whim struck, and left to have misery consume them when all there was around them was misery.... And then, rising above all this cruelty, out of this tragic and nightmarish time, beyond the anguish, the pain and the suffering for all time, we can and must pledge: NEVER AGAIN."

My mother's last wish was for me, her son, Moises J. Goldman, to tell her horrific and triumphant story in a public way. She, too, was adamant that such horror should never again occur anywhere in the world, and she hoped her story would move people to support that aim.

In 1984, my mother was diagnosed with advanced lung cancer. Too weak to write and knowing that she did not have many months left to live, she recorded eleven tapes, forty-five minutes each, describing the war's impact upon her life. In those tapes, she spoke of her father, whom she called *Tatae*—a Yiddish form of the word Father—and how, moments before being murdered by the Gestapo, he had written a note to her, leaving her with his blessing and a promise: You will live; you will tell. These six words rang in my mother's ears and beat in her heart for the rest of her life. She wanted—with all her soul—to honor her father's last behest.

You may ask, *"How did she?"* Painfully, I will tell you.

It has been over thirty-five years since my mother passed away, and while I had attempted to listen to the tapes many times, hearing her voice and story always turned into such a heart-wrenching experience for me that I would have to stop. I could not finish them. You see, my mother meant the absolute world to me. She was my biggest fan and my best friend in every sense of the word. I knew that someday, if I were to fulfill her final wish, I would have to overcome my grief and listen to the entirety of the tapes. But after trying time after time, I just couldn't. Instead, I threw myself into my work as an aerospace scientist, entrepreneur, and businessman.

I do not know if destiny played a role, but after I moved to Austin, Texas in 2018, I met a couple, Sherry and Stephen Maysonave, whom my wife, Terry, and I befriended. Sherry is an accomplished author, and her husband, Stephen, an accomplished businessman. During our many visits and outings together, I told Sherry some of the stories my mom had told me about her Holocaust experiences. As she listened to them, Sherry expressed her abhorrence of what my mother had endured. I inquired about her interest in co-authoring a book with me. Sherry replied, "I feel the pulse of my soul in all this. I would be honored to write your mother's story. It *must* be told. Such atrocities upon the Jews must *never* happen again."

So now *I was on the hook*; no more excuses or reasons for not listening to the tapes my mother had entrusted me with. How could I not go forward? Sherry has authored award-winning books, and her writing style is so detailed and marvelous. My decision was made. Yet, admittedly, it was personally traumatic and extremely painful for me to listen to and transcribe more than eight hours of my mother's recorded material. The process proved complicated, too, as she had spoken in multiple languages, primarily Spanish and Yiddish, which I had to translate to English.

As I finished the initial few tapes, I got up from my office chair and went to my wife. I said, "Honey, I do not know if I can do it; this is going to kill me."

My wife answered, "It better not; your mother lived long enough to tell her story, so you had better do the same."

My grandfather's promise to my mother then became *my* promise to her. I have fulfilled that promise with this book, which tells my mother's story of growing up in Poland, born ninth of eleven into a religious and devout family, to her experiencing cruel persecution and deep loss due to Hitler's Nazi regime, World War II, and its far-reaching aftereffects. The war stole my mother's home, her family, and what should have been happy teenage years. Even still, she not only survived Auschwitz but at the age of twenty-three, she escaped. *And* she got her younger sister out with her.

I proudly say that my mother was extraordinarily bold and brave. I hope these pages of *Tatae's Promise* will fill you with awe of her incredible spirit and triumph.

Moises J. Goldman, PhD

Source for President Reagan's Speech:
Ronald Reagan Presidential Library and Museum Archives, Remarks at Commemorative Ceremony at Bergen-Belsen Concentration Camp in the Federal Republic of Germany. Public Papers of the President. Portions of the speech were omitted as noted with ellipses.

1

A Silent Scream

September 1939 | Zieluń, German-occupied Poland

Black smoke roiled in the village air dense with soot and cinders. Trembling, eighteen-year-old Hinda Mondlak watched the flames rise higher, fiery fingers reaching toward heaven, lighting the starless night sky. A northern wind emboldened the blaze and whipped her dark russet hair, flogging her face as if punishing her further. Hinda stood next to her father, who had his arm around her shoulder, holding her close to him. His presence usually radiated safety, but tonight, it did not stop her shivering nor the tears slipping from her azure eyes.

Hinda's feet shifted, registering the earth's convulsive vibration as the ground under them quivered. Her chest heaved, and her breath slowed. Her hand flew to her mouth. The massive roof and walls crashed downward, crumbling with loud cracks that echoed, multiplying the eerie sounds. Her beloved synagogue disappeared in the blaze.

Government orders. Not Polish ones, but official Nazi commands: Burn all synagogues in German-occupied areas of Poland.

Her heart quaking, Hinda gazed upward to her father—Salomon Mondlak, who was a tall and strikingly handsome man. He appeared remarkably calm in the light of the roaring fire. Yet his face had turned ashen. *Ash,* Hinda thought. Their temple was soon to be nothing but rubble and gray ash. *Is that my fate too?* She pinched the skin on her arm, examining its fragility.

German soldiers marched near them, their pounding boots loud exclamations. One soldier cocked his gun in their direction and yelled, "Go home, dirty Jews, go home."

Hinda remembered when the Nazis had first occupied the village of Zieluń. German soldiers had come to their home, to all the homes, assuring the townsfolk that their lives would not change, only their government. A lie, a colossal lie.

Without a word, and with his head held high, Hinda's father—*Tatae,* as she called him—tucked her arm into his in the most gentlemanly fashion and began walking away as if they were strolling in a serene, picturesque park.

Hinda's back now turned toward the burning synagogue, she felt the heat of the immense blaze spread through her dorsal vertebrae. The heat penetrated her very bones, which then crackled with warnings and foreboding. Her every instinct proclaimed that soon she would witness another Gestapo-ordered fire—one even more personal. A silent scream screeched through her entire body.

Far, Far Away

May 4, 1934 | Zieluń, Poland

At half past four in the morning, chirping birds awakened Hinda. She nestled into the soft mattress and pulled the covers over her head. A rhapsodic feeling curled her lips upward into a smile. Today, she turned thirteen. Yet the birds' melody would be her only birthday song.

Intrusive sounds, loud thumps and thwacks, came through the walls, drowning out the birds' warbles. Hinda bolted upright in her bed. While her large family—eleven children, seven boys and four girls—made significant noise when they were arising to start the day, these were not their typical early morning sounds.

Hinda glanced around the room she shared with her three sisters. Fanny was the oldest; her bed was empty. Hinda's younger sisters, Rachel and Sara, still slept.

Once again, abnormal noises from the other room startled Hinda. Deciding that something big was happening, she leapt from her bed, ran her fingers through her hair, and straightened her nightclothes.

Entering the main living room, Hinda gasped. "What? This is the day?"

Trunks and valises littered the floor. Fanny and her six older brothers—Shio, Leon, Isaac, Manuel, Jack, and Zalel—were dressed in their best clothing. Fanny looked elegant in her navy suit and matching hat and gloves, though the buttons on her suit were faded. The brothers' clothing, hand-me-down jackets and pants, was a bit ill-fitting, their suits either too big or too snug.

Jack strode over to Hinda, making mock boxing movements with his hands and feet. "Sorry that it's today, your birthday, but our passports and tickets suddenly came through late yesterday. This is our only chance." He cuffed her arm, then leaned in, and kissed her cheek. "Can you wake up Rachel, Sara, and Joel? I would like to see them before we leave."

Hinda hesitated, wanting to stand close to Jack another minute. But her father suddenly announced, "It's time to load up. Trains to Mława run on schedule."

Hinda rushed to knock on Joel's door, then to get her younger sisters. In the girls' bedroom, Rachel, who was seven, was already up and dressed. Three-year-old Sara, who clutched a cloth doll to her chest, still lay in her bed. Her eyes were wide open, and her mouth was set in a decided pout. Hinda scooped Sara and the doll into her arms and motioned for Rachel to come with her. Two steps into the hallway, they collided with Joel, who was in his first year of high school. In the order of the eleven children, Joel was just one year older than Hinda.

His eyes barely open, his raven hair wild on his head, Joel groaned. "It's not even five o'clock yet. Why did you wake me?"

"The older ones got their travel papers. They're leaving in a few minutes," Hinda replied. In her arms, little Sara squirmed upon hearing the news. She contorted her body this way, then that, and tossed her head back. Unable to safely hold her little sister when she was in the throes of an emotional spell, Hinda set Sara on the rug.

That is when Hinda saw her mother, Esther, who sat in the corner, a handkerchief to her nose. Esther's shoulders shook, and whimpers escaped from her mouth. She appeared wrung out, as if she had been crying all night.

Amidst the commotion, Salomon, Hinda's father, spoke calmly, but authoritatively. "We must be on our way." To his wife, he urged, "Esther, start saying your farewells. Time is short."

Beginning with her sons, Esther's body fell onto each one. She hugged them, patted their shoulders and their faces. Between cries and expressions of love, Esther pleaded with them to stay. When she came to Jack, she sobbed uncontrollably.

Hinda had *never* seen her mother so distraught. She looked frail and sick, whereas before, she had always appeared sturdy, strong, and uniquely beautiful.

Salomon went to his wife. He stroked her sable-colored tresses; his thumb gently slid over her silky white cheek. He then cupped her face in his hands and peered into her wide-set green eyes. "Esther, it's their freedom, their destiny. Let them go. Let them find safety and better fortunes."

Her chin quivering, Esther attempted to stand erect and compose herself.

"Come now. Let's go outside and give them a proper send off," Salomon encouraged. As he held Esther's hand, guiding her out the door, he tapped Hinda on the shoulder. "Try to smile and wish them well."

With Joel following behind her, Hinda led Rachel into the front yard. On the road, a man waited with a horse-drawn wagon. A friend from synagogue and a nearby farmer, he had readily agreed to use his wagon to transport the travel trunks to the train station.

Hinda had known this day was coming. Even still, she felt ill prepared. She remembered the family meeting that her father had called this past February. His usual serene face had worn a tormented expression when he announced that it was prudent for the older siblings, those who had graduated high school, to leave Poland and seek better lives and safety in North America. On that very day, he stated, each one of the seven oldest had applied for travel papers. Salomon had emphasized that it could be as early as the following week, or it could be months, before their papers were granted or denied. But if approval papers came in, he had said, they would have to leave immediately.

In that same family meeting, Hinda's brother, Jack, who had a keen interest in politics, had then explained that, in addition to Poland's depressed economy, alarming events were occurring in nearby Germany. He rose from his chair at the dining room table, where the family had gathered, and further explained, "One year ago, in January, a man named Adolph Hitler was appointed chancellor in Germany. He's a leader in the Nazi party and has a reputation for being prejudiced against non-Aryan people." Jack looked around the table, eyeing his family members. He pointed his index finger and swept it around the group. He then loudly exclaimed, "That's people like *us!*"

Shifting nervously in her chair, Hinda noted individual reactions. Esther looked questioningly at Salomon. He nodded to her, silently saying yes, it's true. Some of the older brothers shook their heads with contempt. Joel rubbed the back of his neck, appearing disturbed. Young Rachel rested her head on Hinda's shoulder. Fanny looked down at her skirt, and began picking at the raised nubs of the tweed fabric.

Fisting both hands, Jack continued, "Within months, Hitler began using the power of his office to openly attack Jews. Yes, Jews!" Sighing heavily, Jack asked, "Do you want to hear specifics?"

Salomon leaned forward, urging Jack to continue. He said, "Yes, please give details. I know about most of this, but the others do not. It's important that our family be well-informed."

Speaking with moving fervency, Jack spelled out the frightening facts. "On April 1, the Nazi regime declared a nationwide, one-day boycott of Jewish businesses and shops. Then, just one week later, on April 7, Nazi officials expelled Jews from Germany's Professional Civil Service." Jack's eyebrows shot upward in concern as he explained, "This means that Jews employed by the German government or state-run departments, including Jewish teachers, state-hospital doctors and nurses, government lawyers, and administrative staff, were all dismissed from their jobs."

Hinda watched Jack's face as he talked. He was clearly upset, but his face blanched pale when he shared another of Hitler's anti-Jewish actions.

Still standing up, Jack straightened his shoulders as if steeling them. He resumed, "Then, one month later, on May 10, the Nazi regime, under the leadership of Adolph Hitler and another Nazi bigwig, Joseph Goebbels—Germany's propaganda minister—issued a mandate for thousands of books to be burned. Selected books that they considered non-German and not aligning with Nazi philosophy were all torched." Intently, Jack looked around the table, checking the response of the group. He then added, "Do you understand that included *Jewish* texts?" His eyes glazed with worry, Jack glanced heavenward and then said, "And get this. Goebbels had the audacity to make this declaration in his speech on the night of the book burning: 'The age of Jewish intellectual dominance has ended. It has gone up in flames.'"

Recoiling, the older brothers pounded their fists on the table so loudly that the noise awakened little Sara from the other room. Her screeches echoed throughout the house. In response, Esther started to rise from her chair, but Rachel leapt up and rushed toward the door. "Mommy, you stay. I'm really sleepy, so I'll go and lie down with Sara."

Swallowing hard, Jack waited for Rachel to leave the room. Then, he said, "Please indulge me just one more thing. I recently read a book by poet, Heinrich Heine, and he wrote, 'Where they have burned books, they will end in burning human beings.'"

Everyone gasped. Knots formed in Hinda's stomach. Searching the faces of her parents, Hinda saw not just concern, she saw flat-out fear. She then understood why her parents were willing to split the family and to get their older children not only out of Poland, but out of Europe.

When the final travel trunk was hoisted into the wagon, one of the horses snorted and neighed. The noise brought Hinda back to the reality of the present moment. She squinted her eyes at the scene on the dirt road in front of her home. *My family. Over half of my family is leaving, and they're going far, far away.*

On the street, Jack set down his suitcase. His index finger punched the air repeatedly, pointing to Hinda in an exaggerated manner. Silently, he mouthed the words: I love you. Hinda pursed her lips sweetly against her hand and then flung the air kiss toward Jack. She then tried to coax her lips into a smile, but sadness pushed them sideways as she choked back a sob.

Sidling closer to Hinda, Joel muttered, "I wish I were leaving with them." He thrust his hands inside his pockets and cast his eyes down at the grass.

Hinda leaned her head against Joel's shoulder. Then, she gazed across the lawn, checking on her mother, who clutched little Sara tightly in her arms. Torrents of tears pelted Esther's face and dripped from her chin.

Sighing, Hinda inched closer to Rachel, who was weeping audibly and wringing her hands in her skirt, wrinkling and wadding the fabric. Hinda placed her hand on Rachel's shoulder, hoping to assuage her little sister's angst and to find comfort for herself.

The man with the wagon whistled to the horses, and they clomped down the road. The older brothers turned and waved heartily as they walked away. Fanny stared straight ahead and just kept on walking.

After a few steps, Salomon stopped. He called out to Esther and the four remaining children on the lawn, "When they get settled, we will try to get out, too, and join them." He looked upward to the sky streaked with clouds. "God willing, we *will* see them all again."

Suddenly, it felt as if boulders sat atop Hinda's shoulders and were crushing inward on her heart. Her cherished family. Would they ever all be together again? The answer she heard reverberating inside quickened her pulse. Hinda clasped Rachel's hand. Gripping her sister's palm against her palm, skin to skin, Hinda silently mourned the ache that was taking root deep in her soul.

3

The Bubbling Wkra

A farming community, Zieluń was dubbed a *shtetl* because of its proportionately large Jewish population. This morning, on the main street of the village, knots of people huddled together here and there. They spoke in low voices.

Hinda departed from the small grocery, and her skin broke out in chills. The once refreshing village air was now thick with fear. Whispers of *war* crowded the atmosphere as if a dense fog had moved in and cloaked the peaceful beauty —verdant fields, lush forests, and magnificent snow-capped mountains— surrounding the scenic village.

Hinda shepherded her younger sisters, Rachel, who was eleven, and Sara, seven, down the street. The grocery bag, crammed with fresh turnips, carrots, and cabbages, weighed heavily on her arm. Nearing seventeen years old, Hinda was her mother's main support now that the only kids at home were Joel, Rachel, Sara, and her. Memories—of the day, now four years ago, when seven of her siblings departed for foreign lands—flashed through her mind. Saying good-bye to them had been traumatic for the entire family, but it was especially agonizing for her mother. For the remainder of that day, whatever chore her mother was performing, Hinda had heard her mother intoning prayers for the family to be reunited. Hinda's faith was her second skin, yet she had felt unable to honestly articulate such prayers. Her instincts shouted that her mother's petitions to God were futile.

"Hinda, you are *blessed* with good instincts," her mother had told her since she was ten. "You must always trust yourself."

At times, this thing called *good instincts* felt like a blessing to Hinda. Other times, it provided such a stark view of reality that it caused her angst. Esther had also claimed that Hinda's older brother, Jack, was gifted with exceptional instincts. Wishing she could talk with Jack about such things, Hinda wondered if intuition had helped him get along in life, had guided him, and given him confidence as he found his way in a new land.

Last year, word had come in a letter from Jack that Fanny had settled in New York City, and the other brothers and he had all gone to Mexico City. He relayed that they had met a man on the ship to New York who talked about the numerous job opportunities in Mexico City, particularly in the textile industry. Jack reported that, indeed, all the brothers had found secure employment there. Shio, Leon, Isaac, and Zalel were all working in textiles. Manuel was a Hebrew teacher. And Jack had landed an excellent job in journalism.

Hinda pondered her older siblings' choices. New York, Mexico City. Such foreign spheres. Worlds away from Poland. From threats of war. They were the lucky ones, she decided. Abruptly, she was jolted from her reverie when she felt multiple tugs on her skirt. She looked down to see Rachel peering upward at her.

"Can we go to the river after lunch?" Rachel asked.

Hinda sighed at the thought of the river—the bubbling Wkra located on the outskirts of Zieluń. "What a lovely idea. Let's get these vegetables home, and then we'll ask Mommy."

Perhaps, at the river, Hinda could escape her instincts that augured more disruption and heartbreak for her family.

Filling their baskets with mushrooms, Hinda and Rachel scampered through the forest on the way to the river. Feeling free, they danced and skipped among the trees. Hinda had been relieved that her mother had told Sara to stay at home—an unusual occurrence. Not taking it lightly, Sara had fussed, stomped, cried, and begged, but her mother remained adamant that Hinda and Rachel go alone and enjoy the river.

Responsible for the care of her youngest sister, Hinda had become Sara's second mother—in charge of bathing her, dressing her, brushing her thick hair, and teaching her reading and arithmetic. In contrast, her relationship with Rachel was not so maternal. With Rachel, who was six years younger than Hinda and quite mature for her age, she shared a camaraderie, a deep bond that connected them to a powerful force, one even beyond genetic sisterhood.

Hinda's basket now brimming with mushrooms, she eyed the flowing water of the river. It beckoned. "Our work is done, Rachel. Let's go enjoy the river."

Rachel found her spot at the top of the riverbank. She had brought a small notepad and colored pencils to sketch the birds that inhabited the lush foliage along the Wkra, varying species singing their cheerful songs that harmonized with the river's gurgling. Nature's symphony.

Hinda stretched out on the low riverbank. Daring to remove her boots, she dangled her feet in the water. It swished around her toes, tickling her. She reveled in the feeling of the grass and the earth on her back. Her proximity to the water and its bubbling sounds were soothing balms, medicine for her anxious heart. Since childhood, when she had played games among the trees and on the riverbank with her siblings and friends, the Wkra River had been her bliss, her rapturous place. And now, it was only at the river that she could cease worrying and not hear the words *War! War!* reverberating in the very air and in her bones. At the river, her world felt safe. She could relax, be a teenage girl unleashing her vivid imagination, dreaming of true love and a grand life.

Later, when Hinda and Rachel returned home, the happy carefree mood at the Wkra was soon dispelled. Her father sat at the kitchen table talking earnestly with their brother, Joel, who was in his last year of high school. Joel was a strapping young man who had broad shoulders, black hair, and bright eyes that changed from blue to green, depending upon what color he wore.

A letter from the Polish army, recruiting Joel to serve, lay on the table. Salomon picked it up and shook the letter for emphasis. "This is a solicitation, not an official order. You must finish high school first. Education is your ultimate worth."

Joel sighed in relief. "Father, I have no desire to enlist. I want most to continue my education, but I'm scared. The school superintendent says that they may come for us boys, force us to serve."

Upon hearing Joel's words, Hinda winced. She remembered him wishing he could leave Poland when the older brothers and Fanny did. The hair on Hinda's arm prickled. It stood straight up as if an invisible comb had raked it upward.

4

The Mandate

April 1939 | Zieluń, Poland

The spring rain fell in big droplets, a sign of a potential storm. Salomon Mondlak donned his raincoat.

At the door, Hinda hugged him good-bye. "Tatae, be safe in the rain. Wait. Don't you want your rain boots?" She looked up into her father's sky blue eyes and felt such pride. Just the day before, a neighbor had said that she bore a close resemblance to her father. Applause to her ears. She hoped to be like him in all ways, not physical traits alone. His reputation as a wise, kind man was widespread, even beyond Zieluń.

"Rain boots. That's a fine idea, Hinda."

Just then, a businessman from the village came to the door to speak to Salomon. The man, his mouth set in a scowl, explained he'd had a disturbing dispute with another merchant.

A scholar and expert in the Talmud—the collective text of Rabbinic Judaism, both law and tradition—Salomon Mondlak was known as a theological leader. It was not surprising that Jews from Zieluń and other nearby *shtetls* came seeking his counsel as the Talmud was deemed *the* central guide for rituals and for daily life.

After pulling on his rain boots, Salomon leaned in and kissed Hinda's cheek. "Have a good day, my dear daughter."

Taking his umbrella, Salomon asked the man to walk with him as they talked. Before the two men arrived at the *yeshiva,* the religious school, where Salomon worked, they had agreed upon the solution to the merchants' quarrel. Their conversation had turned to war. News had come that in Mława, the largest town near to Zieluń, the Polish army was amassing to defend Poland's borders against a German invasion.

Returning home that evening, Salomon shed his raincoat and presented an envelope to his wife, one bearing an official seal of the Polish government.

Esther searched her husband's face before taking the envelope. Hands shaking, she removed the letter and quickly scanned it. When she looked back to her husband, her eyes expressed both relief and alarm. She exclaimed, "Praise God they're not taking Joel, but how can I possibly have everything ready so soon?"

Salomon took his wife in his arms and whispered, "We can manage this." He placed the letter on the table. "Call the children in."

When the family was assembled around the kitchen table, Hinda noticed immediately that her father's demeanor was more serious than when they gathered at the table for him to read a selected story, which he did every evening.

His eyebrows furrowed, and Salomon announced that an official communication from the Polish government had arrived today. He held up the letter and proceeded to read it aloud: "The German military is advancing on the borders of Poland. To defend the country against a takeover, a mobilization of the Polish military is in full operation. The Polish government hereby issues orders for select citizens of Zieluń to provide shelter to the soldiers who are being assigned there."

Salomon paused to clear his throat. He then read the final sentence: "The Mondlak family is mandated to house three officers beginning Thursday, April twentieth of this year, 1939." He laid the letter upon the table for all to see. Pointing to the date, Salomon said, "The mail was delayed, so this means that the officers will arrive to our home the day after tomorrow."

5
Wolf

April 1939 | Gliwice, Poland

Downstream from the village of Gliwice—located in the Upper Silesia region of southern Poland—Wolf Yoskowitz launched his canoe into the Klodnica River. Fern leaves and lush green foliage skimmed the vessel's hull as he rowed along the river's edge. Arriving at his favorite cove, he cast his fishing line and then settled into a waiting posture. The late afternoon sun cast its glow upon the water, making his lure appear golden. Wolf stared at it, anticipating a bobble. But the glimmer radiated outward, capturing his reflection, which startled him, his face appearing older than his twenty-two years. The liquid likeness detailed his chiseled good looks, including his high forehead. Shimmering, the golden water reflected his dark brunette hair as reddish, which it was not, and filled his spirited blue eyes with gleaming stars.

Sighing heavily, Wolf contemplated his future. Rumors of war with Germany abounded. The Polish army was actively soliciting young men such as him— stout and healthy. Two of his best friends had been forced to enlist last week. The military could come for him, too, although his father's recent stroke had made him the sole provider for his family. Chafing against the cane fishing pole, the calluses on his hands reminded him that he was no stranger to work, having labored in the flour mill since he was ten years old.

Staring into the water, Wolf remembered a conversation with his rabbi, who had suggested that Wolf make a case of his family's hardship if the military questioned him, and to say that he was Jewish, an Orthodox Jew, at that. The rabbi had explained that the Polish army should be reticent to recruit Jews because their presence could incite violence from the Nazis. Then the rabbi had clarified his point. "Months ago," he said, "on November ninth and tenth of last year, Nazi leaders—with the support of Adolph Hitler—actively coordinated attacks on Jewish communities in Germany. For two days, Jewish-owned businesses and homes were vandalized, hundreds of synagogues burned, Jewish cemeteries desecrated, and German Jews beaten and killed." The rabbi had looked aghast as he then exclaimed. "And now in Germany, the Nazis are interning Jewish men, ages sixteen to sixty, in labor and concentration camps. Wolf, do you understand the impact of all this?"

His brow furrowed and Wolf replied, "It's alarming. All so terribly frightening."

"Jewish men between sixteen and sixty. Wolf, that's you and me. And, as for last November's pogroms, you must understand that these were not spontaneous riots against Jews as Nazi propaganda claims. They were state ordered! State-sponsored arson and vandalism! It's now referred to as the 'The *Kristallnacht*' (the night of the broken glass) because of all the broken glass in the massive destruction." The rabbi sighed deeply. "More importantly, I don't believe that this Nazi violence against Jews will stay within Germany. Hitler has his eye on all European Jews."

Lost in memories of the rabbi's disturbing report and predictions, Wolf jiggled his fishing line, but it did not dispel the anxiety that gripped him. Darkness, like a cloud eclipsing the light of a full moon, swelled inside him. Unconsciously, he sank his teeth into his lower lip, causing a blood blister to rise.

From the riverbank, three young boys who Wolf recognized from synagogue began throwing rocks into the water. Wolf watched the waves ripple in his direction and then concentric circles form around his lure.

One boy yelled out across the river, "Wolf Yoskowitz, my sister, Bracha, wants to marry you and make wolf babies." The other two guffawed, hyena-like laughs that bounced across the water. The boy who had spoken wound his arm back and threw a rock at Wolf's canoe. A solid hit, it dinged loudly.

Bracha? Lord, help. She was not a girl he would ever consider marrying, although she was slightly attractive. To his mother's chagrin, not a single female in his shtetl held that kind of appeal for him. From the time of puberty, Wolf had sensed—intuiting angelic whispers in the depths of his soul—that he would instantly recognize *the one*, would know his wife-to-be the moment he looked upon her face.

Wolf watched the boys trot away and then disappear among the trees. A sudden burst of sadness engulfed him. *These boys will not have a carefree childhood if our rabbi's predictions for European Jews are correct.*

Usually, it was a relief to be on the river he loved. But today, being there did nothing to dissolve the knot in his throat or the ache in his heart.

6
Wojtek
April-May 1939 | Zieluń, Poland

Frightened of the soldiers in their home, eight-year-old Sara cried frequently. Yet Hinda found herself humming happily, unburdened by the additional household chores or what it signified to have three soldiers living there. Two of the officers were in their mid-thirties and were married with families. The third, named Wojtek, was single and in his early twenties.

In the evenings after dinner, the older officers retreated to the study and talked with Salomon, while Wojtek visited with Hinda and Joel. Their discussion topics included the military, what it was like as a young officer, fear of being on the front line, and of Joel's being called to serve. At times, Wojtek would tell them about his hometown of Krakow located in southern Poland. A prosperous city, Krakow was a hub for agriculture and manufacturing, and a center for higher education—vastly different from Zieluń.

Spellbound by Wojtek's melodic voice, Hinda and Joel would sit and listen to him for hours as he spoke about his city's culture, his family's bicycle manufacturing business, and his dreams to return and help his father run the operation. At times, Hinda found herself staring at Wojtek, his unique appearance and demeanor markedly different from the young men of Zieluń, who typically had dark hair. In contrast, Wojtek sprouted light flaxen hair that was almost monochromatic with his skin tone and his olive-colored eyes, which bulged, overshadowing the other features of his squarish-shaped face. At five feet, ten inches tall, he was shorter than Joel, but his broad neck and extremely muscular, stocky body made for a presence that was far more commanding.

One morning, Hinda's mother suddenly dropped her dish towel on the counter and turned to Hinda. "Your eyes have a new sparkle these days. I hear you humming, and I see Wojtek staring at you too long." Esther sighed and said, "Hinda, he is Catholic. You are Jewish. Very Jewish."

"Mommy," was all Hinda could say. The realization startled her: the exciting energy bouncing around inside her was about Wojtek. About attraction.

Although she was almost eighteen years old, Hinda fell against her mother, sinking into her bosom as if she were a child.

Esther stroked her daughter's hair as she held Hinda. She pulled back, gripped Hinda's arms, and gazed directly into her daughter's eyes. "You are a wise girl, Hinda Mondlak. I trust your wisdom."

The following week, a day when Hinda was leaving for the forest to pick berries and mushrooms, the soldiers arrived back home after lunch instead of their usual time. Surprising to all, they were free for the afternoon. Wojtek asked if he could accompany her. Hinda looked at her mother and was astounded when her mother nodded yes and instructed, "Don't be late getting back. I need the fruit and mushrooms for dinner."

On the way to the forest with Wojtek, Hinda laughed readily. She felt free, frisky, and daring. Soon, their baskets had been set down, and they were playing hide-and-seek. Wojtek was no match for her practiced skill at hiding among the trees and lush foliage of the forest she knew well. At last, he declared surrender.

"Come see the river, my treasured river," Hinda called back to him as she raced to the riverbank.

"Your river?" he teased. "I do believe the Wkra River is the property of Poland."

"Yes, but it's incredibly precious to me," she said as she found a spot near the water. He plopped down beside her, and they sat listening to the soothing sounds of the bubbling river.

Turning to Wojtek, Hinda said, "I'm very afraid of what's going to happen."

"What do you mean? The war?" he asked.

"Yes, and I fear that I'll never see you or hear from you again."

Wojtek turned to look upon her face. Her large, luminous eyes—blue as a cloudless sky—captivated him. He replied, "Everything is going to be all right. We don't want war, and neither do the Germans."

"But they do," Hinda argued.

"The Nazi leaders do; they want to rule the world. But regular German people don't. Ordinary citizens, like you and me, in most countries are usually scared of war."

"I hadn't thought of it that way."

"As soon as I'm allowed to return home, I'll send an invitation for you to come to Krakow. I'll even make a bicycle just for you." Wojtek's lips crooked into a tender smile as he slid his arm around Hinda's shoulder. In a short while, he moved his arm to her waist, squeezing her closer.

Hinda sighed. Sitting so close to Wojtek—his shoulders smashed tight against hers—felt glorious. A boy had never held her in that way. She did not want it to end. In the next minute, her father's face swam before her mind's eye. Her father, who she respected and admired, would be profoundly disappointed if he saw her cuddled so closely against Wojtek's body. The voice of her instincts arose deep inside, warning, "He's a gentile. Do not get involved."

Wojtek suddenly grasped her face in his hands. His full lips brushed against hers.

"Oh no! The baskets. We left them in the forest." Hinda jumped to her feet, offering him her hand. "We'd better get the mushrooms and berries, and head home." Wojtek's eyes became slits for a moment, but he took her hand, letting her pull him up.

"I'll race you to the forest." Hinda hoisted her long skirt upward and dashed off.

When they returned home, their baskets chock-full, they found Esther waiting on the porch for them. First, she looked at her daughter, checking her out from head to toe. Turning to Wojtek, Esther said, "Hurry, and get your things. The other officers have already left. Unexpected orders. Your platoon is leaving tonight. Going to Mława."

7

Decrees and Handcuffs

Since early June, Polish soldiers no longer protected Zieluń. All available combat troops had been transferred to the trenches to defend Poland's borders. In late August, news had come that the battles of Mława and Warsaw had been lost. Although Poland had put up fierce resistance, the German military had been victorious. Within weeks, Nazi forces occupied vast areas of Poland.

Marching on Zieluń streets, German soldiers cast terror with their official uniforms, loaded guns, and clomping boots. Using oversized hammers, they nailed posters on buildings and street signs, dictating new laws. The posters—emblazoned with the German eagle and Nazi swastika symbols—announced new decrees, primarily for Jews: certain areas, streets, markets, and buildings where they were permitted to go or from which they were prohibited.

The earsplitting hammering sounds invoked agitation. Yet the restrictions the posters delineated alarmed the Jewish villagers. Instead of whispering "*War! War!*" the villagers openly asked, "*Why? Why?*"

Standing near the market, which now heralded a swastika flag over its doorway, Hinda read the detailed stipulations on the poster nailed to the building wall. Tromping in front of her, Nazi soldiers hauled a well-groomed Jewish man bound in handcuffs, kicking him as they shoved him forward. At the corner, the soldiers stopped. Gripping his hair like a lever, they jerked his head upward and instructed him to read aloud one of the posters. Their hands in fists, the soldiers struck his upper back and arms when he recited the section about the newly banned street—the one where he had unknowingly trod. Hinda recognized the man from the yeshiva. He worked for her father, cataloging sacred books.

Not realizing that she had ventured into the street, Hinda jumped back on the sidewalk as a man on a bicycle swerved, narrowly missing her. The sight of the bike stirred her heart with questions, the same ones she had pondered since last May: Did Wojtek survive the Mława battles? Did he get to return to Krakow and help his father with their bicycle business?

Gestapo jostled past her, hauling a group of Jews in handcuffs. People on the streets cowered back, shuddering at the frightful scenes, worrying that they were next.

Looking upward, Hinda searched the sky. It teemed with puffy clouds, appearing as fluffy pillows scattered across the heavens. As she gazed at the clouds, she felt a heaviness descend upon her. It seemed as if the clouds were prayer catchers; each one stuffed with the villagers' desperate pleas to the Almighty. With an ache in her heart, she decided to go to her synagogue, a magnificent building that she believed housed holiness.

The temple was more crowded than Hinda had ever seen it. Hundreds of people sat praying, beseeching God to take pity upon the faithful citizens of Zieluń, to save them from what they feared was coming. A blonde-haired woman, her face stained with tears, exited the doorway where Hinda was standing. "Go home, Hinda Mondlak. They've been praying for hours. And it changes nothing."

Her heart pounding like the hammers attaching the posters, Hinda hurried home. Choking back sobs, she asked her father, "Why, Tatae, why?"

In a surprisingly calm voice, Salomon said, "My dear daughter, throughout history Jews have been persecuted—the Spanish inquisition, the pogroms."

"Why us?"

"Because in the eyes of God, written in the Torah and in the Christian Bible, the Jews have always been *the chosen people*. And even with all the mass slaughter and discrimination, as a people, we have always survived."

"I don't want to be chosen."

"Oh, but you do. It is a privilege to be a Jew. Regardless of what happens, Hinda, do not ever forget that. It will give you strength."

Hinda nodded. "I went to the synagogue. Hundreds of people are there praying. A lady bolted through the door near me and said that their prayers were changing nothing." Hinda checked her father's facial expression, expecting to be chided for speaking of such faithlessness.

Salomon looked down, then steepled his hands together. "Prayer doesn't always change our outer circumstances, but it always changes us in here." He placed one hand upon his heart.

For the first time in her entire life, Hinda heard a tremor in her father's voice. She stared at him, trepidation filling her soul.

"I know you are scared, Hinda. We all are."

The following week, Salomon opened his door to an assemblage of men, all talking at once. Lamenting loudly, many held their fists in the air. Earlier that morning, the Nazis had begun closing all Jewish-owned businesses in Zieluń. Panic, despair, and rage were evident in the men's distressed faces and defeated postures. After lengthy discussion, they decided to return to their homes and start hiding all objects that contained material or sentimental value. Salomon spoke to Esther, instructing her to begin stowing away their valuables too.

That afternoon, between classes at the yeshiva, Salomon experienced a foreboding he had never, under any circumstances, felt before today. Visibly disturbed, he stroked the stack of sacred books on his desk, his fingers gently caressing them. Having difficulty concentrating, which was rare for him, he decided to go home.

At the house, Hinda met him at the door, "Tatae, you're home early."

"Yes, I have work here to tend to." Salomon clutched his satchel, but he did not take it to his desk. He went to the back of the house, opened the latch in the ceiling, and lowered the stairs to the attic. The rickety steps creaked as he climbed upward.

8
The Silver Bell

August 1939 | Mlawa, Poland

With an onslaught of gunfire surrounding him, Wojtek Wiskowski hunkered down in the trench beside two other soldiers from his platoon. Two alive, that is; another lay dead next to him, a bullet lodged in his neck. The Germans had encroached upon the small Polish camp in the early morning hours. It was now midday.

His throat tight and dry, Wojtek reloaded his submachine gun, his ammunition sack now empty. Hours ago, the squadron officer had radioed for help. Yet no troops, weapons, or ammo had arrived.

Suddenly, dirt whirled all around him. A German grenade had landed nearby. Shrapnel filled the air along with rapid gunfire. Wojtek grabbed at his leg, which had been hit; blood spurted wildly from his groin. Then he was knocked back again. When the shell fragments collapsed his lung, Wojtek gasped for air, a name winging on his breath, "*Hinda.*"

His eyes closed. Vivid colors erupted in Wojtek's mind. And then, a scene of a riverbank came into view. A beautiful girl rode a blue bicycle, a bike he had designed especially for her. It had a tan woven basket in front and a silver bell on the right handlebar. The girl's russet hair and eyes of azure came into focus. She waved to him and rang the bell. The chime pealed in his ears. Wojtek's lips parted in a slight smile just as shrapnel from a shower of mortar shells struck his cerebral cortex and rained down upon the center of his heart.

9

The Hulking Canister

Late September 1939 | Zieluń, German-occupied Poland

Doors nailed and barred, Zieluń's yeshivas were closed. Salomon Mondlak had no job now, his teaching salary gone. And with all Jewish-owned businesses shut down, Salomon's previous supplemental income had also vanished. His expert accounting services were no longer required. His private religious tutoring of children was no longer a priority or affordable to Jewish families who had lost their livelihoods.

Plus, notification had come that the Wkra River and the forests surrounding Zieluń were off-limits to Jews, a new decree from the Nazi regime. This meant that the Mondlaks and their Jewish neighbors could no longer enjoy the river and forests. Moreover, two of their major food sources were no longer available to them. No more fish from the river; no more fruits and mushrooms from the forests.

Salomon went to his wife to discuss their larders. Surprised and relieved, he saw the cupboards lined with small jars of meat and vegetables that Esther had been quietly canning, the rumors of war encouraging her. Her eyes glowing, Esther showed him flour sacks and other non-perishable food items that she had collected. With careful meal planning, she had said, they could survive for many months.

After Salomon left the kitchen, Esther studied the calendar on the wall. She flipped its pages, viewing the next six months, calculating meals, and wondering if she had accurately assessed how long their current supplies would last. Deciding that she was correct, she flipped back to the month of September. Today's date jumped out at her. It was exactly two weeks ago that the Germans had burned their synagogue. Tears fogged her green eyes. Unconsciously, she sniffed, remembering how awful Hinda and Salomon had smelled when they returned home that night. For days afterward, she had soaked their clothing in herb-laden water to remove the smoke odor. She wished herbs would as easily remove the weights from her daughter's and husband's hearts after witnessing the horror of it. Salomon had looked hollow-eyed, as if his very soul had burned in the fire. He barely ate the next day and then decided to fast and pray for three days. Hinda had moved in slow motion as if anchors were attached to her feet. Frequently, she would sit in the living room and just stare out the window for prolonged periods. Esther, too, had deeply grieved the unjust loss of their temple, having cried uncontrollably for days.

Ever since the night of the synagogue fire, it seemed to Esther that no place was safe. Even the walls of their home, once secure and warm, emitted fierce warnings. Cooking and cleaning had become distractions, ways to quell her persistent unease. Esther fingered her apron, giving in to the overwhelming desire to make a special dinner tonight, to pretend that all was well, just for this one night.

At dinner, the Mondlaks eyed the array of bowls and platters spread across their table. In the past, it was a typical sight, an abundance they took for granted. Now, such a meal was surprising. Smiling, the family whiffed the air, enjoying the aromas. When everyone was settled, Esther gave the nod to dig in. But within minutes, thunderous knocks rattled the front door.

Salomon rose from his chair and went to the door. Hinda leapt to her feet, following behind her father.

A Gestapo officer waited on their stoop. In the front lawn, three Nazi soldiers stood at attention, their guns in hand, their presence ominous.

"All your books right now, over here," commanded the officer. His voice was guttural, loud, and harsh. He pointed to the yard where the other soldiers waited.

Salomon froze, his hand on the doorknob, not moving.

"Did you hear me?" The Gestapo officer shoved the barrel of his rifle into Salomon's abdomen. "Right now, *all* your books, over here on the grass."

"Tatae, I'll help you," Hinda whispered to her father. Bravely, she pried his hand from the doorknob.

The officer pushed his way into the house and went to the small study across from the entry. He began ripping books off the shelves, throwing them onto the floor.

Salomon regained his senses. His hands trembling, he began gathering the beloved books of his personal library, a lifetime collection, many of which were antique and inherited from his father. He and Hinda carried them to the lawn, piling them onto the grass.

The officer found the other family members cowered in the kitchen. He ordered them out to the front lawn. Esther, Rachel, Sara, and Joel filed out the door. Rachel picked up Sara, who was bawling. Esther's chest heaved, her hands folding over themselves again and again.

One of the soldiers stepped up to Joel, standing nose-to-nose with him as if daring him to fight back. After a moment, the soldier drew back the handle of his semi-automatic service pistol and struck Joel on his right cheekbone. Joel yelped; blood dribbled down his face.

"Weasel Jew boy," said the soldier, taunting him.

After the study had been emptied of all books and journals, Salomon said, "It is done. That is all."

The Gestapo officer threw his head back and laughed, a cackle that made the hair on Hinda's arm prickle. He exclaimed haughtily, "No, you thieving Jew, it is not."

Salomon's jaw tightened, his shoulders instantly sagging.

"How about those you've hidden? The books you stole from the school?" The officer pushed the barrel of his rifle into Salomon's back, shoving him forward into the house.

Raising his arms upward in surrender, Salomon said, "I'll get them." A soldier followed him to the rear of the house. It was then that Hinda understood why her father had climbed the stairs to the attic earlier in the week.

Salomon returned, clutching the sacred texts; all were handsomely bound in leather. Although he showed no outward signs of bruising, he suffered a beating on the inside, his heart pummeled. Carefully, Salomon laid the religious books from the yeshiva on the pile.

The Gestapo officer kicked at the hallowed tomes, stomping and twisting his black boot on them. He nodded to a soldier, who handed Salomon a large container filled with gasoline. Their guns drawn, they forced Salomon to saturate the hoard of books, to dispense the entirety of the hulking canister. Nauseous fumes sickened the night air.

A Nazi officer, who had not yet spoken, handed Salomon matches and a striker. In a full-throated authoritative voice, he said, "Jew Salomon Mondlak, you are hereby ordered to burn these obscene books. Light these matches now."

Striking one match at a time, with the Nazi officer pointing where to drop it, Salomon ignited the fire. Instantly, flames leapt through the parchment paper and bindings. Hinda glimpsed her father's face illuminated in the brightness of the roaring fire. His jaw tight and moving in a grinding motion against his teeth, his eyes flooded with tears. In her entire life, it was the *only* time Hinda had ever seen her father shed even one teardrop, let alone weep.

Books, sacred text and knowledge, had been Salomon's life, his treasure. Helpless against the agony, his mouth quavered, his whole body shook. Looking upward to the sky, Salomon wailed, "Why? Why? Why?"

Watching the flames spike, Hinda remembered the upsetting premonition she had experienced when her father and she had watched the synagogue burn. Her instincts had predicted another Nazi-ordered fire, one more personal. Here it blazed.

Questions clattered her brain: How had the Nazis known that her father had taken the books from the yeshiva? Hinda flashed on the memory of seeing a well-dressed man in handcuffs on the street. He had worked at the yeshiva with her father. Rigor-like chills shook her entire body, paralyzing her arms and legs, rendering her unable to move, unable to offer comfort to her father who she had believed, until now, had all the answers.

10
Dr. Walter

At the University of Frankfurt am Main, Walter Zeilhofen, dressed in a white suit, strode proudly across the stage. Dr. Josef Mengele, a distinguished alum, placed a gold medallion, inscribed with the Rod of Asclepius, around Walter's neck. The medallion hung from ribbons of black, white, and red—the colors of the German flag. Mengele shook Walter's hand heartily, knowing him from their native village of Günzburg located in the region of Bavaria. Mengele then handed Walter a diploma, which certified him as a doctor, licensed to practice General Medicine throughout Germany.

Leaning close to Walter, Mengele posed for an official photograph, as he had done for the other graduates. Striking dissimilarities in the two men dominated this photo. Walter's wavy blonde hair and thin lips contrasted sharply with Dr. Mengele's dark brown hair, heavy eyebrows, and full, lower lip. When smiling, both men displayed straight teeth, but Mengele had a noticeable gap between his upper, center incisors.

The audience erupted into applause. Walter, whose surname began with the letter Z, was the last graduate to cross the stage. The closing comments were brief, inviting the graduates, their families, and friends to join the university officials and staff for a reception.

The crowd flowed into the grand ballroom, which featured a wall of windows that showcased a view of the Main River, a tributary to the Rhine. Walter guided his mother toward the largest window.

Striding across the room, Walter's father toted three glasses brimming with champagne. Joining his son and wife, Mr. Zeilhofen said, "Look who I found in the crowd." Smiling, Josef Mengele bowed in a whimsical way to Walter, his childhood friend. He raised his champagne glass. Just as they clinked their glasses together in celebration of Walter's graduation, a university dean requested Mengele's presence at the podium.

Before departing, Josef Mengele whispered to Walter, "Let's talk later. I have an upcoming vacancy in my staff."

11
Six-Pointed Star
November 1939 | Zieluń, German-occupied Poland

Finished with their breakfast, the Mondlak family bowed their heads as Salomon recited a condensed version of the ritualistic after-meal prayer, *birkat hamazon*. He ended with the words, *"Blessed are You, Lord, who nourishes all. Amen."* Salomon then retired to his study, his skin pale, his hair grayer than it was just one month ago.

Hinda and her mother were clearing the table when they suddenly stopped in their tracks. Raucous raps on the front door boomed throughout the house. Esther gasped, clutching her chest. Hinda rushed to her father's study. Taking Hinda's hand in his, Salomon opened the door.

German soldiers, armed and dressed in formal Nazi uniforms, shoved Salomon and Hinda back and swarmed into the home. While pointing to the living room, the lead officer shouted, "Gather everyone in this house and sit over there."

Hinda dashed to get Rachel and Sara. Salomon retrieved Esther and Joel. They all piled onto the sofa and chairs, sitting closely together, clinging to each other.

Two soldiers stood guard in the living room entry. Opening the chambers of their rifles, they checked ammunition in an exaggerated manner—a deliberate display of dominance—and then aimed their guns at the family.

Other soldiers carried in large crates for packing, while the officers began opening closets and bureau drawers, rummaging through the Mondlaks' possessions, ransacking every room. Anything and everything that had a smidgen of monetary value was confiscated: Sabbath candle holders, wine cups, silver eating utensils, dishes, picture frames, art, jewelry, money, and furs, including coats that sported any fur at all, whether as inside lining or adornment around necklines and cuffs.

When they had plundered the entire house and were satisfied that they had found all valuable items, the eight soldiers surrounded the family in the living room. Guns drawn, they stood in an arc and stared at each family member as if they were suspects.

Abruptly, the lead officer asked Joel to stand. Joel rose from his chair, his raven hair falling across his forehead. The officer touting the greatest number of stripes on his collar instructed Joel to move to the center of the room. He then circled around him, surveying Joel's size and build. When the officer made the second circle and was facing Joel's backbone, he ran his hand crudely down Joel's spine. He grabbed Joel's arms, bringing his wrists together behind his back. At lightning speed, the officer locked on handcuffs and shoved Joel out the front door.

Across the room, Esther screamed, "Why are you arresting him? Where are you taking my son?" Sobbing and wailing, she begged the soldiers not to take Joel. Hobbling over to one soldier, she repeated the same question, screeching, "Where are you taking my son?"

"Enough, you filthy Jew," the soldier shouted. Drawing his arm back, he slapped Esther hard on the face, his fingerprints leaving marks on her snowy skin.

Standing next to her father, Hinda saw that both of his hands had clenched, baring his knuckles. His face blanched pale and then flushed, turning a blood-red color. Hinda sidled closer to him and took one of his fisted hands in hers. Fearing that he was about to hit the soldier, she whispered, "Tatae, *please* don't."

Sighing deeply, Salomon released his fists and Hinda's hand. He went to Esther who now wept mournfully. He put his arm around her shoulder and stroked the handprint on her face.

"All of you sit down. Right now. And stop that sniveling," the officer demanded, aiming his gun at Esther, then at little Sara.

Hinda pulled Sara onto her lap and huddled next to Rachel. Salomon and Esther squeezed onto the sofa beside them. Unable to halt the tears, Esther continued to cry quietly. Salomon sat stoically still, immobilized with rage, fearing for Joel and for what was to come next.

Two soldiers lifted a packed crate, hefting it toward the door. Powerless to change the injustice, the Mondlaks sat in a state of shock and watched the Nazi soldiers haul away boxes crammed full of their treasured belongings. Their tongues held hostage, only the walls heard their muted screams.

Stomping his boot heavily on the wood floor, the officer returned to the living room. With no mention of what he had done with Joel, he thrust his fist in the air and yelled, "Nazi officials have decreed that all Jews, ten years and older, are to wear armbands in public. These badges must be white and must have a six-pointed star outlined in blue affixed to each one."

Salomon asked, "Where do we get such armbands?"

"You make them yourself or buy them. Merchants in some towns now sell them," the officer replied, his tone terse. The officer's eyes narrowed. Then he said loudly, almost screaming, "You are hereby ordered to wear those armbands on your *right* upper arm, atop your outer clothing. If you leave this house without an armband, you will be arrested." The officer paused, eyeing them, one eyebrow raised in a hook. "Understand?"

Salomon nodded.

Before the officer closed their door, he extended his arm up and outward. His lips flat against his teeth, he barked, "*Heil Hitler!*"

Badges of Segregation
February 1940 | Zieluń, German-occupied Poland

Salomon Mondlak shifted in his desk chair, his hands fidgeted nervously, shuffling papers. Once exuding an aura of warmth and comfort, his study now felt hollow and cold. The empty bookshelves matched his heart, which felt barren of positive feeling. Without any books to read and no sacred texts to analyze, Salomon attempted to write an account of the devastating injustices since the Nazis had occupied Zieluń. The pen fell from his fingers. Salomon ripped the paper to shreds. Bowing his head, he retreated into ardent prayer, his constant companion now.

Later, the front door rattled when Hinda returned home. In the entry, she removed her coat and hung it in the closet. She tugged on the white armband, moving it up higher on the coat's sleeve. Her fingertips slid over the embroidered Star of David, and she remembered the day, last September, when her mother had cut up a white bedsheet to make the compulsory armbands for their family. Before her mother had sewn the fabric pieces together, Hinda had used blue thread to embroider the sacred, six-pointed star on each piece. As she closed the closet door, Hinda shuddered.

From his study, Salomon called out to her, "Hinda, is that you?"

"Yes, Tatae," Hinda said, stepping into the archway of the study.

"No flour or vegetables?" he asked, eyeing her empty hands.

"No, they've closed more streets to us. Anyone wearing the white armband was not allowed entry to the market."

Salomon put his head in his hands.

"Tatae, why the armband? And why did the hateful Nazis use the blue star to mark us? It's sacred, but now it makes me feel like a subhuman deplorable."

"Precisely the point. It's intended to humiliate us. And primarily, to mark Jews for discrimination and segregation," he replied.

Hinda winced, noticing how weak and feeble her father had become, having aged dramatically since the German occupation. His stooped shoulders, silver hair, and lined face revealed his constant agony, his endless worry for his family's fate, both individually and collectively. They all had lost weight, but Esther had recently dropped an inordinate amount.

The sunny smiles and hearty laughter of their once cheerful home were distant memories. Now, frantic tears and anxious prayers crowded their days. Raw fear oozed from all their faces. Terror mixed with hunger. Food was scarce.

13

The Lone Fisherman
March 12, 1941 | Gliwice, German-occupied Poland

Wolf Yoskowitz crept stealthily through the forest south of his home in Gliwice—now officially occupied by Nazi Germany. On this windy, chilly day, he wore a bulky jacket, which cloaked fishing line, hooks, and a burlap sack. Wolf limped along, gripping a knobby tree limb that was near his height, as if he needed balance support. Every few steps, he hid behind a tree, watching and listening for any signs of German soldiers, Gestapo, or their snitches.

Finally, after fifteen kilometers, Wolf stood on the edge of the forest. He peered out between the tree trunks and surveyed the countryside. No one in sight, he strode down to the Klodnica River, which had been off-limits to Jews for two years now.

Sharp pangs rankled Wolf's stomach. Hunger was his constant companion since the Germans had shut down the flour mill his family operated. Now, all Jewish-owned businesses were closed, doors locked, and barricaded. Gentiles, fearing punishment, refused to hire Jews. With no job and no prospects of one, Wolf scavenged for food every day not only for himself but, also, for his mother, Miriam, and his sister, Erna, and three younger brothers, Joseph, Samuel, and Alexander.

Choosing a grassy spot on the river's edge, Wolf sat, nestling his body down into a comfortable position. He removed a fishing line from his jacket pocket and tied it onto the thin end of the tree limb—his pretend walking stick. Three fishhooks dangled from the wooden lure. Baiting them with worms he had dug up in the forest, he cast the line into the waters of the Klodnica River. Wolf did not stare at the lure waiting for bites; instead, he looked over his shoulder every few minutes. The corners of his lips turned slightly upward as he contemplated the irony: he wanted to catch fish, but he did not want the Nazis to catch him.

The breeze picked up, creating unfavorable conditions; heavy winds caused fish to go deeper underwater. Disgruntled, Wolf bit his lower lip so firmly that a blood spot appeared. Looking upward, he pleaded for heavenly assistance in hooking small perch. Saliva roiled in his mouth as he envisioned filets sautéing in the skillet. He could almost smell them cooking, which reminded him of his father, who used to sniff the air savoring the aroma.

Thoughts of his father produced a bittersweet piquancy on his tongue. Named Moishe—Yiddish for Moses—Wolf's father had been a stern, demanding, punitive man. Even still, it had been a real shock to Wolf when his father required him to quit school in the sixth grade and go to work full-time in the flour mill. His teachers had protested, saying that Wolf—being highly intelligent and ambitious beyond his years—would have a bright future if he were educated. Wolf's father remained unyielding, repeating what had been done to his father, grandfather, and him.

An intense feeling, a strong intention, jolted Wolf like a lightning bolt, electrifying his mind and heart, causing goose bumps to race down his legs. Silently, he vowed that if he were ever lucky enough to have a son, he would break this inane generational pattern.

Even still, Wolf found it shameful that his father did not have a proper *shiva* after his death, a year ago. At the funeral, the family had torn their clothing and grieved, but no one else came to memorialize him during the week of mourning. No baskets of food had been sent, and the family had no extra provisions to offer guests if they had come to their home for the holy time each evening. Paranoia and trepidation now overrode sacred rituals in the once-friendly shtetl in Gliwice. It was not misplaced fear. Nazi soldiers had burned their synagogue. Their revered rabbi had died in the fire, tied to a pew.

Wolf's body jerked when he felt the tug, then multiple tugs, on his line. Not only was he stunned to be catching fish amid the strong wind, but also for the long lapse of time he had been lost in memories. Anxiously, Wolf searched the landscape for any sign of soldiers, for any humans or animals. Satisfied that he was safe, he removed two small perch, flopping as they were, and placed them in a burlap bag. He tied the bag to a rock so that it floated in the water. His hands moved adeptly, placing worms on the hooks, and then tossing the line into the river.

Gusts of wind brought odd sounds that seemed to come from behind him. Wolf staked his makeshift fishing pole in the mud and stood erect. He looked around, examining every direction of the forest, the meadow, and the riverbank, as far as his eyes allowed. Nothing appeared worrisome. Squatting down on his haunches, Wolf pulled his jacket up closer around his neck and slid one hand into the coat's pocket, checking for the white armband that marked him as a Polish Jew. Still there, the badge's rough texture matched his calloused fingertips.

If not for the deafening harsh wind, Wolf's keen auditory sense would have noted crunching sounds as heavy black boots stepped upon dead leaves on the bed of the forest.

A patrol of German soldiers hid in a grove of trees on the brink of the riverbank, their rifles zeroed in on a lone fisherman—Wolf Yoskowitz.

14
An Abandoned Mill

Early that blustery morning, an axe suddenly crashed through the front door of the Mondlak home. Nazi soldiers swarmed inside.

Hinda jumped back as she had been walking through the front entry to the kitchen when the sharp blade barely missed her head. Her heart raced.

"You have fifteen minutes to pack your most indispensable things," the Nazi officer commanded. "One suitcase per person." From his pocket, he retrieved a stopwatch and set it for exactly fifteen minutes. "And you must wear your armbands."

In shock, Esther sobbed as did Sara, who sucked her thumb constantly now, though she was eight years old. Sara clung to her mother's skirt, hiding her face.

Hinda spoke up, "Tatae, let's get our suitcases from the attic." Salomon did not respond. She shook his arm urgently. "Father! We must do as they say."

"Get busy, now, or you'll be shot," the Nazi officer bellowed, aiming his gun at them.

Hinda motioned to Rachel, and they both ran to the back of the house. Hinda climbed the squeaky stairs and handed down five travel bags to her sister. "Take these two to Mommy and Tatae," Hinda instructed Rachel, who was now visibly shaking. Hinda then grabbed the other three and hurried to their bedroom, calling out to Rachel to meet her there and to bring Sara.

Rummaging through the clothes drawer, Hinda handed five pairs of panties to Sara and instructed her, "Put all these on over those you are wearing, and then this nightgown over your dress, and then this dress and sweater over that."

"Good idea," said Rachel. She and Hinda got busy layering on extra clothing pieces too.

"Sara, go to Mommy and Tatae's room, and tell them to layer their clothing." Sara hid behind the drapery. Exasperated, Hinda said in a sharper tone than she had ever spoken to her little sister, "Do as I say." Sara ran from the room, her thumb in her mouth.

A short ten minutes later, the family of five gathered in the living room, their packed suitcases in hand, their white armbands displayed prominently on their coats—the warmest ones they had after their home had been stripped of valuables.

"Out the door, right now!" the officer yelled. In single file, they strode through the splintered doorway that now exhibited a swastika flag.

A German soldier waited in the yard. He pointed to a military vehicle parked on the street. "Get in the back, in the bed of the truck," he ordered.

"Where are you taking us?" Salomon asked.

"Mława."

Salomon grimaced, knowing that Germany had annexed Mława the previous fall. Rumor was that thousands of Polish Jews, against their will, were being relocated to the ghetto there. With robotic movements, Salomon helped his wife and little Sara into the truck. Hinda and Rachel climbed in behind them.

As the truck's engine revved, Hinda overheard her mother, with faltering words between whimpers, telling Sara and Rachel that someday soon they would return to their home. Hinda then looked to her father. He stared ahead, a blank and distant look in his eyes.

The chilling March wind suddenly picked up, stinging Hinda's cheeks. The wind did not just whisper, it howled, awakening her instincts. Instantly, Hinda knew that they, as a family or individually, would never return to the village of Zieluń or to the residence they had called home her entire life. In fact, all eleven of the Mondlak children had been born in that very domicile.

Although her father owned it outright and held the official deed, their house and the land it was built upon were now confiscated Third Reich property. And, apparently, they were too.

Loaded into the open-air bed of the truck and then hauled, like subhuman pariahs, the Mondlaks suffered a bitterly cold and miserably uncomfortable ride to Mława. The soldiers made one stop where they purchased sandwiches and drinks for themselves, but no food or water was offered to their passengers.

After six hours, the truck drove through the gates of the Mława ghetto. Hinda stood erect, viewing the decrepit ramshackle buildings that begged for refurbishment. Trash and debris lined the streets, which were rough with chuckholes. The rest of her family sat hunkered down away from the blustery wind, as did the other Jews who had been picked up from villages along the way. Most had covered their heads and faces with blankets, their only weapons against the relentless March gales. Hinda's cheeks were chapped and raw; nonetheless, her desire to see exactly where they were going defied her craving for physical comfort.

At last, the truck rumbled to a stop. The soldier on the passenger side jumped from his seat and shouted, "The Mondlak family depart."

He ushered them inside an abandoned mill that consisted of a single large space, approximately twenty-four feet long and twelve feet wide. There was no furniture, except for a rickety built-in table, its top tilted downward, near the front entrance. It appeared useless; two of its legs were broken. Rays from the setting sun streaked through one lone window on the left side of the room. To the right, three people—a man, a woman, and a boy around twelve years old—cowered in the back corner, where clothing and suitcases were strewn across the wood flooring.

Checking names in a black notebook, the soldier pointed to the trio and said, "Jews Shapiro." He motioned for them to come forward. "You are hereby ordered to share these living quarters." He then turned on his heels and stomped out, his boots leaving footprints in the thick dust atop the floor.

Mr. Shapiro pointed his index finger to the right side of the room. In a gruff tone, he said, "We've settled in over there. Prefer that side. Okay?"

Salomon gestured agreement and started to introduce his family, but the Shapiros, as if on cue, turned on their heels in a synchronized fashion. Without another word, the three of them quickly retreated to their part of the room.

"How can this be called *living quarters* when there are no beds, no chairs, and no kitchen?" Hinda asked.

"It can't." Salomon replied. He and Esther both shook their heads in utter disbelief.

"But we got the window, the only window in the entire building," Hinda said with forced alacrity. The view was far from appealing, ghetto buildings in ruins, but at least there was sunlight and a view of life on the street.

The Mondlaks looked around the inhospitable space. Cobwebs hung from the ceiling and clung to the walls. Mud clumps and dirt covered the wood floor. In the corner, a pile of flour sacks caught Esther's attention. She poked around in the heap, fully expecting to find spiders or mice. A sneezing fit from the dust overcame her, but she was relieved to see no critters. After regaining her breath, Esther whispered to her husband and they huddled, pointing this way and that around the room. They examined the low ceiling and walls, which had nails here and there. Salomon—who had packed a hodgepodge of items, not knowing what conditions to expect at their unknown destination—went to his suitcase and retrieved a ball of twine and a small knife.

Amazed at the ingenuity, Hinda and her sisters watched as their parents created a curtain, a smidgen of privacy for them. Threading the twine through the flour sacks, their parents then tied the string to the nails.

Staying away from the Shapiros' zone, Hinda and Rachel explored the nooks and crannies of the mill, looking for anything else discarded that could be useful. Hinda watched as Rachel scrunched her nose, covered her mouth, and backed away. Hinda stepped forward; instantly, her hand flew to her nose. The odor was nauseating. She poked her head around the corner and saw a round hole in the ground—a makeshift toilet. Spotting another curved corner on the other side, Hinda peeked behind it and found a water faucet mounted high on the wall. Rust-colored streaks and splotches, as if the water contained iron or sulfur, marked the peeling paint all the way down to the floor. The only water source, that area would have to suffice as their shower, primitive as it was.

From the main area, Esther called out for her daughters to come to her. Hinda, Rachel, and Sara stopped exploring and hurried to their mother's side. Clasping Hinda's hand, Esther said, "My girl has such good instincts. Clever idea for us to layer clothing on our bodies to make room for household items in our bags." Motioning to Salomon, she said, "Everyone show me what you packed."

Hinda opened Sara's suitcase and her own since she had been responsible for those. At the sight of her cloth doll, Sara's face lit up with delight. In their two bags, Hinda had squeezed in clothing, lightweight blankets, bath towels, toilet paper, soap, female sanitary products, toothbrushes, combs, and one hairbrush. Rachel's bag held comparable items, plus she had placed a sketch pad and box of colored pencils atop clothing and light bedding.

Opening her own bag, Esther showed them the practical things she had packed: washcloths, towels, bars of soap, sewing needles, spools of thread, eating utensils, two small metal bowls, napkins, a paring knife, a bag of dried lentils, and the last jar of their preserved meat.

Then, Salomon revealed the contents of his suitcase. In addition to the twine, he had crammed in two lightweight blankets, a flashlight, extra batteries, a tack hammer, a small bag of potatoes, a folding knife, paper, a writing pen, and clothing.

Taking the tack hammer, Salomon went to examine the broken-down table at the entry. Hinda saw him struggling to detach the top and offered to help. Together, they forcefully removed the cracked legs. Then, they carried the wooden top, all splintered and gouged, to their living area where it would serve as an eating surface.

A mother bird crafting her nest, Esther spread a clean towel over the unsightly tabletop. Her fingers fluttered, working to smooth the wrinkles. She fussed over the cotton towel as if it were fine linen covering formal dining furniture. Her lips curved, appearing almost pleased. Yet the teardrops blurring Esther's vision revealed her suffering: another egregious injustice, her family removed from their rightful home and forced to live in squalor.

In the light of the setting sun, the Mondlaks sat under the window and consumed sparse servings of half the jar of preserved meat and two potatoes —raw, peeled, and chopped. When darkness loomed, Salomon turned on the flashlight and attempted to recite a memorized bedtime story. Halfway through, he choked, too tearful to continue.

Hinda picked up where her father left off, relating the tale as best she could. Soon though, Mr. Shapiro's snoring, blaring train whistles reverberating across the room, made it impossible to hear. "Let's just go to sleep. The end," she declared in a commanding intonation as if those were the last words of the story.

Their only option, the wood floor, minimally padded with towels and their individual coats, functioned as their beds. The blankets were used for warmth as the room was drafty and cold. Just before Hinda tucked the cloth doll into Sara's arms, she kissed its head, wondering if it were time to tell Sara the doll's special story, and how it had been Hinda's, originally. Sara whimpered and squirmed on her coat. Hinda lightly stroked her little sister's back until Sara fell soundly asleep.

Restless, Hinda glanced around the room. With the moonlight shining through the window, she could see her mother's shoulders shaking under the covers as she wept. Her father's hands were held over his chest, steepled together in prayer mode, his lips moving continuously.

Hinda lay on the hard floor thinking of her soft bed in their home in Zieluń. She winced, realizing that she had not appreciated it enough. In her family, material things were secondary. Faith, knowledge, and education were paramount. Flopping over onto her other side, Hinda pondered the education aspect. A Jewish education was deemed imperative for boys, but not for girls. Boys spent up to ten hours a day studying at yeshivas, their religious schools. While girls received elemental religious training, the emphasis for them was on learning household tasks. Orthodox values, Hinda reasoned. Faces of some friends from synagogue flashed through her mind. Then, she realized that God had been the core of the community in Zieluń, its very heartbeat.

As Hinda finally surrendered to sleep, one last contemplation rattled the bars of the confinement cage that she now occupied: God is not the heartbeat of this ghetto. It has no heart at all.

15

A Conditional Offer

March 1940 | Frankfurt, Germany

At the University of Frankfurt am Main, Dr. Walter Zeilhofen browsed the display of advanced degrees hanging in the office of Dr. Josef Mengele. Each was framed in black-stained wood and expertly hung to create an artful grouping. The first set showcased two degrees from the University of Munich— a Master's in Philosophy and a PhD in Physical Anthropology. The next featured a General Medicine degree from the University of Frankfurt am Main. The final frame encased a certificate, an achievement recognition award, from the Institute for Hereditary Biology and Racial Hygiene, Frankfurt University. Walter pursed his lips together in a mock whistle. His friend was impressive.

"Walter! Sorry to keep you waiting." Josef Mengele breezed into his office at the Institute for Hereditary Biology and Racial Hygiene.

"Time well spent, my friend. I've enjoyed perusing your extraordinary achievements," Walter replied, extending his hand to Josef.

"Good to see you. Thanks for coming today," Josef said, gesturing toward a chair near his desk for Walter to sit.

Their talk quickly turned to their respective families, who lived in Günzburg where the two men had grown up together. Josef's family was far more prosperous than Walter's. But since both were staunch Catholics and belonged to the same parish, they had seen each other regularly.

After a brief discussion catching up on family and parish news, Josef checked his watch. "I assume your presence signifies that you're interested in the position at the institute."

"Yes. I've done my research. Your work involving twins is fascinating." Unconsciously, Walter paused, running one hand through his wavy blonde hair. "And I certainly appreciate the opportunity to work with you and your staff."

Josef nodded, but his eyes narrowed as he studied Walter in a peculiar way. "There's one thing, Walter. Are you a member of the Nazi party?"

Suppressing a gasp, Walter felt as if his lungs had suddenly compressed, squeezing all breath from him. He strained for enough air to say, "No, I'm not."

Mengele tapped his desk. "The job offer stands *only* if you join the Nazi regime."

16

Blurry Silhouette

Wolf Yoskowitz, who was typically a patient fisherman, repeatedly raised then lowered his improvised tree-limb pole, checking to see that worms were still secured to his fishhooks. Ever since fishing had been decreed illegal for Jews, he used multiple hooks to increase his odds of making a catch. Wolf dared to take the risk only when his family and he were near starvation.

The afternoon sun shone upon his back. His empty stomach churned, his breakfast bread, a small, solitary piece, now long gone. Wolf contemplated gutting one of the perches floating in his bag and eating it raw. But his esophagus rebelled at the thought, his throat tightening.

The harsh wind, which was rare for southern Poland, had sabotaged Wolf's hopes of snaring ample fish to feed the entire family. He decided to try for one more catch. Then, he would start the slow journey home, sneaking his way through the forest, while hiding the fish in his jacket.

His lure dipped underwater. The tug on his line, which typically spawned excitement, invoked a nervous feeling that tugged at him. Without moving his head, Wolf shifted his eyes to the left and then to the right. There, on the upper riverbank, he saw an odd shadow. A blurry silhouette, it resembled a misshapen man—a giant—holding something pointy. Instantly, Wolf let the fishing pole slip from his hands. Launching from his haunches, Wolf dove headlong into the chilly waters of the Klodnica River.

Rushing awkwardly down the slope, a Nazi soldier, a hulk of a man, fired muilple shots into the exact spot where Wolf had dived into the river. He turned and yelled at his comrades, a squad of Nazi soldiers, who were descending the steep riverbank. Shouting at each other, the soldiers peppered the water with gunfire.

Wolf swam deeper and deeper. The weight of his work boots helped him drop, but it was a challenge to kick his feet to swim in any direction. Bullets whizzed past him.

17
Porthole to Hell

June 1940 | Mława, German-occupied Poland

The sun streaked through the window, highlighting Hinda's russet-colored hair, now dull from lack of shampoo and nutrition, plus the mineral build-up from the dreadful water. She gazed out the glass pane, the window she had once felt lucky to have in their squalid space at the mill. Day after day, she stared into the street, watching the horrors. People of all ages, including babies and children, died right there while her eyes were upon them: untold numbers from sickness, hundreds from starvation, volumes because they just did not want to exist anymore in those circumstances, and others because they moved too slowly in obeying Gestapo commands.

This morning, an elderly man doddered along the street. His walking cane, which looked expensive and handsomely carved, suddenly caught against his foot. He tripped, falling upon the curb. A Nazi soldier demanded that he rise and move to the sidewalk. The man lifted his shoulders but failed at all attempts to get upon his knees. Coughing, the soldier spit phlegm onto him, and then he directed his rifle at the man's head. Blood and gray matter spewed across the sidewalk.

A porthole to hell, that's what the window is, Hinda thought. Yet she felt paralyzed, powerless to turn away. A new scene unfolding, a group of Jewish men and boys—who wore prison uniforms, handcuffs, and foot chains—caught her eye. The Gestapo herded them down the street. Hinda searched the faces of the boys, looking for her brother, Joel. He was not among them.

Word had come from the ghetto's Jewish Council, often called the *Judenrat*, that the Gestapo were forcing Jewish men and boys, who had been jailed, to dig mass graves. Then, they were ordered to carry the dead bodies—all Jewish—from the streets and to *toss* them, not gently place them but throw them, into the deep hole, all on top of each other. Tangled arms and legs. No respect, even in death.

The Jewish men on the Council, who had been selected by Gestapo, had also been ripped from their homes and required to live in the slums of Mława.

The Council's main function was to inform all the Jews living in the ghetto of the newest Nazi decrees and to promote compliance. Its members held the power to help the residents with some of their needs. Salomon had gone to them and requested to purchase cleaning supplies and tools, including a broom and mop, after his family first arrived. When the supplies were delivered, Esther had scrubbed the mill clean, except for the Shapiros' side. They declined.

At times, when the Council's messenger came to the Mondlaks' quarters, he would visit briefly and give tidbits of news, such as the mass graves on the outskirts of town and of specific disease epidemics like typhus, cholera, and malaria. Other times, the messenger would issue warnings to be careful, saying that disease was not only rampant, but escalating. Salomon would nod his assent, but then challenge the notion of how they could be careful when forced to reside in a crowded ghetto that teemed with poor hygienic conditions.

Still at the window, Hinda gasped when the Nazi soldier instructed one of the youngest and smallest prisoners to pick up the dead man who had the bleeding, gaping hole in his head. The supervising officer unlocked the boy's handcuffs so he could grasp the body and place it over his shoulder. Jail rations, skimpy as they were, barely sustained the youth's strength. He struggled down the street, his feet in chains, while carrying the dead man. And if that was not hellish enough, the soldier then ordered a female bystander to remove her skirt and clean the sidewalk with it.

I should go help her, Hinda thought, aghast at the woman's horrible task. Grappling with the idea of rushing out to help, Hinda observed the soldier's menacing posture, which reflected a mood for meanness and even barbarous killing. Fear, like wild horses stampeding, trampled her entrails, reining in her goodwill.

Turning away, Hinda looked around their hovel. It was as if the window rotated, and she viewed their interior Hades from the street, except there were no soldiers inside. Her parents, reclining awkwardly on the floor with only a towel atop their coats for padding, looked as if they were near death—fragile and spiritless. Bones showed through their clothing. They each had lost significant weight, and so had Rachel, Sara, and Hinda.

Raw despair served as the meat of their days, while picayune portions of bread and uncooked vegetables kept them alive. Hinda remembered when they had first arrived at the Mława ghetto. Displacement had been horrific enough. Not having a kitchen instilled further alarm, and then a new Nazi mandate walloped yet another shattering blow. Jews were now prohibited from buying meat, fish, poultry, eggs, vegetables, fruits, nuts, and white flour. Salomon had been enraged, his face turning crimson, his veins protruding from his neck. And in the next minute, Hinda watched him swallow his wrath and retreat into a steely shell.

Days afterward, the Council's messenger delivered a family ration card, which the Third Reich government had recently issued. Esther had kissed the card like it was embossed with gold. Her initial relief quickly turned into despondency when Salomon read the inscription on the back: "This card entitles its bearer to three hundred calories a day, or such, per family member."

The following day, Esther went to the distribution center and returned with shockingly little—a hunk of stale bread, three potatoes, and two carrots. She reported that when the Nazi soldier punched her card, she showed him the label signifying five people, indicating the amount he had given was short. The soldier had then scrunched his face into a scowl and threatened, "Ungrateful Jew. Get out the door now, or I will take back your entire portion."

A few weeks later, a councilman from the Judenrat visited with reports about the rise of the black market, where Jews were purchasing groceries. But he warned that it was quite perilous as those who were caught faced execution on the spot. He also claimed that many people who had chanced it had become seriously ill from spoiled meats that were passed off as fresh. The man asserted that, from what he had observed of the black-market produce, the fruits were near rotten and the nuts rancid, though he believed that the non-meat high-protein goods, such as dried legumes, were decent if you risked being caught by the Gestapo.

"Legumes? We have no kitchen, no way to cook beans, protein, or *any food*," Hinda had railed at the councilman. He opened his mouth to speak but then closed it. His eyes darted around, noting their primitive quarters.

The councilman's affected manner annoyed Hinda. He was clearly not suffering the way they were. Suspecting that he had beds, couches, a kitchen, and superior food, she entreated further, "Why do some Jews have kitchens and an apartment with furniture, and we have this?"

The man's nose wrinkled, and his upper lip raised in irritation. He explained that it was about timing, that when her family had been relocated there, the regular ghetto housing was already filled beyond capacity. Yet, the Nazis continued to move large numbers of Polish Jews there, so now dairy barns, mills, and any such buildings were declared habitable. Apologizing, he said it was out of his control. Salomon told him they understood. The man left immediately, his eyes glazed and cast downward.

Painfully hungry, the Mondlaks barely subsisted on the government rations, which typically included hardened bread, potatoes, and paltry amounts of one other vegetable—either carrots, turnips, beets, or cabbage. No longer did they peel potatoes; they ate the peelings too.

The Nazis are starving us on purpose, Hinda reasoned. She blinked repeatedly, trying to shut out the frightening sights of her frail family members and their despicable living conditions. Her heart ached for all of them, but mostly for Sara, who was so skinny now that her head appeared too large for her body, and her big eyes bulged in a chilling way. *The poor darling has been robbed of her childhood. Does she dream of a better life? Is she even capable of imagination with gnawing hunger throttling her brain?*

Interrupting Hinda's brooding over Sara, Rachel grabbed Hinda's waist from behind and implored, "Please hug me." Sighing heavily, Hinda turned to face Rachel.

"Will we be okay? Are we going home soon?" Rachel's inquiries were like an annoying mantra. Begging for reassurance, she asked Hinda the same questions multiple times every day.

"Get your sketch pad. Let's draw together," Hinda suggested, knowing that Rachel's art was her best therapy.

"No, my pencils are worn down to nubs. Please hold me."

Hinda wrapped her arms around her sister, fully aware that her next words would be lies. But how else could she pacify Rachel's anxieties when everywhere they looked—both indoors and outdoors—there were copious reasons to feel fearful and morose? "Yes, we'll be okay. And I'll never let anyone harm you. I promise."

The next morning, Hinda awoke to Sara's crying, haunting sounds that were not typical. Her little sister lay curled into a ball, clasping her abdomen, groaning.

Sara is starving to death, Hinda concluded. A powerful and fierce feeling arose inside Hinda. Quickly, she got dressed, her brain buzzing. *I am the oldest now. My parents are failing and weak. It's my job to take care of the family. No matter what happens, I must try.*

Hinda whispered to Rachel that she was going out to seek food. With a determined set to her shoulders, Hinda left the mill and strode down the street. No Gestapo were policing the main avenue that morning, but two capos were. Jewish cops, capos were employees of the Gestapo. They wore armbands and carried batons but not guns. They reported infractions and intimidated ghetto residents, keeping them in line. Other Jews did not revere capos. "Our own people are traitors," Hinda muttered under her breath, when she passed two capos on the street. They eyed her armband, making sure she wore it correctly.

Approaching the gate, Hinda stopped. She looked all around. No capos or Gestapo were nearby, but the gate guards were at their posts. A group of workers, men wearing hardhats, came from behind her. At the gate, they halted, surrounding the guards, asking directions. Hinda sidestepped the workers and sneaked through the ghetto entrance—Jews were forbidden beyond that parameter. She swiftly removed the white armband and stuffed it into her skirt pocket.

Emboldened by her escape, Hinda strolled, weaving through the streets. After a while, the houses began to appear more affluent and the neighborhood cleaner. Breathing deeply, she knocked on a door. A man opened it just a slit, then banged it closed. Even after ten or more doors had slammed in her face, Hinda remained determined. She pushed onward, continuing to knock and to be rejected.

At last, a woman, who had blonde curls that fell onto her forehead and along the sides of her round face, opened the door and kept it ajar. "What do you want?" she inquired, but in a tone that sounded kind.

"I am looking for work, any work."

"What can you do?"

"I can clean, do your wash, and I can cook."

"I don't have much money."

"You don't need to pay me with money. All I want is some food to take home."

The woman stared at Hinda for a long moment, studying her face. "What is your name?"

"Hinda Mondlak."

"I'm Mrs. Kowalski. Heenda, please come inside." She showed Hinda around her house and gave her a list of chores.

"Let's see how this goes today," Mrs. Kowalski said with a lilt on the word *today* as if she were posing a question. In the afternoon, she inspected Hinda's work, nodding in hearty approval. Keeping to her word, the woman gave Hinda a loaf of bread and fresh vegetables.

"Thank you," Hinda said, blinking back tears. "May I come back again, another day?"

"You do excellent work, Heenda, so yes." Mrs. Kowalski, her eyebrows raised in thought, gazed at Hinda, then said, "In fact, I could use you every week, Monday through Friday. As long as your payment is food."

"Yes, every weekday, for food."

Tossing her blonde curls, Mrs. Kowalski said in a muffled voice, "But my husband must not know about you or our arrangement. You must leave by four o'clock every afternoon."

"Four o'clock is perfect." Hinda smiled, reassuring her. "What time would you like for me to arrive?"

"Nine o'clock?"

Hinda inclined her head in assent. "Nine, it is. See you tomorrow morning."

Elated and with her head held high, Hinda commenced her trek back to the mill. At the ghetto gates, she slipped through without the guards noticing her. Immediately, she ducked under a low awning and slipped the white armband over her coat's right sleeve. Pushing it upward, she wore the band on her upper arm, as specified. Secreting the food bag in her coat, she wound her way through the debris-filled streets to what was now home.

When she entered the mill, she was greeted with a chorus of multiple voices: "Hinda! We've been so worried." While her family expressed their relief, they also seemed agitated until she showed them the loaf of *fresh* bread and vegetables. Divided, it was small servings, but their stomachs had shrunk so much that the meager portion size did not matter. While eating, she told them about the nice Polish woman named Mrs. Kowalski, her home, the chores, and how she pronounced Hinda's name funny—Heenda. For the first time in months, the family laughed together. Even Sara smiled, which highlighted her dimples.

In an impassioned tone, Hinda announced, "And I'll be working for Mrs. Kowalski every weekday. In exchange for food."

"We thank God, our provider," Salomon said, briefly bowing his head.

Esther reached out and stroked Hinda's arm. "My brave girl."

"But what about walking home with the food?" Rachel asked. "You could be attacked."

"I can tuck the bag inside my coat. Which I will wear every day, regardless of the weather."

"Even still, you must be extremely careful," Salomon warned. "Not only are you in peril by going outside the gates, but in this ghetto, people are crazed with hunger. They have no qualms about, not just stealing, but even killing for a trifling of crumbs."

Her eyes wide and somber, Hinda nodded. "I know. It's dangerous out there."

"And you must be home before sundown on Fridays," Salomon instructed. "We still honor the Sabbath, at least in here." His fist knocked against his chest, indicating his heart.

"I will do my best, Tatae. I am to leave her house promptly at four o'clock. A full hour before her husband gets home from work."

Instantly, his forehead wrinkled. Salomon said, "He doesn't know about you?"

Hinda shrugged. "I don't know why, but Mrs. Kowalski was adamant that my work in their home be kept secret from her husband."

For months, Hinda worked diligently for Mrs. Kowalski. In turn, she was given a fresh loaf of bread, vegetables, and occasionally, roasted chicken or a container of soup. Hinda's pride soared; she had a job. She was feeding her family.

18
Rigors and Chills
March 1941 | Gliwice, German-occupied Poland

Wolf Yoskowitz, his clothes soaked, inched through the dark and empty streets of Gliwice. A quarter moon, hanging in the eastern sky, provided just enough light for him to navigate. Since it was past curfew for Jews, Wolf was vigilant with every step. When he spotted two Gestapo ahead, his heart rate skyrocketed. He lunged behind a storefront wall and inhaled deeply, trying to muzzle his wheezing. His lungs burned from the lengthy periods he had held his breath underwater in the river.

Earsplitting popping sounds caused him to jump and involuntarily exhale with a sonorous rasp. Wolf peeked around the wall's edge. The two Gestapo were running in the opposite direction, firing their pistols as they galloped. Slightly mollified, Wolf decided upon an alternate route home. Shivering from hypothermia and the shock of his narrow escape of the Nazi patrol at the river, and now, these two, he crept forward.

Nearing home, Wolf hastened his pace. When he turned the corner onto his lane, he froze, instantly halting. Nazi flags were attached to the doorways of all the homes on both sides of the street. No lights, not even flickers, could be seen inside the houses. Checking every direction, he stepped warily to his front door. The knob would not turn; a heavy lock hung from it. Guardedly, Wolf stole through the trees to the back of the house. That door, too, was locked and bore a flag with a large swastika symbol.

Bitter liquid rose in his throat. Wolf bent double, retching bile and river water onto the grass. He was chilled to the bone. His head felt waterlogged, his brain numb.

The family home confiscated, now Third Reich government property, could mean only two things for his mother, sister, and three brothers. Either they had been seized, or they were killed on-site. Wolf's shoulders reared up at the latter thought. *I have to know. Have to see if they're in there.* Breathing heavily, he searched the night sky. "God, help me," Wolf whispered, though he wanted to shout it all the way to heaven, knocking the moon and the stars off their orbits.

A light zephyr whooshed across his face, ruffling his hair. Then Wolf remembered: he always left the window in his room slightly cracked for fresh air. Cautiously, he clambered upward. His hand slid over the threshold of the window frame, and sure enough, it was open just a smidgen. His thick fingers blocked him from getting underneath the sash and raising it further. Instead, he tried to hoist the exterior window casement upward—again and again. The house had settled with age. The window was stuck. Mustering all his might, Wolf gave it one more shove upward. It shifted, budging an inch, then another, until, finally, he could push it completely open.

Fatigued from the day's physical demands and weak from hunger, Wolf struggled to climb high enough to get his body level with the opening of the medium-sized window that was set high on the wall. Wincing, he realized that if he hadn't lost so much weight this past year, he couldn't fit through. His broad shoulders posed another obstacle. Repositioning his body at an angle, he thrust himself forward and tumbled onto his bedroom floor.

In the soft glow of the moonlight, Wolf saw his bed covers all mussed and rumpled. That morning, he had made the bed and left the entire room orderly. He gawked in disbelief. Drawers were open; clothing lay strewn across the floor. His room had been ransacked.

Getting to his feet and fearing what he would find next, his heart thumped so arduously that the sound of its beats rang in his ears. Room after room had been turned upside down, valuables taken. There were no dead bodies, and no alive ones either. In each bedroom, Wolf gathered the lightweight and frayed blankets that had been left behind. All the woolen blankets and thick quilts were gone.

Ravenous, Wolf rummaged through the kitchen, searching for even the merest morsel. In the back of the pantry, he found two cans of peas covered with rumpled flour sacks. Retrieving a fishing knife from his jacket, he pierced the lid of one can, lifted its edge, and pried the top open enough to slide in a spoon. He yanked open the utensil drawer, which had been rifled through and was now in a jumble. There, among some old spatulas, he found a dented spoon, obviously not valuable enough for the Nazis to take.

Barely chewing, Wolf gulped down three spoonfuls. Then, savoring baby bites, he slowly chewed two peas at a time. He hankered for more, but self-preservation prevailed. *I must save the other can for later.*

Thirsty, Wolf went to the sink and drank straight from the faucet. Opening the glassware cabinet, he noted that the nice crystal was missing. Only timeworn glasses remained. He selected the tallest mug and filled it. Then he rinsed the knife and spoon and took them, the other can of peas, the stein of water, and the bundle of blankets to his bedroom. There, he shoved the dresser against the door, lowered the window, and closed the curtains. The lamp on the bedside table beckoned. His hand on the switch, Wolf contemplated: *All the other houses are dark too. Had the electricity on the street been shut off?* He shrugged. *Even if not, lights tonight are too risky. I'll find out in daylight hours.*

Past midnight, he had few hours to sleep before dawn, which would be decision time: what was prudent to do next? Wolf removed his soggy boots, stripped off his wet clothes, and dried his trembling body. He donned fresh clothing—work garments, sturdy escape clothes. In the back of his closet, he found a pair of worn-out boots. He unlaced them and set them on the floor near his bed.

Exhausted, Wolf collapsed into bed. Adjusting the covers, he layered all the blankets on top of him. Still not warm, he nestled down into the mattress, hugging the covers to him. Just before going into a deep slumber, the faces of his missing family—his mother, sister, and brothers—floated in his mind's eye. The image of his youngest brother, Alexander, lingered. Wolf shuddered, but nary a tear fell. Weariness sapped all emotion.

Hours later, his body jerked awake with chills, but his skin was burning hot. Rigors shook him hard. Yanking on the blankets, Wolf pulled them tightly around him. But it did not stop the uncontrollable shaking.

A cacophony of honking horns and screeching tires jolted him further, triggering an increased level of shivering. Wolf raised his head. It throbbed. Barely capable of lifting the curtain, he peeked outside. There, he espied the front hood of a large vehicle, a German army truck, parked in the middle of the street. Glaring sunlight almost blinded him. *Lord have mercy, it must be near noon.*

19

Jail of Death

April 1941 | Mława, German-occupied Poland

Despite the war and the German occupation, the Kowalski's home buzzed with festive plans for Easter. All week, Hinda had labored over uncustomary cleaning tasks, ironed table linens, and polished silver. She had cooked elaborate dishes and organized the groceries required for the selected menus. Intrigued, she felt enlivened. The assignments provided glimpses of how Christians celebrated Easter, all so foreign to her.

It was almost nine months now that Hinda had worked for Mrs. Kowalski, who had become more generous with the amounts of foodstuff she rendered in compensation for Hinda's household help. On this Thursday, she bagged an even greater quantity, including nuggets of chocolate. Hinda wanted to hug her but refrained, only saying thank you repeatedly.

"Heenda, you are such marvelous help." Mrs. Kowalski grasped Hinda's hand, the first time she had ever touched Hinda's skin. "Remember though, you don't come tomorrow. Good Friday begins our holiday; my husband will be home. See you Monday morning."

Hinda's head full of the complicated dessert recipes that she had baked that day, she commenced her journey home. The *makowiec* (poppyseed loaf cake) had smelled heavenly when cooking, but the most unique for her was the yeast cake iced with rose water, a specialty for Easter called *babka wielkanocua* in Polish. The entire week had been fascinating to her, the food customs so different from her family's preparations for Passover.

Sweet delicacies waltzing in her mind, Hinda sauntered along unaware of her surroundings. Suddenly jounced by rocky pavement, she looked up. Hinda gasped, flabbergasted to be at the ghetto gates. Quickly, she tucked the bag of food inside her coat.

A Gestapo officer spotted her. He stepped in front of her in an authoritative imposing manner, his feet planted, his hands on his hips. A soldier, wearing a light green uniform different from the officer's dark one, stepped up, flanking the officer.

"What's your name?"

"Hinda."

"Your last name?"

For the first time in her life, Hinda did not want to be a Mondlak. She wished to be Mrs. Kowalski's daughter. *Hinda* was not a typical Jewish name. If she used the Kowalski surname now, the Gestapo might wave her on, let her go on the street where she stood just outside the gate. But if discovered, Mrs. Kowalski could be arrested for letting a Jewish girl work for her. After a brief hesitation, she answered, "Mondlak."

"You are a Jew! Where's your armband?" the soldier demanded.

"It's here in my pocket." Hinda pulled it out, showing him.

"You're not wearing it, you scum," the officer sneered. "And what are you hiding in your coat?"

"Food for my family," she replied, struggling to remain composed.

"Hand it over, right now." The officer checked inside the bag. Seeing the chocolate, he smacked his lips and passed the sack to the soldier. Then he flung his hand far back over his shoulder, adding force, and struck Hinda savagely in the face. Instantly, her eyes watered, her face a blood moon.

"Where did you get this food? You stole it, didn't you?"

"No. A woman gave it to me."

"Who? What's her name?"

"I don't know. A stranger. A woman with blonde hair just walked up to me on the street. She said 'Happy Easter' and handed me the bag."

He eyed her skeptically, his pursed lips and raised brows signaling his disbelief.

"My family is starving, sir."

Both men broke out in uproarious laughter. The Nazi soldier slapped his knee as if she had cracked a hilarious joke.

His mocking risibility vanished. His eyes now snaky and spewing venom, the Gestapo officer held Hinda's white armband with the blue, six-pointed star mere millimeters from her nose. "You knowingly violated the law not wearing this Jew badge. And you trespassed, going outside the ghetto parameters." He grabbed her hands and slapped on handcuffs.

"To jail you go, Hinda Mondlacky."

From across the square, a boy called out, "It's the jail of death, you're going to the *Jail of Death*."

Two hours had passed since the time that Hinda usually arrived home from her day of work. Her family members worried and fretted in their own individual way. Esther clasped her hands together, wringing them anxiously. Rachel stood glued to the window, watching intently for her sister. Clutching her cloth doll, Sara lay curled into a fetal position on the floor, thumb in her mouth. Salomon paced, praying fervently.

Nearing dusk, the light streaming through the window dimmed, casting gloomy shadows. Abruptly, Esther declared, "I can't take it anymore. I'm going to the gate to look for Hinda before it gets dark."

"No, Esther, no," Salomon argued.

Her jaw set and teeth clenched, Esther slipped on her coat, and then adjusted her white armband on the coat's right sleeve. "I'm going. You stay with the girls."

From the window, Rachel watched her mother trudge down the street. She looked weak and crippled, like a mother hen with broken wings. Rachel cupped her fingertips gently on the glass, as if she were caressing her mother's face. She whispered, "Mommy, be careful."

At the ghetto gates, Esther began inquiring about Hinda. Persistently, she asked person after person if they had seen her daughter. Though she loathed the capos, the Jews who worked for the Gestapo, she decided to ask one, a young man she recognized as Joel's friend from their shtetl in Zieluń. His answer was no, as it was with everyone she asked, until she came to a young mother toting a baby, who had his fist in his mouth, his chin wet with drool.

"What was your daughter wearing?" the woman asked, bouncing her baby.

Esther thought for a minute, her mind addled from worry. "I'm not sure exactly, but she had a blue coat."

"Then maybe I saw her. A couple of hours ago," the young woman replied. "My baby is teething. He stops fussing only when I walk him outside. I took him indoors after the episode and have just now brought him back out. I'm trying to lull him to sleep."

Esther's breath caught. "What episode?"

"What's your daughter's name?"

"Hinda. Hinda Mondlak."

"There was a girl who was probably in her late teens or early twenties. She was just outside the gate, and hmm, yes, she was wearing a blue coat." The woman paused. Ruffling her baby's hair, she let her fingers glide through the silky strands.

"Sounds right. Hinda turns twenty next month." Desperate to hear more, Esther focused her eyes intently on the woman and leaned in close to her. "What happened? Please tell me. I *must* know."

"Well, then." The woman paused, swallowing hard. "At the gate's entrance, a Gestapo officer stopped the girl in the blue coat. It appeared he was interrogating her. He and a Nazi soldier laughed haughtily, ridiculing whatever she had told them. Then the officer handcuffed her. I heard him say that she, Hinda Mon-something, was going to jail."

All the color drained from Esther's face. Her breath quickened. She turned from the young mother and the baby. Taking one step in the direction of home, she suddenly keeled over, fainting right there in the street. Her chest crashed against a craggy rock. A loud crack—the sound of Esther's sternum fracturing —clanged in the air.

A Gestapo officer came running, his pistol drawn. The young mother pressed her baby to her bosom and walked briskly away, angling onto a side street. A cluster of bystanders scattered, expecting the officer to fire at least one well-aimed shot, killing Esther on the exact spot where she had fallen. Instead, he walked around her body, studying her. He then radioed for a gurney.

Esther was transported to the ghetto hospital. But not to be treated.

20

A Wicked Germ

Helpless against the high fever that plagued his body, Wolf Yoskowitz struggled to sit up, only to fall back onto his pillow. Although he could hear soldiers on the street in front of his house, he could barely lift a finger, let alone hide. Defenseless, he closed his eyes and attempted a prayer of protection. His brain woozy, the words would not come. Drowsiness engulfed him, demanding submission. Within seconds, he was swept into a deep slumber.

Two hours later, Wolf's eyes popped open. Thumping footsteps roused his awareness, dragging him from the depths of an aguish stupor. Voices—throaty sounds of the German language—reverberated in his room. Nazi soldiers had entered the house. Gauging the volume of their utterances, Wolf guessed they were in the kitchen.

If the soldiers came to his bedroom door and tried to open it, using their typical brute force, the wooden dresser pushed against his door would block them for all of about two seconds. Having no strength to get out the window, Wolf was trapped. Lying perfectly still, he listened intently. He understood enough German to conclude that the soldiers were turning the water off and shutting down the plumbing.

Footsteps trailed. Then, the tinkling of piano keys startled him. Since the piano was in the living room, Wolf surmised that the soldiers were now in there— or at least one was. He listened closely as a childlike pecking of "Jingle Bells" came first, then a surprising ragtime piece, played in quite an accomplished fashion—obviously performed by a different person from the first. Clapping sounds wafted into Wolf's room.

Speaking in their native dialect, the soldiers exchanged several sentences. Wolf understood enough to know that they wanted the piano, and that it had not been taken yesterday because their captain had determined it old and not worth much. The disturbing part was that one of the soldiers wanted it for his mother. Their plan was to come back and get it on another day.

Wolf lay there, barely breathing, listening, waiting. Then, he heard more footsteps and the front door slamming with a bang. Soon, quiet enveloped him; he fell soundly asleep.

At dawn, Wolf awoke. His clothing clung to his skin, moist with perspiration from the high body temperature he had suffered. Yet he felt different; the fever had broken. He sat up in bed and reached for the mug of water that he had brought to his room two nights ago. He downed it all in two gulps, and that amount did not quench his thirst or erase the foul taste in his mouth.

Weak and wobbly, Wolf managed to stand. Hobbling to the dresser, he attempted to slide it away from the door. It didn't budge. He opened one of the drawers; it had been rifled through. Everything was jumbled. He dug around looking for clean underwear. In so doing, and much to his astonishment, he found a quarter loaf of bread wrapped in one of his father's flannel shirts, one used strictly for camping. His mother had known that Wolf was out fishing and would return home. He decided that it must have been her that hid the bread after the Nazi's searched his room. How she managed that, and why she wrapped it in his dad's old camping shirt remained a mystery. Those enigmas begged multiple questions, but he was too hungry to contemplate them. He stuffed the quarter baguette into his mouth, savoring every bite.

Next, Wolf removed the damp sheets and blankets from his bed, tossing them onto the floor. Hurriedly, he dressed in dry clothing. The quick movements made him feel dizzy. He was seriously dehydrated.

Desperate to get any water remaining in the pipes, Wolf pushed and shoved on the dresser again, all to no avail. *That was one wicked germ I swallowed in the river.* Flinging himself onto the mattress, Wolf relented, shedding a trickle of unwilling tears. And in the next moment, he was conked out, dreaming, though his legs jerked in a scissorlike motion. Swimming in murky slime-infested waters, he searched frantically for his armband.

21
A Sliver of Clemency
April 1941 | Mława, German-occupied Poland

Distraught, Sara sobbed and blubbered between gasps for air. In an agonizing tone, she repeatedly screamed, "Mommy! Hinda!" Her wails jangled the nerves of everyone in hearing distance.

A stricken grimace eclipsing her alluring face, Rachel cradled her little sister in her arms, rocking Sara back and forth. Rachel had tried every soothing technique she knew, including plugging Sara's mouth with her own thumb. Nothing helped.

Pacing in a loop, Salomon had pounded the floor for over an hour. Every few steps, he threw his arms up and his head back, looking heavenward, pleading for help. A wise, decisive man in the past, he was stymied by these circumstances. It was past curfew, so he could not go to a Council member's quarters. If he went out on the streets to look for Esther and Hinda, he could be arrested. Rachel and Sara could not fend for themselves. He had to stay with them.

Salomon's soul whispered that something grave had happened to Esther. In his bones, he sensed her life force waning, her flame flickering. Whereas with Hinda, he sensed that she was in serious trouble, suffering terribly. Yet he believed that, somehow, Hinda would survive.

Suddenly, Sara went into an inordinate fit of delirium. High-pitched, ear-splitting squalls beleaguered even the walls.

The flour sacks flapped, and Mr. Shapiro poked his head through the makeshift curtain. "*Feh!* Can't you quiet her down?"

His face flushed, Salomon turned on his heel and faced Mr. Shapiro. The Yiddish term Feh! meant utter disgust—the equivalent of spitting. Ignoring the offense, Salomon replied, "I'm sorry. I apologize for the ruckus. My wife and daughter are missing. God help us."

"God?" Mr. Shapiro asked incredulously. "God is blind and deaf," he exclaimed with a vociferous grunt as he yanked the flour sack divider closed.

Salomon glared. Faithless allegory and insults taxed his nerves more than Sara's wails did. A part of him felt he was screaming with her, venting his bridled fury, giving voice to the horror of all that had occurred and the unjust persecution that continued in their everyday reality.

Suddenly, Rachel shouted, "Tatae, help! Sara's not breathing right."

Heaving Sara upward, Salomon held her upright over his shoulder. He could feel the child's racing heartbeat even through his clothing. In the most tranquil tone he could muster, he said, "Sara, I understand why you're upset. But I need you to calm down and breathe more slowly." His words incited her more. Sara gasped uncontrollably.

"Rachel, get a warm cover for her."

"I am." Grabbing a blanket, Rachel tucked it around her little sister.

"Get your coat and armband. We're taking her to the ghetto hospital."

Hinda crouched in the jail cell. Red welts marked her arms and legs. Soon after she had been locked behind bars, a Nazi soldier came in and flogged her with a leather whip. Hinda's cellmates claimed that a thrashing was the standard greeting, that and the immediate stench. Beyond dirty, the cell reeked of putrid vomit and rotten refuse. High on the wall near the ceiling, an open window, with vertical bars attached, did little to allay the malodorous odor.

Her legs stinging and burning, Hinda rubbed the welts rising on her skin. As she fingered each one, she chastised herself for making such a foolish blunder with the food and the armband. She could not stop envisioning the panic her family must be experiencing. Under her breath, she prayed, "Dearest Lord, please comfort my family. Help me find a way to let them know that I'm alive, but in jail."

The ghetto community called this prison the Jail of Death for good reason. Few people ever got out and returned to their families.

Almost running down the bumpy street, Salomon carried Sara. Her head bobbled on his shoulder; her legs dangled down his torso.

Trotting alongside her father, trying to keep up with his long stride, Rachel strained to see the pebbly pathway. A sprinkling of stars in the night sky and sparsely scattered streetlamps emitted shadowy light. "Tatae, watch out for the rocks," she warned.

As they neared the gates, Salomon dodged a boulder, almost stumbling on the surrounding gravel. He slowed his pace and veered right. There, on the side street, was the entrance to the ghetto hospital that was housed in an old, crumbling structure. He shoved the hospital door open, and they entered the front room, which was a well-lit area. Salomon stopped at the desk. No attendant was behind it or anywhere in the room. To the side, patients on gurneys lined the hallway. Stone-faced, Salomon stood motionless. His skin turning a ghastly gray, he gaped at the patient on the second gurney.

From behind him, Rachel implored, "Ring the bell on the desk. That's what the sign says to do." After waiting a half second for her father to respond, she pressed the buzzer multiple times.

Startled by the peals, Salomon jumped. Regaining his awareness, he realized that Sara lay sprawled across his body, no longer rigid and no longer gasping. His hand moved to the center of her back, which rose and fell with regular breaths. "The chair over there, Rachel," Salomon pointed. "Sit down and hold your little sister."

"I'm too scared."

"It's okay. She's sleeping now. I guess the jogging motion and the night air calmed her," Salomon explained as he transferred Sara into Rachel's arms. "I need you to take her for a few minutes. Yes?"

"Okay, but is that Mommy over there?" Rachel asked, her eyes wide.

A knot forming in his throat, Salomon nodded yes. He stepped quietly to the second gurney and looked upon the face of his beloved. Ghostly white, Esther appeared a mess. Blood oozed from lacerations on her chin. Her dress was torn and bright red, soaked with blood in the chest area. Her coat, which had been pulled back from her neck, was splattered with dirt. Salomon grimaced. *She must have fallen, but she's had no treatment. Not even cleaned up or bandaged.* Her white armband was twisted on the coat's sleeve. Salomon ached to rip it off and tear it to shreds. Placing his hand in hers, which felt cold, he detected a slight pulse. "My precious Esther," he whispered. Her eyes fluttered, yet they did not open. Tears gushed down Salomon's face, dripping onto his coat. He bent over his wife, pressing his cheek to hers.

Suddenly, a wild-eyed nurse charged into the room. She shrieked "What do you think you're doing? Get away from that patient."

"She's . . . my . . . wife," Salomon sputtered, barely able to eke out the syllables.

"How did you get in here?"

"The door was open. My young daughter's heart was racing," Salomon explained. "When we came in, I saw my wife on this stretcher."

"It's after-hours. The door was supposed to be locked." The nurse pulled a stethoscope from her pocket. Pointing at Sara, she said, "I'll examine the little girl."

"Thank you, but please don't wake her," Salomon pleaded. "We've been through such an ordeal. She was overwrought for hours. May I have a moment with my wife? She is—" He sighed, incapable of saying the word, *dying*.

The nurse's black eyebrows shot straight up. "No. Sit down." After Salomon was seated, she strode around the corner and quickly returned with an empty gurney. "Lay your daughter here," she commanded.

Reluctantly, Salomon lifted Sara from Rachel's arms and laid her down. When Sara did not move or even stir, he sighed in relief. "She must be exhausted after getting so worked up."

The nurse placed her stethoscope on Sara's chest. After what seemed like hours, she reported, "Her heart is beating at a normal resting rate, and her breathing is even." Eyeing Salomon and Rachel suspiciously, the nurse said, "Tell me what happened. Why was she upset?"

Salomon could feel time ticking away, hallowed last moments with Esther in jeopardy. Yet, he knew he must placate the nurse for any chance to be by his wife's side again. He took a deep breath and launched into the story. "My older daughter didn't come home at her regular time today. At dusk, my wife went to the gates to look for her. We waited for her to return, but she did not. Our little Sara here was already upset about her sister, Hinda, who is like a second mother to her." Abruptly, Salomon stopped, pushing aside his usual respectful, compliant self. "I can't—" He stood and rushed to Esther.

Before the nurse could react, Rachel, too, lunged from her chair and dashed to her mother's bedside. One glance at her mother's bloody and ashen face, and Rachel cracked. She threw herself across Esther's torso, crying out, "Mommy, Mommy. Please don't die."

"Quiet down, or I will order you to leave," the nurse scolded loudly. "You're disturbing other patients."

Lifting Rachel from her mother's body, Salomon helped her to stand and held her tightly against him. "My sweet girl," he whispered.

The nurse placed her fingertips on the side of Esther's neck. After a moment, she said, "You two take a few minutes with your wife and mother." She turned away, moving to the desk behind the counter.

After standing in silence, Rachel looked up to her father's face. Profound sadness etched a heartsick expression. Removing her hand from her mother's arm, Rachel squeaked, her voice catching in her throat, "Mommy's so very still. Is she alive?"

Bowing his head, Salomon said, "No, my dear daughter, she is not." His chin quivering, he shifted his stance and stood taller. "She was when we arrived, though. Her eyes fluttered when I first talked to her. She knew that we came."

Waking from fitful sleep, Hinda sat up, looking around the jail cell. She wiped her eyes, which were wet. In the dream that had awakened her, she had cried. Struggling to recall the details, intense emotion welled up inside her. Fragments came to mind, then a scene: her mother had stood over her, softly stroking her brow as she wept. She had sung the words, "Shush now, my beautiful, brave daughter," like a lullaby. Her green eyes sparkling, her mother then presented a dainty basket; it was filled to the brim with chocolates. "Go enjoy the river, Hinda. You deserve it."

Yearning to return to the dream, Hinda curled into her coat on the hard floor. Just as she was nodding off, a cellmate cried out during a nightmare, rousing Hinda again. She raised up on her elbows, looking in the direction of the commotion. The girl was moaning and flailing, making fighting motions with her arms and hands while she slept. Earlier, when they were eating the gruel that was served for dinner, that same girl had told Hinda hair-raising tales of the treatment she had received while in jail. Moreover, she warned that every week, on a random day, the Gestapo came and chose three prisoners and took them to the gallows in the square, where they were publicly hanged. Their limp, lifeless bodies, nooses around their necks, were left dangling for days in a ghoulish display, all to terrorize ghetto residents.

A dingy bedsheet in her hand, the nurse asked Salomon and Rachel to step aside. She spread the sheet across Esther, pulling it all the way up to cover her head. "What was her name?"

"Esther. Esther Mondlak." His voice cracking, Salomon asked, "Is there any record of what happened to her?"

"Let me check the charts." The nurse went to the desk and flipped through papers. Her finger went to a line on a page. She moved it under the words. "The notes suggest that she fell on a rock and fractured her sternum. But there's no name here. She must have been unconscious when they brought her in."

"What's a sternum?" Rachel asked, her words faltering.

"It's the breastbone in the chest," Salomon explained, enfolding Rachel's hand into his. Turning to the nurse, he said, "What's the protocol from here? May I take her for burial?"

With a swift shake of her head, the nurse said, "No," in an emphatic and firm tone. She thrust a piece of paper and pen toward him saying, "Write your wife's name here."

Salomon complied, writing ESTHER MONDLAK in neat block letters.

After taping the note to Esther's bed, the nurse turned to face Salomon. To her, he was a broken man. A Jew. Yet his quiet reverence and dignified countenance prompted a sliver of clemency. In a crisp tone, she barked, "Be here at seven o'clock tomorrow morning and bring an official from your people's Judenrat."

The Diabolic Hand

May 1941 | Günzburg, Germany

Visiting his hometown for the first time in months, Walter Zeilhofen parked his 1935 Renault, a black Celtaquatre coupé, on the side street across from the cathedral. He loved his car more than he ever conceived imaginable for a motorized metal object with wheels. Looking skyward, he thanked his Uncle Eckhart for the generous gift. His uncle's recent and sudden death had struck a deep emotional blow. Named in the will, Walter had received his uncle's prized Renault, which was sleek and eye-catching. When walking away, he prayed for the car to not be vandalized. Only recently had the offensive notion come to his attention: a French-made car was not welcome in Nazi Germany.

Entering the Rococo-style cathedral—the Church of Our Lady—Walter was immediately overwhelmed with childhood memories. Near the altar, he genuflected and crossed himself, and then chose a quiet pew to the side. Forever impressed with the architecture of Dominikus Zimmermann, Walter admired the stained-glass windows, the gilded ornate carvings, and the colorful frescoes that were all such a portentous part of his life, from infancy onward. Shutting out the ostensible symbols of God's magnanimous spirit, Walter closed his eyes. Today, though, he could not quiet his mind. Feeling too antsy to sit in meditation, he decided to go to confession, seeking absolution for his recent sins. One, in particular, weighed on him, corroding his peaceful heart.

Afterward, Walter attended midday mass, which he found comforting until Josef Mengele's mother and father arrived late and sat beside him.

Later, when driving to his parent's home, Walter felt the diabolic hand of Adolph Hitler pressing upon him. His stomach churned with acid. The news he was about to deliver to his parents was going to blow the roof off their classic Bavarian-style house.

Swine Buns

March 17, 1941 | Gliwice, German-occupied Poland

Wolf Yoskowitz awoke with a start. Rising from the bare mattress, he parted the curtain. Dazzlingly bright in a cloudless sky, the morning sun beamed as if only happiness and goodness pervaded the earth.

His throat was parched, and his stomach felt empty, but he was free of fever. Grateful to stand erect without dizziness, Wolf shoved the dresser that blocked his bedroom door. This time, it slid easily.

Tiptoeing, he moved through the house, listening at every corner, unsure of who or what he would find. In the living room, Wolf noted that the piano was still there. Sun rays, streaming through the window, danced upon the ebony and ivory keys, although Nazi soldiers had last stroked them. He shuddered, wondering if he had merely dreamt that the soldiers had played the piano. Yet the memory of their coming into the house and shutting off the water was distinct. Also, categorically clear was his recollection of their playing two songs on the piano and then discussing their plan to return for it.

Thirst driving his steps to the kitchen, Wolf searched the cabinets and found two pans. He held one under the faucet, hoping to catch any droplets remaining in the pipes. To his surprise, the pot filled to three-fourths full before the flow waned. While it still dribbled, he filled a glass to the rim. Although he wanted to gulp, he sipped slowly until he emptied the glass.

Retrieving the second pan, he carried it to the bathroom, placed it in the sink, and turned on the tap. Water flowed then trickled, filling the pot to two-thirds full. Making two trips, he carried the water to his bedroom and stowed the pots under his dresser.

Surveying the room, Wolf decided to leave the mess—the sheets, blankets, and strewn clothing—on the floor. Although his preferred style was neat and tidy, he decided it was wiser for his room to resemble the ransacked disorder the soldiers had created in the rest of the house.

Wolf yearned to clean his body. He worried, though, that the water in the bathtub pipes would be needed later for drinking water. Moreover, it was risky to strip down, not knowing what day or hour the soldiers were coming for the piano. He decided upon a sponge bath. Afterward, he donned fresh clothing.

Ready to depart, Wolf noticed the second can of peas on his bedside table. It was empty. Shrugging his shoulders, he guessed that he had eaten it when he was delirious with fever. He peeked through the curtains. Not seeing anything suspicious, he opened the drapes for a wider view. The street was empty of vehicles and of people. The yard appeared clear too. His leg halfway through the window, Wolf remembered his armband. It had been in his jacket pocket when he jumped into the river.

Finding the pile of fishing clothing, Wolf pulled the jacket from the bottom of the heap. He thrust his fingers into the right pocket, and nothing was there. Then he checked the left pocket. Nothing. His heart thumping against his chest, he whispered, "I've lost my armband. I have no identity badge for the streets."

Carefully choosing back streets for his route, Wolf arrived at a familiar alleyway corner. Steps away was the rear door to the bakery where he used to deliver sacks of flour. Leaning around shrubbery, all he could see were trashcans overflowing with garbage. Deciding to take the risk, Wolf stepped into the alley. His mouth watered, remembering the delicious *pączki* holes the owner's daughter, Halina, would sneak to him when he dropped off the flour. This bakery had a reputation for making the finest pączki, Polish donuts, in Gliwice. Today, he did not care about their accolades, only the fact that the owner and his family had been kind to him over the years. And more importantly, they threw away bread and pastry items that were more than two days old. Yet now with the war and the German invasion, he worried that no foodstuff was being tossed, stale or not.

The first trashcan was topped with wet goop. The second one was piled high with wax paper and ordinary refuse. The third can was covered. He raised its lid, and there was nothing inside but old newspapers.

Wolf mustered his courage and knocked on the door, rapping three times. After a few minutes, a young woman poked her head around the door's edge. Her straw-colored strands of hair were twisted into a chignon and covered with a hairnet.

"Wolf! What are *you* doing here?" Halina's brown eyes doubled their size. The boy, who delivered their flour and had grown into a brawny young man, was now a wispy shadow of himself, a skeleton. Although Halina had memorized every feature of Wolf's handsome face, having secretly harbored a crush for years, she barely recognized him.

"I'm sorry to bother you, Halina, but, um, er, I was hoping you had some old bread you could spare." Ducking his head, too uncomfortable to maintain eye contact, Wolf felt like a pauper, a vagrant beggar, a criminal on the run.

"I've missed you, Wolf. I'm so sorry for, for, for what has happened. It's just not right." She cast a suspicious look down the alleyway. "The Gestapo take our stale bread and pastries now. But give me a moment. Wait here." She left the door slightly ajar. Heavenly aromas of bread and sweets all but buckled Wolf's knees.

After a long three minutes, Halina returned and thrust two small white bags into Wolf's hands. "The counter is busy right now, so I've got to hurry back in." She slammed the door.

When he was halfway down the alleyway, Wolf heard the door hinges creak open again and Halina calling out to him. He swiveled to look back at her.

"The Gestapo usually come every Monday and Thursday. Don't come on those days. And be cautious any day. They often surprise us."

Ambling back toward Halina, Wolf said, "Thank you for the warning and for the bread here. Sincerely appreciated."

"On Tuesday morning, I'll have more for you. My father just told me that he heard there were raids in your neighborhood. He asked if your family was all right."

"I don't know," Wolf replied, his voice choked. "I was gone the day the Nazis came and when I returned, well, none of my family was there."

"Oh no! Where are you living? Did the Nazis raid your house?"

"Yes, they took all valuables, ransacked everything, and cut off the water and electricity. I crawl in the window and am managing to stay there. Please don't tell anyone."

"Of course, but may I tell my parents?"

"Sure, as long as they don't report me."

Halina lowered her voice to a whisper. "Definitely not, not *my* family if you get what I mean. I'll see you Tuesday."

"Thank you, Halina. I'm beyond grateful."

"Be very careful." She waved him on and closed the door. This time, Wolf heard the click of the lock.

Hiding the bakery bags in his jacket, Wolf began a circuitous route in the direction of home. It took all his resolve to not rip open one of the sacks and eat as he walked. Passing a park, he was tempted to sit on one of the benches and devour the contents of the bags. But he had no armband. Numerous areas were off-limits to Jews, and the restrictions could change daily. It was too risky to stop anywhere. He pressed onward, his stomach gnawing at itself.

Once he was home, Wolf checked the street for soldiers. Seeing none, he sat on the ground under a grove of trees in the backyard. As if handling precious gems, he carefully opened the first bag. It held five small rolls. Melted cheese oozed out the sides. He broke one roll open. Inside it was a piece of sausage covered in cheese. *Whoa! Swine buns.* Digging into the second bag, Wolf found slices of plain bread, pączki holes, and more sausage–cheese rolls. While feasting on the pączki, he contemplated Jewish law. Pork was forbidden, and it was against kosher dietary codes to have cheese or dairy products touching any meat.

Ravenous hunger overrode compliance. Although not a single shred of pork, and certainly not any meat mixed with cheese, had *ever* entered his mouth, Wolf ate all five of the sausage rolls in the first sack before launching into prayer. "Lord, forgive me. I know I am willfully sinning. Please understand that I'm starving. I'm desperate and destitute. Plus, I need to regain strength if I am to survive. Blessed are You, Lord, who nourishes all. Amen." Although he was still famished, Wolf folded the top on the second bag, vowing to save the bread and other pork rolls until later.

Arising from the ground, Wolf looked upward. What he saw was startling. His window was wide open.

24

The Devil's Maid

May 1941 | Młava, German-occupied Poland

In the ghetto jail, the bell clanged promptly at five o'clock in the morning. Hinda peeped open one eye, then coaxed the other one to face the day. Yawning and stretching, she arose from the hard floor. Morning rations soon followed. Tasteless, watery porridge and a thumb-sized bun comprised her breakfast.

At six o'clock, Gestapo came to Cell Eleven and ordered the all-female group to scrub the guards' quarters. Work was required every day in the jail or in the prison yard, but this was the first time Hinda had entered the living quarters of the police, where eight men shared an apartment-like space. The furnishings were stark, military style, but looked inviting to Hinda, who yearned for any resemblance of a bed.

One of her cellmates gagged and jumped back upon going into a bathroom. The girl held her nose and squealed like a pig. The warden guarding the door grabbed her by the hair and hauled her down the hall.

Trying not to envision the girl's fate, Hinda got busy. In her mind, she heard her mother's voice proclaiming to always bring excellence to whatever chore you were performing. Observing the others' work, Hinda determined that her mother had been a fastidious taskmaster when it came to cleaning. Then, she heard the main guard openly chiding two women about the way they were doing the floors. Her instincts kicked in. She knew they would *all* be beaten if *anyone* did a poor job. Deciding to take charge, Hinda called the group together and outlined the tasks in the order that they should be done. She insisted upon moving beds and furniture to thoroughly clean underneath. Shaking her head in disapproval, she said, "You don't dust baseboards, you wash them." Meticulous about cleaning everything, including corners and behind doors, Hinda even mopped particular floors over again. At five o'clock in the afternoon, with her hands aching from all the scrubbing, she inspected every room and declared the space spotless.

The Gestapo officer, who had guarded them while they worked, yelled out in command mode, "Mondlak!" Hinda jumped back, expecting trouble, then stood erect facing him. Frowning, the officer grunted, "Good work." To the others, he sniped, "The rest of you scum could take more instruction from her."

Back in the cell, there was no sign of the woman who had been carted away. Gruesome speculations of her fate were bantered about like a volley of ping-pong, while three of the girls harassed Hinda. "You'll never get out of here. The Nazis like the way you clean."

Retreating to her corner, Hinda embraced the warmth of her coat. Spreading it on the floor, she reclined, while she imagined that, at the mill, her parents were doing the same. That is, if they hadn't gone mad with worry about her. One question—how to let them know that she was alive, but in jail—echoed continuously in her head and tolled ceaselessly in her heart.

From across the way, one of the girls taunted Hinda, calling her "the Devil's Maid." Anger oozing from her pores, the girl wanted to fight. Every day about this time, usually before the guards brought the evening rations, that young woman tried to instigate conflict. Ignoring her, Hinda pretended to sleep.

After Hinda had finished eating the night meal—hardtack rolls dunked into watered-down barley soup—one of the cellmates came and sat beside her. The girl turned her tall, lanky body away from the others and slipped a pencil and small piece of paper into Hinda's hand. Hinda looked askance at her.

The girl leaned in close and spoke in hushed tones. "Write your name at the top and a few words to your family. Throw the piece of paper through the bars in the window up there." She pointed upward. "The workers that come and go through the ghetto will find it and will notify your family."

"How do I get up there?" Hinda asked. "I'm not as tall as you."

"You can stand on my shoulders. We'll do it *early* tomorrow morning before anyone else is awake."

"How do you know about this?" Hinda inquired.

"My brother. He did it, and a man came and gave us his note."

Hinda clasped the girl's hand. "How can I ever thank you?"

"Teach me more about household cleaning so I can survive here."

Around four-fifteen the next morning, the long-legged girl tapped Hinda on the shoulder, waking her. She hoisted Hinda upon her, saying to climb her body like a monkey would a tree.

Standing atop the girl's shoulders, Hinda kissed the paper, and then tossed it through the bars of the window. Watching her note float, whirl, and turn flips in the wind, she mumbled a prayerful plea when it touched ground, landing in a pothole.

25

Trapped

May 1941 | Günzburg, Germany

Walter rubbed his stomach. "Mother, you've outdone yourself. I'm not accustomed to eating such a hearty lunch anymore."

His mother, beaming with pride, reached over and mussed his blonde hair as if he were ten years old. "I wanted to make your favorites—*schnitzel*, *spaetzle*, and *sauerbraten*. It's so good to have you home, Walter."

"Yes, it is," his father boomed. "And if it's you who gets her to cook like this, then please come every day."

Noting the chocolate cake and tray of gingerbread displayed on the sideboard, Walter sighed. "Can we have dessert later?"

"Sure, let's take our beer to the living room. Or would you rather have coffee?"

"Beer is great for now. I'll have coffee with dessert."

After chitchatting about local gossip and family matters, his father asked about his job with Josef Mengele, now that Walter had worked for him for a year or more. Walter set his beer down and moved to the edge of the sofa. "Well, Dad, I'm not sure it's going well. Josef is, er, uh, different than I thought."

"Overbearing, is he? Like his mother?"

"Well, yes, and I expected that. But."

"Did you get fired?" Walter's mother asked.

His stomach gurgling with heavy food and worried knots, Walter stood up, then immediately sat back down. "Not fired, but I have a confession, and I'm not proud of it." He cleared his throat three times in a row, as if the words were stuck, all bunched together in his larynx. "I didn't tell you last year, but my job offer from Josef was conditional."

"On what?" his father asked.

"That I join the Nazi party. I didn't want to, but I did. To get the job."

His mother gasped and fell back in her chair, as if fainting. His father stood up, his fist in the air.

"I assure you, I have no appetite for it," Walter explained. "But Josef was clear; if I didn't officially join the Nazi party, the job was not mine. And, you know Josef, he was menacing about it. I felt threatened."

"There will be no Heil Hitler in this house," Walter's father yelled. Knocking his fist against his femur, he exclaimed, "We're German to the bone, but we're not Nazis and never will be."

Regaining her composure, Walter's mother added, "But we're not part of the Resistance movement either. That's a death sentence."

Walter pressed his lips together, knowing the worst was yet to come in this conversation. Not ready for the next storm, he asked, "What do you mean, Mother?"

"Anyone who openly disagrees with, or criticizes, Hitler is a dead man. He's having all known Resistance leaders killed. And in Munich, two priests spoke out against the violence and injustice against Jews, Jehovah's Witnesses, and the Gypsies. They were arrested and taken to Dachau, a concentration camp where there's a special priest section, a *Pfarrer* Block."

"That's alarming." Walter's words heavy with emotion, he pleaded, "Please try to understand. I obliged Josef, but in here and in here," Walter said, pointing to his head and then to his heart. "I am *not* a Nazi."

"And you better not *ever* be!" Walter's father exclaimed, shaking his head in disgust. "Folks in Günzburg know that Josef's parents, Karl and Walburga, now support the National Socialism movement—the Nazis—though, they used to be extreme Nationalists. Why, Karl allowed Adolph Hitler to use his farm-equipment factory for a political rally here in this community. He, along with Josef, even joined the Schutzstaffel, the SS—Hitler's major policing organization. But regardless of his family's politics, Josef has gall and nerve demanding you join the Nazi party."

Taking a deep breath, Walter said, "Father, that's not the worst of it."

His father's eyebrows shot upward. "What?"

"There's another ultimatum Josef has issued."

Both parents shifted in their chairs, sitting up straight on the edge of their seats.

"He recently amended my contract, dictating that I sell my Renault and buy a German-made car." Walter waited for the explosion.

At first, there was silence. Then his mother burst. "That was my brother's car, my precious brother," she wailed. "Eckhart wanted you to have it and so did

Claudette. You must stand up to Josef and say that it's a family heirloom from your deceased uncle and his French wife." She pounded her fist against the open palm of her other hand. "Walter, you must. Besides, you're a doctor now. You can easily get another job."

"No!" Walter's father shouted. "Absolutely not. It's too late now. This is far more serious than I'd feared." His father's voice choked; his eyes brimmed with tears. Looking heavenward, he crossed himself. "Dear God, I want my son alive."

Walter stood. Reaching out, he clasped his father to him, hugging his bear-like body as it shook with sobs.

"You are trapped," his father wailed. "If you don't comply, the scumbag, Mengele, will have you killed. By the bloodthirsty Gestapo."

26
The Tiny Paper

Salomon, Rachel, and Sara stood over Esther's grave, which was located in a makeshift cemetery in the field behind the mill. They prayed, saying *Kaddish*, the mourners' prayer that praises and sanctifies the great name of God.

Running his hand over the wood marker, Salomon hoped Esther was pleased with his workmanship—hand carving her name into the wood from the old broken table leg. Grateful that he had received permission from the Council to bury her within twenty-four hours of her death, according to Jewish law, he praised God more fervently.

Holding hands, the three walked back to the mill. Once inside, they all retreated to their respective coat beds.

Reclining, Salomon shifted his position so he could observe Sara. He studied her, not knowing what to do. No longer did she suck her thumb. No longer did she speak. Nary a word or sound had come from her since her delirious screams the night of Esther's death. Mostly, she stared into space, nonresponsive, in a semi-catatonic state. He and Rachel had tried multiple strategies to draw Sara out, but nothing had worked. He feared that the child suffered traumatic mutism.

His eyes going to Rachel, Salomon's heart filled with more worry. He watched her flip through her sketch pad. Stopping on a page, Rachel's finger traced the lines already there, the nearest thing to drawing she could do. Worn down to fragments, her art pencils were incapable of making any marks. Salomon sensed the emotional toll that alone had upon Rachel. Worse yet, with her mother's sudden death combined with Hinda's absence, the starry luminosity had disappeared from his daughter's eyes. Rachel's irises now were almost colorless and flat, devoid of the kaleidoscopic iridescence they had once radiated. Salomon sighed. He could not resurrect her mother or bring Hinda home, but he vowed to find some way to obtain new pencils for Rachel.

Across the room, Rachel studied the troubled expression on her father's face. Abruptly, she rose from her spot and sat beside Salomon. She said, "Tatae, don't worry for me. I'm drawing and painting in my mind. There, I don't need any tools. I can create anything."

"And what do you create on your mind's canvas, my sweet girl?"

"Birds bursting with flames. Flowers on fire. Hinda's face, put together with jagged puzzle pieces."

Wincing, Salomon said, "Well, now, that's compelling imagery."

Glancing over at Sara, who now had her eyes closed and appeared to be napping, Rachel leaned in close to her father and asked, "What do you think happened to Hinda?"

"Something not good. But I feel in my bones that she's alive. Suffering, but breathing."

"Me too. But can we talk about what likely happened? It would help me."

Even though they had already discussed the *what-happened-to-Hinda* subject, Salomon went along. Knowing that Rachel, who missed her sister terribly, needed interaction, he said, "Well, she could easily have been arrested because she was going outside the gates."

"Yes, or maybe she decided to live with the nice woman, Mrs. Kowalski." Rachel offered a new conclusion she had not shared previously.

"Hmm. I doubt it. The husband didn't know that Hinda was working there."

"Maybe he found out and is holding her hostage; she's their slave now."

"That's one I hadn't thought of."

"If Mr. Kowalski is not hurting Hinda and just making her work, I prefer to envision that scenario over her being in the ghetto prison—the Jail of Death, they call it—or her being attacked and beaten bloody for the food bag."

"You stay with your vision of her working at the Kowalskis' house. It's not wise for us to worry excessively about the grim probabilities." Salomon grasped Rachel's hand. "I'm praying constantly for Hinda to walk through that door, unscathed. Or that we learn what happened to her. We must keep the faith."

"And what about Joel? Will we ever see him again?"

"I don't know. Joel is in my prayers every day too."

Looking at her father's gaunt, wearied face, Rachel refrained from saying what she was thinking: *The cable to heaven has been cut. Our prayers do not transmit. The wires are dead.*

On Tuesday of the following week, Salomon returned from picking up their government rations—a half-loaf of bread, potatoes, and one turnip. Before going there, he had taken streets in the opposite direction so he could walk through the square. His heart always beat faster, and his stomach twisted into knots when he viewed the bodies hanging in the gallows. Today, Hinda's body had not been among the new ones. For another few days, he could breathe.

Placing the rations on their makeshift table, Salomon said, "Girls, it's windy today. Get your coats, and we'll visit Mommy's grave."

Rachel gathered their coats. Helping Sara to stand, Rachel tried to tickle her little sister. No response. She struggled to insert Sara's stiff arms into the armholes of the coat. "Can you smile for me?" Rachel asked. She placed her index finger in the slight indentation on Sara's cheek. "I miss your beautiful smile and your cute dimples."

Sara stared straight ahead, a blank expression on her face.

At the grave, the wind whistled, fluttering Rachel and Sara's hair. The sun, low in the sky, cast purple shadows into the clouds, creating sweeping violet swaths in the gray haze. Her fingers plucking strands of hair from her face, Rachel gazed upward into the artful atmosphere. She talked silently to her mother, not to God. On the opposite side of the grave from Rachel, Sara sat down in the dirt. Her eyes cast downward, she stared at the mound of earth that blanketed her mother's body. Standing near to where Sara sat, Salomon said the traditional Kaddish aloud. Afterward, silence enveloped the three of them as if a misty fog had settled in to stay.

Finally, Salomon said, "Okay, let's go."

When they climbed the steps to the mill, a man wearing work clothing and a hardhat waited at the stoop. He shifted his stance, asking, "Do you live here? I'm looking for the Mondlaks."

Afraid to say yes, afraid to say no, Salomon finally answered, "Yes, I'm Salomon Mondlak."

Removing his hat as if paying respect, the man said, "Good, I got it right. I have something for you that I found near the ghetto gates weeks ago. Barely saw it, down in a chuckhole. Sorry, I couldn't make it over here sooner." He pulled a note from his pocket and thrust it toward Salomon.

Squinting, Salomon peered at the tiny paper filled with letters, handwritten in light pencil.

> To: The Mondlaks — The Old Mill
> Dear Family, I am in prison but still alive.
> Hopefully, I will see you one day.
> God Bless. Love, Hinda

27

The Gallows

August 1941 | Mława, German-occupied Poland

In the jail kitchen, Hinda scrubbed the grate of the floor drain. Her reputation for having excellent cleaning skills had led jail authorities to order her to train other prisoners. Today, Hinda was in charge of scouring the entire kitchen plus coaching a team of five from varying cells. Believing that everyone had executed their jobs well and the kitchen was cleaned above the standard, she had sent them on their way. At the last minute, her instincts told her to check everything one more time. That is when she spotted the dirty grille covering the drain. Not wanting to be lashed with the leather strap, she tackled the grime. When the grate sparkled to her satisfaction, Hinda put away the cleansers and tools.

At the door, the Nazi guard stepped in front of her, blocking her way. Glaring at her, his eyes roved over every inch of her body. Abruptly, he grabbed her cheeks, jerking her face up toward his. "You may clean well, but you're nothing but a dirty Jew," he said. Swishing his lips, the guard spit in her face. "Proceed to your cell," he barked.

Back in Cell Eleven, the women were abuzz, all talking at once. The police had come that morning to select three people for the gallows. From that very cell, they took the girl who was always striving to incite conflict.

Trembling, Hinda wrapped her coat around herself, though the cell was warm. This was the first instance of a young female, who was not ill, being chosen for hanging. Hinda remembered the first day that girl had called her the Devil's Maid. From that day forward, that was the name she used to address Hinda. After what had happened in the kitchen earlier, Hinda decided the girl had tagged her correctly.

Leaning against the wall, Hinda closed her eyes, imagining her father and how he must agonize each week over the bodies hanging lifeless in the gallows. What would he think this week when he saw this young woman who, strangely, resembled her?

28
Into the Woods

April 1941 | Gliwice, German-occupied Poland

Early Tuesday, Wolf clambered out his bedroom window. He pulled it down with precision, unlike the last time, when he had been careless and left it open. Cautiously, Wolf crept around the side of the house. In the front, the street was empty. He hoofed it to the corner. There, too, everything appeared okay. He proceeded, taking back streets and alleyways.

Rapping on the back door to the bakery, Wolf looked around nervously, though a slight smile crossed his lips, anticipating Halina's cheery face. The door swung open, and an older version of Halina—her mother—appeared.

"Wolf Yoskowitz! Let me take a gander at you." Mrs. Dutka grinned broadly, then her eyebrows knitted together. "Gracious sakes, we need to fatten you up, don't we?"

"Hello, Mrs. Dutka. How are you?"

"Well, not so good, you know the war and all, but we're okay." Pointing to one of the bags, she said, "Listen, Halina has an extra special treat in your bag today." Mrs. Dutka winked her right eye, tossed her head, and winked again, affected and purposeful.

Wolf tilted his head, silently wondering what it meant. "I look forward to it, and thank you, Mrs. Dutka. I'm deeply appreciative."

"I know. You're a good boy." She handed him the sacks. A buzzer sounded within the bakery. Her face blanched. "Uh-oh, Gestapo, surprising us again. Go quickly, and be extremely careful, Wolf, especially today." Mrs. Dutka pulled the door closed and clicked the lock.

Wolf stuffed the bakery sacks inside his jacket and crept through the alley, his heart rate faster than normal. *I could be one step away from capture. Gestapo are inside this building, and some could be out front in the street.* At the corner, he checked all avenues before veering away from the main street. As Wolf made his way home, he puzzled over what Mrs. Dutka meant about being careful today, especially today. His taste buds were of a different mind, wondering what special treat Halina had put in the bag.

When Wolf rounded the corner to his house, his eyes widened in alarm. German army trucks congested the street. Soldiers were moving items from the trucks into the houses. *Lord help. The Nazis are taking over these homes.*

Barely breathing, Wolf backed away from the corner and headed south. To avoid any streets, he weaved his way between houses and through lawns. His senses on hyper-alert mode, he checked all directions with each step. After an hour of inchmeal advancement, he came to the outskirts of town. There, he found a dense orchard that appeared safe. Sitting under a plum tree, Wolf leaned his back against its trunk and pondered his fate. *I have no home, no place to hide, no safe place to sleep. What am I going to do?* Bewildered, he sat there in a daze. Wolf closed his eyes, seeing the worst. He needed to make a plan, but nothing but the woods came to mind. Knowing the forest as he did, the woods were his best option for a hiding place, but they were heavily patrolled.

Wolf's stomach knotted and rumbled, reminding him of the food. Although his appetite was dampened, he opened the first sack. Three pączkis were at the top. While feasting on one, he spotted the tape holding a white paper to the side of the white bag. If not for the tape, he could have missed it. Wolf removed the tape and unfolded the paper. His breath faltered, and his eyes bulged as he read the letter:

> *Dear W, Father wanted me to warn you that the German military is making a base here in Gliwice. My family is worried for you and offer refuge. The map below directs you to our farm near the south forest. You can stay in our barn. My brothers, who you know, are at home guarding the property. They are aware of the plan. When you arrive, give this paper to one of them for proper destruction. Or if caught, please do your best to destroy it. Be careful, the woods are patrolled. Good luck. H*

His hands trembling, Wolf studied the roughly drawn map. Folding the paper, he tucked it inside the chest pocket of his shirt. After eating, he prayed. "Dear Lord, our provider, blessed are You. Thank You for this protective turn of fate. And blessed are You who nourishes all. Amen."

Having consumed the contents of one bag and part of the other, Wolf put the second bag into the first. Concealing the sack in his jacket, he ducked between the pine and oak trees, their foliage scraping against his face as he scrambled into the woods.

29
After the Fifth Hit
September 1941 | Mława, German-occupied Poland

The women of Cell Eleven marched single file down the hallway, returning from shoveling gravel in the prison yard. One guard led the group, and another trailed the last woman.

Once inside the cell, Hinda went to her coat to recline, her shoulder muscles aching. The Nazi guard who had followed the group remained in the cell doorway, his hands placed on his hips, his elbows protruding. Everyone knew what that meant. Hinda jumped up and stood erect, facing him, as did all the women. It took enormous willpower for her to look directly at him—the guard who had mauled her with his eyes and spit on her in the kitchen two weeks ago.

From his belt, he removed the leather strap. "Mondlak. Step forward."

Bile rising in her throat, Hinda took three steps toward him, though her legs buckled, not wanting to move. The other women fell back against the wall. Some of them shut their eyes and covered their ears with their hands. Others gawked, eyes wide, partaking in the castigation as if their hands were controlling the whip.

The Nazi guard snarled a nasty smile and lashed hard at Hinda, striking her legs, her arms, and her torso. After the fifth hit, he stopped.

"That's so you won't ever forget me." Pursing his lips, the guard growled, "Get your coat, Mondlak. You're free to go back to the ghetto."

30
The Farm

April 1941 | Gliwice, German-occupied Poland

The forest, Wolf's friend in the days before the German occupation, teemed with signs of spring. If not fearing captivity, he would have reveled in the sunlight glimmering on the leaves, highlighting the varying shades of green sprouting from the branches. Mother Nature did not seem bothered by the war. The sun still rose and set every day, and the seasons continued their usual course, even though millions of Earth children were being unjustly persecuted. Wolf contemplated, thinking there was a lesson there. *I must find a way for my inner sun to shine and stay the course, regardless of what happens to me.*

A rustling of underbrush startled him. Frozen in his tracks, Wolf watched as a human foot, naked, with no sock or shoe, withdrew into a mound of branches. *People are hiding here. And, most likely, they are Jews, starving Jews.* Without a word, he placed the bakery bag next to the brush pile and walked on a hundred feet more. There, Wolf stopped behind the trunk of a large oak. Within seconds, he saw long fingers reach out from the brush and snag the bag.

Leaning against the tree, its bark digging into his back, Wolf bit his lower lip, mulling over how to help the person or persons in the brush. *I can't ask anyone to go with me to the Dutkas' place. It wouldn't be right. That entire family is taking a huge risk hiding me on their property.*

Decision made, Wolf proceeded to walk in the direction of the Dutka farm. Moving at a painfully slow pace, ever vigilant, he trudged through the forest. Today, it produced no enemies. At last, he peeked from the trees, checking out a farm. Wolf reviewed the landscape, comparing it to the details on the map. The tool shed sat twenty yards from the main house where, atop the roof, a rooster weathervane twirled in the wind. Chickens squawked in their coop near the barn, which was about ten yards from the shed. Next, he scanned the front fence. Sure enough, there was a metal sign resembling a loaf of bread on the gate.

Wolf inched from the trees, all the while searching for any signs of life other than the chickens. It felt scary and odd to walk in the open, even when he had an invitation. As he got closer, he spotted the well, where he lowered the bucket down the shaft until he heard it splash. When it felt heavy, Wolf raised it and drank thirstily. His throat knotted when he felt the barrel of a rifle poke into his back.

"What do you think you're doing, mister?" a man asked, his tone gruff.

Identifying the gravelly voice, Wolf answered, "Jan! It's Wolf Yoskowitz. Your sister said you knew I might show up today."

"Wolf! I didn't recognize you. Sorry, we have big problems with poachers," Jan said, stepping around in front of Wolf and extending his hand. "I apologize for the gun. Welcome, man. I'm glad you're here."

"I'm immensely grateful to be here. There aren't words to express how I feel," Wolf replied.

"Man, you're a fraction of yourself. Let's get you settled in the barn, and then we'll get a snack, get some calories in you."

On the way to the barn, Jan said, "Do you have Halina's note and map? My father is quite worried about it."

Plucking the letter from his shirt pocket, Wolf gave it to Jan. "It was quite helpful."

"Yeah, Father was concerned about putting the information in writing, but after weighing all the options, we decided it was the most efficient way to communicate the details." Near the barn, Jan stopped and stood over a rusty metal barrel set in the ground. Pulling a match from his pocket, he struck it against the metal. The blue flame surged on the corner of the letter. He tossed it into the barrel. Not taking any chances, Jan watched until the entire paper was blackened ash.

31

Where's Mommy?

At the ghetto gates, the same Nazi guard, who had just whipped her, shoved Hinda down on the gravel. Wielding his black boots, he kicked her through the entrance to the ghetto side.

Her cheeks red and smeared with dirt, her legs sporting bruises and red whelps, Hinda remained on the rocky pebbles until she heard the guard's boots clicking back toward the jail. Raising herself up on her arms, she looked around, making sure the rabid jailer was nowhere nearby. Arising, she brushed the gravel from her clothing. Feeling a bit wobbly, Hinda took steps in the direction of the mill. In seconds, she was running.

At the mill, Rachel peered out the window. The horizon glowed with striated veins of coral and cornelian hues. It was like the Almighty had commanded the setting sun to hurl its art into the heavens before saying farewell for the day. Yearning to paint the scene, Rachel retired to the floor and closed her eyes. Her hand extended, she gripped her imaginary paintbrush, stroking the air.

Across the room, Salomon reclined on his coat, praying fervently. The image of the girl hanging in the gallows a couple of weeks ago would not let him be. His heart had clunked in his chest, beating irregularly when he saw the young woman. He feared cardiac arrest. About the same age and size as Hinda, the girl looked shockingly like her. Trying to erase the image of her lifeless body and gaunt face had only made it worse. Like a raging demon, the vision taunted him day and night, wrestling with his indwelling belief that Hinda would survive. Ardent prayer, his only shield, invoked a trusted fortress.

Lying against the wall, Sara appeared to be sleeping, which she did increasingly these days. Abruptly, she sat up. Her eyes glazed, she stomped to the door and stood stock-still, like a sentry.

"Sara, darling, what's wrong?" Salomon sat up. "Come sit with me," he said, employing his kindest and most convincing voice. Now that he had to be mother, too, he had adopted the sweet language Esther had often used when speaking to her daughters. When Sara did not respond to him, Salomon asked Rachel to please check on her little sister.

Upon hearing her father's request, Rachel's eyes popped open. They strained to adjust to the reality of the mill versus the painting alive in her mind. She went to her little sister and tugged on her shoulder. "Come, Sara, go to Tatae. Or if you want, you can sit in my lap." Sara did not budge from her post, which is what Rachel expected; yet, she was stunned when Sara pointed her index finger at the door. In the tiniest voice, Sara squeaked, "Heenda. Home."

"What did you say?" Rachel tried to maneuver Sara away from the door, but her body was rigid like cardboard. Calling out to her father, Rachel said, "Tatae, Tatae, Sara talked!"

Salomon arose. "She spoke. What a blessing. But did she say what I think she did?"

"I hear steps. Someone's coming," Rachel exclaimed.

Panting breaths and footsteps preceded the silhouette of one they all loved emerging in the doorway.

"Hinda!" Rachel squealed. "You're alive. You're out of jail." She jumped on her big sister, kissing her dirt-stained face and hugging her tightly.

"Praise God." Salomon rushed to scoop Hinda up into his arms. "Dear daughter, what have they done to you?"

"I'm okay. They beat me and then kicked me through the gates before letting me go. I must look a mess."

"You look like an angel to us, a roughed up one, though," Salomon replied, picking gravel from Hinda's hair. He then reached for Sara and Rachel, bringing them into a family embrace, the relief and joy of seeing Hinda ashine in their smiles.

Throwing her head back in laughter, Sara repeated, "Heenda home."

Hinda tweaked Sara's cheek, "Silly girl, pronouncing my name like that. Oh, I have missed you, missed all of you desperately." Scanning the room, she asked, "Where's Mommy?"

Taking Hinda's hands in his, Salomon's throat knotted as he spoke the dreadful news. "I'm sorry, Hinda, I regret to tell you that your mother passed away in April."

"Passed away? Oh no!"

"She was blessed to die the way she did, considering the horrible deaths happening in this ghetto." Salomon paused, clearing his throat. "Mommy is in a far better place now."

Hinda shook her head in disbelief, "I . . . I . . . I. But how? Did she get sick?"

Pointing her finger at Hinda, Sara said, "Mommy gone. Looking for you."

Salomon nodded. "She fainted on the street near the gates. Her sternum broke on the craggy rock she fell against."

Hinda's veins rushed with icy shards; an uncomfortable coldness descended upon her. She inhaled sharply, which triggered pain in her lungs. She exhaled in whispery puffs. The elation of getting out of jail and rejoining her family now thwarted, utter sadness and dismay welled up in her. Yet, Hinda could not cry. Her heart was locked, imprisoned, as if it were still behind bars. Her tears froze, and an inner volcano of grievous emotion sought an outlet. Hinda yelled, "Where's Mommy? Where is she?" Darting around the room, she shrieked, "Mommy! Where are you?"

Salomon chased after Hinda and enfolded her into his arms. "Dear daughter, listen to me. Your mother is with God. Saintly as she was, the Almighty has her . . . is taking care of her now."

Closing her eyes tightly, shutting out the twisted-corpse vision invading her psyche, Hinda whispered, "Did they throw her body into one of those horrible mass graves?"

"No, we were blessed. Come with me. I will show you where she is buried." Nodding to Rachel and Sara, he said, "You two have visited Mommy twice today, so you can stay here." Salomon took Hinda's arm in his, and they promptly exited the mill.

The horizon greeted them with a brilliant reddish-orange fluorescence that streaked the sky and radiated toward them. Hinda breathed in the fresh air and absorbed the gravity of the fact that she had not seen a sunset in months. And now her mother was dead, a momentous luminary in her life snuffed out. Leaning on her father's frail arm, Hinda watched the sun perch on Earth's edge, suspended between worlds, offering its light to both hemispheres.

After a short walk, they came to a mound of hardened dirt. "This is where your mother's body is buried," Salomon said. He pointed to the wood marker, which, at that very moment, glowed with a strangely timed luminosity, a gift from the setting sun briefly situated behind it.

Standing over the grave, Hinda blinked repeatedly, her azure eyes dimming with doleful shadows. Reverently, she crouched down and tenderly placed her left hand upon the dirt, beholding its sacredness. Then she sat fully on the ground, nesting beside her mother's grave. Sweeping her right hand across the wood marker, she fingered the letters of her mother's name, which seemed to wrap around her heart as she felt how lovingly her father had carved each letter. She whispered, "Oh, Mommy. You were such a marvelous mother. And an incredibly good person." Leaning in, Hinda pressed her lips against the wood. Then she began saying Kaddish. When she came to the words of praising God's goodness, especially for the life of her mother, the tears released. Gushing down her face and spilling onto the dirt, her sorrow flowed in rivulets, seeping into the earth, trickling into the dusty remains of her mother's body.

32
Patrols and Poachers
April 1941 | Gliwice, German-occupied Poland

At the Dutka farm, Wolf looked around the interior of the two-story barn. Its high roofline with open rafters rendered a rugged but spacious ambience. Three horse stalls lined a partial wall on the right side, while a tractor, a wagon-like trailer, and a workbench occupied the left. A second-story loft extended out over the horse stalls. Stacks of round hay bales towered along the balcony edges. Behind the tractor, a half door opened to a small room that housed potatoes.

"Have to keep these spuds dry and separate from the animals," Jan Dutka explained. Walking to the back of the barn, he pointed to a rear door that exited into a meadow that flanked the forest. "We keep it locked because of the poachers." Jan fished in his pocket and dug out two keys on a chain. "The short key is for this one; the big one for the padlock on the front double doors. And, oh yeah, I forgot to tell you the outhouse is in the trees around the corner."

"Thank you," Wolf said, transferring the keys to his shirt pocket. "Nice barn."

"Yeah, but man, I'm sorry for you to sleep here, but Father says that if the Nazis find you in our house, we're all dead. If they find you in the barn, we can claim that you hid there without our knowledge."

"He's right. Believe me, I am grateful to be here. To have any place to sleep."

"Confound it, these Nazis. What they're doing to your people is terrible." Jan pointed to a stack of horse blankets. "Mother washed all those and recommended you use them atop the hay in the far back stall, the one near the rear door, in case you need to exit quickly. All the stalls have been cleaned and fresh hay put in. No horses right now. Soldiers confiscated ours."

"German or Polish soldiers?" Wolf asked.

"German. And they often show up demanding eggs. And, sometimes, a chicken. So be on guard, even here on the property."

"For sure. But is there anything I can do to help? Plant or harvest crops, feed the chickens, or trap small animals? I want to contribute."

Jan grinned his quirky, lopsided smile. "Thanks. Chores are aplenty around here. You can probably plow the potato field. The soil is almost warm enough to plant the new crop. I'll ask Father."

The front door swung open and in walked Jan's double, his twin brother, Jakub. "Wolf Yoskowitz, it's good to see you," Jakub said in a gravelly voice similar to Jan's. Except for a red birthmark on Jakub's left cheek, there was trivial difference in the twin brothers' appearance. Even their light brown hair had the same wavy swoop that dipped across their foreheads.

"Great to see you, Jakub. I sure appreciate you and your family helping me," Wolf replied.

"Sorry about your family. Halina told us they're missing. Any news on them?"

"No, nothing." Wolf looked down at his feet, persuading his sadness to remain shackled.

Jakub bowed his head briefly, then said, "On another note, we wanted you to eat dinner with us in the house, but it's not unusual for a soldier or two to show up at our door. Halina or one of us will bring you meals. Hope that's okay."

"Beyond okay." Wolf's voice raised an octave, cracking with emotion. "I don't know how to express how thankful I am."

Jakub shifted his weight from one foot to another. "Father's philosophy has been to be friendly to the Nazi forest patrol out here and the Gestapo in town who come to the bakery. We get more information that way. But in no way are we friends."

"And just two farms over, a couple miles away," Jan exclaimed. "the Nazis confiscated the entire farm and deported the whole family."

"A non-Jewish family?" Wolf asked, his eyebrows raised in surprise.

"Yeah. They were Catholic Poles, like us, but not friendly to the Nazis," Jan explained. He shifted his jaw to the side, sliding his upper teeth against the lowers. "The soldiers said the Third Reich wanted the land for a German family to help instill that culture here in Poland. Dad says we must be extremely careful in how we respond."

"It was hard," Jakub said, "but we were kind to the Nazi soldiers who took our horses. And now they show up wanting our food. Then, we've got poachers trying to steal from us. These are perilous times."

"Speaking of food," Jan said. "I'm going to the kitchen and get Wolf a serious snack. Man, you've lost half of yourself."

33

Sardines and A New Moon

April 1942 | Mława, German-occupied Poland

A villainous devil of death stalked the ghetto. Lifeless bodies—innocents sapped by starvation—littered the streets. The skimpy government rations, a mere three-hundred calories a day of starchy vegetables and bread, did little to sustain health. Hunger and disease pervaded, all part of Hitler's imperious plot, his genocidal blueprint that was unfurling perfectly. In the Mława ghetto alone, thousands of Jews were dying.

At the mill, Hinda gazed out the window, observing a man who searched the pockets of those who lay dead or unconscious. She presumed he was looking for food, a crumb of any kind. Although it approached the one-year anniversary of her arrest and the macabre memories of jail still haunted her, she could not tolerate the ravenous hunger another day. Turning to her father, she proclaimed, "I need to get out of here and find food for us."

"No, Hinda, no. If you try to get out of the ghetto, this time, you will die," Salomon replied, his voice shaking.

"What difference does it make? I'd rather die trying to find food for you and my sisters than sit back and watch all of us die of starvation."

Without another word, Hinda donned a second sweater atop the one she was wearing and slid her white armband upon it. Turning away from her father's ghostly pale face, she exited the mill.

Near the ghetto gates, Hinda ducked behind a vacant storefront and removed her armband. She waited for a group of German soldiers to pass. Then a fight broke out in the square. Bystanders gathered. The Gestapo turned and ran toward the scuffle, their guns popping. When a young boy was hit by a ricocheted bullet, the gate guards left their post, moving toward the ruckus. Amidst gunfire and blood spatter, Hinda braved the territory and slipped through the gates unnoticed.

Traversing the streets, in the opposite direction of Mrs. Kowalski's house, she trudged approximately two kilometers, finally finding the train station. Gestapo officers were out in force everywhere she turned, at every corner, every post, and at every train platform. Yet a peculiar peace overcame her, and Hinda was not afraid. On the contrary, she felt strong and determined. The very thought of finding food for her family emboldened her.

Assessing the vendors who were scattered around the station, Hinda noted that many sold chocolates. The sight of the candy wrappers alone ignited saliva, her mouth watering. Yet she had come for serious food—protein. Then she spotted a man selling cans of sardines along a side ramp. Standing back, she watched him interact with two customers, then decided to approach.

"How much are the sardines?" Hinda asked, smiling and intentionally widening her already large sky-blue eyes. Her thick lashes fluttered against her upper lids.

"How much can you pay?"

Hinda removed her top sweater, the finest she owned. "This beautiful sweater," she said.

The man's eyes darted back and forth from the sweater to her face. "I don't do trades. Cash only."

"My family is suffering dire circumstances, sir. We're literally starving to death."

The man squinted his brown eyes until they were beady. They bored into hers, so penetrating they felt like spikes gouging her eyeballs. Then his head swiveled on his neck as he looked around the pavilion. Satisfied that no one was nearby, he mumbled, "Two cans. For the sweater."

"Two?" Hinda asked. Her disdain for such a small number was audible. "Please, sir, four cans. I have two sisters and my father to feed. And this sweater was costly. See the tiny stitches and tight weave."

He stared hard at her again. "Three cans. That's it, or get out of here."

"Three will do. Thank you, sir."

Grunting disapproval, he plunked the cans into a brown paper bag.

Adroitly, Hinda tucked the bag out of sight under her now one-and-only sweater. She stretched her left arm across her midriff, holding the cans in place, and walked away with the aplomb of a seasoned dealer.

On the way back to the ghetto, she made a wrong turn, adding unnecessary distance to her journey home. Although her legs ached, Hinda worked to remain present and vigilant, not allowing the dreamy state that she often lapsed into when she walked. Approaching the ghetto gates, she hung back, scoping out the situation. It appeared routine; guards were at their posts.

Her breath quickened when she heard heavy footsteps, boots clomping, behind her. Hinda moved to the side as a platoon of soldiers passed her. They marched in synchronized rhythm, goose-stepping with their rifles extended out from their bodies. The captain yelled orders and the soldiers made matching maneuvers with their guns. Just as they entered the square, a throng of workmen wearing hardhats came out of nowhere from a side street, congesting the entrance. Taking a deep breath, Hinda seized the moment and walked through the gates, quickly veering away from the main avenue. It was the longest route to the mill, but she had made it past the guards without arrest.

Unfamiliar with the nuances of this street, her stomach churned as she looked for a place to hide and don the armband. At last, Hinda came to a building that had three rusty sheets of metal leaning against it. No one was in sight, so she scurried behind one of the panels and pulled on the white armband.

In the next block when she rounded a curve, Hinda saw a Gestapo officer standing on the corner. He was talking with a capo who faced her. Deciding it was too late to cross the street now, she kept her same pace. She began rubbing her arm—the one holding the hidden cans in place—as if it were hurting.

At the corner, the officer reached out his hand and lightly tugged on her armband. He asked, "What's wrong with your arm?"

"I sprained it," Hinda replied.

"How?" he inquired.

"Lifting my sister who is sick," Hinda said, turning her head to cough.

The officer jumped back, "Get on home, dirty Jew, and keep your germs to yourself."

The capo jeered at her, though Hinda noted his subtle cringe at the officer's insulting words. She proceeded down the street, the cans of sardines safe under her sweater.

Upon entering the mill, Hinda called out triumphantly, "I did it."

Arising from his coat bed, Salomon rushed to the door, enfolding Hinda in a tight embrace. "Praise God! You made it back."

From across the room, Rachel and Sara came running to see what Hinda had done. They clustered around their sister and father.

Pride ashine on her face, Hinda showed them the sardines. Immediately, they went to their makeshift table. Hinda thrust a can toward her father. He removed the key on the side, placed it in the hook, and rolled the top back. The tin squeaked as it opened, a simple but heavenly sound to them at that moment.

Salomon counted ten sardines on the top layer, then declared there were twenty to share. He parceled out five sardines to each of them. Savoring every bite of the salty fish, the four of them devoured one can in a swift minute. Sara begged for more. Salomon shook his head no.

Turning to face the curtain, Salomon hoped the Shapiros could not smell the sardines. Rubbing his chin, he thought about sharing a can with them, but only briefly for his dear Hinda had risked her life to get the sardines for her family. Moreover, in all their encounters, Mr. Shapiro had been unfriendly and extremely cantankerous. Salomon's eyes widened as a realization struck him: no bad smells or sounds came from the Shapiros' side anymore, not even the raucous snoring. Salomon considered pulling the curtain back to check on them but decided it would be disrespectful of the Shapiros' space, especially since they had clearly indicated that they wanted no contact with the Mondlaks.

His pondering interrupted, Salomon's head jerked sideways when he saw Sara pick up one of the sardine cans and start to engage the key. His mouth open, about to chastise her, he watched Hinda snatch the can away from her little sister. "You can look forward to having some tomorrow, sweetie." Hinda thrust the other two cans back in the brown bag. "We must make these last for a few days."

"How did you get the sardines, Hinda?" Salomon asked. "You had no money."

"I traded my sweater. At the train station."

"That was your prettiest and nicest sweater," Rachel exclaimed.

"Exactly," Hinda replied. "It was my only one that had any value to trade."

Rachel clasped Hinda's hand and said, "You are so generous and good to us." Rachel licked the sardines' oily saltiness from her lips. "We would die of starvation without you."

Salomon nodded in agreement and said, "The train station is dangerous with many police, and it's a long way from here." He shook his head in awe of what Hinda had accomplished.

"I'll clean up," Rachel announced. "Hinda, you go rest."

Exhausted, Hinda collapsed onto her coat bed. Her body ached all over. She turned this way, then that, into another position, and then another.

As darkness emerged, Salomon told a story, as if he were reading, which he had not done in a long time. Enjoying the bit of nostalgic normalcy, Sara and Rachel paid rapt attention.

While her father's metered voice soothed Hinda, the aching in her legs persisted. She attempted to recoup the peaceful feeling she had experienced at the train station. But in addition to the long walk, the fear of being captured had been suppressed and stored in her muscles, which now throbbed like they had been injected with a poisonous stress serum. Even after her sisters were asleep, Hinda continued to toss and turn. And, at times, she moaned.

Salomon went to Hinda and sat close beside her. "My bold, brave, and caring daughter," he whispered. He rubbed his hands slightly together to warm them and began lightly stroking her face. In hushed tones, he spoke blessings over her and prayed, asking God to keep them all safe.

The warmth of her father's touch and the whispered blessings calmed the spasms. When the new moon revealed its soft, curvilinear silhouette in their window, Hinda slept, succumbing to a dream where she and Rachel walked and walked and walked, their legs aching, their feet blistered and bloody.

34

A Red Birthmark

May 1941 | Rural Gliwice Region, German-occupied Poland

Certain that all barn doors, both front and back, were locked properly, Wolf crawled into his hay bed in the horse stall. Up at sunrise, he had labored plowing the potato field, readying it for planting, which they would do tomorrow. Potatoes took ninety days or more to grow and mature, which begged the question: Would he be there when it was time for the harvest?

Stretching out his legs, Wolf reflected upon how Jakub had stood guard with a gun while he wielded the tractor up and down the rows, breaking up the hard soil. In an eerie way, the birthmark on Jakub's cheek had appeared redder than normal. The sun, hidden under a heavy cloud cover, was not highlighting it. Even so, with every turn of the tractor in Jakub's direction, Wolf noticed it, which gave rise to a peculiar feeling he could not explain.

While he and Jakub worked in the back of the property, Jan had guarded the front, including the house. Wolf had been shocked to learn how careful the Dutkas had to be on their own farmland, since the German occupation. Poachers would take anything not tied down, and all machinery and vehicles were a high commodity. Without Jakub standing guard, Wolf could have been attacked and the tractor stolen. The family also worried about Nazi soldiers confiscating the tractor, as they had seized much of their neighbors' equipment, all in the name of war. Wolf now understood why the Dutkas kept their tractor locked in the barn when not in use.

Turning on his side, Wolf realized that his hip bones no longer poked him when he laid upon them. Mrs. Dutka and Halina were quite the cooks and loaded his plate every meal. Thankful for consistent nutrition and his weight gain over the past month, Wolf prayed for abundant blessings and protection for the Dutkas. They could lose their lives for taking him in and hiding him. They were bearing a dangerous risk for a Jewish boy who had just delivered flour to their bakery. The family's brave show of compassion went far beyond simple kindness. Wolf sighed in awe, feeling immense gratitude for this noble family.

Just as Wolf was drifting off to sleep, the image of the human foot he saw withdrawing into the brush pile in the forest floated through his mind. The vision had haunted him since the day he saw the foot, a full month ago now. Incessantly, he puzzled over it and wondered how the people, most likely Jews, hiding there were surviving. He could well imagine they ate berries, mushrooms, and grub worms. But was that enough to sustain them? With all the patrols, they could not risk building fires to cook small animals. Would they become so starved for protein that they would eat the raw meat of a rabbit or a bird? The thought alone stung the flesh of Wolf's stomach.

Drowsiness overcame his worry, and Wolf was swept into sleep. Fifteen minutes later, he jerked awake. That foot. Its details had become enlarged in his dreamy state, as if he were seeing it under a magnifying glass. The middle toes were webbed, almost grown together, and the big toe stuck out to the side crookedly, as if it had been broken. The real clincher, though, was that the foot heralded a red birthmark on the top, above the instep. He gasped. *I know that foot. It belongs to my brother, Joseph.*

35

The Tall Girl

August 1942 | Mława, German-occupied Poland

The ghetto square swarmed with Execution Day buzz. The gallows were erected and prepared; six nooses dangled from a hook. The firing squad stood ready, six gunmen in a line anticipating their human targets. A somber crowd gathered.

The Jewish Council had distributed the news of the recent decrees, which stated that all who resided in the ghetto were ordered to witness the weekly killings. On the specified day, Gestapo or capos would enter homes and corral people, not allowing anyone to evade the executions. If anyone was ill or physically unable to attend, they were selected for execution the following week.

The first event was appalling. Being forced to watch the gruesome murders of the selected residents and prisoners was shocking enough. Worse yet, spectators —including children—who spoke, cried, or screamed were hauled to the platform and shot at close range. There had been no warning to remain quiet. People had unknowingly sobbed or wailed. A massacre ensued.

Today, funereal silence pierced the air. The Mondlaks stood huddled together among the others in the tyrannized throng. This would be the fourth public execution. Each time, for days afterward, Sara retreated to mutism. Since Hinda had returned home from jail, Sara had talked, but only in two- or three-word phrases, as if she were a toddler, although she was soon to be eleven years old. But now, due to the trauma of watching the killings, she did not speak, or even make a peep, three to four days a week.

On the stage, Heil Hitler salutes signaled the start. The hangings were first. Six people marched onto the platform. Soldiers looped the nooses around their necks and tightened the knots.

Invisible hands closed around Hinda's throat, choking back a gasp, when she recognized her friend from jail—the tall girl who had helped her send the note to her family. There she was, standing in the gallows, her neck trussed with a rope. Desperate to shut out the sight, Hinda's eyes blinked automatically, but the residents were not allowed to lower their heads or close their eyes. Attention had to remain on the platform.

After the executions were complete, family members of those killed were called to the scaffold to carry their dead loved ones to the mass graves outside of town. At gunpoint, they were forced to *throw* in the bodies.

A fearsome instinct overwhelmed Hinda. Suppressing her desire to accompany the girl's parents, to tell them of her kindness, she walked home with her own family, holding tightly to Sara's hand.

When they arrived back to the mill, Hinda unraveled. Weeping, her body shook with rigors. She shrilled to her father, "Why even try to be a good person? How could hell be any more miserable than this?"

36
Married French
June 1941 | Frankfurt, Germany

His right elbow on his desk, and his thumb and forefinger cupping his chin, Josef Mengele glared at Walter Zeilhofen, who sat across from him. "I am stunned that I've known you all these years, since childhood, and I didn't know your bloodline included a French lineage." Inclining his upper body forward in an aggressive motion, Mengele appeared primed to lunge across the desktop. "I would never have hired you, Walter, if I had known that you were not fully German according to the 1935 Nuremberg Law."

"French? I'm not any part French. I'm German to the bone, as my father likes to say," Walter replied, a red flush creeping up his neck.

Josef twisted his mouth. "But your *mother's* family is French, right? Your Renault came from her side?"

"I inherited the car from my mother's brother, but he is German as is my mother, and so were their parents." Eyeing Josef's arm extending across the desk with the hand tightly fisted, Walter placed his right hand on his side of the desktop, palm down as if he were swearing upon a Bible. "According to Nuremberg Law, I am classified as fully German. As specified, I have four German grandparents." Walter took a deep breath, running his fingers through his hair. "My lineage, Josef, extends back to even great-great grandparents, who were all German born."

"Then why did your uncle buy a Renault? Was he not a nationalist?"

"He married a French woman from Strasbourg. She bought the coupé for him as a birthday present when it was first released in 1935."

"Married French! Then the man was far from being a nationalist, considering how France treated Germany post World War I." His eyebrows knitted together in a scowl, Josef asked, "Why did *you* inherit the auto?"

"That's a good question," Walter said, shifting in his chair. "I was my uncle's only nephew, but I was dumbfounded when I received notification of his will." Walter lied, not wanting to disclose that his uncle knew that he was bananas about the car. Walter wanted to yell, *it's none of your business*, but he choked back the words, which jumbled in his esophagus and fell like rocks into the pit of his stomach.

"Okay. But why haven't you sold the car as per your revised contract last month?"

"I'm working on it. Most Germans can't afford such a car in these times of war. Today, my father is talking to an Italian collector. I ask for your patience."

"Patience? Bah!" Josef stood, pushing his chair against the wall. "I'm bothered that you don't seem disturbed about owning a French car."

Walter shrugged his shoulders. He immediately regretted the gesture. The contemptuous look on Josef's face sent chills spiraling down Walter's spine.

Raising his voice far above conversational decibels, Josef said, "Walter, it's important that you clearly understand. I, and I alone, oversee this department, and I *insist* that only true German nationalists and Nazis serve on my research team. I believe strongly in what Hitler is working to accomplish with racial purity. For Germany. For the world."

Rubbing his chin, Walter replied, "I understand." Yet his mind rumbled with objections. Even still, Walter flashed a charming smile and said, "I appreciate the clarification."

Mengele stepped toward the door, signaling the meeting was ending. In a more upbeat tone, he said, "Congratulations on your KdF-Wagen. Now, really, Walter, aren't you happier driving a German-made car?"

"Yes, I love it," Walter lied, yet again. "And please know, Josef, it's a privilege to work for you. I am honored to be on your team. I fear, though, that you have misunderstood my situation with the Renault."

"I don't think so. I want proof of sale by Monday, or you're out. I'm departing on Tuesday to return to my duties in the Viking Division. Monday is your absolute deadline."

37

Beans, Not Potatoes

Late August 1942 | Mława, German-occupied Poland

The midmorning sun blazed brightly in a cloudless sky. Hinda drank in the bucolic setting of the vegetable fields, a refreshing tonic compared to the ghastliness of the ghetto. A burlap sack hanging from her waist, she plucked green beans from the vines and tossed them into the bag.

A Council messenger had come to the mill early that morning, announcing that workers were needed to help harvest vegetables. At the end of the day, he had said, there was a chance that workers would be given fresh vegetables to bring home. One person per household could go. Hinda readily volunteered.

After speaking with the Mondlaks, the messenger had then stood at the curtain and called out, "Mr. Shapiro, may I speak with you?" After waiting briefly in the awkward silence, he tugged back the curtain. Open suitcases and clothing were spread across the floor, but no one was there. Salomon informed the messenger that the family of three had not been seen in a long while. The man's face had wrinkled with puzzlement as he directed Hinda to the truck waiting on the street.

At the fields, Hinda noted the flat-bed trailers containing large barrels that were parked in front of each crop's station. Armed guards patrolled the station areas. Additional Nazi guards walked up and down the rows, cracking their whips when workers were not toiling to their satisfaction. When the crew had first arrived, a Nazi officer announced that if workers were caught eating or even tasting any of the vegetables, they would be shot immediately. So far, no gunfire had occurred.

In the early afternoon, when Hinda dumped her fourth load of beans into a barrel on the trailer, an armed guard motioned to her. Uncertain of his intention or mood, she felt a lump arise in her throat.

"Potatoes now," the guard commanded, pointing to the adjacent field. "Go over there and dig potatoes. Same process; empty your bag in their barrels."

"Yes, sir," Hinda said and headed over to the next field.

"What are you doing over here?" The potato-area guard asked gruffly when she arrived at that field. "You're beans, not potatoes. We don't mix the sacks. Carrots and potatoes have dirt, beans don't."

"I am sorry, sir. The guard over there at beans told me to come here."

"Is that right? Well, let's see about that." He grabbed her collar and hauled her back to the bean area. The two guards stood to the side, speaking quietly, looking back at her, their eyes roving up and down her body from head to ankles, and often lingering in between.

Dear Lord, please help me. They are about to beat me or worse. Hinda prayed, while standing tall, her shoulders back, her head held high, though her dress felt flimsy with sunlight filtering through it.

"Green beans, girl. You stay over here," the potato guard said, his tone surly. His face an inch from her neck, his hot breath coated her skin. He grabbed one buttock, squeezing hard. Drawing back his hand, he slapped her derriere three times, and then stomped away.

The bean-station guard guffawed with every slap. In a churlish tone, he snapped at her as if she had taken an undue break. "Back to work, or it's my turn."

Amidst the bean vines again, Hinda rubbed her rear, which stung like it had been attacked by hornets. She shivered, acknowledging that she had come close to being brutally violated.

Focusing on the beauty of the lush greenery juxtaposed against the dark soil dispelled her anger and calmed her angst. It was as if Mother Earth comforted her, radiating her emerald rays upward, speaking to Hinda's heart, reminding her of God's magic: tiny seeds germinating in the ground and growing into plants that produced nourishing, edible beans. *Cultivate miracles*, the earth whispered. *Plant seeds of goodness in the fertile soil of your mind*, it urged, inviting Hinda to daydream of freedom, of abundant food, of a comfortable bed, of a real home with furniture, of true love, and of a splendid future.

At sunset, the guards blew whistles and ordered the workers to get into the trucks to be transported back to the ghetto. Hinda's hopes of taking vegetables home had been dashed after experiencing the guards' attitudes. But, surprisingly, each worker was given a sack that contained substantial amounts of potatoes, carrots, and beans.

At the mill, when Hinda danced through the doorway, jubilant about the food, her father arose and swept her into a hug.

"Praise God," Salomon exclaimed, "You're back and safe." Eyeing the vegetable bag, he whistled softly. He took it from Hinda and lugged it across the room to the shower area. There, she and Rachel washed carrots, beans, and potatoes, far more than they were accustomed to having in one meal. Even better, the burlap bag still bulged.

Exhausted and famished, Hinda spread the array on the makeshift table-top. "Fresh, really fresh, vegetables," she called out in a hawker's tone as if she were selling them.

Eagerly, the four of them partook in the raw feast, their taste buds savoring the piquant flavor of sheer freshness. Having had no greens in well over a year, they all reached for the beans first. Sara, who had brought her doll to dine with them, a rare occurrence, pretended to feed the doll green beans while saying, "Mmm, cake."

Raising an invisible glass, Salomon said, "Let's all toast Hinda. We thank you, dear daughter, for your willingness to work so hard today. And for all that you do for us." He seemed especially jovial and lighthearted.

Hinda watched her father's face as he talked. It appeared lit, like a flambeau burned from the inside, and it was more relaxed than it had been in a long while. She understood. He did not have to worry about her going out in search of food—not anytime soon, anyway.

After they had eaten, Salomon asked them to hold hands. He prayed, praising God, their Provider, for the boon of these fresh vegetables, for their love for each other, and for another day of safety.

For the second time that day, Hinda shivered. A warning wafted over her, imploring her to cherish this peaceful moment.

38
Brown Eyes to Blue
June 1942 | Günzburg, Germany

Walter Zeilhofen drove his 1939 KdF-Wagen to an automotive repair shop on the outskirts of Günzburg. His father, who was meeting him there, had arranged for Walter to see where his Renault coupé had been secretly stored for the past year. Walter yearned to lay eyes upon the car, to touch its fenders.

The Volkswagen that Walter now owned did not inspire his affection. Rather, he held the automobile in contempt. It had been built by slave laborers from internment camps. And for Walter, that fact made the car tainted goods.

Years prior, in 1937, the Third Reich government had founded the Volkswagen company to fulfill Hitler's plan for a "People's Car," one that was affordable to German families. That concept, plus the overall design, were admirable to Walter, considering that previously only one in fifty people in Germany owned a car. Bicycles and motorcycles were the norm; cars were a luxury, only for people of means.

The car's model name—KdF—stood for *Kraft durch Freude*, which meant "strength through joy." Hitler had designated the phrase, the People's Car, as he envisioned happy German families zooming along his autobahns.

Walter felt zero joy. Jewish internment and slave labor were against his principles. Plus, his boss had railroaded him into buying the German-made vehicle. A young doctor, Walter could not afford anything but a KdF, a used one at that. A Mercedes would have been more palatable to him, but even previously owned models sported a price tag above his budget.

His blood pressure rising, Walter pounded the steering wheel, reflecting upon the third ultimatum Josef Mengele had issued last year. He had to present a bill of sale for the Renault, or he would be fired. At that meeting, he would have gladly quit, but his father believed that if he did, Mengele would order the SS to kill him—a bomb planted in the Renault that would blow the car and Walter to smithereens.

Walter clearly understood. Josef despised all things French. And, for what-ever reasons, he harbored an obsessive hatred for Renault automobiles. Deep in his soul, Walter *knew* that his father was correct about the illustrious Dr. Josef Mengele. After working for the man for two years, Walter suspected that his childhood friend, now his boss, was mentally deranged.

To appear compliant, Walter had produced a fake bill of sale, telling Josef that a man who lived in Geneva had bought the Renault. He fabricated an elaborate story of when his father and he took the car to Basal, near the German-Swiss border, where the man met them to receive the Renault.

Patting Walter on the back for getting the abhorrent French car out of Germany, Mengele had seemed delighted, chortling in a Machiavellian timbre.

Pulling into the parking lot of the auto-repair shop, Walter spotted his dad waiting at the side of the building.

His father waved and then put up his hand, palm forward, signaling for Walter to remain in the car. Hopping in the front passenger seat, he said, "Let's take a drive. There's an SS officer inside there."

"Thanks for being my scout," Walter said. "Did you see the Renault?" He put the Volkswagen in reverse and turned in the direction of downtown. If they had to take a drive, Walter wanted to view the unique architecture of the Church of Our Lady, which he found inspiring. Merely seeing the church's exterior lifted his spirits.

"Haven't seen the coupé yet. They have it covered with tarps that are spotted with rust marks and paint splatters. And they removed the left rear tire and jacked up the side. It looks like an old junker awaiting repair."

"Excellent." A slow grin spread across Walter's face. "How long do you think the SS officer will be there?"

"Twenty minutes or so. They're looking at the brakes on his truck. How's it going with Josef?"

Walter tilted his head in a negative gesture, "I've started to question Josef Mengele's sanity. And frankly, the goal of the genetic research we're conducting."

"He's obsessed with twins, right?" asked Walter's father.

"Yes, and now with eye color too. He wants to discover a method to change brown eyes to blue."

"And his purpose would be what?"

"It started with his wanting to fix twins who were born with two different eye colors. But now, Mengele is obsessed with racial genetics and creating an Aryan-German super-race. He believes that blue eyes are superior. He abhors dark brown eyes. Says they're dirty. A result of racial impurities."

"Changing eye color? That sounds crazy."

Walter slowed the car and pulled into a parking spot across the street from the cathedral. Setting the emergency brake, he said, "It's lunacy all right. Dad, I—" Walter paused, staring straight ahead, not looking at his father. "I found a pair of brown eyeballs in a petri dish in the lab. I don't believe they were from a cadaver."

"Oh, God, son, are you saying Mengele cut out a living person's eyeballs?"

Walter pressed his thin lips so firmly against each other that they turned chalky white. "I am witnessing unspeakable procedures." He sighed. "If only I could turn back the clock to March 1940, I would not accept the job with Dr. Josef Mengele."

"You didn't know then what you know about him now."

"In hindsight, a part of me was aware and concerned about his cold-hearted nature, but my ego got the best of me. Josef was so renowned and important in this country." Walter twisted in his seat, his blue eyes fixating on the cathedral. "I don't see a way out. I not only worry for my life. I fear I've sold my soul to the devil."

39
A Grim Prophecy

Halina threw herself onto Wolf, gripping him tightly. "Please don't go. You'll be captured. I feel it." Her wavy blonde hair fell around her shoulders, not in its usual braided bun or chignon with a bakery hairnet securing it in place. Her brown eyes appeared feral, wild with intent.

They stood on the dewy grass in front of the house, the five of them making a casual circle—Mr. Dutka, Jakub, Jan, Halina, and Wolf. An early morning fog created a hazy mist around them.

Mr. Dutka stepped up and gently pulled his daughter back. "Go to the house. Put together a pack of sausage rolls and sandwiches for Wolf to take with him."

Wresting herself away from her father, Halina lunged toward Wolf and kissed him on the lips. "I love you, Wolf Yoskowitz. And I know in my heart, this is it. I'll never see you again."

"You're spooking us, Halina. Enough of the grim prophecy," Jakub said. "And hey, put a thermos of water in his knapsack too."

Hunched over and clutching her abdomen as if a demonic bacterium spasmed her intestines, Halina hobbled toward the house.

"I'm sorry, Wolf. We knew Halina fancied you, but—" Mr. Dutka ducked his head, his word bank empty, devoid of terms to explain his daughter's unexpected fit of feeling.

"She has been known to be psychic. We know that all too well," said Jan.

"Not this time," Mr. Dutka said. "She's just excessively worried for Wolf because she cares. Too much. Such emotion clouds intuition." Mr. Dutka reached out and cuffed Wolf on the arm. "I hope you find your family. At least, your brother. And you know, you're welcome to bring him here." Mr. Dutka scuffed one foot across the grass. "Heck, bring all of them here, should you find them. We'll work it out."

40
Father and Mother
September 6, 1942 | Mława, German-occupied Poland

When the sun was scarcely visible on the horizon, just rising in the eastern sky, two Gestapo officers arrived at the mill.

Earsplitting knocks on the door roused Salomon from an early morning dream. Hinda, Rachel, and Sara sat up, rubbing their eyes as they watched their father shuffle to the door.

Two Gestapo officers, attired in formal uniforms, stepped inside, their rifles hanging from straps on their shoulders. In a deep baritone voice that boomeranged around the room, the lead officer said, "Salomon Mondlak, get dressed. We have orders for you to come with us."

Sara shrieked, "No." Then her voice changed to a deep, heart-wrenching sound as she cried, "Noooooooo."

Hinda pulled her little sister onto her lap, rocking her, which did not soothe either of them. A heavy sensation pressed in on Hinda, as if an army tank had rolled in, flattening her, and parked upon her chest. She watched her father closely. The anguished expression on his pale, gaunt face sent chills zigzagging up and down her legs.

Initially, Salomon's shoulders had slumped, and his lips had twisted with torment, but as he absorbed the inescapable reality, he shifted his posture to a stance of self-possessed dignity. With mindful circumspection, he selected his best tie and sweater.

Jumping from Hinda's lap, Sara ran to her father, tugging on his trousers and hugging his legs. "Please don't go, Tatae, please." It was the clearest she had spoken in months.

"It's not my choice, sweet Sara. I must obey their command."

Upon hearing the stark truth of her father's plight, Rachel fell upon her knees in front of the officers. "Please don't take my father away," she pleaded. "Our mother died. We need him. He's done nothing wrong. Please."

Sara joined Rachel, groveling in front of the officers, begging them. Soon Sara was bawling hysterically, pawing at the men's shoes.

Almost yelling, one of the Gestapo said, "Shut up, little girl. Your crying will not change the orders for your father. And get your Jude hands off my boots."

Flopping onto her back, Sara wailed, blood-curdling yowls.

"Get control of her, or you know what will happen," the lead officer said. He took his rifle from the strap, readying it.

Hinda went to her sister. Placing her hand over Sara's mouth, muffling her cries, Hinda implored, "Hush. Be quiet now." In response, Sara kicked the floor. Her body rigid, she raised one leg at a time and then slammed her foot down.

"You're coming with me, whether you want to or not," Hinda exclaimed. She hooked her hands under Sara's armpits and dragged her across the floor away from the Gestapo.

Hinda corralled her sisters in the corner, but Sara continued her frenzy. She squalled, bawled, and yawped—clangorous, deafening sounds. A resolute strength came over Hinda. She lifted Sara, whose body was uncooperative, and jerked her into a standing position, facing the officers. "See that man. He is going to shoot you now if you don't stop screaming."

In the throes of a seizure-like tantrum, Sara flung herself on the floor with wild abandon. Her eyes registering panic, Hinda looked to Rachel for assistance.

Rachel placed her mouth close to Sara's ear. In a hushed tone, she said, "Remember what happened to the little kids who cried on Execution Day. That will be *you* if you're not quiet."

Instantly, Sara's eyes frosted over. She sat upright and grabbed her doll. Then, as if she were unexpectedly frozen, her body became completely stiff. Her eyes did not budge from the officers' guns. No sound, no movement; she became a statue.

"Stay with her, Rachel, stay close," Hinda whispered.

Donning her sweater, Hinda approached the officers. "May I accompany my father?"

The officers looked at each other. One tilted his head. The lead officer said, "Okay, but just for a short way."

The lower-ranking officer inquired, "What's the deal with the curtain? What are you hiding?"

Hinda crossed her arms on her chest. "We're not hiding anything. Another family, the Shapiros, live there. But we haven't seen them in a long time."

The subordinate officer pulled the flour-sack curtain back and surveyed the space strewn with clothing, trash, and suitcases. He shrugged and returned to stand aside the lead officer.

Salomon said, "I am ready. May I hug my daughters and say good-bye to them?"

"No, that would incite them, and we've waited long enough. Get going." The lead officer pointed his rifle at the door.

Salomon cast a longing glance in the direction of Rachel and Sara. The horror etched on their faces stabbed at his heart, that and the image of little Sara desperately clutching the cloth doll. Resolved to remain composed, he exited the mill with Hinda following closely on his heels.

As they walked, Salomon slipped a tiny purse to Hinda. "It contains a few German marks," he said in a faint voice.

"No, you keep them. You will need them, wherever they're taking you."

"Where I am going, Hinda, I will not need money."

"Tatae," Hinda said. It was the only word she could manage. Her instincts said her father spoke the truth. And she knew exactly what that meant: a death decree, naming him, had been issued. Her throat closed. Her chest tightened. She felt like her heart might explode right there on the street, bursting into bloody pieces as if the Gestapo had shot her at close range.

Reaching for her hand, Salomon said, "I want you to promise me that you will be both father and mother to your sisters."

Abruptly, the lead officer thrust his arm out in front of them, signaling to halt. He instructed Hinda that she could go no farther. "Get back home now," he commanded.

Squeezing her father's hand, Hinda's voice quavered, then found strength. "I promise."

The officer prodded him, and Salomon walked away, a Gestapo officer flanking each side of him.

Standing stock-still, Hinda watched them walk down the street. Salomon was taller than the officers and most others. She kept her eyes on the back of his head, until she could see her father no more.

Turning in the direction of the mill, tears pounded her cheeks, raining from her chin, soaking her sweater's collar. Her hands fisted, Hinda prayed fervently: *Dear God, please, be with my tatae. Save him from suffering. Let his end be as painless as possible. And help me. Give me the fortitude and the wisdom to be both parents—a mother and a father—to my sisters. I am it, all that Rachel and Sara have now.*

Before entering the mill, Hinda dried her eyes. She gripped her own arms, squeezing and patting them. Aloud, she said to herself, "You can do this, Hinda Mondlak. You *have* to."

When she came through the door, Rachel inundated her with questions: "Where is Tatae? Where did you leave him? How was he?" Sara did not speak, but she looked at Hinda expectantly, her eyes pleading earnestly for information.

"Let's eat breakfast." Hinda sighed. "And then we'll talk." She brought out the small block of bread, saved for today's breakfast and divided it into three parts. While chewing the hard crust, Hinda garnered all the willpower she could muster. Shattered as she was, she found her inner strength intolerably insufficient. At that moment, she made the decision to lie to her sisters.

"I left Father with a bunch of men. Soldiers were taking the group to work in a factory. I don't know where or which one, but I think it's far away from here."

"When will he be back?" Rachel asked.

Hinda shrugged her shoulders, fidgeting with the button on her sweater. "I don't know. But, I guess, not for a long while."

Bolting from the table, Sara ran to her coat bed and threw herself upon it.

"Sara, my *Zurele*, my little diamond who used to shine so brightly." Surprised at the Yiddish name Zurele spouting unexpectedly from her mouth, Hinda glanced around the room as if she might see her mother, who had used that endearment, meaning little Sara.

Hinda went to her little sister. Kneeling aside her, she stroked Sara's face and hair. "I miss Tatae too. But we'll be okay. You, Rachel, and me, we will. I promise." She reached for the cloth doll, which usually pacified Sara, but it was not in the wooden box where Sara kept it. Salomon had built the small crate, using wood from the broken table legs, right after they had moved to the ghetto. Sara had played with it endlessly.

"Where's your doll?" Hinda asked. "She's not in her house."

Sara's eyes already dimmed, she had retreated inward. She stared catatonically at the wall.

Hinda opened Sara's suitcase, and there she saw it. The doll. Decapitated. Its head ripped from its body.

Her stomach in knots, Hinda fretted over the headless doll and what it symbolized for Sara's condition. She whispered, "A part of me feels like my head has been severed too. And poor Tatae, what kind of death will he suffer?"

Contemplating her father's death, Hinda suspected that he would be jailed prior to his execution. If so, prisoners would be the ones to carry his body to the burial pits. She thought about the hordes of prisoners who walked in front of the mill every day to and from their assignments with the mass graves.

Using string and old clothing, Hinda covered the lone window in their quarters. The scenes on the street were more nightmarish than ever, but mostly, she wanted to protect her sisters from a sight she feared they would never recover from: their father's dead body being lugged to the graves.

Yet Hinda yearned to see her father, even if he was dead. In the afternoon, she waited until Sara was napping and Rachel's eyes were closed as she painted on the canvas of her mind. On tiptoe, Hinda sneaked out and then climbed to the rooftop. She searched the profiles of the hundreds of prisoners as they walked past, praying to see her father's face, aching to see him one more time. She did this day after day, fantasizing that if she could have just one glimpse of his face, alive or dead, she would yell to the world, "I love you, Father."

Hinda's fantasy never came to fruition.

In the ensuing days, Hinda began to question her lie to her sisters. She railed at herself: *Was it my own denial?* Plagued with guilt, she analyzed the promise she had made to her father—that she would be both mother and father to Sara and Rachel. *I'm not being a good father to them. Tatae would not have lied. He would have told them the truth, regardless of how terrible it was.*

Hinda worried about what to do, how to effectively parent her emotionally disturbed sister. Sara's behavior had become more bizarre. The headless doll was now minus its arms. Then it came to her: she could not bring her father back, and she could not wave a magic healing wand over Sara, but she could make the doll whole again. She rushed to her mother's suitcase, tumbled through its contents, and found the needle and thread her mother had packed from their home in Zieluń. She gathered the doll's parts, hoping to have the doll sewn together again before her sisters returned from visiting their mother's grave.

As Hinda sewed, making the tightest stitches she could to secure the doll's head on its body, memories washed over her, specifically recollections of being ten years old and on a train to Warsaw with her father. She had been thrilled that her father had asked her to accompany him to Warsaw, the country's capital, where she had never been. The train ride proved exhilarating. And then, when they walked downtown together, a warm glow had tingled through her. Soon, though, the store windows' wares summoned her attention. Such merchandise Hinda had never seen. Then, a toy store loomed into view. There, in the window, a beautiful doll sat perched upon a desk. Its golden locks, hanging in ringlets, looked incredibly real, and its startlingly lifelike blue eyes seemed to stare directly at Hinda. She yearned to touch the doll, to have it. Then she saw the price. She looked up at her father, his eyes laden with sadness, and sensed he was feeling bad that he could not buy it for her. Commanding her attention away from the doll's allure, and acting as if she did not care, Hinda urged, "Come on, let's go. There's so much more to see." She tugged on her father's hand, and they walked away. After a full day of sightseeing, they returned to Zieluń in the evening. The next morning, when Hinda awoke, she felt something in her hands—a doll. Fashioned from scraps of fabric, its facial features and eyes of blue had been outlined and filled in with colored pencils. Loops of yellow yarn distinguished its hair. Although it was far from the gorgeous doll in the toy store window, she instantly adored it. Still wearing her nightclothes, Hinda ran to her father's arms, hugging him, and saying thank you. From the other room, her mother had chimed in, "I helped too."

Hinda set the needle and thread down. She hugged the doll to her chest. Reveling in the memory, she whispered, "Tatae, I so treasure that day in Warsaw with you." Tears streaked Hinda's face; her lips quivered. "I miss you so much. Sometimes I think I might burst apart. I hope you know how much happiness and comfort this simple, cloth doll brought me. You and Mommy filled this creation with your love. I pray that Sara can feel your caring in this worn fabric and be comforted by it. She's suffering terribly, and I'm worried that Sara is losing her sanity. Please *help me* to know how to *help her.*"

A fall haze dulled the sky. The leaves of the trees had changed hues due to the cooler season. Rachel delighted in the color, wishing she could see the leaves up close. The artist in her wanted to drink the hues—the sage green, the burgundy red, the bright yellow, and the orange, letting the colors slide down her throat, painting her insides.

Rachel took Sara's hand as they walked. Sara had asked to visit their mother's grave every day since their father had been taken away. Rachel was happy to accompany her little sister, not because she wanted to look upon the grave, but to be outdoors. Tucked back in the field behind the mill, the grave felt distanced from the horridness of the street. The snippets of peace and fresh air rejuvenated Rachel's soul.

As she had for the past few days, Sara marched around the grave like she was performing a ritual. But today, Rachel noticed that her little sister's face held an expression of disturbed puzzlement. "Are you okay, Sara baby?"

Sara held up one finger, asking, "Just one?"

"One what?" Rachel replied.

"Tatae's with Mommy now. Where's his mound?" Sara asked, wide-eyed.

Rachel felt her stomach lurch, folding in on itself. She stared at her little sister, who at times *knew* things. "Oh my, let's go inside and talk to Hinda."

"No." Sara shook her head vehemently. "Heenda too sad."

41

The Letter

Mid-September 1942 | Mława, German-occupied Poland

In the late afternoon, exactly two weeks to the day of when her father was taken away, Hinda played a clapping game with Sara. They sat facing each other on the floor, both sitting cross-legged. Midway through the rhyming chant that accompanied the clapping, there was a knock on the door. Soft at first, then louder.

Tossing her sketch pad aside, Rachel jumped up. "That sounds like a messenger's knock. Maybe it's my new pencils."

Empty handed, Rachel returned with a young man following behind her. A capo, the man was wearing the Jewish Police armband and carried a baton.

Hinda stood and smoothed her skirt. She recognized the capo. He had gone to high school with her brother, Joel, and had occasionally come to their home.

"Hello, Hinda, I'm Zachery Zimmerman. Do you remember me from our old shtetl?" He extended his hand.

"Yes, Zachery, I remember what seems a lifetime ago now. What brings you here today?" she asked, suspicious of his motives. Her arms crossed, Hinda ignored his hand, not extending hers. Now that Zachery was a capo, she had zero trust or respect for him.

Casting furtive glances around the room, Zachery asked, "Could I speak to you alone?"

Hinda's eyebrows furrowed. She looked at Sara and Rachel, worrying for them, especially Sara, to hear what he had to say.

Without any directive from Hinda, Rachel gathered her and Sara's coats. "We will visit Mommy's grave."

"Okay, but don't be long," Hinda said, a lump forming in her throat.

Zachery looked around their hovel, shuffling his feet, until the girls exited the door. "You don't have *any* furniture?" he asked.

"Obviously not," Hinda said. "Is that what you came to discuss?"

"No." He looked down at the floor, breaking away from Hinda's intense gaze. "Your father. Uh. I wanted to tell you that I was with him until the end."

"You? With my father?" Hinda's breath faded. Her insides felt leaden. "How was he? Where was he?"

"First, let me explain. I was assigned to guard him on his last morning."

"Was he in jail?

"Yes, a private cell. The Council arranged for him to have special treatment because of his stature as a religious leader in Zieluń."

"The Council?" Hinda was floored. Her radar ignited and suspicions took wing, flying through her mind like rabid bats. "Please tell me, how was my father?"

"He was serene. And writing a letter to you."

She gasped audibly. "A letter to me? Do you have it?"

"No. When he finished, he gave it to me, but I . . . I—"

Interrupting him, Hinda shrilled, "Where is it? What did you do with it?"

"I gave the letter to the Judenrat, to the head councilman."

Fury billowed through Hinda, rattling her bones, tensing every muscle. Rage tore at her every cell and roiled her aggrieved heart. She screeched, "Why would you do that? The letter was to *me*."

"Because I had to follow compulsory protocol. It's part of my job." Zachery bowed his head. "I'm sorry, Hinda. I didn't think I had a choice, but it's troubling me now. I feel terrible. You should at least be allowed to read it."

"Are you saying they weren't going to tell me?"

He nodded. "They care most about the records. The archives, they say. But I can take you to the council member I gave it to and see if he'll permit you to read it."

"Let me get my coat and tell my sisters." Hinda's hands shook and twitched with such tremors that she wrestled with the buttons on her coat.

At the Council member's apartment, Hinda recognized the councilman. He was the one who had come to the mill warning about black-market food. Peeved— but not surprised—that he did, indeed, have superior living quarters, she worked to contain her anger.

Zachery trailed inside behind Hinda. The man escorted them to his office. "What can I do for you?" he inquired.

"I am Hinda Mondlak, and I want the letter my father, Salomon Mondlak, wrote to *me* the day he was murdered."

"What makes you think there is such a letter?" the councilman asked, casting a disapproving glance in Zachery's direction.

Hinda saw the councilman's eyes, all hawkish. She felt like a mouse that was about to be pounced upon and consumed. Tears flooded her face. Distraught, she leaned against his desk. Through her tears, she saw an open notepad on his desktop. Names were written upon it; Salomon Mondlak's was among them. His name had been checked off and crossed out. The checkmark meant he had been picked up. And that simple, single line through his name indicated that his death was complete. Although she already knew it to be true, the reality struck its blow. She sobbed, her breath catching so that she almost fainted.

"Please!" the councilman exclaimed, saying the usually polite word sarcastically. "Get ahold of yourself." He went to a filing cabinet and withdrew a folded paper. "You may read it only. The letter must remain here for our files."

"Oh? And what do you presume that will accomplish?" Hinda asked, her voice trembling. "Just who will benefit from my father's personal letter stored in your records?"

The councilman cleared his throat loudly. "Do you want to read it or not?" He handed Hinda a napkin. "Dry your eyes. I want it preserved, with no smudges or water spots."

Feeling woozy, her feet wobbly, Hinda unfolded the paper.

Dear Hinda,

Do you remember when your mother died, and I told you that she was privileged to die that way? God did not grant me such privilege. Perhaps I am not worthy. I hurt so badly knowing that I will never see you or your sisters again. I am leaving you with all my blessings, and I beg you to do your absolute best to be both father and mother to your sisters.

My dear daughter, I know that you have immense courage and daring, so please be careful and take good care of yourself. I know for certain that you will live, and you will tell.

With Love and Blessings,
Your Father, Salomon Mondlak

Her knees buckling, Hinda said, "May I sit down? I notice that *you* have chairs."

Although his lips pursed in irritation, the councilman nodded to a bench against the wall. He looked at his watch, checking the time.

A watch? Why didn't they confiscate his valuables? Pushing aside her questions, Hinda read and reread the letter. She ached to touch and caress the curve of every word written by her father's hand. But she felt the councilman breathing down her neck, watching her every move. Worried that he would cut her time even shorter or jerk the letter from her, she asked, "Do you have paper and a pen so that I may copy this?"

His eyes hooded, the councilman said, "No. And one more minute is all I have for you."

She lowered her eyes back to the letter. *Memorize every single word*, she commanded herself. Just then, she heard her father's voice as if he were reading to her. A specific sentence jumped out, searing into her soul: *I know for certain that you will live, and you will tell.*

42

In A Split Second

The sun rose in the early morning twilight, casting its beams upon a freight car that sat unmoving at a junction just past the Breslau station. The previous morning, the train had come to an abrupt halt at that spur, where multiple railroad tracks crossed.

Wolf Yoskowitz sat on the floor of the boxcar with his back to the wood siding. The five-hour ride from Gliwice had been slow and rough. A bucket served as the only toilet. The bilious odor increased hourly. Nonetheless, Wolf felt blessed to have a spot where he could sit. The passenger next to him leaned heavily against him, the guy's head bobbing on his shoulder. Wolf did not mind. His brother, Joseph, slept at last.

Having watched the sun rise, set, and rise again through a slight gap between wooden slats of the roof, Wolf knew they had been in that exact spot for over twenty-four hours. Extreme thirst and hunger rankled his senses. Not one drop of water or crumb of food had been provided to the men in his car. All Jews, from what Wolf could surmise.

His brother's head upon his shoulder, Wolf felt his heart begin to thaw, although he knew the wee warmth would be short lived. He and Joseph were being transported to a labor camp, or so they were told. When their destination of Buchenwald had been announced, another prisoner had cried out, "Labor camp? Pshaw! It's a killing center." The man had been shot dead right there on the station platform.

Without notice, the train inched forward. Closing his eyes, Wolf thought of all that had happened since he left the Dutka farm. *If only I had listened to Halina*, he railed at himself. *But my family. What kind of man would I be if I hadn't tried to find them? Tried to help them?*

As the train rattled along the tracks, Wolf mulled over his capture. He could not stop thinking about it; his brain locked onto the scenes as if a horror movie reeled in his head. One of the few movies he had ever seen and the first horror film, *The Testament of Dr. Mabuse*, had stayed with him for years. Only sixteen years old when the German film had come to Gliwice late in 1933, Wolf had struggled to erase the scary images and gruesome plot from his mind. He shivered at the memory. But now, this real and present horror, his family's capture, fueled a fear like none he had ever experienced.

It all began with his leaving the Dutka farm in search of the brush pile where he suspected his brother, Joseph, was hiding. One kilometer into the woods, Wolf encountered a squad of German soldiers. Hearing their chatter as they approached, Wolf ducked into a grove of trees and crouched behind large vines of undergrowth. The soldiers walked near him, hooting about Halina Dutka, speaking of her female body parts as if they were cheap trinkets. One of them expounded further about what wicked acts he would like to commit on Halina.

Wolf's nerves already nettled by the soldier's objectionable prattle, he was jolted by the fierce feeling that arose in him. The intensity of his protective emotion brought a realization that he held a strong affection and respect for Halina. Yes, he even loved her. She was more attractive to him than any gentile woman had ever been, but his heart fizzled flat when he thought of marrying her.

From what Wolf could ascertain from the soldier's conversation, the Nazi patrol was planning to stop at the Dutka farm for breakfast. After being on duty all night, the soldiers were hungry and hoofing it at a fast clip.

Wolf had then crept through the trees with expert stealth. After a couple of hours, he came upon a clearing, a natural space in the woods where a large, flat rock took center stage. Wolf peeked from the trees. No one was in sight. He inched closer to check out an odd form lying atop the rock. A dead rabbit lay face up, as if it were a sacrifice on an altar. Its abdomen had been slit open, and blood still poured forth. Inspecting the body, Wolf saw no signs of how it had been killed, and rabbits were challenging to catch by hand. The entire scene seemed surreal. Looking around, he sensed an inordinate stillness and quiet. A peculiar feeling overcame him. The idea—*It's a trap! Run!*—exploded in Wolf's mind just as he felt the barrel of a gun push against his spine.

A hand gripped Wolf's shoulder. A Nazi officer asked, "You hungry enough to eat raw rabbit, Jew boy?" In a flash, soldiers surrounded him, their guns all pointing directly at him. Wolf felt a rope go tight on his wrists as his arms were brought behind his back. One of the soldiers shoved him to the ground.

The officer yelled, "What's your name?"

"Wolf," he whispered.

The officer kicked at him. "What's your full name? Loud and clear."

Struggling to sit up, his tied hands inhibiting his movements, Wolf managed to get upon his knees. He looked the officer in the eye and belted out, "Wolf Yoskowitz."

Suddenly, there was a thrashing sound in a nearby pile of underbrush. A young boy staggered out and immediately lunged toward Wolf. Wild-eyed, the boy wrapped his arms around Wolf's neck and squeaked, "Wolfie, you're alive."

His heart shattered, Wolf stammered, "Oh, Alexander."

"He's my big brother," Alexander explained to the officer. "We thought he was dead."

Aiming his gun, one of the soldiers went to the brush pile the boy had occupied. Just as he cocked the trigger to make a blind shot into it, Wolf's mother emerged, her hands held in the air in surrender.

"What's this? A family reunion?" the officer asked tauntingly. He directed his next question to Wolf. "So, you were not living here with them?"

"No, sir." A knot rising in his throat, Wolf swallowed hard.

"Well, then, I don't think an old woman and this young boy could survive alone in these woods." Pointing in various directions, he ordered the other soldiers to shoot into all the brush piles in the area.

Multiple shots were fired at random, then one soldier focused on a giant brush heap about ten yards away, shooting his gun in rapid blasts.

"Stop! My brothers are in there," Alexander screamed. His mouth wide open, bawling, tears spurted like geysers from the boy's eyes.

Wolf's other two brothers, Joseph and Samuel, crawled out of the dead limbs. Samuel's shirt was red with blood. His left shoulder had been hit.

Amidst the ruckus, Alexander ran to the brush pile where he had been living. Sobbing he called out, "Erna, I want us all together." At that moment, Wolf's sister, Erna, showed her face as she came out of hiding.

"All together?" the officer mimicked, with sinister sarcasm dripping from every syllable. "Kid, your Jude family has broken the law living in these woods. Punishment is due." Scanning the group, the officer's sight landed on Samuel. "Looks like I missed his heart. Not this time." He fired one well-aimed shot straight into Samuel's chest.

In a split second, Samuel Yoskowitz, a mere adolescent, fell to the ground, his youth, his innocence, his life force, forever gone.

43
The Chair

Questions of why flooded Hinda's brain. They crowded her heart and inflamed her empty stomach. Awakened by hunger pains and roiling anger, Hinda tossed on her coat bed, the hard floor digging into her bony back. Reliving the previous evening, she thought of the notepad on the councilman's desk. Her father's name had been crossed out, meaning he had been killed. And then, the Council had intercepted her father's final letter to her. They had knowingly kept from her his sacred words of encouragement. If not for Zachery Zimmerman's conscience needling him, she would never have known of her father's blessing upon her and his powerful prophecy that she would survive.

Praying seemed futile. Nonetheless, she extended her spirit heavenward, hoping to gain God's ear, or to merely brush against such holiness that she would find respite from the cyclone of pernicious emotions twisting inside her. Tucking her chin against her chest, she began to pray: *Dear Lord, please help me to be strong today when I tell Rachel and Sara the truth. I'm not sure I can withstand their intense emotion and mine too. Their little hearts are going to break wide open and bleed screams when I tell them the grievous reality: Tatae is dead. Lord, I feel so mad at you. I know you exist, so why, God, why? Why aren't you intervening and stopping this cruelty? I just can't comprehend how you can allow such suffering and injustices against my family, against humanity, against so many good and devout people. Please don't punish us further.*

A loud thump outside the door caused Hinda to rise just before she heard a soft knock. The Gestapo typically rapped loudly, but she had become distrustful of any request for entry. She ran her hands through her tangled hair before opening the door. There, in the dawn's misty light, stood Zachery Zimmerman.

"Good morning, Hinda. Sorry to bother you so early, but I wanted to drop this off to you before I reported to work."

Her eyes widened. "A chair?"

"May I bring it inside for you?"

She held the door while Zachery turned the upholstered chair on its side to get it through the doorway. The stuffing was sticking out from a gash in the rolled arm, and the seat cushion was stained, but it was furniture, a soft place to sit.

"Where do you want it?" Zachery asked, wrestling with the bulky piece.

"This corner right here." Hinda pointed. "Where did you get it?" she asked, sitting down to try it out. "Please tell me this was not stolen. My father would say, I mean, I would say we couldn't accept it if it was."

"It's from my place. I have a sofa, and that's enough."

"What about your family?"

Zachery pressed his lips firmly together, locking in awfulness—the ungodly words needed to describe what had happened to his mother, father, and brother. Their brutal and unjust deaths were the reason he had become a capo working for the Nazis, all in hopes of saving his own skin. "It's just me now," he replied.

"I'm sorry to hear that." Hinda relaxed into the chair, unaware that a sigh was escaping her lips.

"I know it's ugly, but it sits okay, right?"

"Yes! I haven't felt such plushness since—" Her voice broke and tears burst forth, watery globules that made her blue eyes shine like sapphires. She looked up at Zachery, the capo she had despised just yesterday, before he took her to read her father's letter. "I, er, uh. I'm usually not at a loss for words but giving us *your* chair is . . . is—" Hinda stopped abruptly. Sighing heavily, she stood. "It's hard to describe what this means to me. Physical comfort that my sisters and I haven't had in eons, it seems. Thank you." She coughed lightly; the lump in her throat remained. "Seriously, Zachery, we thank you."

Zachery lowered his eyes, although he did not want to stop looking at Hinda. Her uncultivated beauty paired with her undisguised appreciation touched a part of him that he thought, until recently, would require an icepick to penetrate. He moved toward the door, sliding the Ghetto Police armband up near his biceps. "I need to get on to work."

She stepped toward him and placed her hand on his forearm, intending to say thanks yet again. Instead, unplanned questions popped out. "Is there any chance that you know of any news regarding my brother, Joel? What happened to him? Or to the Shapiros, who lived over there?" She pointed to the curtain.

Zachery glanced down at her hand on his arm, a feeling of electricity rippling through him. The muscle in his jaw flinched when he said, "The Shapiros are dead."

"What happened?" Hinda asked.

"They paid a capo to get them false identification documents and were discovered at the train station with tickets to Norway, where they planned to escape to Sweden by boat. All four were promptly executed, the three family members and the corrupt capo. The Gestapo called a meeting of the capos to tell us about it. They came down hard, warning what would happen to us if we had such enterprising ideas. But that all happened last spring. Didn't you know?"

"No one told us. What do you know about Joel?"

Zachery's eyes squinted. "He was in the Zieluń jail, right?"

"We never knew for sure, just that German soldiers took him from our home, marched him away in handcuffs. November of 1939."

"Two years ago?" Zachery's incredulous tone reverberated in the air, indicating his belief that two years was too long to survive a Nazi jail. He winced. "I'll see what I can find out."

Her fingers drumming the dingy brocade fabric, Hinda sank deeper into the chair. A wave of guilt washed over her, realizing that she only felt relief, not a speck of sadness for the Shapiros. Turning her thoughts back to her own sorrowful burden, she watched Sara and Rachel as they slept, her eyes darting from one face to the other. How was she going to tell them that their father was dead . . . that they had no parents at all now?

Rehearsing varying phrases only exacerbated her anxiety—a funnel cloud in her heart that dipped into her solar plexus. Her stomach swirled nervously like a whirling tornado had descended onto her gut, shredding her instincts. She felt intensely confused and desperate to fulfill her promise to her father, to be both mother and father to Rachel and Sara. While it was a hefty responsibility, mothering her sisters was a cakewalk compared to taking on her father's role, which incited such inner pressure that her skin hurt.

Frustrated, she stood from the chair, and it came to her, what her father would do. She turned toward the east, facing Jerusalem, covered her eyes with her right hand, and recited the *Shema: Hear, O Israel, the Lord is our God, the Lord is one. Blessed be His glorious majesty forever and ever. You shall love the Lord your God with all your heart, with all your soul, and with all your might.* Imbued with renewed vigor, she went through all the remaining verses of the traditional prayer.

Once complete, she uncovered her eyes. A dynamic stillness filled her to overflowing. Along with potent peace, a steely determination accompanied this newfound inner strength. It was clear her father's prediction that she would *live* was meant to give her the necessary fortitude to *keep on keeping on* regardless of what happened next. Not a cotton-candy euphoria, it was confirmation, a steadfast sense deep inside that she could effectively parent her younger sisters, and that, somehow, she would survive.

Screams and gunfire from the street startled her calm resolve. Hinda moved toward the window. Her hand on the cloth that covered the glass panes, she shuddered and recoiled. *The Nazis have escalated the killings and beatings on the streets. I'm not looking at horror that I'm not forced to watch. And Execution Day is tomorrow.* She backed away, retreating to the chair, attempting to focus on her surprising good luck to have it.

The noise from outside awakened Rachel and Sara. They both sat up, looking around. When their eyes found Hinda, their jaws dropped.

"A chair?" Rachel squealed. "Am I dreaming?"

Sara looked skeptical, but she arose and ran to the chair to touch it.

Rachel and Sara circled the chair in awe. Hinda stood, her hand motions encouraging them to jump into it. They each tried it out with exuberant grins of delight, such as had not crossed their faces in years.

Oh, to extend their joy, Hinda wished. *Maybe I won't tell them about Tatae today.* Yet reciting the Shema had increased her willpower. Her feet felt bigger. She would fill her father's shoes and push onward. "Let's have our morning bread, then there's something we need to discuss."

After eating, Sara did somersaults over the bulging rolled arms of the chair and flips from the top. Hinda watched. Her little sister was playing, really playing. Once again, temptation to not bring sad news into the lightness reared itself inside her, but Hinda brushed it aside.

"Okay, circus girl, move over. Make room for me. Let's sit in the chair together." Hinda gestured for Sara to get into her lap. "Rachel, come join us."

Rachel perched on the arm of the chair. "What is it, Hinda? Has something happened?"

"Yes, it has. I received confirmation last night." Hinda's eyes filled with tears, her throat tightened. "It breaks my heart to say these sad words, but . . . but Tatae died."

Rachel looked at Sara who nodded her head in assent. "We know."

"What? Who told you? How could you know?"

"Well, we didn't know for sure," Rachel clarified. "But a couple of weeks ago, Sara told me that she saw Tatae with Mommy, that they were together in heaven now."

Sara flung her arms around Hinda's neck, "Sorry, Heenda, sorry."

"We carried rocks and made an edge around Mommy's grave to make it different, to mark it for Tatae too. We cried so hard with each rock that my tear bank is empty. For now, anyway," Rachel explained. "Every day since, we've gone to the grave and said Kaddish for him."

"Come see," said Sara. She jumped from the chair and tugged on Hinda's arm, pulling her to standing.

Breathing in the crisp autumn air, the three sisters walked briskly, with purpose in their stride, to the grave in the field behind the mill. Stones of varying sizes had been placed snugly against each other, lining the edges of their mother's grave perfectly.

Awestruck, Hinda exclaimed, "It's beautiful. What a sweet idea." Then, she began saying Kaddish aloud, praising God and sanctifying the great name of God. Midway, Hinda broke. Deep sobs racked her ribcage. She plopped down on the dirt, stretching her body across the grave, letting yet another stratum of grief seep from her heart.

Rachel completed the prayer and sat on the ground beside Hinda. Her fingers tenderly caressed a nearby rock. She whispered, "Tatae, we hope you didn't suffer a painful death. We miss you terribly, but we are happy that you and Mommy are together."

Dry eyed, Sara stroked Hinda's back. Then she kissed her hands and placed them upon her sister. Again and again, Sara pressed her fingertips to her lips and then patted Hinda—her second mother, her second father. "Heenda, don't cry," Sara implored. "Look. Tatae is standing right there at the end of the grave."

"The word coming down through the ranks, Walter, is that you did a fine job managing the personnel of the department in my absence." Josef Mengele gestured for Walter Zeilhofen to sit in the chair across from his desk.

"Speaking of fine jobs, congratulations on receiving the Iron Cross, First Class award," Walter replied. He paused for a response, but his boss merely nodded. Walter continued, "Pulling those two soldiers out of that burning tank, all while under enemy fire, was quite a feat."

"It was worse than a malignant nightmare. Did you hear about my Black Badge award?"

"Yes. I was about to congratulate you on that one too. I read the newspaper report of what excellent medical care you gave to thousands of wounded Germans."

Josef nodded in assent, his index finger and thumb massaging the outer cartilage of his ear as he eyed Walter warily. "I read a report too. The one outlining what you accomplished with our research projects while I was saving lives in the SS's Viking Division."

Walter shifted in his chair, crossing his right leg over his left.

"It was disappointing to see how close you came to achieving breakthroughs on racial genetics, and then stopped short when it came to performing the final testing procedures."

Hedging on giving an immediate response, Walter uncrossed his legs, transferring his weight to the back of the chair. He assessed his boss's disdainful expression. Clearing his throat, Walter replied, "I'm not as bold as you, Josef."

"Most certainly, you are not," Mengele replied. "That's why I've requested a transfer for you."

"Oh?" A rocket of hope launched inside Walter. Maybe, at last, he could be free from the clutches of Josef Mengele.

"You'll still work under my direction," Mengele explained. "My esteemed boss here at the Institute, Baron Otmar von Verschuer, and I agree that Auschwitz is the perfect place for you to continue our research. It's filled with undesir-ables—racially impure Jews, schizophrenics, Gypsies, misfit dwarfs—and the likes of which I don't think you'll experience such qualms about performing procedures upon."

"Auschwitz? The internment camp in occupied Poland?" Shocked to his core, Walter felt his chest tighten as if it were an overfilled balloon. His heart rate increased; beads of perspiration pearled across his forehead.

"That's the place. The arrangements are made. You report there next week, the fifteenth of October."

45
It's Him
Mid-October 1942 | Mława, German-occupied Poland

Late Thursday afternoon, Hinda washed potatoes in the shower stall, the only water source at the mill. Scrubbing more vigorously than usual, she felt a desperate urge to get the skins ultra clean. Ghetto residents' health was already failing from poor nutrition and rampant diseases, and yet another unidentified illness had struck. People who had seemed to be fairly strong were suddenly sick and dying. Hinda suspected that the Nazis were dusting the rationed vegetable skins with poison or bacteria.

When Hinda was satisfied that the vegetables were sanitized, she departed the shower area. Rounding the corner, her eyebrows shot upward. Sara was standing at the front door, pointing her index finger. She stood chillingly still, like she was in one of her catatonic states.

"Are you playing a game with the door, Sara? Go wash your hands. We're ready to eat." Just as Hinda finished slicing the potatoes, there was a knock on the door. Her head jerked in the direction of the rapping sound. "Sara, are you doing that?" Hinda dried her hands and moved toward the door, anxiety rising with her every step.

Sara stood in the exact spot near the doorway where she had been earlier. Her voice tiny and squeaky—she had not spoken a word all week—Sara said, "It's him."

"Who, baby?" Hinda asked.

Without a single blink, Sara's large eyes stared straight ahead as if seeing through the thick wooden door.

Hinda hurled open the door and was unprepared for what she saw. His black hair was matted, and he had oozing cuts and purplish bruises all over his face and neck. His clothes were shredded threads that barely covered his body.

"Joel!" Hinda's voice cracked. Far from the hale, strikingly handsome Joel of two years ago, her brother looked to be an injured animal, a defeated man.

He fell into Hinda's arms, clinging to her.

46

Circling Vultures

The freight train stopped at the Leipzig station. The schedule showed a two-hour layover before departing for Weimar.

During the seven-hour trip from Breslau, no water or food had been provided to the prisoners. Moans, groans, and curses filled the air in the boxcar, which was now excessively crowded. Wolf and Joseph Yoskowitz stood facing each other, so that it was their bodies that pressed into each other, not those of strangers.

Wolf crinkled his brow. His head throbbed with a dehydration headache. What's more, horrific scenes, reel after reel, of his family's capture in the woods continued to play in his mind. The cruel and abrupt shooting of his brother Samuel had been devastating. His mother, Miriam, had fallen upon her dead son, wailing. The Nazi officer had cocked his gun to her head and ordered her to stand up and be quiet, or she would suffer the same fate.

Miriam asked if they could bury Samuel's body to honor their religion's laws. In reply, the entire patrol had barked and howled like crazed coyotes. The officer pointed to the sky where vultures were circling. "No need for a grave. He's *their* dinner. They've come for the dead rabbit, but now they have a feast."

Wolf's gut kinked into a knot; bile rose in his throat. The thought of Samuel's body being devoured by vultures nauseated his very soul.

The troop separated the family, forcing Wolf and Joseph to stand against a tree with soldiers' guns trained directly toward their heads. Other soldiers bound the hands of Miriam, Erna, and Alexander, then herded them away. No good-byes, no hugs.

Little Alexander, his eyes pleading and anguished, turned to look at Wolf. Panic and raw fear sullied his young face. He cried out, "Wolfie, save us."

Acute helplessness, a poisonous arrow, shot through Wolf, who had been the protector of his family since his father had passed away. Powerless, Wolf stood unmoving, his heart rending apart, his back pushing against tree bark. *Lord help us. This is all my fault.*

47

I'm Cold, so Cold

November 1942 | Mława, German-occupied Poland

The autumn sunset sparked a northern wind that whistled of winter coming. Shivering from the frosty breeze, Joel and Hinda stood beside their mother's grave. Hinda attempted to comfort Joel, who wept inconsolably, although he had visited the grave every day since his arrival two weeks ago.

The first night of Joel's return, he had appeared to be in shock, his eyes glazed, his skin ice cold but sweaty. Weak and fatigued, he could only muster a lackluster greeting to Rachel and Sara, even though he had not seen them in two years. Bewildered by their impoverished living quarters as compared to their home in Zieluń, Joel looked around the mill stupefied and then asked for Mommy and Tatae. When Hinda told him that both his mother and his father were dead, Joel was so stricken, breaking down in such an extreme way, that Hinda feared he had suffered a psychotic break.

Watching the sun lowering on the horizon amidst a bank of gray clouds, Hinda moved closer to her brother's side and put her arm around his shoulder. Joel leaned into her. "Why do you not cry?" he asked, his words spliced between sobs.

"Because I've already shed jillions of tears." Hinda sighed. "Giant ones that pelted my face like a hailstorm, big ones that fell like a torrent, little ones that trickled down my cheeks like drizzle, and tiny ones that seeped from the corners of my eyes against my will. I've screamed, ranted, kicked, and pounded my fist. Nothing brings Tatae and Mommy back. Nothing changes our horrendous circumstances."

Another wave of sobs overtook Joel, his shoulders shaking, his chest cresting. "I'm a fountain. I can't shut it off."

"What happened to you? I haven't wanted to ask in front of Sara and Rachel."

"I . . . uh." Joel's mouth twisted to the side. "I can't . . . talk . . . about it."

"Okay. But where did the Nazis take you the night they took you from us?" Hinda asked, her hand moving in a circle on his back—atop the coat he wore, their father's, which hung to the ground on Joel.

"First, to the jail in Zieluń," Joel replied. "After a couple of months, they moved me to a prison in Warsaw. Then, about six weeks ago, they transported me here to Mława. Never told me why for any of it."

"We prayed for you *every* day," Hinda soothed. "Mommy was distraught and obsessed. We wondered constantly if you were in a labor camp or in jail or even alive."

"I wish I weren't alive, right now today," Joel exclaimed. "It would have been better if the Nazis had just murdered me like they did so many of the others in my cell."

Hinda winced, hearing her brother talk in such defeated terms. "I was in jail here in Mława for several months and had to do hard labor every day. Did you?"

"Yep. I was forced to work, every day, digging huge graves, throwing dead Jews in on top of each other. That is, when the Nazis weren't torturing me."

The sunset cast a coppery glow on the leaves of the nearby trees, which rustled in the wind. Hinda pulled her coat close around her. "I know you're suffering. But, Joel, for your little sisters' sake, I really need for you to try to put on a more pleasant face, to not be so dour."

Joel nodded. Squatting by the graveside, he picked up one of the rocks that represented his father's grave. He turned it in his hand, squeezing it as if he could force it to render something—a soothing balm, a drop of his father's wisdom, a magical metamorphic substance that would transform the world back to the way it was before Hitler, to the days before his spirit had been mortally wounded.

"I'm sorry to ask you to pretend or squelch your feelings," Hinda said. "But I promised Tatae that I would take care of Sara and Rachel, be their mother and their father as best I could. Sara's childhood has been stripped away, her development thwarted. She teeters on the edge of insanity. And Rachel is extremely sensitive. She feels, truly experiences, the emotions other people around her are feeling."

Joel stood and turned to face Hinda. Their eyes locked. His dilated pupils pulled her into a tunnel of death, of even worse horror than she had witnessed to date. A weight fell upon her.

In the early morning twilight, Hinda tossed on her coat bed, feeling as if she had not slept all night. The vision in Joel's eyes haunted her soul. To disarm its power, Hinda had recited her father's promise, *I know for certain that you will live*, which had made it near impossible to sleep. She questioned just how her father could have known for certain? The words "for certain" indicated that it was more than his instinct or intuition. *Did he have a vision?* Then, a realization struck her: *Does Sara take after Tatae? Maybe she's gifted, not crazy after all. But why did Tatae single me out? Why didn't he say that the four of us—Rachel, Sara, Joel, and me—were going to live?* Hinda's thoughts ran rampant, cycling in a circle. Sadness and a knowing of sorts arose in her. From what she had experienced looking into Joel's eyes the day before, it seemed unlikely that he would survive the horrors that she sensed were yet to come.

Suddenly, Sara cried out, her voice congested, "Heenda. I'm cold, so cold."

Rushing to the closet, Hinda grabbed her father's coat and went to cover Sara. One look at her little sister and Hinda panicked. Sara's eyes were sunken, appearing to roll back. She shivered with chills, yet she burned with fever, her skin mottled red, her body drenched with perspiration.

Wrapping her father's coat around Sara while lifting her into her arms, Hinda carried her to the chair. She cuddled Sara, rocking her, using her own body for the rocking mechanism.

"Joel! Rachel! Wake up!" Hinda called out, her voice loud and commanding.

Joel did not move; in a dead sleep, he appeared unconscious.

This time, Hinda directed her voice in the direction of the window, "Rachel, I need your help." When there was no response, she yelled, "RA-CHEL!"

Rachel stirred, then sat up, her fine hair tousled. "What's wrong?"

"Sara is sick. She's burning hot with a high fever. I need you to bring me a cold cloth and then find some aspirin."

Rachel leapt up and ran to the chair. Her hand went to Sara's head. She reeled backward from the heat. "We don't have any aspirin. I had a terrible headache the other day and looked through Mommy's things. There weren't any."

"I know. I meant for you to go and *buy* aspirin. First, please bring me a wet, cold washcloth. I need to bring this fever down."

Rachel raced to the lone water spigot and returned with the cloth. "I hope this is cold enough."

Hinda swabbed Sara's face with it, then placed it atop her forehead. "Get Tatae's purse from under my blanket. Take two of the German marks. Try the hospital. Or knock on doors to see if anyone will sell you any aspirin or even just one."

"What about asking Council members?" Rachel inquired.

"If the hospital refuses, then try them, but hurry."

Rachel threw on her coat, tucking the tiny purse into an inside pocket.

"Wait." Hinda's mouth twisted with revulsion. "Before you go, check the Shapiros' things for aspirin or any medication. I hadn't wanted us to touch their stuff, but this situation merits it."

Rachel ducked behind the curtain and rifled through the suitcases. Soon, she emerged empty handed. Her nose wrinkled, Rachel exclaimed, "Eek! Their things smell nasty." She inhaled, taking in air from their cleaner side of the room. "There's no medication at all," she reported. "And no money either."

"Okay, go scrub your hands." Hinda exhorted. When Rachel returned, she said, "I was thinking that it'd be better if you had the marks ready to show. If you hold up the money, people are more likely to sell you aspirin. But keep the money hidden until asking a specific person."

Rachel removed the purse and took out two bills, noting there was only one left. She clutched the money in her fist, as Hinda had instructed. She ran out the door onto the street where a brawl was already brewing. Without hesitation, Rachel crossed the street and angled onto a side street, heading to the ghetto hospital.

Joel awoke to a humming sound. He sat up, looking around as if not knowing where he was. Then he saw Hinda sitting in the chair, holding Sara wrapped in Tatae's coat.

"Is she sick?"

"Yes, with a high fever. Could you bring her a cup of water? I'm worried she's getting dehydrated."

Arising, Joel grimaced, his knees almost buckling from the pain in his back. He brought the filled cup, then Hinda asked him to please take the cloth and wet it again with cold water. When he walked away, Hinda noticed that her brother was limping, dragging a leg.

"Do you have an injury?" she asked when he returned.

"Too many to name," Joel mumbled.

"I think her chills have subsided. Please help me get this coat from around her." Hinda tried to lift Sara from her lap. Joel struggled to slide the coat from underneath his little sister.

Sara cried out, "Heenda, that hurts."

"I'm sorry, baby. We need to reduce your fever."

"Why does she call you that funny name?" Joel asked in a more normal tone than he had used since he came home.

"I worked for a Polish woman who called me that. Sara thought it to be comical and latched onto it. It's the last of her sense of humor, so I've let it be."

At that moment, Rachel came through the door, breathing hard from running. "No one, absolutely no one, would sell me even one aspirin," she announced. Pausing, she choked back a sob. "The nurse at the hospital said they were out, but I didn't believe her. Two members from the Council said no. Then I knocked on door after door after door." She gulped for air. "Hinda, I tried so hard."

"Don't cry, Rachel. You did your best. Anyway, I'm not surprised. Everyone is too worried for themselves to part with their medication, even for money. And there's been so much trauma and sickness that they may not have any. For real."

"But what will we do?" Rachel implored.

"We'll pray, and I'll keep holding her. You and Joel need to get the food rations today."

Joel looked aghast, as if Hinda had asked him to step in front of a firing squad. Even still, he left with Rachel.

After they left, Hinda moved her little sister to an upright position on her lap and made her drink the water. Sara choked it down, saying her throat wasn't working right. Then she collapsed against Hinda, who silently prayed, *Dear Lord, please let Sara live.*

At that instant, Sara's eyelids flipped up; she gazed intently into Hinda's eyes. Her voice was weak, but she spoke clearly, "I'm not afraid. But if I die, please take me to Mommy. Bury me with her."

Suddenly, a memory flashed through Hinda's mind, and her ears rang with her mother's voice crooning to Sara when she was an infant. As if an other-worldly force spoke through her, Hinda said, "My sweet Sara, it's not my arms that are holding you right now. It's Mommy's arms."

Jarring knocks on the door awakened Hinda. The rising sun barely peeped through the cloth covering the window. Exhausted from holding Sara for multiple days and nights, Hinda dragged herself to the door. Her heart pounded, for she recognized the sound: a pistol handle used as a knocker.

"Hinda Mondlak, come with us," the male voice boomed when she opened the door to two Gestapo officers standing on the stoop.

"Where are you taking me?"

The lead officer grabbed her by the neck, "You piece of garbage. You ask too many questions. Get your coat, you're coming with us."

"May I change out of my nightclothes?"

"Get dressed, and make it fast," he snapped.

"Yes, sir," she replied. Leaving the door only slightly ajar, she crept back into the room. Amazingly, Sara and Joel had slept through the noise. If Sara knew the Gestapo had come to take her, she would throw a hideous fit. Joel would witness his little sister's insanity firsthand, and who knew how he might react.

Rachel sat erect, looking wild-eyed and terrified. She opened her mouth to talk.

Hinda made the shush sign, placing one finger vertically over her lips. Tiptoeing across the room, she bent close to Rachel's ear, whispering, "You're in charge until I return."

"And what if you don't? I'm so scared."

"They didn't tell me to pack a suitcase. That's encouraging. Tell Sara they've taken me to work for the day, and then pray with all your might that it's true."

A Disturbing Assignment

October 1942 | Günzburg, Germany

Walter Zeilhofen parked his KdF-Wagen in front of his family home in Bavaria. He hurried up the sidewalk to the porch where his mother stood waiting, the front door wide open behind her. She wiped her hands on her apron before wrapping her arms around her son. "Wonderful to see you, Walter." She patted his face, pinching one cheek. "Are you okay? You look stressed."

"Sorry, Mother. I was delayed by a military convoy on the autobahn just outside of Frankfurt," Walter explained. "And I detest being late." When he stepped inside the house, a tantalizing aroma greeted him. "Mmm!" he exclaimed.

His father's voice boomed into the entryway. "I'm in the dining room."

"Your father is gnashing his teeth to eat." His mother chuckled but gave Walter a hurry-it-up look. "Lunch is ready, but you've had a long drive. Lavatory?"

After refreshing himself, Walter rushed to the dining room, where his father was already seated, his napkin in his lap, his elbows pressing into the hand-tatted lace cloth. Serving dishes piled high with Walter's favorites were scattered across the table. "Wow, Mom, you've outdone yourself again." Giving his dad a squeeze on the shoulder, he said, "Hey, Dad."

"Son, good to have you home. What happened, though? Did you have a late start?"

Walter seated himself in the chair designated for him since childhood and quickly spread his napkin in his lap. "No. I left promptly at six a.m. But I was delayed a full hour by a slow-moving military convoy."

"That must have been annoying. Let's dig in."

"Dear, don't you want to say grace first?" Mrs. Zeilhofen looked askance at her husband.

Walter's father bowed his head and mumbled, "Bless this food. Amen."

Rolling her eyes, Walter's mother looked apologetically at him. He shrugged his shoulders.

"God will forgive us this once," Walter's father grumbled as he began heaping food onto his plate. "I'm so hungry, I could eat the whole table today."

Walter had intended to chat with his parents before lunch and tell them about his latest orders, but the traffic delay had derailed his plans. Having fumed for days at Josef Mengele's latest ploy, his emotional state was akin to a fiery volcano about to erupt.

Her eyes sparkling, Walter's mother passed a platter of sauerbraten to him. "All prepared with your preferred seasonings."

"Looks like a masterpiece and smells magnificent." Walter forked multiple slices of the roast onto his plate. "I doubt, though, I will see or taste food like this again for a while."

"Why is that?" his father asked, his bushy eyebrows hooked in a question.

"Well. I . . . I have news." Walter cleared his throat—twice, while running his fingers nervously through his hair. Wavy blonde locks fell onto his forehead. "I can't stay long. So can we talk about it while we eat?"

Walter's mother put down her knife and fork, crisscrossing them on her plate, her gaze not leaving her son's face. His father gulped down a bite, staring intently at Walter while chewing. He motioned with his hand, palm up, urging Walter to get on with it.

"I have been transferred to the internment camp of Auschwitz in occupied Poland," Walter announced. Sighing, he added, "I report later this week."

"God in heaven, help us," his mother said, crossing herself.

"Auschwitz? Why there?" his father asked, his face scrunched in obvious disapproval.

"It's complicated." Walter toyed with his napkin, not wanting to reveal the real reason he was being transferred and that Josef Mengele had called him a coward. "Josef believes the people interned there are well suited for our research procedures."

"Is he transferring too?" Walter's mother inquired.

"The current plan is for Josef to visit frequently to supervise the projects." Walter speared spaetzle onto his fork. "Even when he's in Frankfurt, though, I will be working under Josef's direction. Well, to be exact, his, and the directives of Dr. Eduard Wirths, who is chief physician at the camp."

Sipping from his beer stein, Walter's father asked, "What sort of things will you be doing?"

"I'll be performing research procedures, working in the lab, the infirmary, and at the staff hospital. I've only had one conversation with Dr. Wirths, so I am not sure of my exact assignments. He mentioned, though, that he is considering exploring the effects bromide would have on the internees, and if so, I would be involved in that research."

"Bromide?" Walter's father asked, his mouth packed with red cabbage. He swallowed hard, without chewing. "Isn't that a poisonous compound?"

"Yes and no. Bromide is the reduced form of bromine, a naturally occurring element, and is typically mixed with sodium or potassium. It can have toxic effects, though, if consumed in large doses."

"Why give it?" Walter's mother asked.

Using his knife, Walter cut into a slice of sauerbraten. "It *can* function as a calming sedative. And—" He cleared his throat again. "I apologize for talking about such distasteful subjects at lunch." He forked a piece of the roast but held it over his plate. Rich gravy dripped from the tines. "And I don't know how else to say it. So, in short, it stops ovulation and menstruation in women and reduces sexual urges in men."

"Oh, Lord," Walter's mother sighed heavily. "For life?"

"No, just during the time it's ingested."

"But doesn't it put young women at risk of never having children or having ones with birth defects?" she asked.

"Possibly. Current research has not addressed long-term use and resulting side effects." Walter brought both hands above his plate, holding them parallel, palms facing inward. He moved them up and down in unison, underscoring each word. "I hate this transfer to Auschwitz with every fiber of my being, but there's nothing I can do about it." Returning his hands to his lap, Walter let out an exasperated sigh. "Mengele has, once again, issued orders that radically affect my life and entrap me even more into his hateful Nazi regime." He picked up his napkin, dabbing at the corners of his eyes, where hot tears oozed from the corners.

Walter's mother reached over and took his hand in hers. "You have a big heart, Walter. I'm confident that you will find ways to help those persecuted people. God is placing you there for precisely that reason."

"Damn Nazis." Walter's father slammed his fist on the table. "I can't believe they're considering giving these people chemicals simply to make them easier to manage. But your mother is right. You'll be a force for good in this monstrosity of human abuse."

"I pray I can be," Walter said, still dabbing at his eyes.

"See to it that you are, Walter, but carefully so." His father's face had turned beet red, and tears tumbled onto his cheeks. "But more than anything, your mother and I want you alive. Watch your back constantly. As you know, even one tiny misstep, and Josef Mengele will have your head."

Late November 1942 | Mława, German-occupied Poland

Down the street from the mill, the two Gestapo, who had taken Hinda early that morning, steered her to the plaza where a cluster of females waited. Other Gestapo joined with more women in tow. Then, goose-stepping at a rapid pace, soldiers herded the group through the plaza and outside the ghetto gates.

The women exchanged worried and panicked glances, but no one uttered a word. No clues had been given as to where or what they marched toward—their executions or to do the bidding of the Gestapo, whatever that might entail.

When they arrived at Gestapo headquarters, soldiers ushered the women inside. In the main lobby, the soldiers pointed to buckets of water and ordered the women to clean the entire building, top to bottom. One woman spoke up, requesting cleaning rags and mops.

The soldier jeered, "No rags. Today, you use your underwear." The other soldiers laughed lustily.

From a side door, a prison guard, who Hinda recognized as someone who had assaulted her, entered the room. He scanned the group of women and zeroed in on Hinda. "Well, look who we have here. The jail's maid." He motioned to his comrades, including the commanding officer, and they huddled together.

The commanding officer bellowed, "Mondlak, step forward."

Quaking from memories of the guard's brutality, Hinda made her way to the front of the group. She stepped in front of the officer, military style, as she was trained to do when in jail.

Employing a strident tone, the officer said, "You are officially in charge of this group. You organize these women to get the job done. I mean, we want this place spotless." He pulled a bullwhip from his belt loop and cracked it against the floor. "You know what will happen if your work doesn't meet our satisfaction, or there's any trouble."

"Yes, sir," Hinda said with all the respect she could conjure. It also took real effort to repress the acrid hatred that boiled up and begged to slip into her voice. Keeping her tone smooth, she asked, "May I see all the rooms to be cleaned before we start, so I can better organize the tasks?"

Tilting his head to the side, the officer squinted at her. Finally, he said, "Makes sense."

When they returned, Hinda quickly assessed the women. She divided them into groups. Then she noticed two young women, about her age, who were whispering together while scowling at her. Deeming the pair as troublemakers who wanted to see Hinda get a beating, she separated the two by moving one to a different group.

At seven o'clock, the guards escorted them to the rooms on the second level where Hinda told the women to begin. "We'll work our way down," she explained. After seeing that each group was cleaning their assigned area in the order that she had laid out, Hinda joined in and started scrubbing. She had been relieved to discover soapy cleanser in half of the buckets, which improved the odds of attaining the spotless condition the commanding officer had demanded. Yet, the use of threadbare panties as cleaning cloths lowered the odds significantly.

At half past six that evening, the inspection commenced. Hinda accompanied the officer from room to room. She found one sink that was not up to her standard. Though the officer shrugged, she cleaned it again, then and there. An hour later, at seven-thirty, the commanding officer declared that the Gestapo headquarters had been cleaned to his satisfaction. The women were then escorted outside. It was dark, and many women stumbled on the rocky gravel. Soldiers brayed at them to move swiftly. When all the women were through the ghetto gates, the officer yelled, "Get on home now, you filthy dogs."

Although Hinda was insulted and exhausted, she inwardly smiled. No one had been whipped.

Back at the mill, Hinda went directly to check on Sara, who coughed incessantly but did not have fever. Between coughing fits, Sara wrapped her arms around her sister's neck. "Heenda, I worried."

"I'm okay, sweet Sara. Tired, but okay."

In the corner, Joel sat on the floor, appearing lifeless, although Hinda thought she saw relief register on his face when she entered. He nodded to her. "Hard day?"

"Yes, but praise God, I didn't get whipped." From her suitcase, Hinda selected panties and nightclothes, and then strode to the shower area. Eager to be cleansed of the day's drudgery and the Gestapo's leers, she soaped her body into a thick lather, stopping short when she remembered there was just one bar of soap left. After getting dressed, Hinda hobbled to her coat bed.

Immediately, Rachel brought over a dish of sliced turnips along with bread crusts. She said, "Sit up to eat, and I will rub your legs." Her hands moving in massaging motions across Hinda's legs, Rachel leaned in and whispered, "I prayed so hard today that my heart is sore. In my mind, I painted God's court of angels keeping you safe and winging you back to the mill."

"Thanks, dear sister. Can you tuck in Sara for me? I'm aching all over."

Kissing Hinda on the cheek, Rachel said, "Of course, anything for you."

Hinda reclined on her coat. Lying on her side, she curled up, drawing her knees to her chest. Reflecting on the stress and humiliation of the day, a deep fatigue descended upon her, penetrating her bones, and piercing her very soul. Sleep refused to come, even though her eyelids felt as if cast-iron weights sat upon them.

Words from her father's letter took root in her brain, overriding all other thoughts. Even with her eyes closed, the darkness behind her lids did not hinder her mind's eye. The last sentence illuminated, Hinda could see the letters, the preciseness of his handwriting. Each word, a mountain of hope, mended chasms in her fractured heart: You will live, and you will tell.

50

To Each His Own

June 1941 | Weimar, Germany

Heavy rains and storms had laced the day. Yet twinkling stars blazed the night heavens, which showcased constellations that Wolf had not seen since he left the Dutka farm. Ordinarily, he would relish such a sight, would feel a thrill. But tonight, as he trudged through the mud, his bleary eyes could not behold the beauty. Inner ruminations strafed against his stride. *Why wasn't nature in revolt, the moon darkened, covered in blood, the stars refusing to shine? How could nature keep to its usual course, oblivious to the unconscionable atrocities happening on a grand scale to God's children? To his family?*

Wolf's brother trudged along beside him. They trailed a group of men, all Jews, from the trains at the Weimar station. Soldiers carrying rifles led the assemblage and trod behind the rear. Police dogs, large German shepherds, trotted alongside the edges, occasionally barking or growling fiercely if anyone posited even one foot to the side of the roadway.

At first, being in the open air and out of the boxcar with the vile odor was succor to the brothers' souls. But as the trek stretched into multiple kilometers, weakness and weariness overtook them. Starving and dehydrated, many men dropped, falling to their deaths or lying comatose in the muddy slime. The soldiers ordered everyone else to keep going, warning they would be shot if they stopped to help the fallen.

After walking approximately twelve kilometers, they came to a fenced, isolated compound situated on Ettersburg hill. Soldiers dressed in black formal SS uniforms stood at attention, their machine guns focused on the new batch of arriving prisoners.

Suddenly, Joseph slipped in a chuckhole and fell to the ground. At that moment, guards tossed bits of bread and raw vegetables into the muddy trench. The ravenous prisoners fell to their knees stuffing the sludge-laden food into their mouths. Wolf dropped into the mire beside Joseph. They hustled for their share until fights broke out and bullets whizzed in the air.

Guards yelled orders for them to get up and move to another area. They corralled the men through a side gate. Guards then commanded them to remove their clothes and shoes, which went into rusty barrels to be burned. Shivering, Wolf and Joseph stood naked under outdoor water faucets, washing themselves with gritty soap that made no lather. Towels and wooden clogs were dispersed. After wrapping towels around themselves and putting on the awkward shoes, they walked through the main gates, which had wrought-iron letters hinged between posts. German words: *Jedem das Seine.*

Wolf translated the phrase, meaning "*To Each His Own*," and goose bumps popped out all over his body. He knew of this philosophical expression. He squinted as a memory of his beloved rabbi—who was killed by Nazis—bloomed in his mind. He could see the sweet, roundish face of this wise man on the day he had discussed this exact phrase.

Wearing a *yarmulke* atop his head, the rabbi had leaned close, "You must know, Wolf Yoskowitz, that Hitler and his fanatical Nazi followers believe that the Aryan race is superior. Hitler calls it the *master* race; with that, he takes the words—*to each his own* or *to each what he deserves*—to mean that *he* has not only the right, but also the authority, to debase and destroy others that are non-Aryan and whomever he considers an aberration." The rabbi directed his gaze deep into Wolf's eyes and tapped him on the knee as if punctuating with exclamation points. "Do you understand that includes you and me?"

"Yes, because we are Jewish," Wolf had replied.

Dread and trepidation consumed Wolf as he was prodded through the main gates that heralded the words, To Each His Own. Against his will, he crossed into a world of barbarous labor and unspeakable cruelty—Buchenwald, a Nazi-built concentration camp named for the beech tree forest that had been cleared to erect the three primary camps within the massive internment facility.

51
Trickery

December 6-7, 1942 | Mława, German-occupied Poland

A t six o'clock in the evening, there came a pounding knock on the old mill's door. Up until then, it had been a calm Sunday for the typically cacophonous ghetto. Hinda's eyebrows shot upward, as did her blood pressure. She opened the door. A Council messenger requested entry. In his hand, he clasped an official Nazi decree.

The messenger read aloud: "Tomorrow—Monday, December 7—at eleven o'clock in the morning, everyone is to congregate at the ghetto plaza. Each person is permitted to carry one suitcase with their belongings."

"Belongings?" Hinda inveighed. "Not even our life belongs to us."

Without replying or uttering a parting word, the messenger quickly exited.

Struggling to quell her rising anxiety, Hinda whirled, looking around the room, surveying the untenable living quarters that had been forced upon them. Considering the permission to bring a suitcase, she knew they would be leaving the mill, never to return. Her stomach twisted into knots with the realization that the unknown destination might be worse than the ghetto.

From across the room, Rachel arose from her spot and came to Hinda. She pointed to Sara who lay curled in the chair, still coughing and wheezing. Her face shaded with concern, Rachel said, "Sara is very weak. I don't know if she can walk, even to the plaza. But Hinda, don't worry. I'll carry her there and wherever else we have to go."

Hinda cupped Rachel's face, kissing her on one cheek and then the other. She then exclaimed, "I'm so proud of you, Rachel, and impressed with your mature forethought amid this upheaval."

Turning her gaze to Joel, who sat in the corner, his legs twisted on the wood floor, Hinda gauged his response to the decree. He appeared lethargic, not moving, lifeless, and spiritless, as if he were a mannequin, its form discarded in a dumpster. She snapped at him, "Joel! We must pray. That's what Tatae would do. Get up and say the Shema with me."

Reluctantly, Joel got to his feet and stood beside Hinda and Rachel.

The three of them faced east and covered their eyes with their right hands. Hinda led, "*Hear, O Israel, the Lord is our God, The Lord is one. Blessed be the name of His glorious majesty forever and ever.*" Joel misspoke and sputtered the words. Hinda stopped and asked him to repeat each sentence after Rachel and her. He struggled but improved as they went along. *You shall love the Lord your God with all your heart, with all your soul, and with all your might.*" Reciting the remaining verses at a slow pace to accommodate Joel, it seemed to take an eternity. At last, they completed the prayer.

Afterward, Hinda felt strong of mind. Thinking of her father and his prophecy for her, she sensed that where they were going was *not* a better place than the hellish Mława ghetto. Yet a fervent feeling swept over her. However terrible, she was not going to die. She would live.

After the prayer, Joel paced for multiple minutes. Abruptly, he stopped. Throwing his father's coat over his shoulders, he strode out the door.

"Where's he going?" Rachel asked.

"Don't know." Hinda shrugged her shoulders. "And I don't feel worried." For the first time in weeks, Hinda lifted the cloth and peeked out the window. Joel was nowhere in sight, but snowflakes fell from the night sky like pillowy-puffed raindrops, whitewashing the sordid streets. Playing peek-a-boo, a quarter moon—hanging in the eastern sky—twinkled at her, then its face was covered with gray clouds, then it shone anew, then it darkened again. *It's an omen. Whatever is ahead, darkness may temporarily cover me, but my light will not be veiled permanently.* Moving away from the window, Hinda called Rachel to come help wash the potatoes for supper.

Twenty minutes later, Joel returned, snow dusting his hair. He smiled as he withdrew a whole loaf of *fresh* bread from Tatae's coat.

The four of them sat at the makeshift table. Hinda asked Joel to divide the bread. She bit into the crust, which tasted heavenly. Once again, that sentient sensation of her father's promise overcame her. She turned and gave half of her portion to Sara, her weak and ill Zurele.

Monday, December 7, 1942

Around nine o'clock in the morning, guttural voices heckled the air outside the mill. Hinda peered out the window and saw the Gestapo banging on doors. They yelled, "*Schnell, schnell.*"

"Does that mean *fast*?" asked Rachel.

"Yes. And it means they want us to hurry. Let's finish our packing and be on our way."

Across the room, Sara started to cry, and not just ordinary crying, but the sort of keen that indicated one of her explosive fits could easily erupt. "Where are we going?" she wailed.

"Zurele, there's no time for that today. Hear the soldiers on the street?" Sara nodded but continued to sob. Hinda stroked her face. "Close your eyes, sweet Sara, and feel Mommy's arms holding you."

At ten o'clock, the Mondlaks closed the door to the mill for the last time. As they went down the steps, a frigid wind whistled, making a small eddy of snow that whirled around them. Heading toward the plaza, Hinda transported Sara on her shoulders. Joel toted Sara's suitcase along with his. Rachel lugged Hinda's bag plus her own. The streets bustled with people making their way to the center of the ghetto. Countless lumbered along, carrying the elderly and those too weak to walk on their own.

Arriving at the plaza, Hinda scrutinized the crowd that had already gathered. She noticed the councilman who had kept her father's letter. He and his family members held one suitcase each, their fate the same as hers, at least today. She wanted to scream at him, *"So what good are your archives now? I could have packed my father's precious letter to ME."* Containing her ire, she distracted herself by searching faces of people in varying groups. Across the plaza, she spotted Zachery Zimmerman standing alone near the sidewalk. He, too, clutched one bag. Joining the Nazis and working as a capo had saved him only temporarily. Thinking of the chair he had given them and how comforting it had been when Sara was ill, a surprising cordiality arose in her. "Look, Joel, there's Zachery Zimmerman over there. Do you remember him from Zieluń?"

"Yep, he helped me get the bread last night."

For the first time, it clicked with Hinda. Joel had shown up unexpectedly after she had asked Zachery about him. A question whirled inside her: If Zachery had the power to get Joel released, why was he here today? Then, like an echo, the answer boomeranged in her head. *Because in the end, he is Jewish.*

By ten-thirty, thousands of Jews, many of whom were sick and vomiting, had gathered in the plaza. Hinda fretted protectively over Sara, who now sat on Rachel's shoulders. The north wind howled around them. The group they stood among huddled closer together. This offered a warm respite from the frigid air, but Sara shivered, her teeth chattering. Concerned, Hinda said, "Let's put her down between us." Unlatching her suitcase, Hinda withdrew two clothing items. She wrapped one around Sara's neck and tied the other one like a scarf covering her head.

Suddenly, the ghetto gates opened. A squad of Gestapo marched in, all shouting, "Heil Hitler, Heil Mein Führer." Their right arms were extended in salute. In their left hands, they carried tall red banners that blazoned large black swastikas in the center of them.

Verbalized concerns abounded loudly throughout the crowd. "Where are they taking us? What kind of place are we going to?"

A Gestapo officer went to the platform, where he bellowed through a bullhorn, "Silence. Silence now!" He eyed the assembly, his menacing sneer chastising them, demanding quiet. Employing an authoritative tone, the officer announced, "I present Colonel Herpulika of the German army. He will now address you."

The colonel, who wore a black uniform decorated with a myriad of award ribbons and medals, stepped up to the podium. His gaze roved over the crowd, sweeping from side to side, taking in the entire group. A beamy smile plastered upon his face, he began his speech:

> *"We are taking you to a better location where there is good shelter and plenty of food. It's a place where you will be treated with kindness. A place where there is much goodwill for those willing and ready to work. No need for fear, you are going to a much better place than this.*
>
> *The troops, here to my left, will lead you to the train station. Follow their red flags to stay on the correct path. Once at the station, you will board the train. And then, it's a short journey to your new home where you will be well cared for."*

The plaza suddenly swarmed with soldiers. They hustled the crowd through the gates. The exodus commenced.

Hinda, who was familiar with the distance to the train station, said to Rachel and Joel, "It's a heck of a long walk. We must stay together and help Sara." Joel carried Sara initially, and then they took turns. Intermittently, Sara wanted to walk on her own. But after mere yards, she would struggle from weakness.

The icy wind blistered them, making it an extreme challenge to march in rhythm as they were instructed to do. What had been light snow turned into a wintry mix of rain and sleet.

Countless people fell—the elderly, the weak, and the sick. Gunfire riddled the air as the fallen, even those who had merely tripped or lost footing temporarily, were shot on the spot.

Using bullhorns, soldiers blasted warnings forbidding anyone to stop or to help. "And if you do, you'll be shot too," they barked. As more people fell and were killed, grief-stricken wails peppered the ozone. The sounds of bullets pinging continually, while clashing against pain-laden screams, made the trip all the more soul-shattering.

After trudging for one and a half kilometers, they arrived at the railroad station where an elongated train waited. It was impossible to see its beginning or its end as the train stretched endlessly down the track—a duplicitous snake cloaking its head and tail.

Soldiers and Gestapo herded people like cattle, poking and prodding them, through the depot and then loading them into individual cars. An officer directed the Mondlaks to a boxcar that appeared completely full to Hinda; yet, he ordered them to board, anyway. The four of them squeezed inside. "Put your suitcases between your legs," he commanded.

A rectangular box made of two-by-four wood, the freight car possessed no bathroom facilities or seating. People, all standing upright straddling their bags, were packed in so tight against each other that it proved challenging to breathe. The rank smells of sweat, urine, and excrement multiplied the suffocating feeling.

"Heenda, I can't breathe," Sara cried out. Though Sara sat atop Hinda's shoulders, tall men unwittingly pressed in upon her.

Hinda worried that if petite Sara stood on the floor, she would be squashed. Deciding the air up higher was superior, Hinda said, "Joel, you're taller. Please move her to your shoulders."

Joel stared off into space as if occupying a different planet. Rachel shook his arm. "Joel, we need you to help us."

Just then, a man next to them cried out in pain. He clutched his chest, then slumped against his wife's shoulder. Bodies were so tightly compacted around him, he had nowhere to fall. A man who was standing near the wife said, "I am a doctor, may I check his pulse?" She nodded, and he placed his fingers against her husband's neck. A grim expression spread across the doctor's face. He said, "I'm sorry. Your husband has passed away."

The dead man's wife burst into screams and then began spewing vomit. The people who were standing nearby could not move even an inch away from her. Their faces, hair, and clothing were doused with putrid projectiles. Rachel, who was standing nearer to the woman than Hinda and Joel, turned green. Her neck and coat collar were dotted with the woman's regurgitations. Hinda removed the garment from Sara's head for Rachel to wipe the muck from herself.

Oblivious to all the commotion, Joel still appeared in a trance. Hinda shook him, tapping his face, practically slapping him. He roused and took Sara onto his shoulders. Sara's chest heaved. Whistle-like noises accompanied her every breath.

Since the Mondlaks were one of the last families to board, they were closer to the wall, where there were three windows spaced along the car's side. The windows were crisscrossed with iron bars, both horizontal and vertical, on the inside and were locked from the outside. Occasional gaps in the lumber created miniscule air holes.

Every few minutes, more people were fainting, dying, or losing consciousness. Folks who stood near windows knocked on the glass and kicked the wooden sides trying to get the soldiers' attention. In response, an officer glared into the window nearest Hinda. A man yelled to him, "People are dying in here. We need help."

Cocking his gun near the glass, the officer roared, "You Jew dogs, stop making so much noise. If they're dead, throw them out the window." Then he laughed haughtily.

"But the windows are locked and covered with bars," Hinda argued, her words futile.

The train suddenly moved forward, departing Mława station. As it clattered on the track, a foreboding crept into Hinda's very bones, spiraling her thoughts into an oracular vortex. *If the Nazis are moving us to a better place, why are we being treated like pariahs? And to think, the colonel used the words—better place —while smiling cheerily and sounding sincere. Such trickery, all to get us to board the train willingly. I can feel it; we are going to an even worse, more monstrous place.* Fearsome dread chilled her blood, shaking her very soul. *Dear God, where are You in this? Have You been kidnapped?*

52

Work Will Set You Free

December 9, 1942 | Oświęcim, German-occupied Poland

Near the small town of Oświęcim, a gray overcast sky blanketed the late afternoon sun. The long train came to a halt, pulling into the station forty-eight hours after departing Mława. During the trip, the train had made multiple stops to load more Jews from varying towns. Often, it had stopped for hours for no apparent reason.

At the front of the train, SS officers, Nazi soldiers, and Gestapo rode in a car that had amenities: upholstered seats, sleeping bunks, bathrooms, and dining facilities. While in the wooden boxcars, Jewish people were given no water or food, had no toilets, and were compelled to stand upright, all jammed against each other.

Although it was wintry outdoors, the interiors of the freight cars were sweltering. Restricted oxygen plus the heat from hundreds of human bodies confined in a small space exacerbated dehydration. For those fortunate few who were next to windows, condensation on the windowpanes provided liquid treasure. Tongues streaked the glass continually, lapping up tiny water droplets.

Hinda and her family were not among the lucky few. Three men had elbowed them, shifting them away from the window and pushing them to the inside. An inordinate thirst consumed Hinda's awareness. Her eyes were sunken and almost swollen shut. Her lips were puffed, cracked, and bleeding. While Hinda could not see her own face, it pained her to look at Sara, Rachel, and Joel, who mirrored her condition.

After the train had halted, the passengers waited an interminable time. At last, soldiers unlocked the boxcar doors. They yelled, "*Aussteigen! Schnell! Aussteigen! Schnell!*" Meaning *get out fast,* the words incited people to rush out the doors. Desperate for water, passengers were moaning and begging. One woman flopped to the floor and licked up a puddle of urine.

Hinda lugged Sara outside and plunged them both into a snowdrift. Although it was fraught with dirt, Hinda stuffed the powdery moisture into Sara's mouth and then her own. Rachel and Joel followed suit, but only briefly, as soldiers ordered them all to start marching.

Suffering severe dehydration, which caused their heart rates to accelerate, many people dropped from the exertion of marching. The pinging of deadly bullets ensued.

Little Sara pointed to her chest. Hinda understood her communication, as she was experiencing heart palpitations too. Joel bent down and lifted Sara, though he struggled to move.

After marching several hundred yards, they came to a compound. Enormous iron gates marked its entrance. German words were spelled out in iron letters across the top: *ARBEIT MACHT FREI*. Hinda read the phrase to Sara, explaining that it meant, WORK WILL SET YOU FREE. While enunciating each word, Hinda's body sounded its own alarm. Deep in her bones, an ache pulsed: *Honest work, yes. Slave labor, no.*

Hinda noted the buildings behind the gate. While they scaled varying heights and sizes, their identical red-brick exteriors lent a sense of uniformity. As far as Hinda's eye could see, imposing barbed wire fences stretched outward from the gates enclosing the compound. Unlike farmland fences, these stood over six feet high and were constructed with fifty or more thick strands of barbed wire. Tall metal posts, with spikes jutting out from them, connected the wire, which Hinda assumed was electrified. At their tops, square posts curved over the wire, where an attached light spotlighted the fence and surrounding area. Taking in the view, Hinda reasoned: *This is a prison.*

People loitered behind the fences. Hinda gaped, aghast at their condition. Most were shockingly emaciated, their bones protruding through clothing. All had their heads shaved. In a seeming stupor, many sat in the cold mud, looking as if they were senseless.

Under gunpoint and clinging to each other, Hinda, Sara, Rachel, and Joel slogged through the massive iron gates, commencing their confinement at the concentration camp named Auschwitz. As Hinda stepped through the threshold, one thought fractured the core of her will and fortitude to live: *Would it not have been better for all of us to have died inside the train?*

53
Where Are the Infants?

December 9, 1942 | Oświęcim, German-occupied Poland
Auschwitz Concentration Camp

"Walter, have you lost weight?" Josef Mengele—immaculately groomed and handsomely attired in a crisp Schutzstaffel (SS) uniform—placed his hands on his hips and eyed his colleague from head to toe.

"Maybe five pounds," Walter replied, running his fingers through his hair. "The food here is not like my mother's."

"Bah! I just enjoyed a delicious lunch with the camp's commandant, Rudolph Höss. I knew him from the SS as Captain Höss before he became the commandant here. Have you met him yet?"

"Yes, I have. Impressive man. And I was kidding. You know how I am about my mother's cooking." Walter forced a laugh. "The food here is excellent." Cringing, he wanted to yowl, *"But it's not for the internees; they're starving."*

What Walter did not disclose was that he had lost eighteen pounds in the short six-week period he had been working at Auschwitz or Hades, as he referred to it in his mind. While he had plush living quarters and had access to hearty meals three times a day, the conditions for the people imprisoned at the camp had proved shockingly abominable. The first week, his throat had clamped down, refusing to swallow, and his usual robust appetite had evanesced.

"Well, don't lose any more," Josef instructed. "We need you strong. The work you're doing here is changing the world for the better." Mengele's head swiveled on his neck, checking out the room. "Show me around the lab."

"Specimens from twins are grouped here." Walter pointed to the shelves to the left of where he was standing.

"Excellent," said Josef. He moved in for a closer look. "Precise labeling, but I don't see any infant or toddler ages registered."

"For now, there are none." Walter pressed together his thin lips, their natural pink hue blanching to shadowy white.

"That's highly unusual, considering the hundreds of thousands of internees here. Are you sure you have surveyed the inhabitants correctly?"

"Yes, Josef, I have." Walter swallowed hard. "Perhaps you're not aware of what's called the Selection process that internees go through when they first arrive."

"Do you mean the sorting system that categorizes those who are capable of work and those who are not?"

"Yes." Walter's hand flew to his head, his fingers nesting in, then raking through, his hair. He cleared his throat. "Well, in the brief time that I've been here, the policy is to immediately terminate infants. Younger children, too, who are typically sent to the gas chambers."

Mengele nodded. "I wasn't aware, per se, but I see the value in the policy. Those ages require significant care and are incapable of doing any kind of work. Do you have access to the corpses to check for twins?"

Just then, Commander Höss strode through the doorway with a distinct swagger, his deep voice bounced on the walls as he said, "Josef, Josef. I'm pleased to see that you have not departed for Frankfurt yet."

"Oh?" Mengele asked, checking the time on his watch.

"The Mława ghetto has been liquidated. Thousands of Jews from there have arrived and will be ready for sorting first thing tomorrow morning." The commander winked in a felicific way. "I have a time conflict, and I hoped you could preside for me."

"I'm honored you would consider me, but—"

Not allowing Mengele to finish, Höss said, "I know you have important business in Frankfurt tomorrow before you head back to your duties with the Viking Division. But the SS needs you here, and Dr. Wirths agrees that you would do a superb job overseeing the Selections. Can I persuade you to stay the night, or do I need to get your boss, Wirths, to issue the order?"

"With all due respect, Commander Höss, is Dr. Wirths available then? I understand that he fills in for you at times."

"He and his brother, who is a gynecologist, are performing sterilization procedures on women from Block Nine, starting early in the morning. Already scheduled."

"Then, of course, but I need to make some phone calls. And you must brief me on the details of your preferred methods for the Selection process."

"Excellent," the commander said enthusiastically. "Come to my office to make your calls, and then I'll give you instructions for tomorrow."

Mengele nodded his assent, then tilted his head in a curious way. "Commander, I was told that infants are exterminated during Selection. Is this correct?"

"Yes. They're just more mouths to feed, and the little buzzards can't work. Plus, they encumber their mothers who can work. For the same reasons, it's our policy to send toddlers and young children to the gas chambers immediately after Selection."

"Brilliant, the labor force is top priority," Mengele replied as he started walking toward the door.

Höss followed him, then turned back to Walter. The commander slapped Walter on the back. "You're doing an excellent job here, Zeilhofen. This lab is far more organized under your management."

Mengele smiled and nodded enthusiastically, as if he were awarding Walter a trophy.

The rare approbation from Mengele and Commander Höss did not spark even a hint of a smile on Walter's face.

After they left the lab, Walter crossed himself. He inwardly railed at Commander Höss: *You're having all infants and young children killed. Murdered, simply because they require care and cannot work. Costs and the ability to work are your only considerations. Yes, because you do not care one iota about the sacredness of life.*

54

The Selection

After passing through the ominous gates of Auschwitz, the Mondlaks came to a guard tower where soldiers blocked the pathway. Without warning, guards seized their suitcases. They snatched the bags away and then tossed them into a pile as if they contained smelly garbage. Sara screamed and begged to get her doll, all to no avail. Hinda battled with her fury over their suitcases being ripped away. Another loss. Another lie. Now, they only possessed the clothing they wore.

In shock, the family was forced to march onward. Within steps, soldiers whipped them into a long queue and gave no information about the purpose of the line.

Looking at the other people waiting in the queue, Hinda fretted: What is this line? She prayed it was a food line. They had not eaten a single crumb since the morning they left Mława, well over sixty hours ago. Hinda's body ached; every muscle and organ clamored for attention and complained of pain. Dehydrated, ravenous, and exhausted, she yearned to be served a hot meal, to be given a warm blanket, to drink thirst-quenching water, and to rest in a soft bed. She berated herself for allowing such wishes to surface. *Pure folly,* Hinda chided herself. *The colonel was full of blarney, telling whoppers.* She cringed, remembering when he said, "We are taking you to a better place, to a place where you'll be well cared for and treated with kindness." He lied about the journey too. It was not short as he had promised. And they had almost died on the train from being treated so inhumanely. Moreover, the people at the so-called *better* place were imprisoned behind fences. They did not look well cared for; they looked abused.

Hugging their coats close to their bodies, Hinda, Rachel, Sara, and Joel shivered in the cold, waiting in line for the next unknown. The sky's crepuscular light stoked their trepidation, amplifying their apprehension.

Soldiers yelled profanities, issuing orders to remain in the queue and to stand erect. Too weak, Sara could not stand on her own and certainly not with erect posture. At times, a soldier would use his colubrine strap to dispense warnings to her, cracking his whip inches from her.

Every so often, the line would suddenly proceed forward. Darkness prevented Hinda from seeing what was transpiring ahead or determining any reason for advancement. At last, she spotted a building with a doorway that had an overhead light. One small group at a time was allowed to enter. Abruptly, a soldier counted the Mondlaks into the next group. A knot of soldiers pushed them through the doorway.

Inside a dimly lit room, each person in the group was ordered to stand in front of a large barrel. Fierce-looking German women manned the barrels, one woman to each barrel. Soldiers bound the internees' hands with rope and then commanded them to bend over their assigned barrel and to shut their eyes.

Just before her eyes closed, Hinda identified the contents of the half-filled barrel: hair, oodles of it and in varying colors. A razor scraped against her scalp. Her glorious hair began falling away. Hinda's russet strands tumbled into the rusty barrel, and her woe, deep sadness over the loss, burgeoned into heartbreak. Like a cloudburst, a deluge of her tears drenched the locks of hair below.

Exhibiting practiced precision, the German women sheared the newly arrived internees' hair, shaved their heads stark clean until not even stubble remained. Soldiers then untied the internees' hands and hustled them into the far corner, where an interior door harkened. Now bald, they rubbed their heads as if in a daze. They stared at each other, searching for recognition.

A guard, his key rings banging together and making a jangling sound, unlocked the mysterious door. He ushered the group inside a hallway through to a cavernous room, and then corralled them to a counter where a statuesque German woman was filling cups with hot liquid.

Choosing Hinda to go first, the German woman said, "Such big blue eyes. You look a bit German." Handing Hinda a mug, she instructed, "Here, drink this. It has vitamins in it."

Another staff member who was holding a tray stood nearby. She gestured for Hinda to place her empty cup on the tray. Each person followed suit. Their first liquid in almost three days, all in Hinda's group devoured the acrid-tasting coffee as if it were honey-sweetened nectar.

After the coffee station, Hinda and her siblings were shooed to a large area. Hundreds of people milled about; hundreds more slept on the floor. Hinda led the way to an open space where the four of them curled onto the floor. No strangers to sleeping on hard flooring, Joel and Rachel closed their eyes and were instantly asleep.

Little Sara reached over and stroked Hinda's baldness. "Heenda pretty," she said, her voice scratchy and raspy.

December 10, 1942

A blaring siren awoke the Mondlaks. They scrambled to their feet, stretching their aching bodies, their faces contorting into worried question marks of what was to come next.

Booming through the loudspeaker, a male voice cracked, "Breakfast. Line up for breakfast." Hundreds of people began running, all hoping to be at the front of the line.

"Finally, some food," Hinda exclaimed. She gripped Sara's hand as they made their way to the already long queue. Half-asleep, Rachel staggered after Hinda while rubbing the top of her head, testing reality. It had not been a bad dream; her hair was gone. Joel, whose head now looked oversized compared to his emaciated body, limped along after his sisters.

When they finally reached the serving station, they were given a cup of black coffee. Hinda looked around for solid food. The guard shouted at her, "Move on, you ungrateful Jew. You're lucky to get coffee."

Just as the sun was rising, another announcement came through the loudspeaker: "Dr. Mengele will arrive soon to make the selections. To prepare, everyone—every man, woman, and child regardless of physical condition—must get in line outside the building. Mothers may carry babies who cannot walk on their own." Guards then herded the group outdoors, yelling repeatedly to form a straight line.

Required to stand single file, the baldpated Mondlak siblings stood as near each other as the guards allowed. The frigid morning air chilled their every cell. Sara still coughed from her recent illness, and the wintry wind ignited intermittent outbursts of her hacking. Hinda sighed, wishing for the sweater she had used to wrap Sara's neck a few days ago. But when the train had become too warm, she had wrestled it back into her suitcase, which was then confiscated the minute she had walked through the iron gates of Auschwitz. *What a sham. Telling us to pack a bag for the trip was a ploy, just one more lie, to get us to board the train.*

Her worry for Sara mingling with her fear of the German doctor, Hinda's jitters multiplied with every tick of the clock. Burdened with misgivings, Hinda whispered to Rachel, "What does it mean to *select* people. And just what are we being selected to do?"

It was now approaching nine o'clock. Having stood in line for hours, people shuffled restlessly. At last, the man named Dr. Josef Mengele showed his face, which was startlingly handsome. His athletic physique together with his dark hair, precisely parted and combed, and his chiseled features struck an imposing silhouette. Decorated with multiple award medallions, his black uniform fit his body perfectly in a bespoke manner. His boots, black and highly polished, appeared as mirrors. Overall, he was impeccable, crisply immaculate. Adding to his striking look, he carried an elegant wooden baton, which sported a varnish finish that gleamed in the morning sunlight.

Sara began to tremble with seizure-like spasms. "He not nice. He devil."

Hinda grabbed her little sister's shoulders and spun her around. She pushed Sara tight against her own body, trying to shush her and minimize the child's shaking. Placing her mouth near Sara's ear, Hinda admonished, "The soldiers will kill you if they hear you saying such things about this doctor."

Standing to the side, Rachel said, "Here, let me carry her." She lifted Sara up into her arms. Sara's feet dragged against Rachel's shins.

"Put her down. Now!" Hinda's tone sounded unduly strident. "Didn't you hear the soldiers say that, except for babies, every person must stand on their own in this line? The doctor has to see each individual separately." When repeating the mandates, Hinda's hyper-anxious feelings twisted into a harbinger that writhed inside her like a slithering eel. She shuddered.

Surprisingly, the interchange calmed Sara. Her face had morphed into a mask of scornfulness as she eyed the doctor, but she no longer gave voice to her negative opinion of him.

Rubbing Sara's shoulders, Hinda whispered, "I'm sorry, my Zurele. My instincts warn that this is a pivotal process. We must obey the soldiers and the doctor, even if he is . . . not nice."

The loudspeakers blared, "Attention, Attention." A platoon of soldiers, who wore green uniforms and had machine guns strapped to their waists, marched in and stopped near Mengele. Their right arms extended in salute, they shouted,

"Heil Hitler." Josef Mengele nodded to them, signaling he was ready to begin. Five additional men, all dressed in black uniforms similar to Mengele's, formed a horizontal line to the side of the doctor.

Flaunting great pomp and precision, Mengele reviewed the Jews from Mława. He pointed his baton at them, one by one, saying, "You go here. You go there." His baton, and sometimes his thumb, designated the row where the person was to go. The five officers, who wore black uniforms, presided over the five lines, one officer to each row.

When Dr. Mengele came to the Mondlaks, he first appraised Sara, who coughed spasmodically as he eyed her. He ordered her to the fifth line, the furthermost outside queue. Then, he directed Hinda to the second and Rachel to the third. Joel was assigned to the fourth line.

Mothers carrying babies were put into a separate group. Mengele inspected them thoroughly, especially the infants. Suddenly, he issued a command to the soldiers; he spoke in German military code. Immediately, platoon members yanked babies from their mother's arms. The soldiers flung the infants, some close to one year old, onto the nearby grass, as if they were nothing more than plastic dolls.

Mengele raised his baton, then lowered it, signaling to the soldiers who remained in formation. Firing their machine guns in rapid repeat fire, they slaughtered each and every baby. Tiny, desecrated corpses lay strewn across the grass. Their shocked mothers shrieked and wailed, as did other people. Everyone was in an uproar. Heartbreak—so thick, it seemed you could touch it—suffused the air as if a blizzard of weeping snowflakes whirled around them.

In a flash, amongst all the commotion, Hinda reached across to the next queue and snatched Rachel, pulling her into the same line as her.

Watching from across the way, Sara yelled, "Me, Heenda. Get me." Her mouth wide open, bawling, Sara cried out between sobs, "You said we would always be together. You promised."

Just then soldiers stepped between all the lines, pointing their guns, mandating silence, and blocking movement. They spaced themselves down the rows.

Using his baton, Mengele sent a signal to the soldiers who carried machine guns. They surrounded the line that Sara occupied. The row consisted mostly of children, the elderly, and the obviously sick. In gruff tones, a soldier ordered the group to march away, to follow the officer dressed in the black uniform.

Not obeying the soldier, Sara screeched, "Heenda, don't let them take me. If not with you, I want to go where Mommy is."

Placing his gun against Sara's chest, aiming at her heart, the soldier barked, "Shut up and march, you stupid Jude kid, or you'll be dead in one second."

Sara's lips twisted, and her entire face wrenched with hopeless anguish. The expression locked on her face, she looked one last time at Hinda and Rachel before obeying the command.

As Hinda watched Sara march away, the image of her little sister's contorted face, a portrait of excruciating abandonment, freeze-framed in Hinda's mind, forging a vivid, technicolor memory that would torment her evermore. Sara's pleading words were inscribed on the chronicle of Hinda's soul, piercing the depth of her spirit. Her hand flew to her chest, her palm pressing against her bosom as her heart shattered into jagged shards, which then flooded her veins, making her entire body burn and ache. Inwardly, Hinda wailed, *I couldn't get Sara. I've let my father down.*

55
Heterochromia Iridis
December 10, 1942 | Oświęcim, German-occupied Poland
Auschwitz Concentration Camp

Whistling a happy tune, Josef Mengele waltzed into the lab, his eyes alight with glee. "What a magnificent day. Walter, have you ever observed one of the Selections?"

Washing his hands at the sink, Walter swiveled his neck toward his boss and, at one glance, was struck that he had never seen Josef appear so elated. "No, I have not," Walter replied.

"And that, my friend, is likely to change. You were correct about the policy of terminating infants, and I'm told that no one checks those corpses for twins. I plan to speak to Commander Höss and Dr. Wirths about having you take on that job."

Walter nodded, his stomach twisting into knots.

"I've exciting news," Josef exclaimed. "Two sets of twins were in today's group, both between eight and eleven months old. Perfect for research. And, one had heterochromia iridis."

"What color combination?" Walter asked.

"Blue and brown. Highly unusual, as you know."

At that moment, soldiers wheeled in two stretchers. Gray striped fabric, similar to cotton mattress ticking, covered the four dead infants. "Where do you want these?"

"The autopsy room is back here," Walter pointed to the far-left corner of the lab. Escorting them there, he swung open the door. The soldiers transferred the four wee corpses to the autopsy table.

As the soldiers departed, Mengele announced, "I'm delaying my return trip to Frankfurt. I want to personally perform the autopsy on the infant with one blue eye and one brown."

Walter noted the frenetic euphoria emanating from his boss. Having witnessed Mengele's autopsy methods that involved extreme mutilation, he struggled for an appropriate comment. "Understand. Twins and heterochromia iridis are your most favored research domains."

"Indeed." Mengele clapped his hands together. "You know, Walter, when my current assignments, the Viking Division and the Race and Resettlement Office, are completed, I've decided to ask for a transfer to Auschwitz. I love this place."

56

A Five-Digit Number

December 10, 1942 | Oświęcim, German-occupied Poland
Auschwitz Concentration Camp

"Men over here. Women over there," the officer commanded, using a bullhorn to magnify the order. Soldiers milled about the four remaining Selection groups, dividing them based on gender.

Elbowing Rachel, Hinda curtained her mouth with her hand and said in muffled voice, "We're in big trouble if they discover that I switched your line. So, we can't appear like family or too attached to each other. And please stop crying."

"I'm trying," sobbed Rachel. "Will we ever see Sara again?"

Breathing deeply, Hinda wanted to lie. She yearned to say yes, they would, but she could not. "I don't know," she replied. Rachel's face crumpled, tears dripping from her quivering chin.

Across the way, a ruckus broke out in a cluster of men. From the corner of her eye, Hinda spotted Joel standing to the side of a group that was not involved in the scuffle. She turned to look at him, hoping to catch his attention. But just then, a guard kicked Joel and shoved him into the group experiencing conflict. Soon after, soldiers toting machine guns hustled his line away.

Hinda watched Joel limp down the street, his unshaven face, scruffy with whiskered stubble, contrasted sharply with his newly shaved head. Her once strong, handsome, and refined brother looked fragile, tattered, and pitiful. At the main building's corner, where four enclosed hanging gallows stood tall in the grass like sentries warning all prisoners, his group turned onto the perpendicular street. Joel disappeared from sight.

Suddenly, Hinda's knees felt weak and strange. Her intuitive spirit attempted to transmit a message, but her receptors were blocked by stress—being separated from Sara, the day's other unnerving episodes, and gnawing physical hunger. For a moment, Hinda stared at the corner where Joel had faded from sight without discerning that the peculiar sensation conveyed yet another life-long alert: she would never see her brother Joel again, not in Auschwitz, not anywhere.

Although Hinda did not comprehend, a weighty sense of emptiness overcame her. She looked to Rachel, yearning to embrace her sister or to clutch her hand, but she deemed it unwise.

Abruptly, female guards surrounded Hinda and Rachel's group. The guards' faces displaying their penchant for meanness, they yelled and pushed at the women. Wrangling them into the main building, they poked the women's buttocks with barbed sticks as they moved along. Hinda and Rachel, their arms barely touching, kept as close together as possible without calling attention to themselves. Upon entering a large empty anteroom, they were ordered to sit on the floor.

Four at a time, the women were then ushered into a well-lit room where four men sat behind square tables, one man to a table plus a lone chair angled at its side. Each tabletop displayed an array of tools.

Hinda and Rachel were among the first to enter. Soldiers pushed them down into the chairs, which had restraining ropes attached, and proceeded to tie them tightly except for their left arm. The soldier yanked on their sleeves, tugging the fabric up above the elbow. Then, that arm was extended across the table and buckled onto the tabletop area near the man. One strap was secured just under the elbow, and the other came across the palm of the hand, exposing the inner forearm.

Rachel, who had wept on and off since Sara was taken away, now sobbed hysterically. A soldier stepped near, his gun aimed at her chest. "Dry it up, Jude girl, or you die." Instantly, as if she were donning a costume mask, a look of stoic compliance descended over Rachel's face.

Soldiers, who had been scattered around the room, moved behind the chairs, one for each prisoner. They positioned the barrels of their guns between the shoulder blades of the females who were tied to the chairs. "No screaming, or we'll shoot," the lead soldier bellowed. Then, he whistled like he was calling a dog, signaling the men to begin.

The man at Hinda's table picked up a dirty, stained cloth, which he sprinkled lightly with alcohol. He rubbed it across her forearm. While picking up a long needle that was connected to an inkwell, he double-checked numerals written on a tablet. Starting near Hinda's wrist, he began tattooing a five-digit number on her inner forearm. No sterilizing substance was applied to the needle; no numbing agent was applied to Hinda's skin. She sucked in air, screaming on the inside, from the intense pain.

At Auschwitz, there was no more Hinda and no more Rachel. They were now Number 25305 and Number 25306.

57

Singing Horses

December 1942 | Weimar, Germany
Buchenwald Concentration Camp

Light snow had graced the air all day, but in the afternoon hours, windy conditions made for low visibility and chilling temperatures. Wearing only lightweight cotton uniforms and thin-billed caps, Wolf Yoskowitz and his brother, Joseph, wrestled a large stone from the quarry up the hill. As they neared the top, Wolf spotted the wagon that had stones piled flush with its edges. Then he noticed a troop of soldiers standing to the side, plus a black stallion tied to the post of the watchtower. Spine-chilling dread rippled through Wolf, alarming his every muscle.

The quarry supervisor wrote down Wolf's and Joseph's prisoner-identity numbers, which were sewn on the left side of their shirts above the yellow triangle that further identified them as Jews. He measured their stone and then jotted its dimensions in the same tablet, next to their identity numbers. The supervisor nodded, and Wolf and Joseph hefted the stone into the quarry cart, an industrial variety made of metal.

Just as Wolf had feared, the supervisor blew his whistle, a short tempo of three blasts, which meant the four-wheeled wagon was loaded and ready to be moved to the construction site. Soldiers surrounded Wolf and Joseph and then harnessed them to the front part of the wagon. Seven additional prisoners were ordered up from the limestone quarry below. Four of them were also yoked, totaling six men who were harnessed like transport animals across the wagon's front. The other three prisoners, who were to be on call if needed, were handcuffed.

Guards gathered, anticipation dancing in their eyes. In the watchtower above, the commander of Buchenwald, Hermann Pister, who had been alerted to come, looked upon the scene with great enthusiasm. His favorite activity, which he had named "The Singing Horses," was about to begin. Pister shouted to the prisoners, "The chosen song for today is '*Westerwaldlied*.'"

Down below, the prisoners nodded, as it was mandatory for those who worked in the quarry to memorize the words to Pister's favorite German folk-marching tunes.

After descending the stairs, Pister mounted his stallion and commanded, "Hit it!"

The six men struggled to move forward. The enormous weight behind them would have strained the engine of a small tractor. Low on breath, the prisoners' voices were nearly inaudible as the wagon inched forward.

Soldiers marched in front and to the rear of the quarry-cart entourage. Guards walked on each side with the three extra prisoners in tow. Pister rode his black stallion alongside the guards.

"Louder!" Pister yelled.

Wolf, who had a pleasing singing voice, attempted to belt out the lyrics. Afraid of being whipped if they did not sing loudly, too, Joseph and the other four bumped up their volume. Before they could finish the first verse, one of the other prisoners collapsed. Guards snapped their straps, lashing all six of the men.

The main officer barked, "Get up, you scumbag Jew. Commander Pister, the highest official of this camp, ordered you to transport this rock and to sing while doing so." He jerked the fallen man to his feet. "You obey, or you die."

Too frail to stand on his own, the man's body folded in on itself, crumpling to the ground.

From his mount, Pister cheered and chanted like he was at a sporting event, "Death by boot. Death by boot."

The man's body was unharnessed, straightened, and turned onto his back, face upward. Four guards surrounded him. One stomped his heavy black boot on the man's chest repeatedly. One pounded his liver and testicles, alternating between them. Two kicked his head and neck with their boots that flaunted reinforced metal-capped toes. When satisfied that all life had been struck from the man, they tossed his body to the side of the road as if it were nothing more than an annoying fly that had been swatted.

Pister steered his stallion to the ditch for one last gander at the man. His face aglow with jollity, Pister spurred his stallion. Hooves pummeled the corpse as the commander rode up and down, and back and forth, in a figure-eight pattern.

In the dead man's place, one of the extra prisoners was yoked to the wagon. And the chorus began again. Although it was snowing, the six laboring men perspired as if it were a hot, humid day. Their bodies stressed and strained, propelling the loaded wheelbarrow forward, all the while repeating the song verses and chorus. Singing horses. Cantillating mules. Although bipeds, they were beasts of burden. That is *all* they were.

At the top of the hour, they progressed into the southern district of Buchenwald. To Wolf, it looked like a foreign, disparate world from where the prisoner barracks were located in the northernmost zone—the coldest and most barren area of Buchenwald. In veritable contrast, the warmer southern section exhibited lush vegetation, artful landscaping, and spacious, luxury housing for SS officers and guards to reside in comfort. The sweeping acreage of the southern district was also home to the staff hospital, garages, shooting ranges, drilling grounds, a sawmill, and a falconry where birds of prey were kept.

At last, the entourage arrived at the construction site. The grand hotel loomed large on the landscape. It was said to boast a fine restaurant and opulent ballrooms with enormous crystal chandeliers. High-ranking SS officers and top members of the Reich, such as Himmler and Goebbels, stayed there when visiting Buchenwald. The new construction behind the hotel, now nearly complete, constituted an entertainment addition that would house a casino and a movie theater, specifically for the pleasure of SS officers, camp guards, and hotel guests.

Guards unharnessed the prisoners and motioned to the rock in the wagon. Although his legs trembled from muscle tremors, Wolf began unloading the stone in the designated spot. Their eyes hooded, Wolf and Joseph exchanged a look of relief that neither of them had collapsed from excessive exertion and then died by boot or bullet.

The prisoners emptied the cart, stacking the stones according to size, as directed. When complete, the men were yoked again, this time to return the wagon to the quarry.

Leaning down from his saddle, Pister spoke to the head guard, giving him instructions for the return trip. The soldiers and guards alike all saluted him, saying, "Heil Hitler." Pister then galloped away, his stallion's black tail swooshing in the air.

Although the metal wagon was empty now, the prisoners labored to pull it, exhausted from their extreme output on the first leg of the trip. The guards popped their whips, urging the men to move faster, not satisfied until the men were at a full trot. At a fork in the road, guards blocked them from turning toward the quarry, forcing them to go the other direction—the long way through the main camp.

As they loped along, they glimpsed the fields and pig farm of the eastern section. The eastern area was farmed, producing a myriad of crops that included prodigious vegetable gardens. Closer to the main camp, they passed the indoor equestrian riding hall that had been built for the wives of the SS officers. Adjacent to the entry gates were the stables and jail, or bunker, as the jail was called. Wolf's skin prickled as they passed that building. Rumor was that brutal punishments and executions took place in the bunker.

Nearing the parade ground, they passed the small zoo that was for the enjoyment of the SS officers' children. Wolf noted that the bears were standing erect. This meant it was near their feeding time, which coincided with evening roll call for prisoners. A tall, electrified fence separated the zoo and the roll call plaza. Prisoner barracks were located in a building to the right, inside the fence. Wolf longed to return there and crawl into his hay-strewn bin. He and Joseph shared the crib, so it was a bit cramped, but many prisoners had to sleep in bins with three or more other men. Tonight, though, Wolf knew, however uncomfortable the bunk, he would pass out the second he was allowed to lie down.

Arriving back at the quarry, soldiers unhooked the six men. Although they were weakened, exhausted, and starving, the men had to scramble back to the main camp for evening roll call, where they would stand at attention for a full hour.

Wolf, whose every muscle knotted with cramps, struggled to walk. He longed to fall into the snow and roll around—moaning. Employing extraordinary effort, he toughed it through five steps. He paused, turning back to his brother. "Joseph, I know it's killing you to walk, but we've got to hurry. If we're late for roll call, well . . . you know what that means."

"No dinner," Joseph said, barely able to catch his breath. His feet bled from fresh injuries to existing sores. Shooting pains surged up his legs. "Do you think we'll get meat in our soup?"

"We qualify. Exceeded our quota of stone today. Don't know if the guards will keep their word, though."

"Tonight, we *must* eat," Joseph said, as he managed a couple of steps. For eighteen months now, they had been confined at Buchenwald; yet, Joseph still had immense trouble walking in the ill-fitting wooden clogs he was issued when they had arrived. And after marching for miles today and pulling the wheelbarrow at a trot on the return, his feet appeared nonhuman, purple and hugely swollen.

"Hey, man, go on without me," Joseph implored his brother.

"No way. We're in this together," Wolf replied.

Joseph pried off the splintery clogs and plunged his feet into the icy slush.

58

Zyklon B

"Remove all your clothing—shoes, socks, everything. Put them in these labeled bins. You grimy animals, we're giving you a bath. A group shower," the SS officer shouted through a bullhorn.

Reluctantly, people started taking off their clothes. Not little Sara. She stood unmoving, her back ramrod straight, her eyes fixed on some unknown.

"What's wrong with you, kid?" A guard poked Sara with his gun barrel, yelling at her. "You were commanded to get undressed. Now get busy."

Sara did not budge. People stepped away from her.

Another guard spoke up. "She's retarded. Just shoot her."

From a side cluster of folks, an elderly woman, who was naked except for shoes and socks, stepped forward. She placed her hand on Sara's shoulder. To the guard, she said, "Sir, if you'll allow me, I'll remove her clothing."

Shrugging his shoulders, the guard replied, "She looks stiff and uncooperative. But, okay, you have two minutes and no more."

The woman bent close to Sara's ear and whispered, "My name is Rivka. You remind me of my beautiful granddaughter. Can you pretend that I'm your mother or your *bobeshi* so I can help you?" Without waiting for a reply, the woman pulled Sara's sweater over her head and unbuttoned her blouse. Her breathing labored, the old woman stripped Sara down to her shoes and socks. Sara's skirt and panties hung around her ankles. The woman was incapable of bending down and lifting Sara's feet.

Still catatonic, Sara did not move.

Once again, the woman placed her mouth close to Sara's ear. "Now, it's your turn. I really need you to help me. I'm old and can't bend over far enough to reach my shoes. The soldiers will shoot me if I don't remove them. Please, can you take off my shoes and socks?"

Still as a statue, Sara did not budge.

Rivka sighed heavily, her breath ragged.

Suddenly, Sara plopped down on the floor and untied the woman's shoes. Ever so gently, she lifted the woman's legs and removed her shoes, sliding the socks off next. Sara promptly discarded everything of her own: skirt, panties, shoes, and socks. Clambering back up, she took all of their things and placed them in the correct bins, precisely as the soldier had instructed earlier. Returning to Rivka's side, Sara clasped the woman's hand.

Whistles blared. The officer instructed, "Time to proceed to the showers. There are pipes and faucets that will come on automatically and shower you with water, then soap, and then more water to rinse. You can sit on the benches or stand, as you wish. Afterwards, towels and uniforms will be distributed. Lunch will be served before getting your work assignments."

Walking awkwardly, many people covering their privates with their hands, the group entered the room that had the words *Desinfiziente Wasche* (Disinfectant Wash) inscribed above the door. Ceramic tiles lined the walls and floor, which had multiple drains throughout. The old woman guided Sara to a bench. They sat down, side by side.

When the entire group was situated, the doors were bolted shut. No guards or soldiers remained in the room. When the lock clicked, the faucets began to spew.

In less than a minute, people began gasping for breath, suffering internal suffocation. Many vomited. Countless people screamed as they ran to the door, trying to open it, realizing there would be no disinfecting shower—only a dousing of death—as a cyanide-based pesticide, Zyklon B, circulated throughout the locked chamber.

Looking upward, Sara pointed her finger at the spigots. She choked out the words, "Not water. Not soap." Glancing at the old woman's face for the first time, Sara saw calm, kindness, and a glint of green in the woman's eyes. "Like Mommy," she whispered. Sara snuggled closer to the woman and closed her eyes—for the last time.

59
The Alien Vegetable

The spacious room was empty of any furnishings but teemed with zombie-like women who milled about, hollow looks in their eyes. Other women wept broken-heartedly; untold numbers lolled or slept on the wooden floor. The female guards, robust German women, who had been in charge of Hinda and Rachel post-Selection, ordered them and their entire female group into the huge room. One of the guards shoved their backs, pushing them inside. Her tone snarky, she said, "Get a move on; get in there now." No explanation or additional orders were given.

Surveying the room, Hinda led Rachel to a corner where they reclined on their coats. Her arm throbbing and stinging from the tattooing, Hinda examined her bruised skin. Swelling distorted the shape of her arm; she could barely distinguish the numerals, 25305, the five-digit number that was now her name. *I am nothing but a number, a branded animal.* Her spirit wanted to fight and bellow, *I am Hinda Mondlak, child of God. I am valuable.*

Turning to Rachel, Hinda said, "Dear sister, we have ample reasons to be upset, but is it your arm that's making you cry?"

"My arm hurts terribly. And I can't stop thinking about Sara," Rachel replied. With her chin quivering, she added, "Visions are haunting me."

"Visions about what?" Hinda implored.

"Mommy hugging Sara." A series of sobs made Rachel's shoulders shake. "Hinda, what does it mean? Is Sara dead, and now with Mommy in heaven?"

"It could be symbolic," Hinda replied. "Sara could be having one of her fits, and Mommy's spirit is trying to soothe her."

"Whatever it means, I feel incredibly sad."

Desolate emptiness swept over Hinda. Her heart aching for Sara, she reached over and stroked Rachel's back. After making sure that no guards were watching, she inched closer and curled into her sister. Nestled together, they surrendered to their inordinate fatigue, succumbing to heavy-eyed drowsiness, then slumber.

After about thirty minutes, shrill whistles shocked the air. Hinda staggered up from the floor, frightened of what was next. Rachel stretched and yawned.

German soldiers entered and walked around the room, cracking their whips. "Get up. Make a line," they shouted, whipping people indiscriminately, lashing near to others.

One of the straps popped inches away from Rachel's leg. Hinda helped her from the floor, and they hurried to the line, expecting something vile to happen. Surprise fanned the sisters' faces when they were given a spoon and a small bowl, which resembled a wide cup.

Using a bullhorn, the officer instructed, "These are your eating utensils, the *only* ones you will ever get here. Guard them with your life. If you lose them, you lose the chance to eat. You get no food. Understand?"

A throng of women screamed out, "Yes, we understand." Hinda fingered her bowl and spoon like they were made of gold. Rachel clutched hers to her chest.

After another set of stentorian whistles, the soldier yelled, "It's time to eat. Form a line outside."

Hinda grasped her sister's hand, and they rushed to the queue, which quickly trailed around the building. One hour elapsed before they arrived at the serving station in another building, where a guard ladled soup containing a white substance into their bowls.

"What is this vegetable?" Hinda asked, noticing its odd texture.

"This vegetable is enriched with vitamins. It's good for you," replied the guard.

A memory flashed in Hinda's mind of when she was a young teenager visiting a friend who lived on a farm near Zieluń. They had fed the animals—cows, pigs, and goats—this same white vegetable that her friend's father had said was not fit for human consumption. Yet, today, Hinda chewed and swallowed every fibrous granule.

After lunch, groups of women were escorted back to the spacious room they had occupied earlier. Hinda and Rachel found their spot in the corner. They reclined on the hard floor, making certain their eating utensils were secured and hidden.

Rachel tossed and turned, complaining of stomach pains. "Ouch. I have terrible gas."

"I'm bloated too," Hinda exclaimed. "It's that white thing. I bet it's not really a vegetable." After an hour of misery, they napped.

Later that evening, around seven o'clock, the whistles blasted again, and they were ordered to form a line for dinner. The slow process ended with them receiving black coffee, which was thick like mud, and two small hunks of dark bread. The guards measured the exact weight of the bread before giving it to them. Hinda overheard one say her portion weighed one hundred grams, but it appeared far short of that to her.

Days passed, all spent in that same room. Identical menus and food-service schedules were followed: black coffee for breakfast; thin soup laced with the alien vegetable for lunch; thick coffee and sparse bread for dinner.

One afternoon, an officer entered, and for once, he did not pop his whip. Speaking into a bullhorn, he announced, "The central office is still working to coordinate your identity numbers with your housing and work assignments. It's a complicated process. Rest, for now, because soon you'll be on the job. But let me be clear: you do not have permission to leave this room except as directed for meals and for exercise outdoors on Sunday morning. Every door is guarded. If you attempt to leave, you will be killed."

Hinda shivered. She turned to Rachel, who had lost all the color in her face, and whispered, "Start praying now about our housing assignments. That we are not separated."

"I couldn't bear that, to be apart from *you*." Rachel sobbed quietly. She bowed her head. Her chin trembled and glistened with tears. "If I'm separated from you, I will attack a soldier, kicking his shins until he shoots me dead."

60

Geological Plates Shifting

Labeling specimens from the infant autopsy, Walter worked alone in the lab. His face displaying a disgruntled frown, he wished he were in his private quarters, lounging with a cup of freshly brewed coffee. Sundays were his day off, barring emergencies.

His boss, Josef Mengele, had stayed the weekend to complete the autopsy on the infant with the rare eye condition. Mengele had worked like a fiend, dissecting the baby's eyes and body. Plus, he had chopped away at the three other infant corpses. Walter doubted that anything groundbreaking had been discovered. Nevertheless, Mengele had ordered Walter to preserve the designated tissue and organs, and for everything to be completed no later than noon on Sunday.

Without lifting his head to check the time, Walter knew that it was precisely ten o'clock when the camp loudspeakers began broadcasting classical music, a tradition on Sundays. This morning, strains from *The Flying Dutchman* by Wagner wafted through the windows.

The camp commandant, Rudolph Höss, demanded that only masterpieces by Hitler's favorite composers be selected. Although Hitler enjoyed Beethoven, primarily, he was a Wagner enthusiast, not only because of the composer's elaborate operas, but also because of Wagner's anti-Semitic viewpoints—expressed in his writings as early as 1850. When giving a speech in 1922, Hitler cited Wagner's musical works and essays as glorifying the heroic Teutonic nature—a compatible embodiment of Hitler's vision for Germany.

Distracted by the overture, its stormy chords and dramatic crescendos, Walter decided to take a break. Moving to the window nearest him, he took in the scene down below. Pitiful-looking internees roamed about inside the fence, which they were permitted to do on Sundays, their day of rest. Walter worried for them living in such harsh and unsanitary conditions. And now, new outbreaks of typhus and malaria had been reported, which he had observed firsthand when on duty in the infirmary. Rotating schedules with other camp doctors, he worked in the infirmary on a part-time basis.

Authorized to only give non-curative treatment to the prisoners, Walter wrestled with the oath he had taken when becoming a doctor. Medications effecting a cure for malaria and typhus were available, right there in a locked cabinet in the infirmary, but they were restricted for the treatment of staff, SS officers, German military, and guards who became ill.

Chilling screams from below jolted Walter out of his ethical quandary. An older Jewish woman had thrown herself against the electric fence, clinging to it until death freed her from the relentless persecution. The other prisoners jumped back, scattering away from the fence.

Standing to the side of the disturbance, two young women caught Walter's eye. They were dressed in civilian clothing. *Newcomers*, he assessed. One woman, appearing to be in her early twenties, had the most perfectly shaped head he had ever seen. It had been a shock to Walter that all the internees were shaved bald upon their arrival. Most looked unsightly, but this young woman was beautiful. Suddenly, she turned and looked up at him standing in the window. Walter caught a glimpse of her large blue eyes and was transported to a different world. Like geological plates shifting in the center of the earth, something deep inside him stirred.

61

Block Thirteen

Housing assignments had been in process for hours. Now late in the evening, neither Hinda nor Rachel's number had been called. Rachel rocked back and forth, chewing the skin on the inside of her cheek. Hinda paid rapt attention, listening intently as the announcer's voice had begun to drone in a boring monotone.

Unexpectedly, the officer's tone altered to a lower pitch but louder volume. "Numbers 25305 and 25306 assigned to Block Thirteen," he boomed. "Report to UNIFORMS, then go to your Block, and get to bed. Work starts at five o'clock tomorrow morning."

Thirteen seemed an unlucky number in such a villainous place. Yet Hinda (25305) and Rachel (25306) celebrated their profound luck in being assigned to the same Block. As they walked to the next station to get their uniforms, Hinda buzzed with relief.

Now wearing the blue-striped garb of Auschwitz, the two sisters cautiously crept through the doorway of Block Thirteen. At first glance, they thought it was livable. Yet dim light skewed their initial assessment. When they moved closer to their assigned sleeping bins, rats scurried out from the hay strewn across the wooden bunk. Hay would function as their mattress and pillow. Dirty bug-infested hay, that is.

After inspecting the nooks and crannies more closely, Hinda turned to Rachel, "This place is a hellhole, but at least we're together."

Rachel shuddered. "I wish we had our coats to lie upon. This musty straw is repulsive."

"Those idiot guards, confiscating our coats, what were they thinking? It's winter, and these lightweight uniforms feel like summery pajamas," Hinda lamented.

"They were thinking they wanted to torture us even more. But, at least, the pants of the uniform have roomy pockets to store our eating utensils," Rachel replied.

A female voice suddenly interrupted them. From three bunks away, someone screeched, "You rude newcomers, be quiet. Some of us are trying to sleep."

Stunned, Hinda looked around the room and saw that women occupied the nearby bunks. "I'm sorry, the light was so dim, we didn't see you," Hinda replied, employing her kindest tone.

The woman grunted, "You owe me one."

Without speaking, Rachel made hand signs toward their bunk.

Her question clear to Hinda, she replied in a barely audible whisper. "You get in first, so you'll be more protected. I'll take the outside."

Exhausted from the day's job of scrubbing the large holding room they had occupied since their arrival and then enduring the stress of housing assignments, the sisters curled onto the hay, nestling their bodies close together. Just as Hinda entered into the pre-slumber stage of grogginess, Rachel whispered, "Do you remember the woman who threw herself onto the electric fence yesterday?"

Not lifting her eyelids, Hinda murmured, "Yes. What about her?"

"I want to do that, want to die. On Sunday, let's do it together. Please, Hinda. It's only going to get worse here. We could be released from it all in less than a minute."

62

The Zookeeper

April 1943 | Weimar, Germany
Buchenwald Concentration Camp

When the gunfire commenced, the monkeys scampered into their stone enclosure situated in the middle of their gargantuan cage. Two brown bears that were near the entrance of their rock cave moved from all fours to standing on their hind paws.

Wolf Yoskowitz, who stood at attention for evening roll call, watched the animals out of the corner of his eye. He and Joseph were near the rear of the prisoner assembly; they had not been released from their work in the quarry until time for the compulsory attendance check. This placed them alongside the electrified fence, and just on the other side, a mere ten steps away, was the camp's zoo. The bears were growling and acting agitated. Wolf puzzled over why they had not been fed yet and why the zookeeper had been showing up later than normal.

At the quarter hour, the zookeeper appeared, talking to the bears like they were old comrades of his. He tossed large slabs of red meat toward one. It immediately began feasting. Then he chunked three more identical thick cuts to the other bear. His eyes hooded, the zookeeper sneaked a look at the prisoners, who had stood at formal attention for well over the usual hour because two prisoners had not shown up. The zookeeper suspected that the men felt dizzy at the sight of the meat, but he could not wait any later to feed the bears.

When he had been hired for the zookeeper position, he was told that the zoo had been placed next to the main camp because it was the coldest area of Buchenwald, which was good for the bears. Weeks later, he learned that the previous camp commander's wife, Ilse Koch, had specified that the zoo be located close to the electrified fence because she had a yen for taunting the prisoners. Specifically, she wanted the prisoners to witness the *tenderness* with which the staff treated the zoo animals. A stark contrast to the harsh, abusive treatment the human prisoners received. What's more, she intentionally set the bears' feeding schedule to coincide with morning and evening roll call so that the prisoners would be forced to see the quality and abundance of meat the bears were fed twice a day. Such meat was not included in prisoner food, which consisted of watery gruel and stale bread.

Shifting his shoulders, Wolf struggled to avert his eyes away from the bears devouring the fine-looking meat. His stomach rumbled, and his legs throbbed after working a twelve-hour day and now standing at attention for over an hour. Next to him, Joseph battled to retain a neutral expression while enduring sharp burning pains in his feet. Although they had not exchanged words, Wolf surmised that his brother's feet were hurting badly. Joseph held his body tensely in a way that went beyond maintaining the at-attention stance. For Joseph, who had toe deformities, the wooden clogs were torture.

More gunfire erupted. This time the monkeys caterwauled and chattered with every bullet. Wolf prayed for strength, hoping this latest round of fire meant that the second prisoner had been found. The gunshots were for show, attempts to further intimidate the prisoners, who knew the ones missing were incapable of making roll call, or they would have been there. Most likely, they were already dead or near dead. Nevertheless, until those absent were found and accounted for, the other prisoners would stand at attention.

The zookeeper stepped near the electrified fence, now boldly eyeballing the prisoners. His tampering with the feeding schedule had not saved them from seeing the bears eat meat. He shook his head in dismay, knowing what it meant for the entire group that two prisoners had missed roll call. No dinner. Although the men had labored for twelve hours with scant breakfast in their stomachs, and only black coffee and a hunk of bread for lunch, they would get zero food this evening.

When the zookeeper walked away, readying to feed the monkeys, he happened to catch Wolf's eye. The ravenous hunger and torment in the young man's face startled the zookeeper, ripping the scab from an old childhood wound. Intense emotion roiled up like bile in his throat. His hand slipped into the large pocket of his overalls. It contained a bag of monkey food—a mix of apple slices and seeds. Looking back over his shoulder at Wolf, he reversed his steps, turning toward the fence. Careful to not touch the wires, he tossed two apple slices that landed near Wolf's feet. He dug his hand into the bag, going for an entire handful this time. Lost in his altruistic thoughts, the zookeeper did not see the guard approach.

"What do you think you're doing?" The guard spun the zookeeper around, aiming his gun at the man's abdomen. "And just what are you up to, changing the bears' feeding schedule?"

The zookeeper said nothing, his mouth agape.

"Answer me, now," the guard commanded, raising the barrel of his rifle, and poking it into the zookeeper's chest, shoving him slightly backwards.

Knocked off balance, the zookeeper's body went reeling against the electrified fence. He screamed. The monkeys screamed. High-voltage electricity pulsed through him, stopping his heart. His body slumped. Apple slices and seeds spilled from his pocket.

63
Fertilizer

In the wee hours of dawn, a soldier, outfitted with a machine gun, entered Block Thirteen. He shouted the command, "Numbers 25305, 25306, 18302, 18303. Come with me."

Sleep riddling their limbs, Hinda, Rachel, and two other women stumbled from their bunks. They grabbed their shoes and reported to the soldier. A military Blitz truck, with its motor running, was parked near the door. The soldier thrust a small hunk of bread at each of them and ordered them to climb into the bed of the vehicle, which already held about twenty other females.

"May I ask where we're going?" Hinda asked.

"Nope," he replied, slamming closed the tailgate of the truck.

After the truck lurched forward, one of the other women said, "Budy. We're going to Budy to work in the vegetable fields. At least, that's where I've gone in this truck every day for months."

Hinda's mistrust of the soldiers and guards had intensified. Without cause, they frequently threatened her and other prisoners with the gas chambers and execution ranges. When in the square this past Sunday, Hinda and Rachel had watched smoke pouring from the crematorium chimneys. The guards there jeered at the two of them, laughing that those wisps of smoke could be all that was left of their families, their bodies reduced to ash.

Two of the women in Block Thirteen had met that fate when they had become ill. Hinda had made friends with the woman, Debora, who had complained to her about the noise the first night. One morning, Debora awoke with a high fever, as did her bunk mate. Before leaving for work, Hinda and some other women in the Block covered them with blankets and hay, trying to hide them, but upon returning that evening, they found the two were gone. The Block warden said they had contracted malaria, so they were sent to the gas chambers.

Unlike Rachel, Hinda did not want to die. She wanted to live, however horrible life was. Rachel begged Hinda every day for the two of them to throw their bodies against the electric fence. Repeatedly, Hinda told Rachel no, confessing that she was a coward. But then, she came to realize that she was not a coward. Deep inside her, Hinda had a compelling need to fulfill her father's prophecy: you will live, and you will tell of the unjust persecution. It had been agony to feel that she had failed her father when she had not saved Sara during the Selection. So, now, she had to keep living. She had to do her part to accomplish Tatae's promise.

Riding in the back of the truck, Hinda shivered in the chilly spring air and wished for warm head coverings. Every few weeks, just as their hair started to grow, they were sent to the barrel room where their heads were shaved anew. Administrators claimed lice as the reason. But even with no hair, lice were a pesky problem. The sucking parasites thrived in the fabric of the uniforms and in the hay where they slept.

After thirty minutes of being jostled around in the truck, they arrived at a small sub-camp located near the southern end of the Auschwitz property. Barracks and other scattered buildings were surrounded by fields growing varying crops. Sure enough, there was a sign that said BUDY. Hinda scanned the entire area, estimating that two hundred or more prisoners were already at work in multiple fields.

The soldier, who drove them, pointed them toward a gate that opened to a medium-sized tract of land, a lush vegetable garden. An electric fence surrounded the plot, and it was heavily guarded by soldiers, all carrying machine guns.

Counting an unusual number of guards and soldiers, Hinda surmised that this garden grew special produce, perhaps reserved for the officers. The sight of the healthy vegetables made her drool. She hankered to bite into any type and wondered if it were her acute hunger that made them look so perfect.

Leaning in close to Hinda, one of the women from the truck whispered, "The bones and bodies of Jews, *our people*, were the fertilizer for these crops. I've worked here for six months now, and we've spread ashes from the crematorium many times."

Hinda's appetite instantly turned to nausea. The delectable vegetables now appeared repugnant. *Grown from evil to feed evil,* she reflected.

Blasts from a bullhorn interrupted her ruminating. A brawny guard announced that any worker caught eating or stealing any vegetable would be killed immediately.

Full-bodied German women, who were there to police the prisoners' work and had bullwhips attached to their belts, began dividing the new arrivals into smaller groups. Rachel inched closer to Hinda. The policewomen did not seem to notice and counted them as a pair.

Assigned to the tall-plant section, the sisters worked side by side picking green peas. They were the finest pods Hinda had ever seen, but her fingers kept reminding her of why. She thought of Debora dying in the gas chambers and could not dispel from her mind the concept of people's remains fertilizing food that other humans would then eat. *Is that a form of cannibalism?* She pondered.

After laboring all morning, the workers had a ten-minute break for lunch consisting of a single slice of bread and one ladle of soup. A different recipe from the main Auschwitz kitchen, the Budy soup contained nettles, rye, and bits of fishy-tasting carp.

When back at the vines, Hinda and Rachel worked diligently plucking the pea pods, each sister in her own world. Working on the row adjacent to Hinda, Rachel played a game of counting the pea pods, then tired of it and began to visualize painting them, using varying shades of green on her imaginary canvas. When she heard multiple gunshots nearby, lethal ones, indicating that workers had been murdered, she added a red bird to her all-green painting. To match the fury flaring inside her, Rachel affixed a spark—a flickering flame—to the bird's wing.

On her row, Hinda questioned the post-lunch increase in gunshots. She mulled over possibilities. Had the workers found the meager meal so insufficient that they succumbed to the temptation of eating the vegetables? Or was it that people were collapsing from exhaustion and weakness? Or did they feel more at ease now, believing they could sneak a vegetable into their uniform without notice? Or did the soldiers have quotas that cited the exact number of Jews to kill each day? Speculations sprinted through her brain with every bullet she heard.

Later that afternoon, one thought in particular struck Hinda hard: *What if Sara's ashes are in this garden?* While contemplating the possibility, a stabbing pain to her heart and soul, her body jerked. She lost her footing. Her ankle twisted in the wooden clog, making her slip in the uneven soil. She fell, then rolled sideways. She tried to get up before the policewomen saw her, but the channel between the rows was more like a ditch.

One of the German guards, an amazon of a woman who saw Hinda fall, stomped over to Hinda's row. She pulled out her leather strap and began whipping

Hinda. The woman shrieked, "No napping on the job. Get up, you lazy Jude girl." She lashed at Hinda in a seeming frenzy. As if a crazed vampire dwelled under her skin, the woman bellowed, "Get up and get back to work, or I—will—see—blood."

Malnourished and physically weaker than she had ever been, Hinda clawed at the dirt, struggling to get up on her knees. The woman drew back her boot and kicked Hinda in the head, flattening her on the ground. The sky spun in circles around her as she almost passed out, which only enraged the woman more. Pain skyrocketed through Hinda as the policewoman then walloped her harder with each strike of the bullwhip. Again, and again, she flogged Hinda's head, her arms, her legs, and her torso. Blood flowed from a gash in Hinda's forehead and seeped from her legs. Nearing unconsciousness, she lay rumpled on the ground.

Upon seeing Hinda's blood spilling onto the soil and not able to endure any more, Rachel rushed in and helped her sister get on her feet. Trembling, Hinda could barely keep her balance.

"And just who do you think you are?" The commando woman reared her arm back and smacked Rachel across the face so hard that it knocked her down into the pea vines. Then the woman proceeded to whip Rachel in the same monomaniacal way. Rachel could not contain her screams as Hinda had, so the woman beat her for a longer time, as if Rachel's cries fueled the leather whip. When Rachel was a bloody lump, the woman laughed heartily, deep belly cackles that clanged in the air. Hefting her shoulders back with pride, she strode away.

64

Hiding the Savage Truth

May 1943 | Oświęcim, German-occupied Poland
Auschwitz Concentration Camp

Chromatic chords, from the opera *Tristan und Isolde* by Wagner, blasted through the camp speaker system, drifting into the open window of the lab located in Block Ten. Once again, Dr. Walter worked on a Sunday, his usual day off. Today, though, it was his preference.

Struggling with depression, Walter found that focusing on work, perfecting the organization of the lab, was his best therapy. When he tried relaxing in his living quarters on Sundays, the horrific reality of Auschwitz overwhelmed his spirit. Dismal helplessness invaded his already lugubrious thoughts about the inhumane persecution occurring behind the camp's heavily guarded gates.

Recently, Walter had taken a walk, trying to calm himself after learning that he would not be permitted to leave Auschwitz and visit his parents this summer. Furthermore, his parents were not allowed to visit him there. At all. Ever. He had strolled near the entrance gates, wanting to kick them into oblivion. Abruptly, he had stopped and squinted his eyes, questioning what he was seeing. He double blinked, but the sight remained the same. He mumbled in surprise, "The letter *B* in the word "*ARBEIT*" is upside down." Tilting his head to the side in a curious manner, he mused: Yes, *the larger part of the letter is on the top, not at the bottom as it should be.* Then a memory flashed in his mind. Dr. Wirths had taken him on a tour when he had first arrived at Auschwitz and relayed that the gates had been made by Polish prisoners in the metalworking labor detail. Standing there, Walter contemplated the error of the upside-down *B*. Had it been accidentally forged that way by a dyslexic prisoner? Or was it a sign of disobedience, of resistance? More importantly, why had it not been reported by staff and then corrected? The latter question sparked thoughts of possible resistors existing in the camp. A hint of a smile crossed Walter's face when he decided to begin closely observing all staff members. If he noticed the subtlest signs of what might be construed as resistance attitudes, he could, perhaps, make some like-minded friends.

Today, in the lab, while rearranging the tissue samples of twins, Walter thought about friendship. When he was a kid, he had counted Josef Mengele as a friend. But now that the two were adults, Walter found Mengele's Nazi dogmatism and racial-science obsession so offensive that he didn't even like or trust the man. When speaking with him via phone yesterday, Walter learned that Mengele was soon to complete his assignment at the Race and Resettlement Agency in Berlin and would take up residency at Auschwitz on the thirtieth of May.

While weighing the pros and cons of Mengele's daily presence, Walter frowned. The cons list could fill tomes. Then a slight smile upturned the corners of Walter's thin lips as he thought about the one and only upside: He would spend less time in the lab and more time treating patients in the infirmary and the staff hospital.

Clattering noises from outside ruffled Walter's reflections. He went to the window and watched as a portable stage and folding chairs for the camp's new orchestra were set up in the square. The Sunday concerts were touted as an effort to boost morale. Walter was not fooled.

Two months ago, while at dinner one evening, he had been privy to a discussion that included the highest officers of the women's camp: the director, Franz Hössler, and head supervisor, Maria Mandel. They told Walter about the all-female orchestra they were forming. Mandel spoke in zealous tones, saying the small orchestra would perform a concert of classical pieces every Sunday afternoon. She was quite excited about the group, which was to be composed of prisoners, such as musically inclined homosexuals and Jehovah's Witnesses. But no Jews, she had adamantly averred.

Walter asked, "Is the government supplying the instruments?"

"The government would supply them," she affirmed. "But it's not necessary. High-quality instruments are confiscated from new arrivals, especially from the Jews, right here at the front gates of Auschwitz." Mandel then laughed merrily.

Concealing his chagrin and acting politely puzzled, Walter asked the reason for prohibiting Jews from the orchestra. He suggested that those who came in with such fine instruments were surely accomplished musicians. Specifically, he asked Mandel why she would not tap that talent and make her orchestra superb.

Maria Mandel wrinkled her nose at him.

Hössler then shared that the orchestra initiative had come about because of Hitler's directive that they create a propaganda tool of the women's camp, specifically for newsreels that would be released to the German people. Perhaps, even to the world, Hitler had suggested, if the films were ultra favorable.

Ah, yes, Walter thought, *an orchestra. Such a cultured sight. Concentration camp prisoners, all dressed up and outfitted with fine instruments, playing beautiful music would hide the savage truth.*

65

Rhino

May 1943 | Oświecim, German-occupied Poland
Auschwitz Concentration Camp

In the early evening hours, Hinda and Rachel slunk through the doorway of Block Thirteen after working all day in the vegetable field at Budy. It was exactly two weeks from the day of their brutal beatings. Still recovering and dog tired, they immediately went to their bunk, ignoring the cluster of women who were chatting in the aisle.

"We have newcomers from Vienna," one of the young women called out to them.

"Sorry, my sister and I are too tired to visit tonight," Hinda replied. "We'll meet them tomorrow."

"I know that voice," one of the new arrivals said. Then she squealed, "Hinda Mondlak! Is that you?"

Hinda turned and her jaw dropped. "Annie!"

In a tearful reunion, the two young women hugged tightly, trying to smile, even while acknowledging they were both imprisoned in a Nazi internment camp. A close childhood friend of Hinda's from Zieluń, Annie—a child prodigy—had moved to Vienna in her early teen years to pursue a life in classical music. The two had not seen each other since, but they had communicated via letters until the German occupation, which censored mail to and from Jews.

Annie released Hinda from her tight grip. "If I seem unduly happy in this horrible place, it's because I've just had a bit of encouraging news."

"Encouraging news? In Auschwitz?" Hinda asked, her eyes clouding with skepticism.

"Do you know about the women's orchestra that was started here in April?"

"Yes, Rachel and I have watched and listened for two Sundays now."

"Well, here to now, they haven't allowed Jews to be part of the group. But wait, let me back up and start at the beginning." Annie's hand went to her head, stroking her scalp, her newly shaved pate. "So, I arrived here yesterday. When the guards confiscated my suitcase right after we stepped through those horrid gates, I thought I would keel over dead because it had my violin in it. The guards scoffed, saying under no circumstances could I keep it."

Hinda nodded, knowing the scenario all too well.

"Anyway," Annie continued, "I began touting my musical credentials and citing what an expensive instrument my violin was. Luckily, one of the female guards, who was on duty at that time, also works as a warden for the new orchestra. She contacted Officer Maria Mandel, who played a key role in forming the group. When Officer Mandel saw the quality of my violin and found out that I had played regularly in the Vienna Symphony, fifth chair no less, she said I could audition for her orchestra. Oh, Hinda, as painful as it is to be incarcerated here, I'm thrilled about having a chance to play regularly. It's a touch of normalcy for me. My music. My violin. You know?"

"Yes, your passion. And I'm sure you'll ace the audition," Hinda encouraged. She noted the brightness of her friend's smile that radiated genuine delight, a quality she had not seen in any face for years. "I'm happy for you, Annie, and it's *so* good to see you. I can't believe you got assigned to Block Thirteen."

Annie put her arms around Hinda again. "My dear friend, I barely recognize you." Tears popped from Annie's eyes. She shrilled, "Hinda, you are so thin, and you look so very sad."

A dark shadow crossed Hinda's brow. "My family is gone, except for Rachel and my older siblings who left Poland before the war. Rachel and I have been through—well—hell. Such unjust torment, I cannot describe. We are starving and beaten down, literally." Eyeing Annie, who still had meat on her bones and appeared vibrant, Hinda added, "Hopefully, you haven't been so abused. But in this monstrous place, you will be."

"No one arrives to Auschwitz without enduring abuse, but obviously, I've not gone through all that you have. Did you come here straight from Zieluń?"

"No, our home was confiscated, and we were taken to the Mława ghetto, which was beyond terrible. Food had already been scarce due to the war, but there, we lived in squalor and on a starvation diet for almost three years. Both of my parents died there, and then just this past December, we were transported to Auschwitz. How about you?"

"My mother and I lived underground for three years. Gentile families hid us. They were all part of the secret society." Annie paused, her lips puckering into a sorrowful pout. "Exactly a week ago today, the SS busted the group protecting what was left of the Viennese Jews, captured us, and threw us on a train bound for here."

"What about your father?" Hinda asked.

"He was executed by the Gestapo in 1939, and for no reason of wrongdoing."

"I'm deeply sorry, Annie. My father suffered a similar fate."

Abruptly, Annie grabbed Hinda by the shoulders and looked directly into her eyes. Tears spilled in rivulets down her cheeks. She implored, "You have to be strong, Hinda, and keep fighting to stay alive."

"And as I listen to your words, I say to you, dear Annie, you must do the same."

When Hinda crawled into their bunk, Rachel was already sleeping soundly. Reaching in her pocket, Hinda pulled out a tube of salve. She began applying the balm to the cuts and sores on Rachel's face. Then she rubbed a small amount into the lesion on her own forehead. Additional lacerations and mosquito bites needed doctoring, but that would have to do for tonight, she was so fatigued her bones ached.

The tube of salve slipped from her hands onto the hay. She caressed it as she slid it back into her pocket, feeling thankful for it, and for the surprising way it had come to her on the day of the whippings. Recollections flooded her mind. She and Rachel were in such a desecrated, crippled state, they could barely walk. When it was time to leave Budy, the other two women from Block Thirteen, numbers 18302 and 18303, helped them get to the rear of the truck.

The rabid policewoman, who had scourged Hinda and Rachel, had come running. She hollered, "No. Do not help those lazy, impudent girls. Let them do it on their own or die trying."

The soldier who had driven the truck that morning stepped up, his hand resting on the handle of his rifle. He barked, "This truck is my domain, not yours." He nodded to the other passengers to render assistance to Hinda and then to Rachel, who had to be lifted into the bed of the truck.

The woman glowered at the soldier and pawed the dirt with her boot as if she were a mad bull striking its hoof. Dust flying around her, she stomped away, spewing profane curses.

When the military truck arrived back at Block Thirteen, their block mates, 18302 and 18303, helped the sisters down. The soldier turned off the engine, giving them time to get out without further injury. He came to the door with them. In one deft movement, he slid a tube of salve into Hinda's hand.

In a low whisper, the soldier said, "Looks like you're both going to need this. When you've used it all, go to the infirmary, and ask for Dr. Walter. Tell him Rhino sent you. He'll give you a new tube."

66
Burning with Fever
Mid-June 1943 | Oświęçim, German-occupied Poland
Auschwitz Concentration Camp

At seventy-two degrees and with low humidity, the Sunday afternoon air felt agreeable as a light breeze ruffled Walter Zeilhofen's blonde hair. Enjoying the outdoor concert, Walter sat in a folding chair in the front row next to Josef Mengele, who had officially taken up residence at Auschwitz two weeks ago, on May thirtieth.

Mengele appeared delighted with the music. He tapped his foot to the *da-da-da-duuum* theme prominent in Beethoven's Symphony Number Five in C Minor. Although enjoying the instrumentation, Mengele did not look at the musicians who played passionately. Rarely did he take his eyes away from the attractive and talented conductor, Zofia Czajkowska.

To the contrary, Walter's eyes roved over the prisoners gathered to the side behind the fence. He searched for the young woman with the perfectly shaped head. She had stirred his dreams, although he had seen her just one time. He yearned to catch even the slightest glimpse of her. Not seeing her this afternoon, Walter checked the time on his watch. Familiar with the score of the symphony, he knew it was soon to end. He hoped to slip away unnoticed to meet his new ally, Soldier Rhino, in the infirmary.

At the concert's end, Josef Mengele stood, giving brief, enthusiastic applause. He excused himself, making a beeline to the conductor's side. Exactly as he had done the previous Sunday, he asked Zofia to have dinner with him that evening. Yet again, she declined, saying that she must start preparations for next week's concert.

Mengele inquired about having dinner another evening that week. Before she could reply, he took her hand in his and said, "There must be immense talent in these cells."

Sliding her hand from his, Zofia shuddered. She explained that her evenings this week were filled with mandatory rehearsals.

Accustomed to having his way, Mengele furrowed his brow in disbelief of Zofia's rejection. Thinking about his wife, Irene, who chose to visit him only periodically in Auschwitz, Mengele felt a familiar loneliness engulf him. Even still, he smiled cordially at Zofia. He claimed to understand, but said he would discuss her schedule with camp superiors and arrange an evening off for her.

Standing at the back of the prisoner group, Hinda and Rachel listened to the orchestra's rendition of Beethoven's Fifth. They had chosen the rear area so that Hinda, who had been ill all night with vomiting and diarrhea and was now suffering a pounding headache, could lean against a tree trunk. Although barely able to walk to the plaza, Hinda was determined to see her childhood friend, Annie, play first-chair violin in today's concert.

As Hinda had predicted, when Annie auditioned for the orchestra, she was instantly accepted. What Hinda had not expected was for Annie to be promptly moved from Block Thirteen. The following day, Hinda overheard inspection wardens chatting about how all orchestra members had been moved to apartments located near staff's quarters. That did not seem too surprising, but then one warden mentioned that the musicians would receive staff-quality food for months or until the film was made. Hinda had wrinkled her brow, finding it suspicious that orchestra members were being fattened up for a film.

A few days later, Rachel and she bumped into Annie outside their block. Her face aglow, Annie had told them how the orchestra practiced long hours every day. She disclosed that orchestra members did not have to shave their heads anymore, and they had been measured for formal dresses. Annie had barely caught her breath, the words tumbling from her mouth in a hurried cadence. All this, she relayed, was in preparation for a premier concert that was to be filmed by government officials and released in news reels to the German public and to other countries. To Hinda's surprise, Annie did not seem to question the reason for such a film. She had only raved about it with excitement and pride.

Today, from the other side of the electrified fence, Hinda observed Annie totally engrossed in the music and gleefully playing her violin. Her friend had broken the barrier, being the first Jew allowed to join, which engendered a sense of pride for Hinda. She noticed that the orchestra was now larger than the initial small chamber ensemble in early May. Camp rumors claimed that Officer Mandel had been so impressed with Annie's talent and work ethic that she had admitted more Jewish musicians, doubling the orchestra's size.

When there was a pause in the concert, Rachel whispered, "How's your headache?"

"Awful," Hinda replied. "And I'm feeling nauseated and achy. I need to go lie down."

Placing her hand on Hinda's forehead, Rachel shrieked. "Ouch!" She jerked her hand away and wiped it on her uniform. "You're burning with fever. And sweaty." She squinted at her sister. "Your skin looks a bit yellowish. Let's get you to the infirmary."

"Maybe later. I don't know if I can walk there right now."

"Hinda Mondlak, listen to me. You need medical attention. Some aspirin, at least. And if you wake up sick tomorrow morning, you'll have to go to the fields regardless. Besides, we need more salve. What was the name of that doctor we were supposed to ask for?"

"Walter, Dr. Walter," Hinda said, her breathing irregular. In the next minute, she was in the throes of a hard rigor, shaking with chills.

Rachel gasped. "It's typhus or malaria. Dear God, help us. The gas chamber." Tears burst from her eyes. Her lips quivering, Rachel begged, "Let's go throw ourselves on the fence right now. We'll die together. Hinda, please. I can't make it without *you*."

"No fence, not today. And I've changed my mind about the infirmary. Please, just help me get there." Hinda choked out the words, her teeth chattering from chills. "I know it's a risk to be diagnosed, but my instincts say to go now."

67

Mental Coercion

June 1943 | Weimar, Germany
Buchenwald Concentration Camp

Wolf Yoskowitz lay in his bunk listening to his brother breathe heavily while sleeping. He tried synchronizing his breathing rhythm with Joseph's, while urging drowsiness to engulf him. Although Wolf was weary, completely exhausted, sleep did not come and rescue him from the hunger that gnawed at the lining of his stomach like a starving dog attacking a bone.

He and Joseph had far exceeded their quota of seven stones in the quarry today. They had delivered *ten* stones of qualifying dimensions. This authorized them to receive double meat in their soup tonight. Yet no food, not even bread, had been distributed.

Wolf had expected to receive consistent sustenance when Pister, the camp's commander, instituted a *food-for-output* plan for quarry laborers, who worked in pairs. The plan stated that meat would be added to dinner soup when workers met their daily quota of seven stones. As further incentive, double meat would be added when workers surpassed the quota by three stones, qualified by size. Wolf had been confident that he and Joseph could exceed quota. They were proficient, and they toiled assiduously.

Stone excavation skills were specific, requiring training. But quarry laborers were dying at higher rates than other prisoners, due to extreme exertion in all types of weather and being fed a starvation diet. To maintain the quarry's robust profits, Pister implemented an incentive plan for the weakened workers to earn the chance to ingest protein on a regular basis.

Buchenwald limestone was a hot commodity, in high demand throughout Germany. Owned and operated by Nazi SS, the quarry was one of the most profitable endeavors in all the concentration camps, a source of pride to Pister. Due to Buchenwald's no-cost labor force—imprisoned Jewish men—profits were soaring, but they hinged on trained workers who had stamina for twelve-hour days.

The hitch with the *food-for-output* plan was that it depended upon the mood of the guards who, at the end of the day, determined what and when the prisoners ate. At frequent, random times, the guards on evening duty did not distribute the soup at all, deciding they just did not want the bother. For the quarry workers, meeting quotas or exceeding them were useless then. There was no supervisor to oversee or report the abuse.

Tonight, the guards were in such a mood. Hatred for the Nazis roiled up inside Wolf. The taste was vile as he tried to swallow it, to bury the intense feeling. When Wolf had first arrived at Buchenwald and experienced the severity of the labor requirements combined with the lack of nutrition, he questioned if he could survive even two months. One night, a poignant memory overwhelmed him: On the day he turned thirteen, his rabbi had looked him square in the eye and said, "Wolf, you are blessed with superior mental strength. You can achieve *whatever* goal you set your mind upon." The memory had tingled through him, and—in that very moment—Wolf set his intention to live. From then on, in the name of physical survival, he downed every smidgen of gruel the camp offered, regardless of how noxious it tasted. He ate potato peels and all, whereas other prisoners spit out the bitter vegetable skins even if they were the only solid floating in the broth. Occasionally, small fish and chicken bones were in the potage. Most prisoners would toss them on the floor, afraid of choking. Not Wolf. He chewed the bones and would collect the discarded ones, however dirty. He would then grind them with his teeth and swallow the gritty residue. In the quarry, when digging for rock, they often came across worms and crickets. Wolf would snatch them up, pop them into his mouth, and swallow them whole. He aimed to stay alive, even when malnourished and overworked as a slave laborer.

Wolf turned on his side. He closed his eyes and mandated positive thoughts and images, which seemed foggy and worlds away. On nights when he had eaten meat, it was effortless to engage in his visualization and mental exercises, which fed his inner flame. Tonight, he strained. Although it took intense mental coercion, at last, Wolf envisaged true love with a beautiful Jewish woman, who would then become his wife, his queen. Next, he conjured up images of an abundant life where he was a free man and was paid well for work that he enjoyed, a life where he had ample food, a real home, and a family—children whom he adored and who loved him.

Cycling through the visions again, Wolf ended with pondering what it would feel like to hold his wife to be. His fisted hand relaxed, his fingers unfolding. A warm sensation enveloped him. At last, his breathing slowed, and sleep transported him into a dreamy world where he held her closely. Dancing cheek to cheek, they twirled and glided around the dance floor, keeping perfect rhythm to the triple-time beat of the Viennese Waltz.

68

Treason

Inside the infirmary, Walter pulled up a chair next to his friend, Soldier Rhino, who sat on an examination table, his sleeve rolled up, a blood pressure cuff around his arm, all in pretense of needing medical aid.

Rhino exclaimed, "The beatings in the fields, Walter, are unbelievably brutal. In most cases, the workers have done nothing wrong. Plus, the mosquito swarms are rampant, especially in the late afternoon." Rhino tapped the sheet. "I need more tubes of salve."

Just then, the front-door buzzer rang. Walter arose and hurriedly donned his medical jacket. To Rhino, he said, "You know what to do if that's Mengele."

Rhino winked, his broad face breaking into an ear-to-ear grin.

When Walter opened the infirmary door, his eyes widened to double their size. It was her, the woman with the perfectly shaped head. She stood in the doorway, leaning against another young woman.

"Is Doctor Walter here today?" the younger woman inquired.

"I'm Dr. Walter. How may I help you?"

"A soldier, named Rhino, gave us salve and told us to ask for you when we needed more, which we do. But most importantly today, my sister is very sick. She's 25305, and I'm 25306."

"Ah, my friend, Rhino, a good man he is." At one glance, Walter could see that 25305 was seriously ill. But even still, he was captivated by her unique beauty, especially considering the oppressive environment. His breath caught in his throat when he looked into her large blue eyes, which today appeared dull, resembling foggy mirrors. Pointing to the green curtain on the right, he said to 25306, "Let's get her to the bed back here."

The second 25305's head touched the pillow, a rigor shook her body. Walter instructed her to turn on her side, draw up her legs, and to wrap her arms tightly across her chest to minimize the shaking. Inserting a thermometer into the patient's mouth, he looked to her sister. "She's still trembling. I need you to hold this outside tip to keep it under her tongue. I'll return shortly with aspirin and ice packs. But before I go, may I ask your names? I despise using serial numbers for human beings."

"She is Hinda. I am Rachel. Mondlak is our surname."

"Hinda and Rachel, under other circumstances, I would say I am *very* pleased to meet you."

From behind the curtain, a male voice said, "Doc Walter, shall I come back later?"

Walter exited and motioned to Rhino to step back. In a hushed tone, Walter said, "I prefer that you stay, if possible. I'll need your help with this situation, if it's what I think it is."

Walter did not have to tap or push on Hinda's spleen to see if it were enlarged; she was so thin, he could see the organ protruding through her skin, swollen and obviously inflamed. Upon closer examination, he noted that her liver was distended, and the whites of her eyes appeared yellowish, her skin already slightly jaundiced. All that, plus her labored breathing and about twenty mosquito bites—one of which looked badly infected—were strong indicators. Then, considering her fever of one-hundred-four degrees, profuse sweating, severe chills, nausea, headache, muscle pain, and additional symptoms, the assumptive diagnosis was malaria. But Walter could not be one hundred percent certain without a blood test. The problem, though, was now that Mengele was running the lab, the woman's test would be labeled with her identity number, and if it were positive for malaria, she would be sent directly to the gas chamber.

His hands shaking, Walter inserted the key into the infirmary's locked medicine cabinet, which contained medications that were restricted from use on prisoners. Weighing his options, he withdrew an antimalarial agent, chloroquine phosphate tablets, although he was not certain she could tolerate oral medication in her distressed gastrointestinal condition. Walter then reached for the serum, chloroquine hydrochloride, and held the vial, contemplating. The woman's case was severe, and she was compromised further from weakness and malnutrition. She would die in the next twenty-four hours without substantial doses. A dilemma loomed: would both medications be too much for her fragile state? Rubbing his chin, Walter pondered briefly, and then put both the serum and the tablets in his lab-coat pocket. He would first give her an intramuscular injection to jumpstart treatment, and then decide about the timing for the tablets. While selecting a sterile syringe, he remembered that injections and serum amounts were monitored more closely than pills. Later, he would figure out how to falsify the records.

Fully aware that he would be punished, even executed, if discovered administering any of these medications to a prisoner, Walter relocked the cabinet and headed toward the kitchen.

When Walter slipped through the green curtain, his eyebrows raised in a question as he eyed the patient.

"She seems a bit better after the aspirin," Rachel offered.

"The aspirin was merely balm for her headache and fever. It will do nothing to cure what ails her," Walter explained. He set a cup of water and a brown bag on the counter.

"Do I have malaria?" Hinda inquired.

Impressed with Hinda's valor to be forthright, asking about what could mean a death sentence, Walter stepped closer to her bedside. "Yes, I believe you do."

"Lord, help us," Rachel cried out. "She's going to the gas chamber."

"Not on my watch." Walter placed his hand on Hinda's shoulder. His insides quaking, he looked directly into her eyes. "I want to help you get well. And I believe I can, although I will be in woeful trouble if discovered. So, it's going to take clandestine effort, which has risks. Would you be okay with that?"

"Yes, for sure," Hinda replied, her voice weak and her breathing raspy.

Turning to Rachel, Walter said, "And what about you, as for the risks?"

Rachel bobbled her head up and down vigorously, giving her consent. "Anything for my sister to get well."

Satisfied, Walter turned back to Hinda and announced, "I have decided upon a medication plan for you. The first step is an intramuscular injection, a shot, to accelerate your treatment. Later, the second phase includes tablets, if you can tolerate them. There is one thing. You can tell *no one* that you have received antimalarial medications. Can you promise that?"

"Yes, I promise in God's name. My sister won't tell either. We give our pledge."

Unprompted, Rachel said, "I promise on my own. And I keep my word."

"Very good, then. Guess we're ready. I'll prepare the injection, which must go in your hip." After the injection, Walter covered Hinda and stepped to the counter. He dunked the hypodermic into a jar of isopropyl alcohol. At the sink, he scrubbed his hands.

"Do you think you could sit up in the bed?" Walter asked. Acknowledging her slight nod, he lifted Hinda's head and helped her into a sitting position, propped up on pillows. He then reached for the brown bag and withdrew soda crackers and bread. "It would be beneficial if you could keep some food down, especially since you vomited earlier." He placed the cup of water next to the bed. "Sip this while taking intermittent bites of crackers, bread, or both."

"My stomach is rolling, but I'll do my best," Hinda whispered.

"Take your time. I need to step out anyway. A trusted friend is in the next room, and I want to pick his brain about the plan I'm hatching for your extended care."

Astonished, Hinda's words faltered. "Thank . . . you . . . Dr. Walter."

Halfway through the curtain, Walter turned back. "Please forgive my manners. Rachel, I'm sure you could use sustenance too. There's extra bread in the bag. Please help yourself." He disappeared through the green drapery.

"I know those two girls. They were almost beaten to death a couple of months ago at Budy," Rhino said. "I gave them salve. They're in Block Thirteen."

"Budy? Block Thirteen? So, you take them back and forth in your truck every day?"

"Yep, I do."

"What a boon that is." Walter exhaled, although his brow remained furrowed.

"How so?" Rhino asked.

"The older one has a severe case of malaria. And I feel—" Walter paused and placed his hand upon his heart and looked upward to the ceiling as if omniscient divinity resided there. "I feel compelled to treat her with curative medication. And that must remain confidential as it's against policy. But for her to survive, she cannot work in the fields this week. Are you willing to break some rules?"

"What do you have in mind?"

"I'll log her in as having influenza and write a prescription for rest, but that's only good for twenty-four hours. Plus, she needs nutrition and liquids, and she won't get either in the Blocks." Walter paused, his fingers combing through his hair as if that clarified his thoughts. "I would like to keep her in the infirmary in the back room during the day, so I can administer the medications properly.

Any ideas about how we can manage her *not* going to work at Budy this week? Tuesday through Saturday, that is."

Rhino looked at the floor, staring hard at it, his best thinking ally, that and raw earthy ground. "On Tuesday, I could check her in as Present. And if the commando witches inquire, I could say I had orders for her to work in the orchards for the remainder of this week and had dropped her there." He cast his eyes downward, blinking multiple times. "The fruit trees are a half mile from the vegetable gardens. They wouldn't walk that far to check it out. Besides, those women enjoy the policing too much, always watching for a chance to use their bullwhips."

Walter flinched at the mention of bullwhips. "Sounds like a solid plan to me. Do you need more time to think about it?"

Returning his gaze to the floor, Rhino studied for a minute. "There's one more problem. Two other women from Block Thirteen work at Budy. They would notice her absence."

Walter sighed heavily.

Continuing to stare at the floor, Rhino said, "I suppose the younger one could say that her sister was transferred to work in the kitchen. That's believable because prisoner jobs are rotated frequently." Lifting his head, Rhino pronounced each word emphatically. "This plan will work. I'll see to it."

The two men locked eyes and clinched their fists, raising them in opposition to Hitler and the Nazi regime.

When Walter left the room, he made the sign of the cross. Murmuring under his breath, he asked for God's blessing upon what they were about to do: commit treason.

"How's it going in here?" Walter asked. He set a small, covered bowl on the counter.

"Not so good," Rachel replied.

Hinda lay curled under the blankets, moaning. Her uniform and the bed sheets were soaked from her continuous sweating.

Walter's eyes darted to the pan on the bed. He sighed in relief; the pan was empty. She had not vomited up the bread, which meant he could start oral medication. To Hinda, he said, "These damp sheets have to go. Let's get you into the chair." He leaned over her. "Place your arm around my neck." In one swift movement, he lifted her gently into the chair, but she leaned, as if she might fall.

Grabbing pillows, Walter placed them behind her head and back for support. Then, he reached into one of the upper cabinets and retrieved fresh bed linens.

Inching closer to the bed, Rachel said, "I can change the sheets, if you'd allow me."

Walter hesitated but then said, "That would be helpful." Noting Hinda's drenched uniform, he wished he could have her change it, but hospital gowns were not stocked at the infirmary. And even if they were, he could not send a prisoner's uniform to laundry without raising such suspicion that the matter would be investigated. Later, he would ask Rachel to blot the uniform with towels and then dry Hinda's body underneath.

Fishing around in his lab coat pocket, Walter withdrew a flaxen-colored tablet. Handing Hinda a cup of water, he said, "This pill begins the second phase of your treatment. Though, if this works, it's going to be a full week before you feel significant improvement, and then another few months or more to feel recovered."

Hinda swallowed the tablet and said, "Thank you, Dr. Walter." Silently, she praised God for this miraculous favor of fate. Her prayer quickly turned to asking for help to keep down the golden pill. Nausea nettling her gag reflex nerve, she leaned against the pillows.

Walter removed the lid from the bowl on the counter. "Here's some cherry gelatin that should go down easily. Can you manage a couple of bites?"

Hinda inclined her head, signaling yes, although she was far from sure. It felt as if she were going to toss up the pill at any second. Using the spoon, she slid a red cube into her mouth.

Walter ran his hand through his hair, causing a wave of blonde strands to fall onto his forehead. "We've devised a plan that we believe is cogent. Is it okay with you ladies if my friend, Rhino, joins us to go over the details?"

The sisters both agreed. But just then the buzzer to the infirmary door rang. Then they heard a key in the lock.

Walter wriggled through the green curtain and came face-to-face with Josef Mengele.

69
Bar Talk

In the bar area of the formal dining room reserved for officers, Commander Rudolph Höss stirred his cocktail. Checking his watch, he muttered, "Damn it, Mengele, how dare you keep me waiting this long?" His thoughts drifted to the beauteous prisoner, named Eleanor Hodys, soon to arrive at his secret apartment for their Sunday night tryst, and he became even more disgruntled. Unexpectedly that afternoon, Josef Mengele had demanded they meet for a drink, providing no explanation of the business to be discussed.

"Commander Höss, please accept my apologies," Mengele said, as he sauntered into the bar. Settling into his chair, he explained, "I encountered odious circumstances in the infirmary."

"Late means you owe me. What about the infirmary?" Höss waved over the waiter to take Mengele's drink order.

After requesting a glass of Riesling, Mengele said, "I stopped by the infirmary to see if Zeilhofen wanted to join me for dinner as I knew you had another commitment. But three extremely ill people were there. Two had influenza, and a soldier had dysentery. He couldn't contain the regurgitating. And for me, that's intolerable. The place was a germ fest. I had no choice but to go take a quick shower and change my clothing."

Placing his whiskey back on the table, Höss curled his upper lip, not hiding his disdain, "What urgent matter did you want to discuss?"

"Did I say it was urgent?"

"Yes, you did. I changed my plans to meet you."

Mengele dropped his head. Lifting it again, he said, "I sincerely apologize, sir, for my miscommunication and for delaying you. I simply hoped we could have a friendly drink, and I wanted to discuss the duties and time commitments of the orchestra director."

"Zofia Czajkowska? You interested in her or the orchestra?"

"Her. She seems talented, very accomplished."

"Good-looking dame." Höss winked. "But she is soon to be replaced. Are you aware that she is imprisoned here because she is an activist, a *resistor* to the regime?"

Frowning, Josef exclaimed, "Political prisoner? Zofia is not staff, not a paid director?" Fury rose inside him as if someone had unexpectedly kicked his groin.

"That's correct." Höss raised his glass, holding it mid-air. "Do you know about the upcoming publicity film?"

"No, sir, I don't."

After a long drink, Höss said, "Hitler ordered propaganda tools that could be used in newsreels. In particular, he wanted compelling material from the women's camp. Officer Mandell, the women's camp supervisor, conceived of the all-women's orchestra. Brilliant, right?"

"Indeed. A sophisticated endeavor."

"Mandell found well-qualified musicians but not a leader. To get the thing off the ground, we temporarily approved Zofia. She's an acclaimed conductor, but there's no way that Hitler would allow her to be in the film."

"Understand. Who is replacing her?"

"Alma Rosé, a Jewish woman. She's due to arrive August 1. Being transferred from the Drancy internment camp in Paris."

"Paris?" Josef protested. "Hitler's okay with a French woman, considering how France has treated us?"

"She's not French. She's Austrian. And the daughter of Arnold Rosé, who was once the conductor of the Vienna Philharmonic. She's Jewish and from a high-brow family, which is perfect for the goals of our film."

Mengele sipped his wine. "Excellent. It's a compelling idea for the public to see her in a lead cultural role here at Auschwitz."

Höss pushed back his chair, readying to leave. "You know, Mengele, if it's foxy musician broads you're after, the director of the new women's choir, an informal group, would likely turn your head. You can meet her next Sunday. The choir is performing a few numbers with the orchestra."

After taking two steps toward the door, Höss turned. Slapping Mengele on the back, he said, "Since you owe me one, can you oversee the Selection process early tomorrow morning? A large group of Greek Jews are arriving from Salonika."

Mengele's eyes brightened as if a splendid toy had been dangled in front of a five-year-old. "The Selections? I would be delighted. Consider it done." He tapped his fingers on the table, "And I want Zeilhofen there to check the infants for twins and eye disorders. Then those corpses can be moved to the autopsy room in my lab."

"Fine. Let Zeilhofen know tonight. And remember, we do the Selections now on the ramp as they depart the train. You'll need to take a jeep to the site."

70

Am I Dying?

Mid-June 1943 | Oświęcim, German-occupied Poland
Auschwitz Concentration Camp

Rachel rolled blankets together, narrowing them at one end, then plumping them midway to the top. She then molded a shape resembling a human head. Stepping back to survey her creation, she decided to bend what would be the knee area. Then, she pushed more hay around the entirety of the blob. Taking her usual blue blanket, Rachel covered the blob, hoping it simulated a person sleeping on their side. It had to be good enough. Doctor Walter had given her three blankets to make it appear that Hinda slept in the bunk, and she had used all three. Next, she affixed his note to their berth. It was written on official infirmary paper and signed by him: #25305— INFLUENZA—Bed Rest Required.

Tonight, Rachel would sleep on the outside of the bunk, her back against the fake Hinda. That is, if sleep would come, as plagued with worry as she was.

Late that afternoon, after eating the cherry gelatin, Hinda had vomited up the golden pill. Doctor Walter's face had turned ashen. Reading his expression, Rachel felt as if his thoughts leapt from his brain into hers. They echoed in her head like alarm bells: Hinda could die tonight.

Walter sat beside Hinda's bed, watching her. He could not move his eyes away from her face, one he wanted to behold for a lifetime. Feelings of that nature were alien to him, like strangers trespassing on the avenues of his heart.

Hinda stirred, opening her eyes. "Am I dying?" she asked, her breathing labored.

"You're extremely ill, but from what I can see, you're strong in spirit," Walter replied, employing as convincing a tone as he could muster. At that very moment, he decided to give her another injection of chloroquine hydrochloride, although treatment protocol dictated that he wait another six hours.

The phone in the infirmary office rang multiple times as he was completing the shot. Whoever it was hung up, then called back seconds later, the phone screeching again. He placed the hypodermic on the counter and raced to the phone.

"Okay, I'll be there," Walter begrudgingly said, although he was relieved that Mengele had called and had not stopped by. But then, he knew Mengele would not come to the infirmary again tonight because of the perceived germs—thanks to Rhino, and his talent for making believable and gross vomiting sounds.

But now, what was he to do? Scratching his head, Walter wrestled with the dilemma. Hinda needed constant monitoring. If she lived through the night, where could he safely hide her in the morning? Another doctor or a nurse would have to be on call in the infirmary while he fulfilled corpse duties for Selection. He sighed, then mumbled, "Damn it, Mengele, you and your gruesome, racial-science obsessions."

71

Telling the Truth

In the quarry, the supervisor paced atop the hill watching Wolf and Joseph work. He jerked off his hat and slapped it against his pants. Trudging down the hill, he yelled, "What's wrong with you boys? Is all that beef making you sluggish?"

Wolf put down his pickaxe and shovel. He stood at attention facing the supervisor—a hulk of a man. "Sir, I apologize if we're slow today."

"Were you sick last night?"

"No, sir," Wolf replied.

"You boys are my best workers. Do I need to get the whip after you?"

"No, sir. We'll do better," Wolf said, maintaining direct eye contact with the boss.

"I'm taking the meat protein option away from you both for a week, and I expect you to exceed quota anyway."

His eyes darting wildly, Joseph blurted out, "It makes no difference anyhow. We exceeded our quota by three stones yesterday and didn't get anything last night. No soup, no meat, no bread. Nothing at all because the guards didn't want to mess with serving food."

Wolf cringed. Swallowing hard, he said, "Sir, I apologize for my brother's outburst. It will not happen again."

The supervisor cocked his head to the side. "Are you saying your brother is lying?"

"No, sir. He's telling the truth about not having anything to eat last night. But we cannot be certain of the reason the guards didn't serve."

"Has it ever happened before?" The supervisor squinted his eyes at Wolf.

"On occasion, sir," Wolf replied.

Shaking his head in disagreement, Josef protested, "Happens all the time, at least once a week, if not two nights."

"I will investigate this," the supervisor said while scrutinizing the other workers. "Looks like they're all slugs today." He started to walk away, but he suddenly veered back. His massive hand fisted, he landed a punch smack into Joseph's jaw, knocking him to the ground. "You need to learn how to show respect and how to keep your squealer Jew mouth shut."

Sometime after midnight, Wolf slept soundly while Joseph lay awake, his face to the wall, his jaw swollen and bruised. The supervisor's blow had dislodged a molar, causing intense pain. Hearing rustling sounds nearby, Joseph sat up. Blinding light flashed in his eyes. Then he saw them.

Two guards stood over his and Wolf's bunk.

Overhead lights on high, the entire barrack awakened. The other prisoners quaked in silence, watching as the two brothers were lashed, whipped, and beaten until no sound came from either of them.

72

Snatched from Death's Threshold

July 1943 | Oświęcim, German-occupied Poland
Auschwitz Concentration Camp

At five forty-five in the morning, the Blitz truck roared to a stop, parking in front of the vegetable garden at Budy. Hinda stood back, letting the other workers get out first, then took her time getting down. Rachel assisted; yet, she restrained her efforts, not wanting to draw attention to Hinda's infirmity.

Soldier Rhino stood at the bed of the truck. As the women descended from the tailgate, he checked off each one's identity number on the Present/Absent list attached to his clipboard.

When the sisters turned in the direction of the squash vines, Rhino bumped shoulders with Hinda. His clipboard tumbled to the ground. A small piece of paper found its way into her hand as Rhino reached down to pick up his items.

Tucking the paper into her pants pocket, Hinda hastened the pace of her steps as she walked away. At the squash vines, two policewomen patrolled her row. The note from Walter would have to wait. In anticipation of reading today's message, a slight smile swept her lips upward. But it was short-lived. When Hinda bent down to pluck the zucchini from the low-growing vines, a stabbing pain in her left side caused a frown. Her spleen remained enlarged. Dr. Walter had said it might take another two months for it to not feel sore, especially when she torqued her waist area. Walter had wanted Hinda out of the brutal environment of the fields, claiming it was necessary for her to fully recover from such a severe case of malaria. Soldier Rhino had worked his end of it, submitting paperwork for her to be transferred to an indoor work area. Administration had denied the request.

While Hinda worked, thoughts of the good doctor encouraged her entire body to feel healthy and strong. Although Hinda picked the squash and placed them in the burlap bag, her mind occupied a different space. No question about it, Dr. Walter had saved her life, which had hung in the balance. To her, it seemed that Walter had reached across death's threshold and snatched her away. And why he had remained perplexing. Going beyond the ethics of his medical license, Walter had risked punishment, even his own life, when he defied policy by administering curative medications to her, a prisoner, and when he devised schemes to keep her from working in the fields, fed her nutritious food from the staff menu, kept her hydrated with *clean* water, and hid her in the storage closet of the infirmary.

Spared from the gas chamber, Hinda sensed that a confluence of sacrosanct miracles had swooped upon her and upon Dr. Walter—their clandestine plot was not exposed or discovered, although there were scads of close calls. The fastidious care Walter provided not only saved her life, but it also helped her to feel human again, to feel released from emotional numbness, and to feel the drumbeat of her soul anew, healing her beyond her physical edges.

When extending her arm to reach for a zucchini, her sleeve slipped upward. She noticed the tattoo on her wrist, her Auschwitz identity number that, prior to meeting Dr. Walter, had caused her to feel like she was nothing but a cockroach. The morning sunlight cast its glow on the inky numerals. A peculiar prescience rippled through her. Opposing voices collided in her mind:

—*There will come a day when that tattoo saves you from a horrific demise.*

—*There will come a day when that work of the devil will vanish from your arm.*

73

The Pleasure of Your Company

August 1943 | Oświeçim, German-occupied Poland
Auschwitz Concentration Camp

The mid-afternoon sun cast an odd coppery aura upon the choir director, Elisa Gaensel, a young woman in her twenties. It was as if the reddish-brown glow highlighted what was once her thick auburn tresses, even though her pate had been shorn.

Her hands gracefully swooping one way then another, Elisa directed the all-female prisoner group in a lively number while the orchestra played accompaniment. In the past weeks of Sunday concerts, it had become tradition for the newly formed choir to perform two vocals as part of the finale.

At the zenith of the ending note, the audience applauded wildly. Josef Mengele leapt to his feet, and others around him arose, awarding the musicians and singers a standing ovation. The newly appointed orchestra conductor, Alma Rosé, and the choir director, Elisa Gaensel, bowed to the audience—officers, guards, staff, and their families.

Ignoring concert protocol, the young choir director turned and curtsied to the cluster of prisoners who had gathered behind the fence. A popular inmate, Elisa was known for her rare ability to enable those who were tone deaf to sing on pitch. Her infectious delight in comedic absurdity and use of her operatic mezzo-soprano voice to mitigate the suffering made her a favorite in the women's camp. It was said that when she witnessed Block mates feeling devastated, Elisa would belt out ridiculous lyrics about their collective plight in Auschwitz until their tears disappeared. Or, as some would say, she hypnotized them.

The choir had been a morale-boosting addition to the Sunday performances, although the group was not as sanctioned as the orchestra. When performing together, the two all-female assemblies fashioned a striking, visual contrast. Not accorded special treatment, the women in the choir sported shaved heads and smacked of inadequate nutrition. Yet orchestra members appeared well fed and modeled stylish coiffed hair, although they were internees too.

After receiving accolades and dismissing the musicians, Alma huddled with Elisa to debrief and discuss selected vocals for next Sunday's concert. Midway in their conversation, a guard tapped Elisa on the shoulder.

"The renowned Dr. Josef Mengele requests the pleasure of your company at dinner this evening." The guard spoke in a brusque, demanding tone.

Elisa's eyebrows shot upward. Baffled, she tilted her head, looking askance at her new friend, Alma, who narrowed her eyes, assessing the guard's demeanor. Duly noting the machine gun, Alma leaned close to Elisa and whispered, "I don't think you have a choice."

Directing his communication to Elisa, the guard expounded, "A warden will take you to cleansing within the hour and provide appropriate attire. I will call for you at your Block at exactly 5:45 p.m. and then escort you to the officers' dining facility. Dinner is served at six o'clock. Sharp." His instructions delivered, he walked briskly away.

At dinner, Josef Mengele openly ogled the young choir director. He found her physically alluring, especially now, while she was wearing a black slim-cut dress that featured a plunging V-neck. The warden had chosen well for her, he thought, including the light pink head drape that framed her face beautifully. Moreover, she was proving to be delightful company and, thus far, was displaying shockingly perfect dining etiquette.

Shifting in her chair, Elisa noted Mengele's keen observation of her manners. She concluded that he believed all Jews were uncouth. She resolved to show him, to rattle his cage of prejudice, although she yearned to gnaw the bones of the lamb chops to glean the tiny shreds of meat hanging there and to lick her fork for the remaining bits of buttery mashed potatoes—a real meal, the likes of which she not had in years. Yet, with intentional preciseness, Elisa followed each and every decorum rule her high-society parents had taught her.

By the time dessert arrived, Mengele was entranced. And then to discover that Elisa had been singing in chorale groups and playing the piano since she was a young child thrilled his curiosity. Lifting his wine glass, he felt the *unrest* expanding inside him, as he experienced an overwhelming urge to see inside her larynx and its vocal folds, her heart, her brain, her cells, her hands. He yearned to explore her body and find physical evidence of musical talent.

In fact, a deep unrest had been surging in him ever since Zofia Czajkowska had rebuked his dinner invitations. Although he had performed autopsies and chosen random prisoners for experiments, all of which had been enormously satisfying, the unrest continued to intensify.

Tonight, when he was gazing at Elisa, the face of Zofia would appear, out of nowhere, as an overlay. At first, it had been infuriating to him, especially since Elisa was prettier, although she was racially impure: a Jew. Zofia was German and a Catholic, like him. She was racially clean, but she was a political resistor to Hitler's regime. For that, Mengele despised her. Enraged, he silently brooded about her daring to reject him, and then having the audacity to interfere this evening. Then it clicked. This was an intervention of sorts, a magical one like he had experienced years ago with his friend, Diesbach, who had incited his scientific curiosity to such mythic proportion that he felt as if he'd had an encounter similar to Athena visiting Odysseus in the form of a deer. Later, Mengele had wondered if his friend were truly Athena in disguise. Tonight, as Mengele mulled over that memory, it seemed that Athena was speaking to him again. He could have his way with Zofia, after all. Her face on Elisa's face was a sign. They were the same.

Across the table, Elisa returned the crystal water glass to its proper place. An uncomfortable feeling had settled over her. One minute, this man named Dr. Josef Mengele smiled brightly at her, showing keen interest, and the very next, he blinked repeatedly and then glared at her with disdain. Concerned that his eyes now appeared glazed, she asked, "Are you okay?"

"Never better," he replied. "I was just thinking that the evening is young, and I would enjoy showing you my lab. I keep an array of cordials there. We could have a nightcap while I give you a tour."

"That sounds lovely," she replied. "But I have to report for roll call at exactly half past four in the morning and then work."

"Bah! I can make arrangements just like that—" Mengele snapped his fingers in the air. "For you to be late or even absent from roll call and work tomorrow. And with no penalty to you. Come now, be my honored guest."

Stripped naked, Elisa lay atop the autopsy table in the lab located in Block Ten. Hovering over her, Mengele gaped at the sublime thinness of her body, which facilitated his exploratory desires. He smiled, seeing there was no fat to slice through, no fat to slow him down.

When they had first arrived, Elisa had acted tickled with the fancy liqueur glasses, commenting on the incongruity of such in a research laboratory. "I imagined we would imbibe from beakers," she had joked, while he poured her a particular apple brandy that he kept locked in his liquor cabinet. For himself, Mengele chose a shot of Jägermeister.

Sipping the brandy as he showed her around the lab, Elisa had dropped in minutes. Unconscious from the sedation-laced potion, she did not feel the needle of the lethal injection when it plunged into her heart.

Hyper-focused, Mengele picked up the scalpel and made an elongated incision.

Late in the evening, at half past eleven o'clock, whistles blew. Guards entered Block Thirteen and ordered all internees to the square. Roused from deep sleep, Hinda and Rachel dragged themselves from their bunks, as did their Block mates.

Arriving at the square, Hinda experienced a jolt when seeing female prisoners from all Blocks in the women's camp assembling there. Most rubbed their eyes from sleepiness, wondering why they had been summoned. Fearful speculations were whispered: "Was a massacre about to occur? Would a certain number of women be selected for the gas chamber or for beatings?"

Shivering, although the night was balmy, Rachel clung to her sister. "This could be it for us. I'm so afraid they're going to shoot us all, just mow us down like blades of grass."

"We're all scared, Rachel, but it's unlikely they will kill everyone at one time." Hinda tried to reassure her sister, although a knot had formed in her stomach, her instincts on high alert.

After ten minutes, a brigade of soldiers arrived, all toting machine guns. Following the entourage of soldiers, guards wheeled a wooden crate to the center of the square.

An SS officer stepped up to the podium. Using a bullhorn, he announced, "Herr Doctor Mengele has commanded that you pay respects to your choir director. You are hereby ordered to walk past this crate and say your good-byes before her body is taken to the crematorium."

Guards removed the cover to the box, and there the young choir director was, barely recognizable. Flabbergasted and horrified, Hinda and Rachel joined the mandated procession. Women wailed, screamed, sobbed, and gagged as they staggered past the severely mutilated and dismembered body of Elisa Gaensel.

Later, when Zofia Czajkowska was forced to walk past the crate and view the atrocity, she gasped. Aware that Elisa had dined with Mengele earlier that evening, she realized that this could have been her if she had accepted one of his dinner invitations. Chills shook her. She edged over to a nearby tree and retched, aiming her gushes away from the rose bushes underneath it. She questioned how flowers could bloom in such a wicked place. Peering heavenward for answers, she beheld the starry night sky. It was spinning in circles. Just before fainting and falling to the ground, Zofia felt as if Mengele's scalpel were slicing into *her* throat.

74

Evidence

September 1943 | Oświęcim, German-occupied Poland
Auschwitz Concentration Camp

Huddling under the blanket in her bunk, Hinda completed her note to Dr. Walter and folded the paper. She thrust her hand deep into her pants pocket and returned the small pencil and the tiny notepad—items Walter had provided for their secret correspondence—to their hiding place.

The gong to arise for roll call would be sounding soon, but Hinda wanted to savor the warm feeling engendered by writing to him. Having stretched her brain to find expressive words, she hoped Walter would perceive the immense gratitude that she imbued into each syllable she penned. When reading Walter's notes of encouragement to her, she felt his sentiments reach into her soul, buoying her spirit with optimism. Often, he would write: *Stay strong. The war will be over soon.*

Hinda tugged on her lower lip, contemplating Rachel's recent claims: the good doctor was in love with Hinda, and he looked at her sister exactly the way Tatae used to look at Mommy. Rachel also asserted that her sister loved Dr. Walter in return. Hinda did not believe she was *in love* with Walter, although, admittedly, she felt something.

The clanging gong ended her sweet ruminations. Another long day at Budy awaited.

In the early morning dim light, Hinda and Rachel exited Block Thirteen, heading toward the new meeting point on the corner. Rhino no longer came to each barrack; he picked up and dropped off at designated street corners. Rumors claimed that he got in trouble for helping select women in and out of the truck and to their door. Others said it was an administrative decision to reduce gasoline costs. Many asserted that it was merely another way to punish the internees, adding to their twelve-hour workdays, making them walk farther and be exposed to the elements longer.

Encountering a knot of women on the sidewalk, Hinda bent down, pretending to scratch her leg. "Drat, those mosquitos," she fussed. After the women had passed, Rachel tapped Hinda on the back, signaling the sidewalk was clear. Still bending over, Hinda plucked a small piece of paper from underneath a flat-topped rock, while sliding her note under it. Just as she started to stand, she saw someone else on the sidewalk. Quickly, she bent down again, pretending to adjust her shoe. Although it was only thirty seconds, it seemed like minutes before Rachel tapped her back again.

"Did you see that person?" Rachel asked.

"I got a glimpse, and that was enough. Creepy face."

"I couldn't tell if *it* was female or male, a kid or a midget," Rachel retorted.

"Male prisoners and kids are not supposed to be in this area, not unescorted anyway, but I don't care. I want to read today's note before someone else comes along." Hinda unfolded the paper. It was as if she could hear Walter's voice: *Dearest H, Today and always, remember how amazingly strong and beautiful you are. I pray this day gives you at least one reason to smile. You are at the heart of my every thought. Love, W*

"What did he write?" Rachel asked.

Hinda handed her the note.

Rachel's eyes bulged. "He used the word *love*. I told you."

At first, Hinda tried to stifle the emotion that involuntarily curled her lips. But she decided that would be unfair to Walter's prayer. The day had already brought her two reasons to smile. Earlier, she had been surprised by the bubble of joy she felt when writing to him. And now, reading his message to her, she wanted to skip and hop down the sidewalk, even though it was mere steps away from the infamous Killing Wall where condemned prisoners were executed.

Inside the infirmary, Walter peered out his office window. Red and orange hues blazed on the horizon announcing sunset. Studying the varying swathes and streaks, some a blood-red color, he thought of Josef Mengele, and his insatiable desire to mutilate people. The senseless murder of the young choir director had capsized the women's camp, stimulating unrest and self-destruction—a hundred or more bodies found lifeless on the electric fence the following week. Conversely, Josef Mengele whistled happy tunes. Auschwitz Commander, Rudolph Höss, granted Mengele unlimited scope with his research. Any experiments the doctor performed on Jews or on those deemed as misfits were condoned and encouraged, including killing or maiming at his whim. No backlash. No reprimands.

Weary of the barbaric injustices, Walter cast one more glance at the vibrant sunset. Soldier Rhino, who had been the essential cog in Hinda's and his communication system for months, should be arriving soon to deliver today's message. Walter smiled, anticipating reading Hinda's words, which was the highlight of his evenings. Reaching into his lab coat pocket to reread his note to her, prepared earlier that morning, he found only a tongue depressor for examining patients. He searched the other pocket. Nothing. His face blanched pale. Tossing the tongue depressor in the trash, he turned the pocket inside out. White threads hanging from the stitched seam were its only contents. He shuffled through papers atop his desk. No note. Tugging on the center drawer, he pulled it forward as far it would go and retrieved a small notepad. He ran his fingers through his hair as he thought, *I distinctly remember tearing it from this pad, folding it, and placing it in my lab coat pocket.*

Recalling that he had removed the jacket while eating lunch in the kitchen, he leapt forward. With the quickness of a spooked cat, Walter bounded around the corner and immediately bumped into Benjamin, Number 81264, a prisoner newly assigned to work in the infirmary. Such proximity magnified the man's unusual appearance. He had a facial disfigurement, a cleft lip. And then, his deep-set eyes, paired with sunken cheeks, caused the man's pointy nose to appear as a beak of a bird. Even though Walter experienced a peculiar uneasiness around Benjamin, he felt sorry for the guy, who not only had a cleft lip but also appeared as a young boy, even though he was thirty-two years old. From what Walter could determine, the man's stature combined with a short torso were characteristic of a condition called disproportionate dwarfism.

Walter worried, knowing that if Mengele came into the infirmary and saw Benjamin, he would immediately take him for experiments in the name of genetic research. Of this, Walter was certain. Mengele's second doctoral dissertation was about the hereditary factors of oral cleft. What's more, Walter knew for a fact that Mengele had set up a second lab in the Gypsy camp and was researching growth anomalies—dwarfism and giantism. Mengele had confided that, in addition to gaining information on the genetics of these conditions, he was collaborating with Verschuer, the head of the Kaiser Wilhelm Institute of Anthropology, to discover how to purge them from the Aryan race. Walter remembered how Mengele had then chuckled and said that, after Germany won the war, he hoped to write a post-doctoral thesis using all his research from Auschwitz. Walter had then realized that Mengele was focused on academic advancement and was not interested in medicine, only science, as he called his racial, genetic research.

Having accidentally knocked Benjamin against the wall, Walter said, "I'm so sorry, Benjamin. I thought you'd already gone for the day."

Benjamin, who held a broom and dustpan, eyed the clock on the wall. "Since I was delayed this morning, I wanted to stay later to make up the time. And earlier, I saw dead spiders on the floor around your office window. I wanted to sweep them up before I left."

"Dead spiders aren't going anywhere. First thing in the morning is fine." Walter reached for the broom and dustpan. "I'll take those. You hurry on so you don't miss roll call and the guard escort back to the men's camp. Consequences are too severe."

Tightening his grip on the broom, Benjamin scowled at Walter. Moments passed, then he said, "Yes, sir," and handed over the cleaning tools.

"Go now. Don't be late." Walter pointed to the rear staff exit down the hallway. "I'll lock the door behind you." He followed Benjamin only a few steps when the buzzer to the front door rang two times, one right after the other. Walter pressed Benjamin to hasten his pace. When the man's pants leg had barely cleared the threshold, Walter yanked the door tight and locked it. After leaving the broom and dustpan in the utility closet, Walter jogged toward the front door.

The front buzzer sounded again four times in succession. Walter mumbled, "Must be a really sick patient, or Mengele has misplaced his key." Unlatching the door, Walter sighed in relief to see Soldier Rhino.

Stomping into the entry hall, Rhino grunted their code, "Bees stinging today?"

"No bee stings," Walter replied, indicating he was alone. "What's wrong?" Unaccustomed to his friend acting agitated and impatient, Walter's eyebrows raised in concern.

"There's no note from Hinda today. Nothing was under the rock."

Walter crossed his arms. "Hmph. Well, she either didn't write one or couldn't leave it without being seen. It's happened before. But that's not why you're upset."

"I've been transferred to the men's camp." Rhino blurted out the words, his forehead wrinkled in a scowl.

"What assignment?" Walter asked, his throat suddenly feeling dry.

"The same paperwork, but I'll be transporting men, instead of women, to and from Budy. Completely different route from the men's camp to those remote fields. I won't be driving by here every morning and night anymore. And you know what that means."

His fingers raking through his hair, Walter exhaled heavily. "Yes, I do."

"I can still take your note for tomorrow, though," Rhino offered.

"I had it ready. But now, I can't find it. Take a seat in my office while I check the kitchen for it." Walter raced down the hallway.

Rhino eased himself into a chair in Walter's office. His bulky body filled the frame. He leaned forward, an elbow on one knee, his thumb and forefinger stroking his chin.

Stomping into the room, Walter complained, "My note to Hinda was not in the kitchen."

"Sorry to hear that." Nodding to Walter, Rhino said, "Doc, I've been thinking. Something about this transfer doesn't feel right."

Sighing loudly, Walter plopped down in his desk chair. "Agreed. It *is* unusual for Auschwitz staff or military to be transferred unless they've requested it. Though, administration rotates prisoner jobs quite often."

"Yeah, to keep guards and staff from getting attached or showing favor. And that's what worries me." Rhino rubbed the back of his neck as if it ached. "There's a policewoman at Budy that has it in for me. She's been circling me like a vulture these past few months. Ever since the day I stopped her from further injuring Hinda and Rachel."

"But would she have the authority to get you transferred?"

"Not the authority, but she could have complained to higher ups, like a *snitch witch*." Rhino squirmed in his chair. "Her stalking me is the reason I had to stop passing your notes to Hinda at the vegetable garden."

"And that's when we went to Plan B, hiding them under the rock." Walter reached for his notepad. "I must let Hinda know that my communication will be intermittent now."

"Good idea." Rhino stretched, noting the intense expression on Walter's face. To keep himself from overtly staring at Walter, Rhino glanced around the room. A glint from behind the drapery caught his eye. He sprang from the chair and jerked the curtain back. "What the heck? How did this get here?"

Walter turned in his chair. Then, he stood up. His hands on his hips, his mouth agape, Walter exclaimed, "Is that what I think it is?"

"Yep. It's our rock. See its flat top. I chose one that was markedly different from the others on that sidewalk."

"How can you be certain it's the same one?" Walter asked.

Rhino flipped over the rock. "I scratched an X on the bottom." He held it out for Walter to see.

Knitting his brows in suspicion, Walter jerked the other side of the drapery back. Examining the floor in front of the window, he said, "There are no dead spiders here."

"What do spiders have to do with this?"

"The new guy, Benjamin. After it was time for him to leave today, I bumped into him as he was coming in here to sweep up dead spiders, or so he said. And this morning, he came in late and walking funny, like he was carrying something heavy in his uniform." Walter slammed his fist on the desk. "I've had a weird feeling about him from the moment I met him, but I let sympathy cloud my judgment."

"You think he's the one who put the rock here in your office?"

"Yes, I do. To hide it for the day."

"But why your office? Seems like the utility closet would be a better hiding place."

"For sure. But when he arrived this morning, I was in that closet getting cleaning supplies to sanitize the bed and counter after treating a flu patient. Ordinarily, I would have asked Benjamin to do it, but he was tardy. Then, I found him in my office. He claimed he was emptying the trash. But I'm betting that he decided to dump the rock before he was caught with it. Probably planned to move it later."

Rhino twisted his lips to the left and ran his fingers across the hollow indentation on the right side of his jowl. "Is he small? I mean, like a midget?"

"Yes, he has dwarfism. Why?"

"Someone fitting that description was there this morning when I arrived to get Hinda's note. The person's small size puzzled me. I knew it couldn't be a kid in that area, so I decided it was an ultra-petite woman from the gypsy camp. If it was him, he was over by the Killing Wall, his hand pressed against it. I waited in my truck until he moved on. Then I checked the rock, but nothing was there."

"Hmph. Maybe Hinda did leave a note this morning, and he took it," Walter speculated.

"The guy probably lifted it before I got there. Then, after I left, he seized the rock."

"I wager that he also stole the note I wrote this morning. Then, he would have two notes and a rock to turn in or sell as evidence."

"He's minus the rock. But, Doc, it's here, which is a bad sign. If he has the two notes, we will be swimming in scalding water, and soon."

Feeling lightheaded, like he might pass out, Walter bowed his head and made the sign of the cross—sequentially touching his fingertips to his forehead, his heart, his right shoulder, and his left shoulder. "Blessed Mother of Mercy, God help us." He bit his lower lip, subduing quivers. "The Nazis will kill Hinda. If they haven't already."

75

Lavish Pleasures

September 1943 | Weimar, Germany
Buchenwald Concentration Camp

Holding ten-inch nails between his teeth, Wolf Yoskowitz plucked the hammer from the tool belt that hung from his waist. The rickety ladder he stood upon leaned against studs of the framed interior. Next to him, Joseph hoisted up a nine-by-twelve squared timber, placing it close to the adjacent rafter. He held it there while Wolf hammered multiple nails at sixteen-inch intervals, securing the beam in place. Guards, who yelled threats to hurry them, stood below, overseeing the two brothers' every action.

The entire construction site crawled with workers and frenzied guards, all striving to accommodate Commander Pister's demands that the pavilion be completed within the next twenty-four hours. Rushing the job was no excuse for sloppy workmanship. Pister required excellence at every step.

High-ranking, Third Reich guests—Heinrich Himmler and Joseph Goebbels —were due to arrive on Friday to celebrate the railway that had been laid from the Weimar station to Buchenwald. Accomplished in unprecedented time, using internees as slave laborers, the rail connected the camp to the freight yards in Weimar—a boon to Buchenwald's quarry.

Disgruntled that only a small loading platform marked the Buchenwald terminus, Pister had conceived the pavilion plan a mere five days ago. In the next breath, he decided to build his concept—a station-like portico and a covered walkway for guests to use when exiting the passenger car. To have it completed by Thursday, he instructed camp supervisors to organize hundreds of prisoners to work on the short-term project. Demanding precision, he asked all supervisors to select their most skilled laborers and to remain present on-site with them. Wolf and Joseph had been pulled from the quarry to work on the pavilion. The job demanded eighteen-hour days and allowed only five hours of sleep a night.

After double-checking that the beam had been buttressed properly, Wolf descended the ladder just as a whistle blew three times in succession. Wolf called up to his brother, "Finally. Our turn for lunch."

In a halting gait, Joseph followed, taking one ladder rung at a time. His right kneecap had been fractured, the patella bone crushed, in the brutal beating that Wolf and he had endured in June. Wolf had survived with no apparent permanent damage, although it had been weeks before his soreness and deep bruising were diminished. Joseph still suffered the effects, walking with a pronounced limp.

Wolf rushed to the queue. He had been astonished the last two days to be served sausage rolls instead of the usual lunch of bread and coffee. No illusions of humanity, he knew it was all about Pister impressing the Third Reich's top brass. And to do so, Pister's blueprint must be flawlessly executed in record time. In the first two days on the project, dozens of men could not hold up to the heavy labor requirements. Their dead bodies were now stacked high, like kindling for a bonfire, behind the construction site.

Pister then realized that training replacements was wasting precious time. Just as engines require gasoline to work, he had reasoned, slaves require fuel for maximum output. To facilitate the speedy completion of his prized pavilion, he ordered meaty lunches for the workers. Smirking, he had instructed the kitchen cooks, "Make sausage rolls. Pork ones."

Hyper-focused on the progression of the pavilion, Pister checked continually on all aspects of construction. He shouted commands from the saddle of his black stallion. Fixated also on the planning of Himmler's and Goebbels' upcoming visit, Pister's brain worked overtime, tweaking to-do lists and making mental notes on their accommodations and entertainment. He had alerted the warden of the officers' bordello to prepare the women for entertaining premier guests. Buchenwald's only female prisoners, the brothel women had been commanded to bathe daily that week, to shampoo and style their hair, and to oil their skin. The warden reported that new, seductive lingerie was due to arrive tomorrow. The hotel and casino were being readied too. Chandeliers were being cleaned, silver was being polished, and bedsheets were being ironed. Fine wines, liquors, exotic fish, and specialty meats were on their way. No cost would be spared for the fanfare and celebration that Pister envisioned. Due to the stunning success of Buchenwald's quarry, dubbed as one of the most profitable enterprises in the SS, the camp could afford the price tag of providing lavish pleasures for these top Nazi leaders. Pister's chest puffed with pride.

Goading his stallion, Pister circled the lunch groups. In the cluster of workers standing next to Wolf, a man heaved and gagged, vomiting foaming sausage bits onto the grass. Within seconds, bullets popped into him, and he dropped. Two other men standing near him fell from ammo gone astray.

Regurgitating equaled sickness; the penalty was death. Fighting was on par with disrespect; the penalty was death. Wolf suspected that many of the men working on this job intentionally picked fights or stuck their fingers down their throats to be released from the harsh torment that never ceased. Their method of suicide.

Amidst all the ruckus, Pister reined his stallion near where Wolf and Joseph were standing. Pointing directly at them, he yelled, "You two, move those bodies to the back. And clean up this mess."

Wolf immediately said, "Yes, sir." He stuffed the lunch rolls into his pocket and motioned for Joseph to follow.

Upon seeing Joseph hobbling, Pister bellowed, "He's a cripple. Shoot him."

Guards drew their guns, aiming at Joseph, ready to slaughter him.

Wolf's eyes doubled their size, immobilized in wide-open shock mode. Not a single blink fluttered his eyelashes, but his pulse skyrocketed, causing his heart to flutter and skip beats.

Unexpectedly, the head supervisor for the quarry stepped between Joseph and the armed guards. He shouted, "Commander Pister, sir, with all due respect, these two boys are my best team in the quarry and have been for over two years. Production and profits will be compromised if I lose one of them."

Pister scowled at the supervisor. "Even in that condition?"

"Yes, sir. He's remarkable and dependable."

"Stand down," Pister barked at the guards. To Joseph, he bellowed, "I've got my eye on you, Jew boy. If you don't maintain a high performance, it will be *death by boot* for you."

76
Pitch Black

October 1943 | Oświęcim, German-occupied Poland
Auschwitz Concentration Camp

In the warden's office located in Block Thirteen, the hour hand on the wall clock shifted, pointing to the numeral one—1:00 a.m. The warden arose from her chair and went to a specific bunk. She grabbed the collar of Hinda's uniform, shaking her awake. "Get up, 25305, you slut. You're being moved to a different block."

Sleep crusted in her eyes, Hinda jumped from the bunk. "Moved? Why?"

"Because you've been a bad girl, passing love notes to the good Dr. Walter."

"I. I. They weren't love notes," Hinda stuttered.

"Don't argue with me." The warden tugged on the whip attached to her belt.

Jerking awake, Rachel cried, "What's happening?"

"Your bunk mate is being punished, moving to Block Eleven."

Terror shot through Hinda, like sky-to-earth lightning bolts electrifying her jagged nerves. Block Eleven was known as the most vicious Block in Auschwitz. Worse, it was the Block where Dr. Mengele selected internees for his experiments. Next door to Mengele's lab that was located in Block Ten, Block Eleven had become known as *The Waiting Room*.

Sobbing, Rachel said, "Take me too. I must be with my sister."

"Please, can she come too?" Hinda pleaded.

The warden scoffed, "Sisters, are you? Well, little one, let's see how much your big sister loves you." She withdrew her whip and began flogging Hinda, striking her repeatedly. After ten hits that had knocked Hinda to the floor, she said, "Do you still want your sister to move with you?"

Writhing and moaning, Hinda choked out the words, "Yes, please."

Proceeding to whip Hinda again, the warden struck her hard another six times. "And now, have you changed your mind?"

Yelping like she was the one taking the beating, Rachel pleaded, "Please stop. I'll stay here in Block Thirteen."

"Shut your mouth. I didn't ask you."

Sucking in air, Hinda asserted, "My mind is the same. Please, I'll do whatever you say for my sister to go with me."

Squinting her eyes, the warden gawked at Hinda, stretching seconds into a protracted minute. Then, she threw her head back and crowed, "Begging for your little sister to go to the worst prison in the women's camp, are you? Well, why not? Okay with me if you both go to the Block of Punishment."

When the sisters stumbled into Block Eleven, the chief guard scowled and said, "It's about time." Signaling them to remain quiet, she showed Hinda and Rachel to their sleeping area. Relief lit the sisters' eyes; they would be sharing the bunk together, just the two of them.

Expecting to crawl into the bunk and return to sleep, Hinda sat down, rubbing the bloody welts on her legs from the whipping she had sustained. The guard raised her open palm and slapped Hinda across the face. "You're in Block Eleven now. There will be none of that. Both of you, come with me." She ushered them to a back room where a policewoman was in charge. Winking at the policewoman, the guard pushed Rachel, then Hinda toward her.

The policewoman kicked Hinda, shoving her to a table that had handcuffs dangling from its end. After handcuffing Hinda to the table, she directed Rachel to a wooden box on the side. "Put your feet inside this box," she commanded. One foot at a time, Rachel stepped inside the wooden structure. The woman then secured Rachel's feet with chains, and barked, "Stretch your body across this table."

The flogging table, called the Goat, easily accommodated Rachel's petite frame. The woman withdrew her whip. "Okay, Jude girl, you must count each lash aloud. If you get a number wrong at any time, we'll start over. As many times as it takes to get to twenty. And after each one, you say the correct number plus the words *received with many thanks*. Let's practice." She lashed at Rachel, who cried, "One, received with many thanks." She struck her again. Rachel groaned, "Two, received with many thanks."

"Smart animal. You've got it. So, here we go, starting over at one."

After the fifteenth lash, Rachel faltered, getting the number wrong. The whole sequence began anew.

Hinda winced with every blow Rachel endured, which was thirty-seven in total, counting the two practice ones. Inwardly, she prayed, *Dear God, I was so stupid and selfish, begging for Rachel to be allowed to come with me to Block Eleven. Please forgive me.*

Back at their bunk, the sisters prepared for bed. Hinda stroked Rachel's arm, asking for her forgiveness. Rachel would hear none of it. "That flogging nearly killed me," she complained. "But I'm with *you*, my sister. That's what matters most to me."

At precisely three o'clock in the morning, the same policewoman approached the bunk. She yelled, "Number 25305, get up."

Hinda arose, and the woman grabbed her by the collar, hauling her away. "Off you go to the *Stehbunker* in cell twenty-two. You'll be there for two nights." The policewoman jeered at Hinda, "That is, if you survive the first."

Hinda had heard hair-raising stories about the Stehbunker—a standing stall. Nevertheless, when she entered it, wriggling her way through the hatch in the floor, she panicked. Entirely windowless, it had one tiny vent for air. And the vent grate had been covered with a perforated sheet to further restrict air flow.

The policewoman adjusted the sliding walls to fit Prisoner 25305 before locking them in place. Hinda's back was pushed against a wooden wall, and her face was smashed against the front wall. Completely closed in on all sides, Hinda was forced into a standing position.

"The countdown of your forty-eight hours begins now." The policewoman announced through a wall speaker that blared into Hinda's ear.

Swallowing hard, her throat already dry, Hinda knew that neither food nor water would be provided. Choking back screams, she prayed, asking for God's help in programming her mind to endure this punishment and to survive the next forty-eight hours.

High-pitch noises screeched through the speaker again. The policewoman's scratchy voice squawked, "Before I turn out the lights, there's something you should know as you contemplate your wrongdoing. Your lover boy, Dr. Walter, has been banished from Auschwitz. His punishment takes place underground; he is now a slave laborer in a coal mine. And he will be, forevermore. Because of you."

A clicking sound preceded the darkness. The standing stall turned pitch black. And so did the light in Hinda's spirit.

77

Höss vs. Hössler

October 1943 | Oświęcim, German-occupied Poland
Auschwitz Concentration Camp

Soldier Rhino zipped up his packed duffel bag. With one hand, he flung it onto the floor near the door. Plunking down in the chair, he reached to the side table for the official papers addressed to Arno Rhinehardt, his legal name. He had read the document multiple times. Still, his finger traced under each sentence of the military directive assigning him to an assault troop, a specified tank battalion, in Western Russia. The directive was clear. There was no escaping it. He was headed to the front line.

His eyes fixed on the floor, Rhino relived the captain's interrogation of him. "No, definitely not," he had answered. "I'm not in love with, nor have I had physical relations with 25306 (Rachel), and not with 25305 (Hinda) either."

The captain had grilled him, asking why then did he get involved, giving the women salve, requesting a softer work transfer after one had influenza, and committing willful acts of hiding and delivering forbidden notes for Walter Zeilhofen? Badgering him, the captain pushed Rhino to confess other wrong-doings involving medical treatments that would aid and abet Dr. Walter's plans. Getting nowhere, the captain returned to the subject of Hinda and Rachel. Finally relenting, the captain said, "You seem certain that you're not infatuated or in love with either of those two female inmates. How are you so sure?"

"Because I care for someone else."

"And who would that be?" the captain asked, his eyebrows lowered in suspicion.

"A girl back home. We're engaged to be married."

"My gut says you're lying," the captain retorted. He squinted hard at Soldier Rhino. "But that doesn't matter now. We have enough evidence to convict you, but we've decided on another strategy for you." The captain handed him an envelope. "Pack your bags, Rhinehardt. You're being transferred to a post in the Pskov Oblast region, near Nevel in Western Russia. German troops there are fighting to stave off the Russians from further encroachment after our losing the Battle of Stalingrad. There will be no women, certainly no female Jews, to feel sorry for and coddle there. You'll be battling for the Homeland and for your very life."

Rhino could not let go of those last words. Yet, he felt relief, recognizing that he had escaped death on this very day because his captain had not discovered the truth about him. It was treasonous enough to be an inside resistor to the regime as he was. And then, there was the other issue his captain would find intolerable: it was not a girl back home whom he loved.

In Nazi Germany, homosexuals were considered social misfits and subhuman aberrations who were sent to concentration camps or to the gas chamber. More importantly, the German military judged homosexuality as criminal. Rhino clearly understood that he would have been executed had his captain learned the name of the person he loved even more than himself: Dr. Walter Zeilhofen.

In the conference room adjacent to Commander Höss' office, a self-important aura surrounded those who waited for the meeting to commence. Dr. Eduard Wirths, Auschwitz's chief physician, sat at one end of the rectangular table. Dr. Josef Mengele, who tapped his fingers impatiently, occupied the chair to Wirths' left. Near the opposite end of the table, Auschwitz Commandant, Rudolph Höss, stood gazing out the window. The multi-hued autumn landscape, which Höss typically enjoyed this time of year, incited his annoyance today. Tree leaves were changing colors, and his life would soon shift along with them.

The door opened and the women's camp director, Franz Hössler, entered. "Sorry to keep you waiting. A guard dispute detained me." Hössler carried two folders. One he placed on the table in front of his chair, and the second, he pushed toward the empty chair at the other end of the table.

Commander Höss swaggered to his seat near the window. He opened the folder and glanced at the first page. "What do you have on Zeilhofen?"

"No actual crime that we can document. His amorous affection for a Jew is the most egregious offense we have on him. He admits that he fell in love with 25305, a female prisoner. He's not the only officer who has done such with other women inmates." Franz Hössler fixed his stare directly upon Commander Höss.

Shifting in his chair, Rudolph Höss felt the heat rising, traveling up his neck into his face. He clenched and unclenched his hands, yearning to punch Franz Hössler so hard that his teeth flew from his mouth. Reining in his anger, Höss asked in an even tone, "Did Zeilhofen have sexual relations with 25305?"

"Sir, I can speak to that," Dr Wirths interjected. "My brother, as you know, is the camp's gynecologist. I asked him to examine the woman. He reported that her hymen was intact. She is a virgin."

"The same was true for Number 25306, her sister." Franz Hössler added. "I requested that she be checked to either disprove or corroborate Soldier Rhinehardt's testimony."

Commander Höss scowled, "Sister? It's our policy to separate families."

Shrugging his shoulders, Director Hössler said, "We've only discovered their kinship in this investigation. They look nothing alike, but we're not sure how they slipped past our notice at Selection. The two have not been a problem until now."

"How old are these women?" Commander Höss asked.

After checking his folder, Hössler replied, "Number 25305 is twenty-two, and her sister is sixteen."

"Young. Are they carrying their fair share of work?" Höss probed.

"Report says both are highly productive, especially the older one," Hössler replied.

Höss nodded. "And when did their gynecological examinations take place?"

"This morning, sir," Dr. Wirths answered. "We removed 25305 from arrest in the Stehbunker but returned her there afterward. The warden adjusted the clock accordingly for her to serve the full forty-eight hours consecutively, uninterrupted—as per Director Hössler's orders."

"Fine," Höss replied. "And what about the investigation into unauthorized medications Zeilhofen allegedly administered to 25305?"

Dr. Wirths rubbed his forehead as if he suffered a headache. "Mengele and I have gone over the infirmary records multiple times. We can find no violations. We've counted all restricted pharmaceuticals. Inventory matches the written records. And those registers align exactly with patient data."

Shifting his weight in his chair, Commander Höss, said, "What's your recommendation for Zeilhofen, going forward?"

Josef Mengele spoke up. "As you know, Commander, I recruited Walter. He's an excellent diagnostician, and overall, an exemplary doctor, though he has many cowardly weaknesses that I loathe. And it's unacceptable to me that he loves a Jew. According to the Nuremberg law, Protection of German Blood and German Honor, race defilement—sexual relations between an Aryan and a Jew—is a criminal act. Should there be proof of Walter engaging in any sexual activity with this Jew or giving her restricted medications, I believe the relationship should be classified as treasonous, and Zeilhofen should be hanged."

Wirths raised his thick eyebrows, creasing his forehead up to his receding hairline. "Since Director Hössler has presented no additional evidence this afternoon, I will stick with my earlier assessment. I recommend that Zeilhofen be removed from the infirmary and placed in solitary confinement for thirty-six hours, no food, no water. Zeilhofen is an excellent doctor, so I propose that after his chastisement, he be transferred to the officers' hospital. Lastly, he is forbidden to have any contact or communication with Jewish prisoners 25305 and 25306. If he violates that order, he will be executed."

Höss rubbed his chin. "Okay, I agree with the recommendations for Zeilhofen. Solitary confinement, then a transfer to the officers' hospital. Apprise him of his restrictive orders and resulting consequences should he violate them. And what about 25305, what has she been told of Zeilhofen's punishment?"

The corners of Hössler's mouth turned slightly upward. "She was told that Dr. Walter was sent to work underground. To a coal mine where the doctor will slave away for the rest of his life."

"Excellent." The commander's eyes flared with Machiavellian delight. He flipped through the papers in the folder. Then, he leaned forward. "And what reward did prisoner 81264 receive for turning in the evidence?"

"The bird-faced, rabbit-lipped dwarf got a whole loaf of bread. Stale and a bit moldy." Franz Hössler grinned widely.

Poised to rise from his chair, Mengele asked, "Rabbit-lipped?"

"I guess the right term is harelipped," Hössler replied.

Mengele cleared his throat loudly. "The correct medical term, Director, is cleft lip. My second doctoral dissertation was on the hereditary factors on oral cleft abnormalities. Furthermore, I am exploring growth anomalies, both dwarfism and giantism right here at Auschwitz. This unusual combination of cleft lip and dwarfism is perfect for my genetic research. You may remember that Rudolph Hess, Hitler's deputy, once said that Nazism is applied biology. For racial hygiene purposes, I must take this man to my lab for examination and testing."

Scowling, Hössler barked, "Genetic research or not, hands off, Mengele. He's a valuable informant. I have more jobs for him."

Rocking back in his chair, Commander Höss glowered at Franz Hössler, the man he wished he could castrate for reporting his adulterous affair to Hitler's right-hand man, Heinrich Himmler. Ordinarily, Hitler did not object to his team having sexual relationships outside of marriage. But this woman, Eleonore Hodys, was a German political prisoner who the regime held in contempt.

Nevertheless, her extraordinary beauty and hour-glass figure had been irresistible to Höss. And now, he awaited official communication of his fate.

Franz Hössler was unaware that Himmler had recently spoken with Commander Höss, alerting him to his potential transfer from Auschwitz and confirming that it was Director Hössler who had squealed. Moreover, upon hearing the description of prisoner 81264, Höss recalled a dwarf who had a cleft lip and beaked nose cleaning the quarters he kept solely for rendezvous with Eleonore. The puzzle was unraveling. Prisoner 81264 was who Franz Hössler had exploited to garner evidence on his extramarital activity.

A satisfied sneer rippling his lips, Höss said, "Number 81264 is an inmate in the men's camp, which is not in your jurisdiction, Hössler. Only the business of the women's camp falls under your domain. Mengele can do whatever he wants with the misfit." Rapping the table with his knuckles, he snarled, "I'm still the head boss here."

Mengele leapt from his chair. "Thank you, Commander Höss. Please excuse me." A gleam in his eye, Josef Mengele strode from the room, closing the door behind him.

Franz Hössler rose from his chair, preparing to follow Mengele and stop him from abducting 81264 (Benjamin).

"Sit down, Hössler. This meeting is not adjourned yet. Not for you, anyway. I have another matter to discuss with you and Wirths." Plucking a cigar from his pocket, Commander Höss slowly lit it, taking his time to savor the look of utter shock emblazoned on Hössler's face. Vaporous wisps of cigar smoke whirled in the air of the small room.

Turning his head away from the cigar fumes, Dr. Wirths looked in the direction of Franz Hössler, where he saw a different sort of fuming. Wirths grimaced. The two men were waging personal war, and today, he was caught in their crossfire.

Pointing to Wirths, Commander Höss said, "Before we move on to the other business, what time this morning did 25305 have her vaginal exam?"

"Around ten o'clock, sir."

"And what time did she first go into the Stehbunker?" The commander looked to Franz Hössler to answer.

Hössler could barely speak. His lips twisted with rage as he managed to say, "Three a.m."

His eyes narrowing, Commander Höss duly noted the lack of respect. Hössler had not added the usual title of *sir* or *commander* to that statement, or any others of his, when addressing him during the entire meeting. That was a green light to proceed with his plan to further enrage and undermine the director of the women's camp who, to Höss, was a tattletale weasel.

"Let's see now." Höss tilted his head back on his neck, calculating hours. "That timeline would put 25305 in the standing stall for nine hours or so initially. And let's say, after seeing the gynecologist, she returned at eleven o'clock. It's now four o'clock. That's another six hours. Fifteen, total." Abruptly, the commander pushed his chair back and stomped to the front of the room, where he picked up the receiver of the rotary phone. Using the finger-hole marked 0, he dialed the switchboard operator. "Connect me with Block Eleven, cell twenty-two." While waiting, he took a long draw on his cigar and then blew perfect smoke rings toward the ceiling.

Static roared on the line, then a female voice said, "Cell twenty-two, Freida speaking."

"Freida, it's Commander Höss here. Release 25305 from the Stehbunker now. My orders. This sentence of punishment has been commuted. But she is to remain in Block Eleven. Understand?"

"Yes, sir, Commander Höss, I copy. May I ask if Director Hössler has been informed?"

"He is in the room with me now. If he's listening, he has been notified."

78
Stark Naked

In Block Eleven, the gong clanged at precisely half past four in the morning, rousing the female prisoners. Wardens and guards stomped through the aisles, whacking inmates with sticks. To avoid the painful prod to arise, Hinda and Rachel staggered from their bunk and shuffled outdoors to use the latrine. Causing dread in and of itself, the toilet constituted narrow wooden slats laid across a deep ditch.

Balanced precariously on a plank, the sisters squatted next to each other. Women crowded in close on both sides of them. Guards shouted, urging everyone to hurry, showing no respect for the time necessary to properly empty bladders and bowels.

A woman who suffered dysentery parked next to Hinda. Her bodily fluids splashed and spattered onto Hinda, soiling her uniform and contaminating her skin with foul-smelling fecal matter. The first time it happened, Hinda had gagged, vomiting into the trench, almost falling from the plank into deep excrement. Now, it seemed an everyday occurrence. Nothing to wipe or clean with was ever dispensed—no paper, no towels, no soap. Odious odors sheathed the female inmates like a noxious nimbus that shadowed them wherever they went.

The dark sky, without a single streak of sunlight, intensified the dreadful latrine experience and the frigid temperature. Wintery weather had arrived, and so had it settled into Hinda's heart. Aching for contact with Walter, she sorely missed his caring and encouraging notes. Tormenting visions of what abuse Walter was enduring in the coal mine swirled in her head—blustering snowstorms in her psyche.

The whistle for roll call blared. Hinda and Rachel discontinued their toilet functions. Desperate to get in the line on time, they willed their bodies to move quickly. If they were tardy for roll call, even one second late, they would be whipped until they bled.

After getting in the correct roll-call queue, Hinda blanched pale as panic invaded her body. Her entrails looped like roller coasters, tangling together, and tying tight knots. Three SS officers stood at attention next to the wardens and guards who typically presided over morning attendance check. The last time this SS line-up occurred at roll call, ten inmates were randomly selected to be hanged.

After one hour, when prisoner attendance had been completed satisfactorily, one of the SS officers dressed in a formal black uniform stepped to the podium to address the group. "Tomorrow, honored guests will be visiting the women's camp and inspecting all Blocks. Instead of going to your usual work today, you are to clean your Block, scouring it well from top to bottom. After your Block has passed inspection, your group is to gather back here in the roll call area. You will remove your prisoner uniform for cleansing, and then stand at attention until the time that your uniform is returned to you. Now, get to work."

Later, in the bleak afternoon hours, a frigid wind raised goose bumps on Hinda's flesh. Stark naked, standing ten paces apart at rigid attention, the women in Block Eleven had been waiting for what seemed like two hours for their uniforms. The sun was soon to set, lowering already chilly temperatures. Hinda reflected back on her time in the standing stall. Every muscle in her feet, legs, back, and neck had throbbed and ached unbearably, as they were beginning to now. Today, it was the cold and being naked that gave rise to the feeling of palpable vulnerability. There, it was being locked into an unyielding standing position and utter darkness that had ignited intense powerlessness. Moreover, the policewoman's blistering words about Walter's fate had cast a poisonous spell upon her as surely as if she had been thrown into a witch's cauldron of boiling potion.

When daylight dimmed to dusk, wardens and guards marched down the rows, returning the washed uniforms, folded, but still damp. When a guard came to Hinda, she checked her tattoo, and then said, "Here you go, 25305." Before handing the uniform to Hinda, she puckered her mouth and spit into the interior part of the jacket. "That's for the good Dr. Walter. Shame on you, ruining his life like that."

In the early morning hours of the following day, Commander Höss escorted Third Reich aristocracy—Heinrich Himmler and Arthur Liebehenschel—into Block Eleven. Höss gruffly greeted the women, who saluted him and said, 'Heil Hitler,' as they had been ordered to do.

The men looked around the Block, eyeing the clean conditions and the bunks stoked full of fresh hay. After the brief tour, Commander Höss stood at the front of the room. His voice thundered, "You Jews are privileged to live here in this tidy and comfortable Block. Yet, you are still ungrateful for all the good that we, the Nazi regime, are doing for you animals. It's appalling, and I'm certain your new commander has noticed the unappreciative looks on your faces. Yes, you have a new commander. I have been promoted to a higher position back in Germany. So today, I pass the baton to Commander Liebehenschel."

Arthur Liebehenschel scanned the group of women as he stepped forward. "I am honored to be appointed the new commander of Auschwitz, but I am not happy with what I see here in Block Eleven today. Because of your selfish and ungrateful attitudes, when you return this evening, you will get no soup or bread, and you will each receive ten lashes. Now, get on with the day's work."

79

Saving Two Lives

November 1943 | Oświecim, German-occupied Poland
Auschwitz Concentration Camp

In the officer's hospital, Walter Zeilhofen tread down the hallway, making morning rounds on the second floor. When he neared room 206, the very room he had recently occupied as a patient for two full weeks, he paused. Recollections of almost dying flashed through his mind. When he was initially jailed in solitary confinement as punishment for falling in love with Hinda, he had no clue that he was borderline diabetic. The thirty-six-hour sentence decreed that he was to be deprived of food and water, which elevated his blood sugar to a dangerous level of hyperglycemia. The guard, who came to release him, found him unconscious, in a diabetic coma.

Shaking off the morbid memories, Walter moved on down the hallway. Noting his flagging energy levels, he questioned Dr. Wirths' judgment to schedule him for full-time duty on his first week back.

A rustling sound from behind him startled Walter. He turned to see a nurse rushing toward him. She panted, out of breath from running.

"Didn't you hear us paging you?"

"No. I did not. What do you need?" Walter replied.

"Dr. Wirths has called for you to come to his office at once. He says it's an emergency."

Walter's mouth fell agape. His hand flew to his abdomen, resting there. "You are asking me to perform an abortion?"

Dr. Wirths sat behind his desk, leaning forward, an urgency evident in his tone. "Yes, Zeilhofen, I am. Except, I'm not asking. I'm *ordering* you to do it."

Walter's fingers raked through his hair. "But I'm not a gynecologist; I have no experience. What about your brother? What about Mengele? He would be delighted with such a process."

Sighing heavily, Wirths replied, "My brother and Mengele are in Frankfurt this week. And this must be done today. Orders from Commander Höss."

"I thought Liebehenschel was now the lead commander of Auschwitz, as of today."

"He is, and he signed the order that Höss had originally issued. The woman —Eleonore Hodys, a German political prisoner—who has been confined in the Stehbunker for the last thirty-two hours, is mandated to have the abortion today, and it's to be completed before Höss departs this afternoon. While in the standing stall, she hasn't ingested solids or liquids, which makes it timely to administer anesthesia. As for the steps of the procedure, my brother will instruct you over the phone."

Walter slumped against the chair. "I am Catholic. Abortion is against my beliefs, my moral code."

"First and foremost, Zeilhofen, you are a Nazi. Your religion and morals matter not at all." Wirths grimaced. He was expecting ready cooperation from Walter, not argumentative resistance. Wirths' eyes narrowed, studying Walter's inimical expression. Then it clicked, and he had a clear memory of Josef Mengele confiding that he seriously questioned Walter Zeilhofen's loyalty to the regime.

Wirths' hand curled into a fist as he came to decision. He raised his chin upward and declared, "You *will* perform this abortion, Zeilhofen, and as of now, you'll do it at gunpoint. An armed guard will be present in the operating room. If the nurse gives him the nod that you're not proceeding to terminate this pregnancy, you'll be shot. You will die. And those are *my* orders."

Walter swallowed hard; his Adam's apple bulged on his neck, appearing twice its size. "I will follow your command, Dr. Wirths, performing the abortion to the best of my ability." Sighing, Walter added, "For the record, and with all due respect, sir, the oath I took when I became a doctor supported saving lives, not intentional killing."

"You'll be saving a life, two lives actually," Wirths said emphatically. "Your own, for one. And secondly, if this abortion is not done within two hours, Eleonore Hodys goes to the gas chamber this afternoon."

In the privacy of his living quarters, Walter Zeilhofen knelt in front of the toilet, vomiting into it. The shocking sight of the well-formed body of the male fetus, which was beyond a seven-month developmental stage, had shaken him to the core. When the nurse left the room to dispose of it, his stomach had roiled. Hours later, he was still vomiting.

At first, it had seemed to Walter that he was throwing up his iniquity, purging it from his body and spirit. But now, it felt more like the devil had hijacked his gut, twisting it into forked fangs, making him vomit up himself, emptying all his goodness too. He heaved and gagged again. Dizziness overcame him. Walter rolled onto the bath rug. Moaning, he mumbled, "Lord have mercy. I'm dehydrated. And it's time for my insulin shot."

Surmising that standing up would trigger another round of heaving, he crawled to the bathtub. Adjusting the faucet, he dribbled water into his mouth. On all fours, he crept from the bathroom to the kitchen. There, he reached his arm upward to a lower shelf and retrieved the cracker box. He crunched on soda crackers, then stretched out on the floor.

Lying there, Walter recalled his parents urging him to be a force for good at Auschwitz. His friend, Soldier Rhino, then came to mind. Together, the two of them had schemed and broken the rules to save Hinda's life when malaria threatened to defeat her. Walter closed his eyes, intending to say a prayer for Rhino's safety, but Hinda's face, floating like an angel, came into view in his mind's eye. He seized upon the ethereal vision of her; nevertheless, another image—the well-defined head of the fetus—intruded. He blinked his eyes in rapid succession to dispel the disturbance.

Knowing that cranial contour was genetic, he wondered who Hinda resembled, her mother or her father. Her sister Rachel was pretty, but not like Hinda, who had such a beautifully shaped cranium. Walter's hand reached into the ethers above him; his index finger traced the mirage as if outlining Hinda's head shape. He felt as if his hand were touching her, gently cupping her cheek. "I so wish we could marry and have a baby together," Walter whispered to the imaginary Hinda. Gazing into the unknown, he pondered the genetic probability of Hinda's and his child inheriting her perfect pate.

Walter turned on his side. Hot tears gushed from his eyes. Inwardly, he lamented the unfair situation. Commander Höss had a full-on affair with a prisoner, even getting the woman pregnant, while he had fallen in love with a prisoner, but he had never touched her in a sexual way, never even kissed her. He mumbled, "Why am I punished more for less?" In a matter of seconds, the answer reverberated through him: *Because the prisoner you love is a Jew.*

Weeping, Walter wondered, *My beautiful Hinda, what unjust cruelty are you suffering tonight?*

80
The Chosen Ones

Early December 1943 | Oświęcim, German-occupied Poland
Auschwitz Concentration Camp

A fearsome beast of prey stalked the women of Block Eleven. Sunday was no exception. The *day of rest* had become another day of dread. Multiple times each week, Dr. Josef Mengele would barge through the doorway, soon after morning roll call, and select women for his research experiments. Although Mengele could take subjects from anywhere in the camp, he preferred Block Eleven, not only because of its proximity to his lab in Block Ten, but also because it was the Block of Punishment. These women ranked even lower than those in other Blocks.

After surveying the day's group of female prisoners, he would point his burnished baton at individuals. Smiling sardonically, he would then say to the chosen ones, "Please, come with me." His polite words, the use of *please*, disguised his intentions and suggested the women had a choice. Mind games.

The chosen females would disappear through the door, going to his lab next door in Block Ten. When they returned, they were in excruciating pain, some from missing body parts—bones taken from arms or legs, eyeballs cut out, fingers cut off, toes severed, and clitorises removed—while some were bleeding profusely from other procedures such as vulva, vaginal, cervix, and uterine surgeries and biopsies.

This Sunday morning, Hinda and Rachel were cleaning their bunks when Mengele entered. They had hoped to be allowed outdoors in the afternoon when chores and inspections were completed—their only free time for the entire week. Hence, they had begun scrubbing their area earlier than usual. Yet, when the doctor banged the door closed, all dusting and sweeping stopped. Obeying Mengele's command, the sisters dashed to the middle of the room and stood in a rigid military-style At-Attention position.

Hinda had warned Rachel—who was nearing a nervous breakdown from the fear of being mutilated by the monstrous doctor—to not show emotion, especially angst, around Mengele, as that drew him like a hungry hawk to a fledgling bird. Lately, women who cried, trembled, or appeared openly defiant were certain to leave with him.

Today, Mengele circled Hinda. Unconsciously, her jaw clenched. He raised his shiny baton to the notch just above her ear lobe, then traced a line down her jaw bone to the middle of her chin. She managed not to blink. In her mind, she recited her father's letter, his last written words to her: *You will live; you will tell.* Then, Mengele lowered the baton, pressing it firmly into her navel. Just as suddenly as he had shoved it against her, he removed it, twirling it through his fingers. Hearing weeping across the room, he sauntered in that direction.

That Sunday afternoon, when the sisters were allowed to go outdoors, they were surprised to see snow, five inches or more on the ground, and boxlike snowdrifts scattered around the square.

Running to a glistening snowbank, Hinda called out to Rachel, "Let's skip today's concert and cleanse our faces." She grabbed handfuls of the white-powder crystals and rubbed them vigorously all over her cheeks, nose, chin, and forehead. Disgusted at the brown ice then in her hands, soiled from the grime on her face, she dropped it and grabbed fresh snowflakes. Repeating the process multiple times, she scrubbed until handfuls of unsullied snow remained white, and her face had begun to sting and tingle.

A heavyset German woman, a warden named Gerda who supervised guards, approached the snowbank where Hinda and Rachel made snowballs. Her eyes popped wide when she saw Hinda's face—creamy pink skin and enormous blue eyes framed with lush dark lashes. "For a Jew dog, you're quite attractive," Gerda remarked. "What's the secret to your beautiful skin?"

Hinda studied the warden, who had whipped her and then moved her to Block Eleven. The woman seemed in a lighthearted mood today, although her posture and the set of her shoulders spoke of stress. Noting that, an idea pitched a tent in Hinda's mind. Deciding to optimize such a rare Auschwitz moment, Hinda followed her instincts and fibbed. "I've studied cosmetology and massage therapy."

"Yow! That's interesting," the warden exclaimed, her feet shuffling in a jig of eagerness. She popped her neck as if it ached. "I could sure use a massage. And a facial," she groused while scratching her cheek. "Hmm," Gerda mumbled, appearing to be mulling over something. "I'm now the manager of the kitchen where meals for staff are cooked." She looked intently at Hinda, then declared. "I'm transferring you to work there, starting tomorrow."

Hope burst through Hinda like exploding fireworks in a night sky. Employing her most convincing voice, Hinda pointed to Rachel and said, "She is trained too. If you let both of us work there, we'll give you a massage every day and do frequent facials."

The warden cocked her head to the side, scrutinizing Rachel, whose face also glowed from snow exfoliation. Returning her gaze to Hinda, Gerda spoke with certainty, "Deal." She dug in her pocket and pulled out a notepad and wrote down their identification numbers, 25305 and 25306. "What was your work assignment before this?"

"Budy," Hinda and Rachel said in unison. "The vegetable field," Hinda added.

"Okay. I'll put in the proper paperwork and see you both in the kitchen tomorrow morning. And I want the massage first."

Preparing for bed that evening, Hinda bounced with excitement. Working in the kitchen meant the *chance* to get extra food. And it was indoors. Having no coats to wear, the onset of winter had turned the climate of Budy to that of a freezer. What a relief it would be to toil in a warm kitchen.

While fluffing the straw in their bunk, Hinda said to Rachel, "This was the only good thing that came from the commanders' visit. We have more hay than normal because the wardens wanted to impress those wicked men."

Standing to the side of the bunk, Rachel simply nodded in response. In a seeming daze, Rachel rubbed the skin on her face.

"Your skin looks so smooth," Hinda exclaimed. "Does it feel soft now?"

Her brows furrowed, Rachel turned to her sister. "It does, but Hinda, we know nothing about cosmetology and massage. What are we going to do? That warden, Gerda, will beat us and send us back to Budy if we're not any good at it."

"We'll figure it out. I already have ideas of what to do."

"Like what?" Rachel asked, her eyes fixated upon her sister, who possessed a spunky boldness that she could not find in her own reticent nature.

"We could use gritty coffee grounds to remove dead skin, like we did with the snow today on our faces. That's what Mommy used and remember what pretty skin she had."

"Mommy had the creamiest skin, like you, but is that all there is to a facial?"

"That's just the first step. I'm trying to recall information I saw years ago in one of her magazines. I was only nine, but for some reason, the article made an impression on me."

Rachel's eyes widened in astonishment. She exclaimed, "Mommy had magazines?"

"It wasn't wartime then. You wouldn't remember; you were only three years old." Hinda clenched her fist, an unconscious action. "Anyway, I think we can satisfy the warden. She knows we don't have access to skin products and will need to use items from the kitchen."

"So, what will we do?"

"I'll come up with something. Don't worry."

"But what about the massage. Do you think she meant her whole body? Like, she would be naked?"

Wrinkling her nose at the thought, Hinda replied, "She will sit in a chair, and we'll massage her through her clothes and work extra on her neck and shoulders. I noticed that she carries her shoulders high, like up around her ears. I bet her muscles there are tense and tight. And don't forget, you are terrific at massaging hands and feet."

At that moment, the door to Block Eleven opened and in hobbled three of the prisoners who Mengele had taken that morning for his experiments. Hinda gasped, "Rachel, don't look."

Ducking into the bunk, Rachel turned her face to the wall, her eyes squeezed tightly closed.

The women's wails were unnerving. Having had no medication since the initial drug to knock them out was administered—given solely for Mengele's comfort, so they would not fight him while doing his cutting—the women suffered intense pain. One by one, the women began giving detailed accounts of their grossly appalling procedures.

Moving closer to the group, Hinda watched and listened intently. One of Mengele's victims clutched wads of bloody rags to her breasts. That woman reported that both of her nipples had been removed. She explained that she had been born with an abnormality, inverted nipples, or medically speaking, inverted mammary papilla, as the doctor had said. Mengele found the condition curious, so he manipulated her nipples until they were exterior. Then, he had lopped off both of them, including the areola surrounding each one, merely to determine whether her condition was genetic or a random irregularity.

Another woman's left eye was swollen and bruised from chemical injections into the eyeball in attempts to change its color from brown to blue. She was now blind in that eye. Her face and neck were flushed with hives—a reaction to the toxic chemicals.

The third victim was missing her right hand. Mengele had claimed it perfect for research because the thumb joint was severely enlarged and knotted from arthritis. She relayed that significant amounts of blood had gushed from her wrist when her hand was severed. Mengele had been intrigued by its lack of clumping, so he tested her blood and discovered her rare type—AB negative. He then drew countless vials from her arm to use in experiments on a particular set of twins. She reported, through sobs, that when she fainted from blood loss, she had fallen onto the doctor and accidentally scratched his face. Annoyed, Mengele had taken medical pliers and ripped off the fingernails from her remaining hand.

Inmates cried along with the day's victims. Yet, Hinda did not. The horror clearly registered in her heart and mind, but nary a tear dusted her eyes.

Across the room, Rachel was curled into a fetal position. She pressed her hands over her ears; nonetheless, she could still hear the women's chilling tales laced with their pained moans. Their piercing groans, like those of sick dying animals, were bombs detonating in Rachel's fragile psyche. Her eyes closed, Rachel focused on the imaginary canvas in her mind, where she painted Mengele with flames all over his body. In her picture, the doctor was afire, burning, his mouth wide open, screaming. His eyeballs lay upon his cheeks, having popped from their sockets. But suddenly, he spread his arms outward, like a magician, and the fire stopped. He stepped from the canvas and thrust his scalpel into her, slicing her open from her neck to her pubic bone. Rachel's body began to tremble and jerk. Odd-sounding, high-pitched shrieks escaped from her mouth.

Racing to their bunk, Hinda quickly covered Rachel with a blanket. When her shaking did not diminish, Hinda climbed into the bunk. Hugging Rachel tightly, she gently rocked her sister back and forth. Speaking softly into her ear, she said, "My sweet Rachel, what happened?" When the only answer was jerking and shivering, Hinda sighed. Instinctively, she began stroking Rachel's face, kissing her cheeks, telling her she was okay, and whispering how dearly loved and valued she was.

After a while, the tremors calmed. Opening her eyes, Rachel looked to Hinda, surprised that her sister was there, cuddling her. "I had a bad dream," she mumbled.

Hinda nodded, but she knew that it was not a dream; she understood that Rachel was even closer to a complete nervous breakdown. "Do you want to talk about it?"

"Not the dream. Just the electric fence. Hinda, please. We must throw ourselves onto it next Sunday. That is, if we are not chosen by *you know who* this week and then sent to the gas chamber because we are sick from infection or too weak to work."

"Remember, Tatae promised that we're going to live, going to tell the world of all this unjust and horrible cruelty."

"He promised you, not me. And I can't take it anymore. I'm not afraid of dying, but I am terrified of my body being carved up into pieces, like a cow after slaughter, all while I am still alive."

Hinda winced. "I know you're scared. I am too. But we have to take it one day at a time. Just look at our good luck today. We escaped Mengele's selecting us this morning. And in the afternoon, we had a friendly exchange with that warden, and she is transferring us to work in the kitchen. Do you realize how miraculous that is?"

"I guess," Rachel sighed. "I'm sorry. I'm just so scared. And so tired of all this."

"Let's get to sleep." Hinda yawned. "I want you to think of something happy and good when you close your eyes. Like paint pretty flowers in your mind."

Turning on her side, Rachel pressed her back against Hinda. She nestled against the warmth of her sister and reveled in the pleasant sensations of Hinda's fingertips lightly stroking her face. When Rachel closed her eyes, she saw Mengele's burnished baton pointing directly at *her*. Quickly, she painted a large black X across the scene, which then disappeared. Next, she saw the electric fence. She ran towards it and then floated on a fluffy cloud, safe, secure, and free. Soon, her breathing smoothed, becoming even and regular as she fell into a deep slumber.

Withdrawing her hand, which cramped from caressing Rachel for such a lengthy time, Hinda yawned and nestled her head into the hay. Sleep did not come. The lump in her throat and ache in her heart were like clamps on her eyelids, propping them open as she fretted over Rachel: how to calm her anxiety, how to help her retain sanity, and how to make her *want* to live.

Sighing, Hinda decided that, for her own good, she must put the worry for Rachel aside and be her own psychiatrist. Lying there, Hinda reflected upon

Walter and the good feelings she had experienced because of his caring and kindness to her. Pulsating warmth rose up inside her. She clung to the enveloping sensation, begging it to stay forever. Visualizing one of Walter's notes, Hinda focused on his encouraging words. Then, it was as if she could hear Walter's voice soothing her. "Hang on, Hinda, you're strong. The war could end soon. Please know, you're in my heart, in my every thought."

Drifting into welcomed drowsiness, Hinda felt a jolt. Like a thunderbolt in a storm cloud, the burden of Walter's fate rumbled, making itself heard: Walter is a gentle soul, a professional accustomed to working in good conditions. How can he survive belowground, laboring in a coal mine hellhole?

81

A Brumal Wind

December 25, 1943 | Oświęcim, German-occupied Poland
Auschwitz Concentration Camp

It's Christmas. Time for a bath. The edict was announced at roll call that Saturday morning, which normally would have been a workday. For Hinda, suspicion and trepidation sprouted deeper roots with each step she took while following instructions.

Guards circled, nudging the internees like animals, pushing them to march close together. Soon, quite a congregation traipsed along the roadway as additional groups of inmates and their guards merged. Curiosity peppering her apprehension, Hinda counted clusters of inmates while she marched. She strained her neck to better see the sprawling horde, but soon suspended her calculations when the guards ordered them to speed up their pace.

A soldier trotted up nearby. Speaking to an SS officer, he thumped his clipboard and said, "All accounted for in the Blocks selected today. Five hundred inmates, total."

Overhearing the official tally, Hinda gulped, concluding that something major was taking place. Worry overtook her and was exacerbated by the German shepherds that now flanked the sides of the throng. Barking continuously, the dogs snapped viciously at anyone who slightly veered from the others.

A brumal wind whirled the early morning air, intensifying the chill factor. After marching two kilometers, they came to an imposing stone building, the bathhouse. Concern furrowing her brow, Hinda reached for Rachel's hand. A vestige of peace washed over her, then vanished as disturbing notions rankled her volition to survive. The building looked like a gas chamber. This could be their end.

Once inside, their group was commanded to strip naked, to hold their eating utensils and clogs, and to toss their uniforms into large barrels lining the side wall. Guards aimed their loaded guns, cocked and ready for those who did not comply. While Hinda was now accustomed to having no choice, the orders still vexed her independent disposition. Irritated, she felt as if coarse-grain sandpaper abraded her spirit, grinding it down to a sliver.

Visibly ogling the naked bodies, male guards prodded the group through a doorway into an enormous room. Tiered from the floor upward to a high point upon the wall, the space resembled an auditorium, except for the seating. Backless, slatted benches filled each row. Giant spigots were spaced across the ceiling and down the sides of all walls.

People began climbing to the top areas. Her instincts beckoning, Hinda grabbed Rachel as she started to ascend. "No, let's stay near the floor." Choosing an empty bench on the first row, Hinda pulled Rachel beside her.

"If we're going to die, why not be close to the top, closer to heaven?" Rachel asked, tears slipping from her eyes, wetting her cheekbones.

"I have a bad feeling about going up there. And if this doesn't kill us, we'll want to exit quickly and not be stuck in a horde of naked people."

"Does dying in the gas chamber hurt?" Rachel inquired.

"I don't know. You've begged for the fence, and the electricity would hurt before it stopped your heart." Hinda squeezed her little sister's hand. They sat with their shoulders and legs touching, skin to skin. "Pain or not, whatever this is, Rachel, I love you with all my soul."

Just then, the double doors slammed closed, and steam began pouring from the spigots. Scalding steam filled the room like a thick fog, dousing their bodies in a pounding rhythm. The room became unbearably hot and humid. People audibly gasped for breath, especially those sitting near the top. Many screamed as their bench mates keeled over, collapsing upon them.

After an excruciating ten minutes, the steam stopped. The double doors opened. Guards shouted for them to exit. Hinda and Rachel were two of the first to escape the sweltering room. Next, they were hustled into the adjacent area that was outfitted with showerheads. Water spouted from each faucet. Hinda urged, "Be quick, Rachel. Let's shower while we can."

The sisters set their eating utensils and their clogs on the floor nearby and stepped under the stream. Icy water shocked their overheated skin, traumatizing their nervous systems. Even still, they reveled in the clean water flowing over their bodies, which had not been cleansed in over one year.

Abruptly, all the showers stopped. Guards handed them thin towels as they went through the doorway. Giving them little time to dry off, the guards jerked the towels from them when they were outside. The arctic temperature did not register at first, their naked bodies still cold from the frigid shower. But soon, they were shivering. Huddling together was not allowed. All the prisoners were forced to stand a precise number of paces apart.

The steam had opened Hinda's sinuses, and her nose dripped. She swiped at it, afraid it would freeze on her upper lip, which already felt chapped and split. Her toes tingled from numbness even with her feet inside the wooden shoes. Without the clogs, though, she knew her feet would soon be frostbitten, then frozen lumps. To keep her fingers from icing over while gripping her eating utensils, she switched the bowl and spoon from hand to hand in a ping-pong rhythm.

After Hinda and the others had stood at attention in the wintry air for twenty minutes, baskets of clean uniforms arrived. The guards distributed them according to the color-coded identity system. Hinda and Rachel were, once again, given uniforms with the inverted red triangle with an overlapping yellow triangle, which made a "Star of David" shape. The two triangles together signified that they were Jewish political prisoners.

Hinda quickly donned her uniform. It soothed her freezing skin, but it was far bigger than her old one. When she dropped her eating utensils into one of the pants pockets, they plunked down near her knee.

Whistles shrilled the air, signaling that it was time to move. Hustling the inmates into a knot, the guards herded them like sheep down the roadway.

While making the two-kilometer return to the base camp, Hinda listened as guards talked about past Christmases at Auschwitz. One guffawed about how Commander Höss would set up a giant lighted tree in the square and then, on Christmas Eve, demand that all roll calls extend to three hours. The bodies of inmates who died from standing so long in glacial temperatures were then artfully arranged under the tree, like presents.

Disappointed that the new commander, Arthur Liebehenschel, had nixed that tradition, that guard yelled out, "I miss Commander Höss. He was the wicked best."

Nearing the plaza where the crowd would disperse to return to their individual Blocks, Hinda's eyes roved over the assembly as she counted small units. It appeared that only half of the people had survived their Christmas cleansing.

Feeling grateful that the two of them had endured, Hinda reached for Rachel's hand, pulling her sister close. A high-pitched whistling sound ruffled through Hinda's ear. The worrisome noise reverberated from Rachel, who was wheezing, her chest rising and falling at a rapid rate.

Hinda quickly turned her face to what she hoped was true east. Inwardly, she prayed, *Dearest Lord, I ask you to put your hand upon my sweet Rachel and prevent her from getting pneumonia. Please God, I can't bear to lose her too. I need her—desperately.*

82

On Their Own Terms

February 1944 | Weimar, Germany
Buchenwald Concentration Camp

Tossing in a fitful slumber, Wolf Yoskowitz dreamt of his sister, Erna. In the dream, she was huddled under human cadavers stacked in a ditch. She looked emaciated and wild-eyed, like a rabid dog that had not eaten in weeks.

Before going to sleep that evening, Wolf had employed his imagination, conjuring up images of the wonderful life he would share with the beautiful Jewish woman he hoped to marry and have a family with someday. That possibility kept his heart beating. His existence had begun to feel futile. Physically and mentally depleted from the brutal year-to-year reality of Buchenwald, Wolf struggled to find reasons to live, reasons to hope for survival, and reasons to believe the war would end.

Tonight, Wolf could not maintain the mental positivity of his conjuring rituals and had lapsed into worrying about his mother, sister, and youngest brother. Visions of them in the woods, when soldiers had hauled them away, haunted him grievously. These thoughts of his family and the day he had found them in the woods triggered more memories, especially of the Dutkas and his time on their farm. When thinking of the Dutka family, a deep sense of gratitude washed over him. And finally, the grace of sleep embraced him.

In the dream of Erna, seeing her so desperate and ravaged, his heart had physically ached. Wolf had reached out to her and felt a hand take his. But it was not the slender long-fingered hand of his sister; it was the soft plump hand of Halina Dutka.

Sensing a presence and hearing a faint voice, Wolf sat up. Lo and behold, there stood Halina, right there at the edge of his bunk. She whispered sweetly, "Wolf, dearest Wolf, I love you. I will always love you." She looked like an angel with her flowing golden hair and white satin dress that draped beautifully around her shoulders.

Wolf blinked, and the vision of Halina disappeared, a fleeting apparition that left a leaden feeling in the pit of his stomach.

February 1944
Rural Gliwice Region, German-occupied Poland

At the Dutka farm, the double doors to the barn were open, wide open, the panels clanging against the barn's exterior wall. The tractor was not in its usual spot; it was parked in the front yard near the well. A German soldier strutted around it, admiring its superior quality. "This magnificent machine is going to make our life far easier. You boys sure don't need it anymore." He spoke to Jan and Jakub, whose dead bodies lay next to the well, their throats slashed.

Inside the house, Mrs. Dutka, who the soldiers believed was in town at the family's bakery, hid behind the curtain, peering out the kitchen window, watching the entire scene. Her twin sons had not put up a fight. Trusting what the officer had said—that they were taking the tractor for one day to complete a project—Jakub had willingly driven it to the front lawn. But when he jumped down from the seat, Jakub felt a gun barrel jut into his spine. At the same time that the soldier's arm came around him and the knife sliced into his neck, Jakub saw his twin brother, Jan, lying on the ground, his throat slashed.

After dragging Jakub to lay beside Jan, the soldier ambled over to the front gate. He pulled wire cutters from his pocket and cut away the metal loaf of bread that had been the family's emblem for forty-plus years. He tossed it on the ground near the roadway. From his vest, he retrieved a flag and hung it on the gate, the swastika claiming the property.

Inside the house, Mrs. Dutka beheld the Nazi flag and her sons' bodies lying completely lifeless on the grass. She felt her heart splinter apart, and her spirit depart her flesh as she glimpsed the fate of the entire family. The day she and her husband had most feared had arrived. There was no denying it; her sons were dead, and her husband and daughter were being held at gunpoint in the next room. Moving robotically, she tiptoed to the storage closet behind the kitchen.

In the living room, the Nazi officer aimed his gun directly at Mr. Dutka. Forced to his knees, Mr. Dutka knelt in front of the officer, his hands behind his back, his wrists locked in handcuffs.

"She is mine," the officer snarled, nodding in the direction of Halina. "And so is this farm. Orders from my commander came down from the Führer himself for us to confiscate this property and Germanize this region." Eyeing Halina's shapely silhouette, he sneered. "I will have her. And I'll do it right here in front of you, if you don't surrender all the keys to your vehicles, the barn, and this house."

"No! Don't do it, Daddy. I'd rather die," Halina screeched from the arms of the soldier who restrained her in the corner beside the fireplace. She bucked and kicked to get away.

"She's a hot one." Halina's captor grinned widely. "You sure you can manage her?"

"I sure can," the officer drawled. "Been dreaming about her for a while now. Tie her up on the bed in the next room, and I'll show you."

"Wait," Mr. Dutka pleaded. "I'll give you all the keys, and anything else you want, if you leave my daughter alone and let us walk away from here. And if not me, then her and my boys."

"Not going to happen. And it's not about the keys, which we *will* find." The officer's voice tone lowered, oozing with disgust. "It has come to our attention that you and your family have been harboring Jews here. And that's an egregious crime, punishable by death." He thrust his gun against the right temple of Mr. Dutka's hairline, and barked, "Do you understand?"

Mr. Dutka locked eyes with the officer. Ever so slightly, he nodded. "Yes, sir. I do."

"You and your family are now officially charged. And just so you know, your bakery in Gliwice, where you've also hidden Jews, is afire, burning to the ground, right now." The officer moved his gun, jabbing it against Mr. Dutka's throat. "And your wife is trapped inside." A derisive smirk darkened the officer's face. He gestured to the soldier to take Halina to the bedroom.

Just as the soldier shoved Halina forward, Mrs. Dutka emerged through the doorway. Her usual pleasant face had turned stonelike. Eyes glazed, she stared straight ahead as if she were sleepwalking. She gripped two pistols, one in each hand. Her fingers pressed on the triggers, firing six rounds from each gun. Bullets flew in all directions. Halina and the soldier dropped to the floor. He had a gaping hole in his skull. Blood spurted from the center of her chest. Mr. Dutka tumbled. The officer fell upon him, but not before he fired a single shot that hit Mrs. Dutka square in the forehead.

At peace, Mrs. Dutka's spirit floated heavenward. She had saved her daughter from being violently molested. And she had fulfilled her husband's merciful plan for them to die quickly—on their own terms—when it became clear that there was zero chance of their escaping the cruel claws of a Nazi-decreed death.

On the lawn, the soldier, hearing more gunfire than he had expected, vaulted from the tractor seat and sprinted to the house. A bloody knife hanging from his belt, he walked around the Dutka's living room, poking the barrel of his gun into the bodies, looking for life. Except for his own breath, there was none.

83

I Don't Pray Anymore

February 1944 | Oświęcim, German-occupied Poland
Auschwitz Concentration Camp

In the utility closet located at the rear corner in the staff's kitchen, the warden named Gerda sat sprawled in a chair, her head tilted back while Hinda patted lemon juice onto her face. At a makeshift sink, Rachel rinsed dish towels that were used minutes ago to remove coffee grounds from the warden's face and neck.

"Now, I want this one to be exactly the same as before. It worked so good." Gerda let out a hushed hoot, unable to contain her excitement but tamping it down so that she was not discovered getting a facial from two inmates. "I haven't had a date in twenty years or more," she exclaimed. "It can only be that you girls made my skin look so pretty."

"A date would be exciting," Hinda answered, attempting zeal, although she was bone tired and had not wanted to stay after working hours tonight.

"Yow! I can't believe it. Tomorrow night, I have a real *date*." Gerda performed a wiggly dance in her chair. "Did I smash up the cucumbers good enough?"

Inspecting the contents of the bowl, Hinda began applying the mash to the warden's face. "Looks perfect."

Even though they were certified workers in the kitchen, the sisters were not allowed to touch any food, utensils, or appliances. Their duties were limited to housekeeping, primarily scrubbing the floors and emptying the garbage. In preparation for the facial, the warden had followed Hinda's instructions. She had cut and juiced one lemon into a bowl, peeled and finely chopped a cucumber, placed it in a separate dish, and smashed it with a potato masher. And then, she added two teaspoons of cornstarch and stirred well.

At the sink, Rachel finished cleaning the coffee-ground mess. Then, she sat on the floor and began untying the warden's boot lace.

"Whoa, 25306, let's just do the hands tonight," the warden squalled.

Relieved to not touch the warden's toenails, all yellowed from fungus, Rachel happily retied the boot.

"My hands ache terribly because of the many years I was in jail," Gerda shared.

Standing next to Gerda, readying to apply the cucumber paste, Hinda almost dropped the bowl. Her eyebrows shot upward. "What happened that makes them hurt?"

"The detention officers would jerk my fingers really hard and pop my knuckles, every day. Their brand of fun."

Question marks flew like a skein of geese through Hinda's mind. She wanted to ask where, what, why, how long, and—especially—the reason the warden was in jail in the first place. Deciding she was walking a tightrope named *you better show respect*, Hinda swapped her questions for empathy. "Ouch, I'm sure that hurt," Hinda said, as if it pained her too. "But you obviously got out. You're employed here at Auschwitz now."

"Yep. Thanks to Commander Höss. He came to the penitentiary in Munich and chose one hundred German women—all oversized and strong, like me. All of us felons, and some, like me, were serving life sentences for first-degree murder. He ordered us to be released and brought us here to work as policewomen. Yow! I was so lucky."

"And now, you're a warden."

"Yep. Lucky again. I advanced to the guard level quickly. Then, before long, I was promoted to warden status."

Feeling her skin prickle, Hinda yearned to grab Rachel and run from the room. This woman had committed murder at least once. And she had been promoted because she controlled the Auschwitz inmates with callous, insidious cruelty.

Finished applying the cucumber paste, Hinda gave the warden a tray to hold under her chin to catch any drips. Inwardly, she implored the Almighty: *Dear Lord, please let this bogus facial work as well as the last one. If it causes even one tiny pimple or rash, she will murder me and Rachel, smash us up like cucumbers.*

Hinda swallowed hard. She needed to complete the process, and in the manner of a professional cosmetologist. Though her heart rate was elevated, she spoke in a soothing tone to the warden. "Close your eyes. It's time for deep relaxation." Hinda placed a round cucumber slice on each of Gerda's eyelids, then she began massaging the warden's shoulders.

"Yow! That feels amazing," Gerda sighed, her broad shoulders shifting downward as she relaxed into the massage.

"Remember to not talk until the paste has dried like a mask," Hinda said in the sweetest tone she could invoke, although her mind was whirring with worry.

Later that night in their bunk, Hinda reached into her pocket and retrieved scraps of food she had taken from the kitchen trash. Stolen orts. A wedge of potato, a sausage link, and a crust of bread. "This is all I could get today when I emptied the garbage. Did you grab anything?"

From under the blanket, Rachel produced her eating bowl that held two slices of carrots, a chunk of roast beef, and a flattened dinner roll. "Not as much as usual. And I couldn't steal the mini bread loaf tonight with Gerda there. But this looks good. I'm starving."

The sisters divided each and every scrap, placing them into their respective bowls, so that each had equal portions of the day's yield. They tried to chew slowly and savor each bit. But, within minutes, their tongues were rimming the empty bowls, licking them clean.

Returning her eating utensils to her pocket, Hinda said, "Don't you think it's bizarre that German officials brought in convicted criminals to police people who have done nothing wrong? Who thinks like that?"

"Nazis do. They wanted patrols they could count on to be cruel and hateful to us Jews." Rachel sighed. "Remember those German women who nearly killed us at Budy? I bet they were from that penitentiary too."

"It's all about dominating us, abusing us, before they employ their extermination plans." Hinda licked her lips. "I'm still so hungry. We missed dinner—the glorious mud coffee and moldy bread that's better than nothing. I can't believe that Gerda didn't give us soup or a crumb of bread for staying late to do her facial." Yawning, Hinda whispered, "Last time, she gave us a bowl of stew and soda crackers. Wonder why nothing tonight?"

"Either we're her personal slaves now, or she was so preoccupied about her date that she forgot. Hinda, after what she told us today, I'm really scared of her. Just think what she might do to us if she gets pimples or breaks out in a rash."

"I went easy on the lard as a moisturizer this time, worrying about blackheads. We must pray that she looks good for her date."

"I don't pray anymore," Rachel confessed. "It does nothing."

"What? My dear sister, I know that we're incarcerated, treated worse than rodents, but we're working indoors this winter, and we're getting extra nutrition.

In the short two months that we've eaten the food foraged from the kitchen, I feel stronger, and I see color in your face again." Hinda pinched Rachel's cheek affectionately, then in the next second, shook her finger disapprovingly. "I prayed for you to not get pneumonia after that awful bath, and you didn't. Plus, we've been in this horrid place for over a year, and we're still alive. And we survived years in the ghetto before that. How can you say such a damning thing about prayer?"

Shrugging her shoulders, Rachel reclined into the hay, "I don't think God likes me or listens to me the way He does you."

The following Monday, Hinda vigorously scrubbed the kitchen floor. Her knees ached from the pressure of the hard tile. The sisters' main assignment, their hellion, the floor required constant upkeep due to dirty boots coming and going across it throughout the day. If it wasn't spotless at all times, they were whipped, which had happened once when the cook dropped a gallon of milk. The glass instantly shattered and milky liquid mixed with sharp shards had spilled all across the floor. The chief dish washer, who was putting away plates, slipped and fell into the mess. Although it happened so fast that the sisters had not a second to grab rags or mops, the main cook had removed his belt and walloped away at both of them, like it was their fault, as if it were their hands that had dropped the milk jug.

This morning, the tantalizing aromas filling the front kitchen stalked Hinda like a predator trouncing her lank stomach. Along with apple cobbler, loaves of yeast bread were baking in the oven, chicken-and-dumplings simmered on the stove top, and a beef roast sizzled in another oven. Iced cinnamon rolls sat on the counter, leftovers from the staff's breakfast. Hinda had taken out the trash, but nary a crumb of bread or cinnamon-sugar goo had she found, which was grossly disappointing, knowing that her lunch would be a thin soup made from sub-par ingredients.

In the back kitchen where prisoner food was prepared, huge pots of the gruel, barely warmed, sat atop the stove. A study of disparities, the front kitchen produced abundant feasts while the back kitchen served up starvation—malnourishment in one scarcely filled ladle at a time.

At ten o'clock, the outside kitchen door slammed, and Gerda pranced in, a clipboard in her hand. She spoke gruffly, practically snarling, "Numbers

25305 and 25306, you're being transferred to Laundry. Finish this floor, and I'll accompany you there."

Hinda drank in the news, a cocktail of relief, frustration, and angst. She was relieved to see Gerda's skin perfectly clear, without a single blemish. Yet, upon hearing the transfer notice, Hinda's shoulders slumped. The realization struck her hard. Rachel and she would now have zero opportunities to obtain extra nutrition. One fearsome question surfaced: *how could they continue to survive on the dwindling camp rations when the harsh labor requirements remained the same?*

84

Pink Triangles

Walter Zeilhofen jiggled the key in the lock, opening the door to his private quarters. The movement caused two boxes to fall from his arms. Postmarked envelopes flew from his hand and crisscrossed the threshold like paper airplanes crashing against each other. Grumbling in annoyance, he bent down and picked up the mail. Then he kicked the boxes inside.

Locking the door behind him, he chucked the envelopes on the dining table and went to retrieve the boxes. One was from his mother, and the other was labeled with a name he did not recognize. He checked his watch and sauntered to the kitchen to administer his insulin shot. Returning to the living area, he ripped open the package from his mother. A fragrant aroma of gingerbread wafted upward, crinkling his nostrils. He sighed. His mother had sent *lebkuchen*, even when she knew that he was now diabetic. Walter fingered one of the iced cookies, then before he could have counted to ten, he had consumed three large ones. He lamented the fact, then consoled himself with the thought that if he started feeling woozy, he would take more insulin.

Walter reached for the mystery box, examining the name of the sender— Rhinehardt. Thinking there was a mistake, he double-checked that it was addressed to him. His brow wrinkling, he used a knife to open the heavily taped box. A sealed envelope with his name written in block letters lay atop wadded newspapers. Setting the letter aside, Walter started to remove the wrinkled newsprint, but an ache assaulted his stomach. Questioning why, he answered himself aloud, "I ate too many cookies, too fast. My blood sugar is elevated."

Glancing at his watch, Walter determined that he should not inject another dose of insulin just yet. He went to the kitchen and returned with an orange to have it ready in case he felt faint. Sitting down in a dining-room chair, he reached for the mysterious envelope. Using a silver letter opener kept on a tray on the table, he sliced through the closure and pulled out a handwritten letter.

Dear Doctor Zeilhofen,

I am grieved to inform you that I have received official notification from the German army that my son, Arno Rhinehardt, who you knew as Soldier Rhino, was killed in action on the front line defending his mother country against the Soviets. His final battle transpired in December of last year.

Rhino mailed me his special belongings last November before he left for Western Russia. After going through his things, I became aware that you meant a great deal to my son. His affection for the "good Dr. Walter," as he referred to you, is repeated plentifully in his journal entries.

Thank you for being his friend. I have taken the liberty of sending you a few of his keepsakes that I believe may have meaning for you. I hope you will treasure them and remember Rhino fondly.

If this war ever ends and you travel near the village of Garmisch, I would so enjoy meeting you and having you join me for tea, should your time permit.

Sincerely, Hildegard Rhinehardt

His eyes watery, Walter laid the letter on the table. His dear friend and co-conspirator, Rhino, was dead. Looking upward to the light fixture in the ceiling, he said, "Rhino, you were a good man and an extraordinary friend."

Walter lifted the wad of packing paper and peered inside the box. He squinted his eyes skeptically, unsure as to what he was seeing. Carefully, he removed the contents: an object wrapped in pink fabric and a framed four-by-six drawing. Dumbstruck, Walter looked closely at the drawing and instantly recognized his own face. The pencil sketch captured him perfectly. Scrutinizing the signature in the corner, he made out the initials, AR, scrawled with sweeping curls. "Rhino, I had no idea you were such a fantastic artist." Walter issued the compliment aloud as if his friend were present in the room with him.

Next, Walter inspected the scrap of pink material, which had been cut into the shape of a triangle. Inside it was a small rock. Walter picked up the rock, a common gray sedimentary stone, and turned it in his hand. On the underside, etched marks caught his eye. Capital letters A and R were etched on the first line, a double-heart symbol—one upside-down and layered in a staggered fashion on top of the first—was carved on the second line, and the letters W and Z were scratched on the third. Walter studied it for a moment. His hand flew to his mouth as he realized that AR stood for Arno Rhinehardt. The implication was clear. The carving indicated that Arno loved WZ. Bowing his head, Walter exclaimed "Lord have mercy. Those are my initials."

Grabbing the fabric triangle and the rock, Walter rushed to the kitchen. Striking a match, he burned the pink triangle in the sink then scrubbed away the scorch marks. He looked around the room in bewilderment, desperate to dispose of the rock. Pacing and saying, "Oh, God, oh, God," with every breath, he darted to the pantry and rummaged through his miniature tool set for a file or sandpaper to abrade the etching and disguise his initials. Not seeing a suitable tool for the job, Walter grabbed a tack hammer. In the living room, he placed the stone on top of the rug. Slamming the hammer into the rock repeatedly, Walter cracked at it, but it still remained whole. Not satisfied, he turned it over and pounded every inch of the etched message as if he were a convulsing madman.

Collapsing onto the rug, Walter whispered, "Oh, Rhino, I love you, too, but not in *that* way. No wonder you were willing to risk your life to help Hinda. It was all for me."

Walter lay there, staring at the ceiling, his thoughts pulling him into a vortex. The pink triangle made sense now, for that was the classification badge that male homosexuals were forced to wear at the Dachau concentration camp. At Auschwitz, he reflected, there were some homosexuals, but they were not interned there for that reason, like they were at Dachau.

At Auschwitz, all prisoners had colored symbols affixed to their uniforms to typecast them. Flashing upon the labels of shame, as Walter called them, he thought about the color-coded triangle system. Red triangles denoted political prisoners, which included Jews, but they wore a different badge from non-Jewish political opponents and activists, who wore red triangles only, the tip pointing upward. Jews wore an identity badge that was made of a red, inverted triangle overlapping a yellow triangle, which together formed a Star of David shape. Purple triangles designated Jehovah's Witnesses, who refused to swear allegiance to Hitler or to any state. Loyal only to God, their faith forbade them from uttering the words "Heil Hitler," and from registering for the draft or taking part in the war; thus, they were considered a threat to the Nazi regime. Black triangles signified the asocial—Gypsies, the perceived mentally/emotionally ill, the perceived mentally handicapped, the physically handicapped, and more.

Walter sighed. He hated the badges that, in the eyes of the Nazi government, marked the impure—the despicable humans. Fear spiked inside him. Soon, he could be one of them, incarcerated at Dachau and wearing a pink triangle, if he couldn't figure out how to dispose of the inscribed rock. If he dumped it in the trash, housekeeping might find it. He couldn't flush it down the toilet. If it clogged the drain, a plumber might retrieve it. He *could* drop it in the grass on the way to work at the hospital. But then, with his recent trouble and directive about not ever contacting Hinda or Rachel, Walter never knew for certain when he was under surveillance.

Pondering the rock, Walter surmised that Mrs. Rhinehardt believed that Rhino and he were lovers, that Walter was also homosexual. Although Walter had no objection to people who were not heterosexual, he understood that in the Nazi regime, there was minimal tolerance. As a German medical officer at Auschwitz, if he were thought to be homosexual or was even accused of being such, he would likely be imprisoned and tortured, potentially even hanged.

Cringing, Walter remembered hearing reports of horrid happenings at Dachau, where it was not uncommon for male homosexuals to be used as live targets for soldiers who were practicing their marksmanship. The prisoners, all with pink triangles on their camp uniforms, were forced to run in circles while the soldiers tried to shoot the exact center of the triangles. Many prisoners would drop to their deaths. It was also said that quite often these marksmanship practice drills served as entertainment for visiting Nazi leaders, such as Himmler and Goebbels.

Abruptly, Walter jumped up from the rug and hurried to the box that Rhino's mother had mailed. He turned it in every direction, examining each side. No official government mark could he find, while his mother's box had the stamp in obvious sight. All mail, coming in or going out of Auschwitz, was censored. This box sporting such obvious, heavy tape would not have been missed. His mind spun webs of questions: Who taped it so rigorously? Mrs. Rhinehardt or the postal censors?

With precision, Walter removed layers of tape, searching for variance. Holding up strips to the light, he grimaced. There were two distinct types of tape. His flesh prickled. It was highly likely that a government agent opened the box, noted its contents, and retaped it.

Snatching his rosary from the tray on the table, Walter paced, caressing the beads frantically. "Blessed Mother of Mercy. Did they read the letter? And exactly what did they surmise about *me* upon seeing the pink triangle? Did they examine the rock and match up initials?"

A vision of Hinda waltzed through his mind. Plopping down in the chair, Walter leaned his head back and spoke in a soft voice. "My beautiful Hinda, I so wish I could see you and tell you about the loss of our dear friend, Rhino. I know you appreciated the risks he took to help save your life. And then, he was such a willing messenger, delivering our notes."

Walter reached for the orange and peeled back the colorful rind. Ripping away the stringy white layer, he tugged the segments apart and popped one into his mouth. When the citrus flavor exploded on his tongue, an epiphanous insight bloomed in his mind.

Moving to the window, Walter gazed at the lambent light cast from a street lamp. His lips parted, slightly curving upward into a smile. Wide-eyed, Walter stared straight ahead, as though he were in an enlightened trance, allowing the realization to unfurl its rationality. *Falling in love with Hinda got me in serious trouble, and now, it could be the very thing that saves me.* Walter exhaled, a deep audible sigh of relief. *My feelings for Hinda provide the proof, or at least make a compelling argument, which I will need if they come for me with accusations of homosexuality.*

85

A Liar and a Thief

May 1944 | Oświęcim, German-occupied Poland
Auschwitz Concentration Camp

A diamond. Hinda's hand began to spasm with tremors as she gripped the loose unset stone, an emerald cut. Its perfect symmetry and the mirror-like quality awed her sense of elegance.

Glancing furtively around the room and deciding that none of the guards were watching her, she eased the diamond of many carats into her pants pocket. Searching for additional valuables, she dug her fingers deeply into all other compartments of the jacket, a brown tweed with moss-green velvet collar and lapels.

Rachel, who was working alongside her sister, said, "That's a handsome jacket. But what's wrong?" She reached across and lightly stroked the plush velvet lapel.

"What do you mean? Nothing is wrong."

"Then why are your eyes so big that they're bulging right out of your head?"

The sisters worked at Canada now, a workstation warehouse where the suitcases of recent arrivals to Auschwitz were unpacked after being confiscated. Jewelry and valuables found in the luggage or clothing were turned over to wardens who catalogued them as German property. A hostile milieu, soldiers outfitted with machine guns were stationed in all corners. Armed guards milled about the space, surrounding the workers.

After workers searched and sorted all wardrobe pieces into categories—male, female, and children—the items, along with shoes, accessories, and suitcases in good condition, were crated. Expensive jewelry and finer garments were packed separately. Those specific boxes were labeled Chancellor & Principal Officials—Third Reich. Then, all crates and boxes were loaded onto a train bound for Germany.

It galled Hinda that soon-to-be prisoners were told to pack a bag for their new home, a better place the government claimed to be providing. She had sized up the situation correctly: It was a way to control the people until they were imprisoned at Auschwitz. And it was a way to increase the coffers of Germany —confiscating personal items of the Jews, oftentimes, wealthy Jews.

Today, Hinda and Rachel unpacked the belongings of people—eight hundred Jews—who had arrived on an early morning train from Hungary. Not going through the usual screening process and not tattooed, the entire group was sent directly to the gas chambers. Mass killings, large groups gassed at one time, occurred multiple times each week. Hinda wondered why and had noted that crematorium chimneys now continuously poured forth billowing smoke.

The workstation Canada was named after the country Canada in North America, which was believed to be an abundant place. At least, that was what a guard told the sisters when they were first assigned there. After working in the warehouse for one month now, Hinda understood. She had found costly watches, strings of pearls, nuggets of gold, and bejeweled necklaces, rings, and bracelets stashed inside clothing pockets or luggage compartments. She had promptly turned them all over to the wardens. Until today.

The diamond felt heavy in Hinda's pocket, her angst encrusting the stone, making it feel like a weighted anchor on a sinking ship. Even still, she could not bring herself to turn it in just yet. It was not that she wished to keep it, although in other circumstances, she would treasure such a gem. What she wanted most, what she needed most, was *food*. The large diamond had sparked a daring idea.

Due to the latest reduction in prisoner rations, Hinda now experienced ravenous, raw, corporeal hunger every waking second. Along with food allotments, coffee portions had also decreased. Rumor said it was because the Russians were invading Germany, who had lost its stronghold. Plus, it was touted that news of the persecutions had reached other countries, such as the United States of America and Great Britain. Hinda believed that the Nazis had reasons for, yet again, lowering prisoner food and liquid rations. Their strategy, she surmised, was to kill off as many Jews as possible before other world powers forcibly stopped them.

Questions, exploring how she could continue to exist on such sparse nutrition, plagued Hinda's empty stomach and gnawed at her brain constantly. And now, both Rachel and she were so thin that they cast the merest shadows—wisps in the air.

As she worked, Hinda reflected upon how severe hunger was making her do stupid things. One day last week, Rachel discovered a sausage link in a clothing pocket. She had held it to her nose and instantly made a face. Hinda had sniffed it and declared it bad, but she was so starved that she broke it in half and stuffed her portion into her mouth, anyway. Rachel gobbled her half too. Later, they paid a painful price—food poisoning. The inmates in their Block had managed to hide the two of them and their gastrointestinal distress. Otherwise, she and Rachel would have been dragged to the Killing Wall just outside Block Eleven and been shot, execution style.

Hinda pondered two questions: *Was the diamond scheme stupid also? Would it have a poisonous ending too?*

While unpacking this particular suitcase—filled with tasteful, dapper menswear, the likes of which she had never seen—Hinda paid rapt attention. Thrusting her fingers deep into a side pouch that bulged, she pulled out a pair of elegant gold cufflinks—three-dimensional lion heads with billowing manes. Mesmerized, Hinda stared at the ferocious faces. For a moment, it seemed that one of the lions spoke to her. *Have courage*, it insisted, commanding her to action. Hinda felt a warm rippling sensation in her heart, feeling as if the lion were gazing earnestly into her eyes.

Using her thumb, Hinda snapped shut the case. Stepping quickly, she marched over to the jewelry wardens. With a dramatic flourish of her wrist, she turned in the set of cufflinks. Hoping her display was enough of a decoy, Hinda promptly returned to her area and began unpacking a different bag. Intentionally, she wrinkled her face into an expression of intense focus. After five minutes, she looked up to see the jewelry wardens huddled around the cuff links, oohing with admiration.

Donning her mantle of boldness and bravery, Hinda scrutinized all the guards in the room. One had a different air to his stance; he seemed less truculent than the others. He stood to the side, and no soldiers were nearby. Holding the diamond tightly in one hand, Hinda carried the brown tweed jacket in the other. Her shoulders straight and her spine stiffened, she approached him, asking if the elegant suit coat should be separated from the stack of common garments. The guard turned toward the wall to examine the fabric in better lighting. Hinda opened the palm of her hand over the velvet lapel, revealing the large diamond.

The guard's eyes widened, but he remained silent. He tilted his head in a good-natured manner, and his bushy eyebrows raised not in alarm but in a quizzical expression.

Barely audible, Hinda asked, "Would you like to have this in exchange for some substantial food for my sister and me?" She closed her fist around the stone and dropped her hand to her side.

While appearing to appraise the quality of the jacket, the guard turned the coat inside out, inspecting its silk lining. "How about a cooked rabbit? I could bring it tomorrow."

Hinda's mouth watered in anticipation. "Yes. How will I get it?"

"There's a large rock in the field on the south side of this building. You can't miss it. It's the only one in that area that has a peaked top. Early tomorrow morning, I'll place a brown sack there in the tall weeds next to it."

Hinda opened her palm. In one swift sleight of hand, the guard nabbed the diamond, while returning the jacket to its front side. His eyes suddenly hardened, losing their affable luster. "If you say a word about this, I'll proclaim you a liar and a thief, and shoot you dead on the spot. Understand?"

"Yes, sir," Hinda said. She had expected him to make such a threat. Even still, her stomach fluttered with fearsome distrust.

Pivoting to face the room, the guard announced loudly, "I think you're correct about this jacket." He pointed to the lead female warden standing beside the jewelry counter. "Take it to Officer Wilda for proper appraisal."

Block Eleven was in an uproar when Hinda and Rachel returned for the night. Mengele had selected Helga, Hinda's cherished friend, that morning for his experiments. An accomplished ballerina in Poland before the war, Helga was a Block Eleven favorite. Boldly humorous, she often entertained her Block mates with graceful ballet moves between jokes. Helga's dream was to return to dance. But tonight, she lay in her bunk with her left foot minus its three middle toes. Helga would never dance professionally again. Mengele. He had destroyed her dream.

Hinda cracked. Breaking down in sobs, Hinda leaned over the bunk. She kissed Helga's cheeks, her tears dripping onto her friend's face.

Lifting her head, Helga said, "You're like a sister to me. But, please, Hinda, stop crying! I'm alive. I'll be okay. I promise. By tomorrow night, we'll be having mud coffee together."

Hinda nodded and forced a slight smile. She tugged the blanket up around Helga's neck and bowed away.

Gripping Hinda's waist, Rachel helped her sister to their bunk. "Oh, Hinda, I haven't seen you cry in years," Rachel whispered, her own eyes moist.

"Obscene . . . unjust . . . cruelty. Will it ever stop?" Hinda muttered between gritted teeth.

That night, the sisters' usual roles reversed. Rachel was the one to console and comfort Hinda. She snuggled next to her and stroked her arm and head, patting her intermittently.

When drifting into drowsiness, Hinda thought of the diamond and the cooked rabbit. She wanted to whisper to Rachel about the prospect of having some real food in the morning but decided against it. Hinda fully understood another likely possibility: The guard could greet her with gunfire instead of warm protein.

Early the next morning, Hinda and Rachel departed for Canada immediately after roll call. Rachel had put up a fuss, complaining about skipping the coffee and meager bread the camp's staff called breakfast. Even still, Hinda had urged that they had to leave then, saying that she would divulge why later.

Still trying to convince her sister, Rachel fretted. "What about the guard escort? We're supposed to march with them."

"Don't worry. Many prisoners go on their own now that there are fewer guards. Remember, hundreds from Auschwitz were called to serve in the German army. Anyway, it's the guards at Canada who check us in as *present* for work."

Yawning, Rachel mumbled, "I wish I could feel good about this, but I don't."

Hinda ignored her sister's comment. She was too tired and her head too full of worry. All night, frightening visions had plagued her. The images alternated between the guard gunning her down and of Helga's mutilated body. Combined with her concern about Walter, Hinda's anxieties had booted sleep out and locked the door. And now, as she walked, she worried that she had been an idiot to expect the guard to bring food in exchange for the diamond.

As they trod along, Rachel inquired, "Did you check on Helga this morning?"

"She was feverish," Hinda answered. Hatred for Mengele swam in the mire along with her apprehension about the diamond guard.

"A fever. That means infection—" Rachel stopped abruptly, glancing at her sister. "Hinda, you aren't acting like yourself. And I don't understand why we're doing this."

"My heart is breaking for Helga," Hinda replied. "And, well, I'd rather not talk about why just yet. We'll soon know my fate."

Looking heavenward, Rachel took in the breathtaking sky. "Glory be, look at that beautiful sunrise. Maybe it's a sign of hope."

"The Almighty hasn't stopped the sun from rising just because we, and millions of other Jews, are incarcerated in hell." Hinda paused her step, then said sharply, "Turn here."

"We aren't at Canada yet."

"I know." Hinda turned the corner anyway and proceeded to walk another ten yards. Although confused, Rachel followed her.

Scanning the area, Hinda looked for signs of betrayal—a guard, a soldier. She grasped Rachel's shoulders, looking her sister in the eyes. "Wait here, Rachel, and don't move from this spot unless you hear gunfire. If you do, run for all your life. Get inside Canada as fast as you can."

Hinda then made her way through the weeds to the peaked rock. After searching all around it, she mumbled to herself, "No brown sack. Maybe I'm too early." She leaned against the rock. Her chest felt tight. Realizing that she had been holding her breath, she inhaled deeply and decided to expand her search. And there it was tucked in the weeds, about two feet away from the rock. The brown bag was smaller than she thought it would be, but it was warm. She crouched down and tore open the paper. Instantly, her eyebrows shot upward. The shrunken shape did not resemble a rabbit. Yet a meaty aroma drifted upward, making her mouth fill with saliva. Using the sharp side of her spoon, she cut down the length of the body. It appeared fully cooked and tender. Standing up, she waved to Rachel to join her.

The sisters sat in the tall weeds, their backs to the rock, facing away from the main walkway. They ducked their heads and began to feast, licking their greasy lips and fingers between bites.

Rachel crooned, "Mmm. Delicious. What did you have to do to get this rabbit for us?"

"Don't ask. Just eat." Within minutes, they had devoured every smidgen and shred of the meat and even sucked the bones.

"That was one tasty rabbit. I feel so full, but my mouth wants more," Rachel exclaimed.

"Mine too." Hinda said, though she believed that what they had just eaten was not a rabbit. It was a cat.

In the afternoon, a warden carrying a clipboard approached Hinda. "Number 25305, you've been transferred to work at the Sola River. Report there tomorrow morning."

Before Hinda could respond, the warden turned to Rachel, 25306, and issued her the same order. Relieved and grateful to not be separated from Rachel, Hinda said a silent prayer, something she had not done in a long while now. Then it dawned on her. The Sola River was located near the end of Auschwitz property, close to the crops and vegetable fields of Budy. How would they get there? She looked all around, but the warden carrying the clipboard had vanished.

When Hinda had scanned the room, she saw the guard with whom she had traded the diamond. When their eyes met, he grinned triumphantly, a wickedly smug upturn of his lips.

Even still, a triumph of her own washed over her. It had been a remarkable day. She was not shot. She was alive. And, amazingly, she was not hungry. As long as Rachel and she did not become ill from eating cat meat, her daring plan had worked. Hinda's stomach had gurgled incessantly with digestive juices. Yet the animal protein had supplied enough nutrition to clear the fog in her brain and renew her energy.

Hinda reflected back to the lion cufflinks. Unexpectedly, she laughed aloud. The golden lion had urged her to be courageous and trade the diamond for food. Funny thing, lions are in the feline family. They are cats, big cats.

The second Hinda crossed the threshold to Block Eleven, she dashed to Helga's bunk. It was empty. Frantic, she began asking what had happened. Most said they did not know. Many averted their eyes. "Please, I want the truth," Hinda called out to her fellow Block mates.

The woman, who bunked next to Helga, took Hinda's hands in hers. She bit her lip and said, "I know that you and Helga shared a special bond. I'm sorry to tell you that she developed a severe infection in her foot where the toes had been removed. Dr. Mengele refused to give her antibiotics. This afternoon, he ordered the guards to take her to the gas chamber."

Hinda's hands curled into fists. Her mouth quivered, then opened wide, and she burst into sonorous wails.

The night warden arose from her chair and kicked it back against the wall. She squinted her eyes, making them snaky slits. "Shut up, 25305, and get to your bunk."

Bent double, her head hanging past her waist, Hinda stumbled blindly to her bunk where Rachel was fluffing the hay. Rachel wrapped her arms around her sister and helped Hinda into bed. Between sobs, Hinda tried to instruct Rachel, but her words came out so garbled that Rachel could not decipher them. She climbed in the bunk and lay beside Hinda, holding her, rocking her, until finally, Hinda could make sense between sobs. "Go ask the warden. How we get transport to the Sola River. For work tomorrow morning."

Rachel, who was quite timid when it came to speaking to wardens and guards, trolled deep inside herself and fished out buried bravery. Quaking in her clogs, she did as Hinda had asked her to do. When Rachel returned, she found Hinda unraveled. Her body shook uncontrollably, and continuous tears coursed down her face, drenching the collar and neck of her uniform.

Her chin quivering, Hinda sputtered the words, "What did she say?"

"A transport truck will be at the same corner as the pickup point for Budy. She said to board the green army truck, not the Blitz truck that goes to Budy."

Hinda curled into a ball. "Thanks. I know that was hard for you."

An attempt to distract her sister from the loss of her friend, Rachel said, "I wonder what kind of job we'll have at the Sola River. I thought only men worked there."

Rachel saw Hinda's shoulders shrug slightly before they started shaking, and she launched into another bout of sobbing. For hours, Hinda quietly cried and moaned. Rachel, who had given up trying to comfort her sister, tossed and turned on the hay. Reaching her tolerance threshold, she sat up and said sternly, "Hinda! Stop crying. Don't you see that Helga is in a far better place than we are? She's the lucky one. I wish we were in heaven right now with Helga."

Raising up on her elbows, her eyes dripping, Hinda exclaimed, "What you say is blasphemy. Tatae wants us to live. Tatae wants us to tell of this horror."

86

No Longer Privileged

May 1944 | Oświęcim, German-occupied Poland
Auschwitz Concentration Camp

The infectious exuberance innate to Annie—Hinda's childhood friend who was first-chair violinist in the camp orchestra—had withered into dispirited downheartedness. Her ebullience languished soon after the propaganda film was completed, and she was not practicing and performing classical music every day and evening. Moreover, she was now forced to play German marching scores at dawn and at dusk for hours, and in all kinds of weather.

No longer classified as a privileged prisoner, Annie had come face-to-face with the brutal reality of Auschwitz. Her blonde curls gone, her head shaved, Annie now bore the mark of an ordinary inmate. There were no more pretty black dresses, either, even for concerts. She now wore the unattractive striped prisoner uniform. Eating regular prisoner rations had shocked all her bodily systems as she dropped thirty pounds in two months. Desperate hunger fogged her brain, making it nearly impossible to focus even on her passion—music.

Standing near the south gate of Auschwitz's women's camp, Annie struggled to play the march tune with fervency. Her musical ear registered that she was not the only one straining. The group of thirty-five should be putting forth a robust sound. Instead, the up-tempo piece sounded lackluster and discordant, falling flat in the matutinal air. Annie reasoned that the entire group would soon be harshly punished. Their task was to play their instruments perfectly, striving for their music to boost the morale of the prisoners going through the gates for work in outside posts.

Instead of focusing on the notes, Annie questioned how one beaten-down group could boost the morale of another beaten-down group. At times, she saw a smile or a wave of appreciation from the inmates, but most turned an indifferent ear. The German marching tunes the orchestra was required to play only served to remind the prisoners of the goose-stepping soldiers who held them captive.

The orchestra itself now battled to keep up its morale, which had plunged when its members had lost their special privileges. Plus, their beloved and renowned conductor, Alma Rosé, had suddenly died in April.

With the final stroke of her bow on the violin for that particular piece, Annie felt her pants begin to slip from her waist. Once again, the food portions had become even smaller, and she had lost more weight. She thought of her childhood friend, Hinda Mondlak, and how extremely thin the poor girl was when Annie first saw her at Auschwitz, and that was one full year ago. She wondered what Hinda looked like now and if she were even alive.

When Annie struck the first note of the new tune, a Blitz truck filled with female prisoners roared through the gates. Following closely behind it was a green army truck. Its driver braked, slowing to acknowledge the orchestra. Annie glanced at the women standing in the bed of the vehicle. One in particular caught her eye. *That's Hinda. I would recognize Hinda's unique and pretty head shape anywhere. She's alive, but Lord help her, she's in the truck that takes workers to the Sola River.*

87
Aizik

May 1944 | Oświęcim , German-occupied Poland
Auschwitz Concentration Camp

Barefooted, Hinda stepped upon the ridge of sediment at the edge of the Sola River. Her feet prickled, then throbbed. Otherworldly screams and sorrowful wails of the dead assaulted her, as if the soles of her feet had sprouted ears. Her arms and legs broke out in goose bumps. Peering downward at the gray sludge she stood upon, she stammered, "What is this?"

A young woman, who was stacking rocks nearby, replied, "Don't you know? The ashes and ground-up bones of hundreds of thousands of people, Jews and other prisoners, have been dumped here. Such massive amounts of silt, they've made these deep ridges. Like sandbars."

"So that's why we're placing all these rocks here, to divert the water?"

"Yes. The river is clogged and doesn't flow well anymore. Serves the idiot Nazis right."

A guard stepped up and jerked the woman's collar, throwing her down onto the sediment. He kicked her upper body into the river and put his boot upon her head, holding it underwater. Her arms and legs flailed, then went still. The guard kicked at the girl's lifeless body until it was swallowed by the river. He pointed his gun at Hinda and said, "Now, you wouldn't want to speak poorly of us Nazis, would you?"

"No, sir," Hinda replied, her blue eyes as big as platters.

The guard winked at her. "You're rather good-looking for a scummy Jude girl." His eyes roved over her body in an overtly lascivious manner.

Hinda's eyes blinked unconsciously, but she dared not look away from the guard.

"The grass under those trees over there makes a nice mattress." He leered at her while taking steps to get closer. Just as he was inches from standing nose to nose with her, a series of gunshots rippled the air. He checked his watch and grimaced. "I'll see *you* later." His lower lip thrust forward into a haughty pout, the guard leapt up onto the riverbank and disappeared.

Block Eleven was all abuzz when Hinda and Rachel returned. The inmates were chattering excitedly. Women were exclaiming, "Can you believe it?"

"What's going on?" Hinda asked.

"There were male prisoners working at my station today," an inmate said, her tone brimming with surprise.

One woman, who had a broad scar across her chin, replied, "It's true. After years of strict separations, they're now intermingling men and women prisoners on job sites."

"We noticed that at the river today," Hinda said. "Why have they changed the rules?"

Pursing her lips, which puckered the scar, the woman said, "I overheard the wardens talking. They said that there's a new camp commandant, an SS Major named Richard Baer, who replaced Liebehenschel. Maybe it was the new guy's decision because the wardens also said that the administration does not have enough able workers now and has decided to mix the women and men to better fill the jobs."

"Of course, they don't have enough. Tons of prisoners are dying from starvation every day," Hinda protested.

Another woman piped up, "I heard that there's a shortage of guards now because the Russian army has invaded Germany, and many of them were called to fight."

"Does this mean that the men's and women's camps are no longer separated—"

A shrill whistle interrupted the chatter. The night warden shook her finger at them. "Stop this nonsense and get to bed." The cluster of inmates quickly dispersed.

Once the sisters had fluffed the hay and were settled into their bunk, Rachel whispered, "You had a close encounter today with that fat, ugly guard."

Hinda shivered, "Indeed, I did. Dear sister, we must pray for a quick transfer. I'm grateful to be near water and for the fresh air and sunshine. But the Sola River is the scariest workstation I've experienced."

"The guards have such lecherous attitudes. One kept winking at me today. Plus, it feels so odd to have men prisoners work alongside us. I felt nervous on both counts."

"The Sola River guards are more than lustful goats. They're wickedly mean. Did you see that fat guard, the one who almost attacked me, intentionally drown that young woman? She looked to be around seventeen, your age."

"I saw," Rachel said. She stared off as if in a trance, wishing it had been her. Hinda sighed. "We'd better get to sleep. Tomorrow will surely hold challenges."

After five minutes of wide-eyed insomnia, Hinda whispered, "Rachel, can you snuggle me? I need to feel you close."

The next morning, Hinda struggled to lift the rock and then carry it to the assigned point. She mused that, in her weakened condition, she really had no idea if the rock was genuinely weighty. Yet one thing, she knew, was truly heavy—her heart. She ached for Walter and for her friend, Helga. And every time she walked on the sediment to place a rock, her feet prickled, and her ears burned with ghostly rattles. Calculating estimates of the sheer amount of ashes and the number of ground-up bones that it would take to clog a river had seared her soul.

When she placed her stone in the pile, Hinda noticed a group of men striding toward her. They carried huge rocks. She stepped aside to make way for them, and her foot slid into the bog. A hand reached out and grabbed her, pulling her back onto drier silt. About to say thank you, she looked into green eyes, such vivid green eyes—shockingly similar to her mother's.

"Hinda, is that you?" the young man exclaimed. "It's Aizik, your cousin."

"Aizik! You're a welcome sight." She reached out, then backed away. "I so wish I could hug you."

Glancing up to the two guards standing at the top of the riverbank, Aizik said, "Me, too, but we ought not embrace and should keep our expressions neutral." He reached down to adjust a large rock. "I must know, though, is my Aunt Esther, your mother, still alive?"

Hinda turned her back and fiddled with the opposite side of the rock pile, hoping to buy more time with him without attracting the attention of guards. "No. She died three years ago in the Mława ghetto. My father too."

Aizik nodded, his green eyes turning misty. "Let's try to meet here again."

Towards the end of the day, Hinda had spoken briefly with Aizik three separate times. Longing for family connection, Aizik proposed they meet later in what he called a hideaway, a secluded side yard behind a grove of trees, located between the women's and men's camps.

Hinda agreed to take the risk. Immediately after Rachel and she had consumed their meager evening rations, Hinda told her sister where she was going.

"He's my cousin too. Why can't I go?" Rachel complained.

"I'm not sure it's safe. I need to scope out the place. If all goes well, you can come with me next time."

Later, when Hinda returned, Rachel was sleeping soundly. She crawled into the bunk, her heart feeling soothed because of the cousin-time with Aizik. They had cried together over the unjust losses in their families and then had become giddy talking about all the good times they'd had as children back in their shtetl of Zieluń. Unexpectedly, the shared camaraderie patched the hole she felt after losing her friend, Helga.

That night, Hinda did not need to employ her usual reflection therapy of trying to relive the wonderful feelings she experienced when she received notes from Walter. Tonight, for the first time in months, she did not push sleep away, worrying about Walter's fate in the coal mine.

The next day at the Sola River, the guards gloated over the game they had devised for their Friday afternoon fun. They were hollering, sniggering, and slapping their knees in delight.

Aghast, Hinda and Rachel watched as four male prisoners, all with heavy rocks tied around their necks, were pushed into the river and ordered to swim across. The men struggled to keep their heads above water and stay afloat. Hooting and yelling, the guards placed bets on which man would make it to the ledge on the opposite side.

Clenching her eyes shut, unable to watch, Rachel asked, "Is it over yet?"

"No. Don't look. Two are drowning now. Oh, my, it's so terribly awful."

Rachel exhorted, "Then close your eyes or turn your head."

Sputtering the words between gasps, Hinda said, "I. Can't. Seem. To. Do. It." She breathed heavily. "Oh no! They're pushing four more men in."

Her eyes still tightly shut, Rachel gasped. "Is Aizik one of them?"

"No, thank God, he works in the leather factory, as of today. He told me last night about his transfer."

The sound of demonic, sardonic laughter rang all around them. Then gunfire.

Breaking into sobs, Hinda grabbed her sister's hand. She screeched, "Oh, God in heaven, are you paralyzed? Please stop this heinous, cold-blooded heartlessness."

88

A Poisonous Worm

"Jew fat? This green soap is made from dead Jews?" Rachel asked, her brows knitted together in disgust. Recently transferred from the Sola River to work in the Officers' Laundry, Hinda and Rachel examined the green bar.

"Rumor says it is," Hinda asserted. "You know the Germans don't waste anything."

"The letters RIF are stamped on the bar," Rachel said, turning it in her hand. "Besides, the Jews I've seen here at Auschwitz are starving. Most don't have an ounce of fat on their bodies, so I don't believe it."

"RIF stands for Reich Industry Fat, or so I was told. Whether or not it's made from humans, we are going to seize the opportunity to use real soap," Hinda exclaimed. She bent over the sink and lathered her face, then rinsed it well. "Ahh, that feels so good."

"We're supposed to use it to get stains out of the uniforms. What if we're caught? It's hard to hear with the noise from the washing machines. The warden will do more than whip us till we bleed." Her face scrunched with concern, Rachel rubbed her hands together nervously.

"You go iron shirts in the front room while I cleanse my body. Then I will stand guard while you clean up."

Rachel's shoulders sagged downward. "I despise ironing those shirts with the lightning symbols embroidered on the collars. That's what the monstrous Dr. Mengele wears. The SS officers, always acting all high and mighty, are the most villainous of all."

Eager to show Aizik her freshly cleaned face, Hinda rushed to their designated meeting area. Expecting to see her cousin in his usual spot, leaning against a tree trunk, she was surprised to find the entire tract vacant. Exhausted from working a long day, Hinda readily sat down on the grass to wait for him. Rachel had declined to join them tonight, claiming that she was just too tired, that work in the officers' laundry was nerve-wracking.

Months of grime all washed away, Hinda stroked the clean skin on her face and felt a flicker of gratitude for the green soap, although she now loathed all German-made things. The guards' laundry, where they had been assigned for two months in the spring, had been less demanding work than the SS officers' laundry, where Rachel and she were the only workers. The benefit, though, was it stocked the green soap.

Waiting in the quiet, Hinda pondered just how good it felt to have a clean body, which sparked the desire to scrub her dirty heart with the green soap, to wash away the built-up guilt from a specific memory from two years ago. An idea flashed in her mind. She could confide in Aizik, telling him the secret that had come to feel like a massive boulder that she lugged around every day. Tussling with her thoughts, Hinda stepped back in time and relived the event that now tormented her with rueful regret.

One Sunday afternoon, when Rachel and she were in the square listening to the orchestra, they heard children laughing and playing in the distance. Rachel, who knew how bold Hinda was, begged her to go to that area—forbidden to adult prisoners—to look for Sara among the group of kids. Without forethought, Hinda pushed through the crowd of inmates gathered in the square and edged close to the fence of the children's area.

A policewoman, who was posed to strike her down, stepped in front of her. In a brusque tone, she said, "Just what do you think you're doing?"

Explaining politely, Hinda replied that she thought she heard her little sister's voice and just wanted a glimpse of her. Hinda extended her wrist, showing her identity tattoo, 25305. "My little sister came in at the same time as I did and should have a similar number. Do you know if she's here with these children?"

Her hand fondling the whip on her belt, the woman asked, "Which line was your sister put in at Selection?"

"The outermost line, the one farthest from the administration building."

"People in the outside line aren't assigned serial numbers and aren't tattooed. They're sent directly to the gas chamber."

Staring intently at the woman's face and eyes, Hinda observed no guile, only clarity and neutrality. She heard no taunt in the woman's matter-of-fact tone. The answer confirmed Hinda's suspicions, but the finality was agonizing to hear. Choking back tears, Hinda thought of Rachel and how she would handle the devastating news. Rachel, who wanted to throw herself on the electric fence, could crack, could have a complete psychotic break if she knew the truth about Sara. Riddled with concern, Hinda took her time returning to the opposite side of the square where Rachel waited. Arriving there and seeing Rachel's hopeful expression, she proceeded to flat-out lie. Hinda looked into Rachel eyes and said convincingly, "I saw Sara! Got a glimpse of her, anyway. She looked thin, but okay."

Squealing in delight, Rachel hopped around gleefully. "Did she see you?"

"No, I hung back out of her sight, worrying that if she saw me, it could trigger one of her fits. Besides, she wouldn't be allowed to talk to me or come with me."

"You're so wise," Rachel exclaimed. Elated with the news that Sara was alive, Rachel grabbed hold of Hinda and shuffled her into a dance sway, hugging her joyously.

Ever since, for almost two years now, Hinda had perpetuated the lie.

As Hinda sat there in the grass, weighing the consequences of telling Aizik, she bit her lower lip, then twisted her mouth, and nervously nipped at the skin inside her cheek. She concluded that if she confessed to Aizik what a sinner she was, lying about such sacred things as her little sister's death, he could refuse to meet with her. After losing her friend, Helga, Hinda felt desperate to consort with Aizik. Their talks and time together lifted her woeful spirit. Deciding to keep the secret buried in her heart, and hers alone, Hinda refrained from reflecting further.

Looking up to the darkening night sky, far beyond dusk now, Hinda was stunned to realize that a considerable chunk of time had lapsed. Apprehension assailed her senses. Aizik was *never* late. She heard footsteps crunching the leaves and quickly got up from the grass.

A young man stepped from the trees. "Hinda Mondlak?" he asked, a distinct formality infusing his tone.

"Yes," Hinda replied, relieved that it was not a guard, but concerned that it was a stranger who knew her name.

"Your cousin asked me to give you a message." He tucked his chin down onto his chest, not looking at her. "Number 38617, I mean, Aizik, isn't feeling well and cannot join you."

"He's sick? With what?"

"He has an infection."

"Oh no! Please don't tell me that Dr. Mengele performed experiments on him."

The young man looked up at the rising moon, then down at the grass, and stammered, "He did."

A knot formed in Hinda's throat. "He cut on Aizik's green eyes?"

"No. His privates."

When she pressed the hot iron onto the black shirt, Hinda gasped. A hole appeared right before her eyes. Frayed fabric with burnt edges stared back at her, as if it were an evil eye casting a curse upon her. She set the iron upright on the board and adjusted its temperature settings. *I'm so upset, I didn't pay attention. Now I will be beaten—again.* She slumped against the wall. *And God doesn't seem to care, and today, I don't either. I'm so oppressed and depressed that I just don't have it in me anymore to continue the fight to survive. Maybe this time, the whipping will kill me, and it will all be over.*

A poisonous worm burrowing into Hinda's very soul, a deep depression overwhelmed her like never before. Since news of Aizik's castration and resulting infection, Hinda had languished, feeling that her spirit had been sorely and irreparably injured. Twice, she had returned to the hideaway at their usual designated meeting time; Aizik had not come. Hinda presumed he was dead, sent to the gas chamber.

Taking the damaged shirt, Hinda went to the back room where Rachel was working. She exclaimed more loudly than she had intended, "Look what I did. Be prepared for beatings today."

Surprisingly, Rachel replied, "Not necessarily. I've discovered their garment counting system. They keep the records in the sink room."

Hinda's eyes widened. "Show me."

In the room where the soaking sink was located, Rachel climbed upon a stool and stretched to reach the top cabinet. She moved a box of detergent and then dangled keys in front of her sister. Rachel jumped down and inserted one of the keys into the padlock that was attached to a side cabinet. The lock instantly opened. Rachel tugged the cabinet door and revealed a stack of notebooks. Hefting the top one onto the counter, she flipped back its cover and expertly located the page that listed today's laundry records—specifically, the numbers of shirts and pants.

Astounded, Hinda asked, "Since when did you become a detective?"

"See that little hole in the wall over there? I've been watching the supervisor mark the columns after counting what we'd washed and ironed."

"But shouldn't the number of shirts and pants be the same?

"No, look here at these pages. They often don't match. And they're written in pencil. We can change the number of shirts that were brought in last night."

Flabbergasted, Hinda realized that she had not been present with this job, which was unlike her. She had been an unthinking zombie, too mired down in abject melancholy. She nodded to Rachel. "Go ahead. Change it."

Rachel took the pencil and erased the last digit that denoted the number of shirts designated for laundry today. She licked her upper lip as if concentrating. She reviewed the numerals, focusing on the style details of exactly how all the sixes on the page had been written—noting just how big the circle at the bottom was, and just how curved the top line was. Taking a deep breath, she applied what she thought was the right pressure on the pencil lead, and wrote in the numeral six, changing the total of shirts from one hundred thirty-seven to one hundred thirty-six.

"That looks perfect," Hinda exclaimed.

Rachel put the pencil back in the notebook pocket and flipped the cover closed. After making sure the padlock was back in place, she handed the keys to her sister. "You're taller. You put them back under the detergent box."

"Okay. But what are we going to do with the damaged shirt?"

Grinning mischievously, Rachel said. "Let's cut it up into small pieces, keep them in our pockets, and use them to wipe ourselves at the latrine. We can toss them down into the muck. They're black, anyway, so they won't be noticed."

"Now who's the bold one?" Hinda said sarcastically, as if she had taken affront.

"I thought you would laugh, or at least appreciate the irony of doing such a thing with a Nazi officer's shirt," Rachel said, her face a cameo of disappointment.

Hinda turned away from her sister. "How can you think in humorous terms in this place of vile wickedness?"

Rachel grabbed Hinda by the shoulders and twirled her around. "Snap out of it!" She glared at her sister, as if slapping Hinda with her eyes, which were afire with vehemence. "You are drowning in morose waters. For weeks now, I've watched you schlep around and just give up, wishing and hoping to die." Underscoring her point, Rachel shook her sister's shoulders and leaned in close to her face. Fervently, she exclaimed, "*You*, who have not let *me* die, were always intent on surviving to keep Tatae's promise. Do not let me down now. And not Tatae either. Hinda, please. Get . . . a . . . grip."

89

Death Warrant

September 1944 | Weimar, Germany
Buchenwald Concentration Camp

Wolf Yoskowitz and his brother sneaked into the grove of trees behind the quarry. The aluminum foil in their pockets felt warm. Ducking into bushes, Wolf unwrapped the foil to discover chunks of roast beef. His lips were dripping with *au jus* by the time Joseph got settled next to him. Trying to slow the pace at which he was gobbling down the beef, Wolf placed his hand over his mouth and forced himself to chew.

Having already devoured his portion. Joseph eyed his brother who showed more restraint than he did. Then, he craned his neck, looking all around to be sure he would not be overheard. In a near whisper, Joseph said, "The guys in the next bunk are joining the rebels, saying they're going to be part of an upcoming insurrection."

"How was your beef?" Wolf asked.

"Good. Just not enough of it. Brother, did you hear me about the guys?"

"I heard. I'll have no part of it. Not yet."

"Why?"

"Because of this." Wolf stuffed the last chunk of beef in his mouth.

"I don't understand," Joseph said, using his finger as a drawing tool in the dirt.

Wolf shook his head in dismay. "Joseph, don't you get it? We're being fed meat, extra rations, three times a week. All around us, men are dying from starvation."

"What if we could escape? Be free!"

"Do you really think those emaciated men can achieve that? And you're still limping."

"They say hundreds are joining in. Legions of guards have left to fight in the army. And we're hearing bombing noises more frequently now."

"Our supervisor is taking a risk giving us this meat to keep us alive."

"All for the Nazi quarry profits, and so he gets his bonus when we exceed quota, which nearly kills us. We're his slaves," Joseph grumbled.

"If we have *any* chance of surviving until the war ends, extra food, this meat protein, is key to our strength. It significantly increases our odds of survival."

Joseph nodded slightly. "But I've heard others say that there's a Resistance movement that includes some officers and administrative people."

Wolf stared at his brother, the set of his jaw meant he had made up his mind, a stubborn mind. "Joseph, if you do this, you'll be issuing my death warrant."

"How so?"

"We work as a team in the quarry. If you participate in the insurrection, you'll either die or escape. I can't make quota on my own. Not only will the supervisor stop the extra food, but he'll also have me executed. I will die by noose, boot, or bullet."

90

By Her Own Hand

September 1944 | Oświecim, German-occupied Poland
Auschwitz Concentration Camp

In the square, a sepulchral aura surrounded the platform. Nazi flags rippled in the gusty breeze, and the two readied nooses swayed in the air. High overhead, cirrus clouds scattered the morning sky, appearing feathery and ghostlike as the wind fluttered the filamentous tendrils.

Commanded to attend, the inmates—male and females from all Blocks—stood in somber silence. Large numbers of them hung their heads, dreading to see the hangings of their comrades: Mali, a Belgium girl in her twenties, and her boyfriend, Gelden. But watch, they would, or else they would be shot.

Hinda fidgeted, shifting her weight from one foot to the other, while Rachel stood stock-still, barely breathing.

Three SS officers climbed the steps to the platform. The lead officer, the one with the most stripes, medals, and decorations displayed on his crisp black uniform, spoke through the speaker system. "Today, you will witness the hanging of two inmates who foolishly believed they could escape Auschwitz and its widespread tentacles. Captured when trying to cross the Bohemia-Moravian border, they were promptly returned. Let their fate serve as an example for you." Increasing his volume to a screaming decibel, the officer snarled into the microphone, "You cannot escape us. It's impossible. And, if you attempt it. You. Will. Be. Hanged. Now, all eyes forward."

Armed guards shoved Gelden, a young man in his late twenties, to the first noose, and forced him to stand upon the assigned wooden box. They pushed his head through the rope and cinched it tightly around his neck. Another guard hustled Mali onto the platform and hefted her up onto the adjacent box. The guard, who was assigned to Mali, chortled at his plan to torture her further, forcing her to watch the hanging of her boyfriend in ultra close propinquity. Hence, he did not place her neck in the noose. Instead, he turned her toward Gelden, then he stepped back behind her box.

The SS officers saluted the flags and yelled out three times consecutively, "Heil Hitler." On cue, the guard behind Gelden kicked the wooden box, knocking it out from under the young man. Instantly, the noose clenched Gelden's throat. His body flailed and writhed and, after a time, went still. Limp and lifeless, Gelden's unmoving body dangled from the rope.

The audience of prisoners uttered not a sound.

Neither did Mali, although tears spilled from her eyes. And now, blood gushed from her slashed wrists and from the femoral artery in both thighs. A gesture of unadulterated defiance, Mali held up a small knife for all to see just seconds before she stabbed her neck underneath her jawline, slicing into the carotid artery. Ghostly pallid, she collapsed onto the wooden box and took her last breath looking upward to the empty noose the Nazis had intended for her. A sly smile adorned Mali's face. She had not hanged as ordered; she had died by her own hand.

Hinda wanted to applaud Mali but dared not. Today, the Nazis did not have it their way, not with Mali and not with Hinda. A brazen thought had germinated, sprouting seeds that resounded repeatedly through Hinda's mind, heart, and soul—one word: ESCAPE.

When Hinda and Rachel returned to Block Eleven, inmates were weeping. One woman screamed out, "Lord, how much more do you think we can take? How much longer will we be persecuted?"

Another woman screeched, "Lord Almighty, Mali just wanted freedom. Do you think she didn't deserve that? Do we not too?"

Questions and curses—barbed darts directed at God—flew with fury around the room.

The warden stomped from her office and ordered silence. She stood in the middle of the room until all prisoners were in their bunks.

Later that night, Rachel whispered, "How do you think Mali got the knife?"

"Had to be a resistor, somebody in administration, a guard, or maybe a capo, who gave it to her." Hinda yawned, then added, "Mali worked in the SS office, so she had access to information. Maybe she sold or traded reports."

"Was Dr. Walter a resistor?"

Hinda flinched at Rachel's use of the past tense when referring to Walter. Sighing heavily, she replied, "For sure, in that he gave me curative medicine and allowed himself to have feelings for me, a Jewish prisoner."

"And he made negative comments about the Nazis and how they were treating us Jews. Do you think he's still alive?"

"I pray so." Hinda turned onto her side, facing her sister. She pulled up their one blanket around them. "Rachel, there's something I've been thinking about all day." She paused.

"What? Out with it," Rachel said, yawning.

"I want us to escape. I'm hatching a plan."

Her mouth agape, Rachel rose up in the bunk. "How could you possibly say such a crazy thing after watching Mali and Gelden die today?"

"That's exactly what gave rise to the idea. My gut instinct spoke, which I have not experienced in a long time now."

"Lord, help us. Hinda, *you* have gone mad, totally insane."

91

Diabolical Disguise

September 1944 | Oświęcim, German-occupied Poland
Auschwitz Concentration Camp

Inside the Central Pharmacy, Walter Zeilhofen counted pills while listening to the Chief Pharmacist, Victor Capesius, talk with Dr. Josef Mengele on the phone and commit to deliver copious quantities of the chemical compound, phenol, to him that afternoon. Walter ran his fingers nervously through his blond strands, thinking about the medical uses for phenol. He could not stop the rage from welling up like a tempest inside him for he knew for certain—having witnessed it himself—that Mengele used phenol unethically. The doctor administered phenol in lethal doses to achieve quick deaths, so he could begin cutting and carving his test subjects into pieces. Since phenol had a scent that was reminiscent of sterilizing products used in medical environments, the unsuspecting prisoners waiting in Mengele's lab had no idea that they were about to die.

Before hanging up the phone, Capesius said, "Keep up the splendid work, Josef. Your research accomplishments are staggering. The world will soon be at your feet." A high-ranking Nazi SS officer, Capesius knew exactly how Mengele used the compound and had no moral objections with such usage of phenol on prisoners. In fact, he applauded it, especially when it involved Jews, deeming them as enemies of Germany and genetically defective deplorables who must be completely purged from the human race.

The phone in his hand, ready to dial another number, Capesius turned to Walter. "How's that hospital order coming along?"

"I'm working on the final prescription now. Then, I'll be on my way," Walter replied.

Capesius nodded and proceeded with another phone call. After less than a minute of conversing, he yelled into the receiver, "Not acceptable! We did *not* receive this week's supply as outlined on the purchase order. So, now, we need five hundred more canisters by tomorrow morning. Get your supervisor on the line or let me speak to Herr Tesch, the owner."

Behind the counter, Walter had now completed the hospital order, but he stalled, pretending to count tablets into an apothecary jar. He listened intently to the conversation between Capesius and the agent of the German company, Tesch & Stabenow, about his purchase of Zyklon B.

At his desk, Capesius, who was now red in the face, screamed into the phone, "What do you mean this week's order was cancelled?" He lowered his volume and quietly asked, "Was it a male or a female with whom you spoke?"

At that moment, a prisoner named Matija from Axis-partitioned Yugoslavia, accidentally dropped the mop near the pharmacy counter. Its handle clanged loudly against the floor. She looked nervously at Capesius, then at Walter. Quietly and respectfully, she apologized.

From behind the counter, Walter nodded his assent to Matija, who was a certified pharmacist. Imprisoned at Auschwitz simply because she was a Jew, she now mopped floors and ate slop. Walter watched as she picked up the mop handle and began scrubbing a dirty splotch. Her head down, she moved her arms and the mop back and forth in a vigorous, crazed rhythm.

Across the room, Capesius continued his phone conversation. His tone full of angered curiosity, he inquired, "A heavy accent? What kind?" Capesius tapped his fingers on the counter. Narrowing his eyes in disbelief, he said, "French? I have no male employees who are French. I'll get to the bottom of this later. Right now, though, I want a guarantee that your fake Red Cross truck will show up here early tomorrow morning with those five hundred canisters of Zyklon B." After a short pause, he said, "Then I'll call Degesch, your competitor, and get it *all* from them. Do I have your guarantee or not?" Raising his fist in the air in triumph, Capesius slammed down the phone. He then took his pen and scribbled on a notepad. Stomping over to Walter, he thrust the paper in Walter's face and commanded, "Read this."

Walter scanned the message, which featured a French proverb—"Qui court deux lièvres à la fois, n'en prend aucun."—that he knew well. Yet, in a faltering pace, and intentionally speaking in guttural German tones versus nasal French ones, Walter proceeded to butcher the phrase that meant, *who runs after two hares at a time, catches none.* Acting embarrassed, Walter apologized, "I'm sorry, sir. Should I know what this says?"

"Didn't you take basic French in school, or at least in college?" Capesius asked, his eyebrows knitted together in skepticism.

"I took Latin in college in preparation for medical school. I was exposed to French in grade school. I can speak basic greetings and classic menu words." He pointed to the paper. "But speaking or reading such as what is written there is an entirely different matter." Walter stared directly into the eyes of his boss, Victor Capesius. He maintained eye contact and did not blink, all the while silently apologizing to God that he had become such an expert fibster.

Tilting his head back in arrogance, Capesius walked away from Walter. He strutted over to Matija and showed her the note, demanding that she read it aloud.

Walter cast his eyes downward to the floor, holding his breath while Matija read the words. In a painfully slow measure, she enunciated the first part decently, but then crudely mispronounced three of the words in the second half. She spoke in a higher-pitched voice, not her normal one, which was low for a female, almost being a baritone.

Capesius stared intently at the woman, whom he had expected to read the proverb fluidly. He was surprised at Walter too. Most Europeans of their educational levels were fluent in multiple languages. Capesius wadded the paper in his hand and looked back and forth between the two of them. "Sounds like you both need language lessons." Turning to Matija, he said in a condescending tone, "Go wash your hands, 46139, and then bring me fresh coffee." Capesius stomped to his desk and chose a file from the drawer. Donning his eyeglasses, he pored over the pages of the registry that showed who worked in the pharmacy and exactly what days and times they did.

When Matija brought his coffee, Capesius swatted her away without a word of thanks. Sipping from the cup, he noted that there were only five people who had worked in the pharmacy in the last month. The names, though, that reappeared every few lines were Dr. Walter Zeilhofen and prisoner number 46139, which was Matija Banovic. Looking up to the ceiling, Capesius leaned back in his chair. His mind whirred with suspicion that this cancelled order was not a simple error, and that someone was deliberately sabotaging the supply of Zyklon B, which was needed to operate the gas chambers effectively. Whoever was to blame, he believed, was also working to undermine the *Final Solution*. He sighed heavily, crossing his arms across his chest. Pieces of a mystery fell into place. Now, it made sense why there had been so much trouble with the supply chain in the past few months. He vowed to investigate and find the traitor or traitors. Friend or foe, he declared, he would see them hang.

One day the following week, Walter was assigned to run the pharmacy while Victor Capesius was out on business. After completing orders for hospital pre-scriptions, he headed to the small kitchen located in the back to make a fresh pot of coffee. When he passed Capesius' desk, he remembered a day in April, earlier that year, when he had read a nefarious document. The folder had been left in plain sight atop the desk of Capesius, who had been out for the afternoon. Disbelieving what he was seeing, Walter had read the title three times. Shock had rippled through him. Printed in bold letters across the front of the folder were the words, THE FINAL SOLUTION: *The Question of the Jews*.

Brazenly, Walter had opened it. Dated January 1942, the document he proceeded to read curdled his blood. In ordinary language, the mission was spelled out clearly. At that stage of the war, it had been determined that the most expedient directive was to exterminate all Jews within grasp.

Disease and starvation had an impact but were not producing immediate sweeping results. Bullets proved to be too costly and were too slow for the execution of large groups. Gas chambers, housing hundreds of Jews at a time, maximized objectives. To effectuate the desired outcome, Zyklon B had been selected as the poison of choice and was to be delivered in hermetically sealed canisters, and arrive at camps in red trucks that resembled official Red Cross vehicles. Walter had gasped. His mind had whirred as he thought, *Zyklon B is intentionally delivered in trucks that display the red medical cross on a white background, an emblem that symbolizes safety and help. Yet, it carries human poi-son. What a diabolical disguise.* Shaking his head with revulsion, Walter had read on. Guards, wearing protective gear and gas masks, were to unseal the canisters and administer the toxin into the chambers through a specifically designed pipe in the roof.

The document outlined exact logistics to be followed. Subjects' clothing and all jewelry were to be removed and collected prior to entering the chamber. To ensure that subjects entered the chamber calmly and without protest, announcements verbalized that after the cleansing bath subjects would receive uniforms and a hearty meal. Then, they would be allowed to retrieve personal belongings. In actual practice, armed guards were to herd them inside the bath-house, packing the room to full capacity. Once the gas was switched on, subjects inside would die within fifteen minutes or less. Guards would wait one hour for the toxins to clear, then remove the bodies. When the facility was readied anew, another group was to be ushered in and gassed.

Calculations regarding how many thousands of Jews it was feasible to exterminate in one day, how much Zyklon B would be required, and how many bodies the crematoriums could handle at one time had made Walter feel so nauseated, he thought he might lose his lunch. He was about to close the folder when he saw an amended proviso dated December 1943. Auschwitz Chief Pharmacist, Victor Capesius, was responsible for ordering all toxins and securing an ample supply for all gas chambers in the Auschwitz and Birkenau camps and subcamps. Two German manufacturers of such chemicals and compounds had been selected as official suppliers: Tesch & Stabenow in Hamburg and Degesch in Dessau.

Shuddering from the memories of reading such chilling decrees, which had blatantly charted mass genocide, Walter rushed to the kitchen and made fresh coffee. Returning to the pharmacy counter, he sipped from his mug, thinking of the murderous mandate, which repeatedly used the word "exterminate" as if Jews were bugs or rodents. He grimaced, but hope leapt in his heart when Matija, his resistor ally, entered the pharmacy. Soon, she would be on the phone with an agent from Tesch & Stabenow cancelling the next order of Zyklon B. She had the talent of a professional impersonator and had recently perfected the tenor tone and Austrian accent of chief pharmacist, Victor Capesius. Although Walter had noticed Capesius acting suspicious of the two of them, Matija and he remained morally committed. They would take precautions, but they would persist with their sabotage operations and continue fighting the Nazi regime's evil goals.

92

An Electric Feeling

October 1944 | Oświecim, German-occupied Poland
Auschwitz Concentration Camp

The *human* train stretched from the warehouse named Canada to German buses on the main street. Links in the labor chain, Hinda and Rachel, who had recently been reassigned to work at Canada, passed the packed boxes to the next person in line and so on until the boxes were loaded onto a bus.

Every Friday morning, the buses arrived at Auschwitz and then departed in the early evening, transporting the week's accumulation of confiscated goods to varying cities throughout Germany, specifically to Third Reich offices. Such bounty the Germans were garnering from the Jews, who the Nazis were slaughtering in legions, multiple train loads, every day now.

In the late afternoon that Friday, one of the boxes felt particularly heavy when Hinda handed it to the woman in line next to her. For a moment, she felt she would faint. Then she decided it was the weight of her sorrow-laden heart as she contemplated the profound injustice of it all. Not only were the Nazis unjustly confiscating property from the European Jews, but they also were intentionally destroying great humanity—including brilliant minds of scientists, engineers, educators, surgeons, inventors, and the keen talent of writers, artists, poets, and musicians. Intellect and genius obliterated. Burned to ashes in crematoriums.

Hinda blinked, clearing tears that welled as she thought of all the tragedy, and especially the multitude of Jewish children who had never had the chance to grow up, like her little Sara. She placed her fingertips on the side of her head, applying pressure to the temple area. She chided herself for allowing her mind to whirl with such unjust realities that she now felt lightheaded. Fearing that she might pass out, she planted her feet wider apart for stability. Yet, in the next hour, the faint feeling returned again and again.

A new box was passed to Hinda, and she turned to face the woman next in line, preparing to heft it to her. When the woman saw Hinda's face, she gasped, "*Oy gevalt!* 25305, you're as yellow as an egg yolk."

Extreme thirst and nausea engulfing her feverish body, Hinda flipped onto her left side, then flopped onto her back. All positions provoked intense achiness. Yet lying on her right side was especially painful, which engendered worry that her liver was swollen.

Earlier that evening when the sisters darkened the doorway to Block Eleven, Hinda had dashed straightaway to her bunk. She was not feeling up to conversing. But more importantly, she did not want the warden to see the color change in her skin. When getting into her bunk, she overhead mutterings from the bunk next to hers: "Whoa, 25305 looks jaundiced."

Upon hearing those words, Hinda's fears of having hepatitis or typhus duly fueled, she curled into a fetal position and prayed more ardently than she had in a year or more. Just last month, bogged down in the abyss of a hellish depression, Hinda had wrestled with her beliefs in God, though she had been raised to be devoutly religious. In those dark hours of despair when she wished to die, it seemed that her faith was no more than myth and bunk. Questioning if the Almighty existed, she concluded that either God was deceased, or the Nazis had converted God to their way of thinking. How else, she reasoned, could the all-seeing Lord watch such gross inhumane atrocities perpetuated upon the Jews or any group of people?

A startlingly high number of women in Block Eleven had maintained their faith. Hinda had listened to them discuss their belief in God's wisdom and watched them pray, just as her father used to do. Hinda envied the peace and strength the women found in their faith, compared to the turmoil in her mind. Even still, on that day, she had declared them to be simple minded.

Tonight, as she felt death brush against her once again, her father's prophecy that she would survive was not enough. She needed more. Her soul reached heavenward, pleading for mercy, for Divine intervention, and for healing. Plunged back into the convictions of her youth, she repented for having been a doubter. Feeling awkward, she stumbled through prayers, attempting to connect to the Lord Almighty, whom she had renounced.

Late into the fitful night, her father's face appeared, hovering over her. His lips moved as if he were talking to her. While Hinda could not hear what he was saying, she suddenly remembered her father speaking the phrase, *Praise God*, regardless of negative circumstances. Sensing that she had interpreted his message correctly, Hinda focused her thoughts upon the praise-worthy favor that

God had bestowed upon her while she had been in Auschwitz. Her heart fluttered as she reflected upon their day of Selection when she had seized opportunity and dared to switch Rachel into her line, keeping them together. It was utterly amazing that she had not been caught and killed on the spot. Furthermore, it was astounding that she still had Rachel with her. Even after discovering the two were sisters, the authorities had not separated them, although it was a strict camp policy to do so with family members. Miraculously, the two of them had been allowed to work together and to sleep together. In awe, she remembered yet another wonder: the Sunday she went to the infirmary and met the good Dr. Walter. His heroic actions saved her life when she had a severe case of malaria. And then, after two years of enduring horrendous beatings, strenuous labor, and malnutrition, she was still alive. Although barely, it seemed tonight.

Seconds before she fell into deep slumber, she whispered, "Thank you, dear Tatae, for reaching down to Earth tonight to help restore my faith. Praise God."

Although seriously ill for two full weeks, Hinda arose for roll call and showed up for work at Canada every day. If she did not, she knew her jaundiced skin would be scorched and reduced to ash in the crematorium. Hepatitis and typhus were rampant but going to the infirmary for a diagnosis equaled a death sentence. Now, any sign of sickness or disease in a prisoner and the immediate prescription was the gas chamber.

With Rachel's help, Hinda made it through the daylight hours. After work, rather than stand in the food line, she retreated to her bunk for rest. Most nights, Rachel saved a bit of bread for her. Hinda's appetite was nil, but she forced herself to choke down every crumb in the name of getting well. Although far from completely recovered, she was physically improving, and without medication and the liquids her body needed. Moreover, she could feel her mental clarity returning.

The women in Block Eleven continued to keep their distance. Unabashedly, they eyeballed Hinda, noting the details of her outward symptoms. The expression in their eyes her mirror, Hinda knew that her yellow coloring was improving. Since Rachel had remained well, Hinda surmised that she had not contracted typhus but had suffered a strain of hepatitis that was not contagious.

One evening toward the end of the month, Hinda was alone in Block Eleven, a rarity. Her Block mates were at the food hall getting their nightly rations. Plus, the warden had stepped out, saying she would return shortly. Lying in her bunk, Hinda soaked up the peaceful solitude, which triggered thoughts of her father and how strong-minded he had been. In the face of extreme persecution and loss, Salomon had kept his faith, his dignity, and his integrity. Exhibiting incredible fortitude, he had trusted God to his final exhalation. And he had possessed the foresight to leave Hinda with inspiring words, a powerful prophecy.

Suddenly, an electric feeling jolted through Hinda. She began shouting zealously, "I WANT TO LIVE! I WANT TO LIVE! I WANT TO LIVE!" In a calmer tone, she issued a potent declaration, proclaiming "My dear father, Tatae, said I would live to tell. And I *will*."

93

Harvesting Gold

Paradise in Auschwitz. Hinda chuckled at the oxymoron, the absurd paradox applied to any workstation in Auschwitz. Yet, in comparison, she claimed Canada to be her utopia. The work was indoors where it was warm, except for when they loaded the buses on Fridays.

What's more, she and Rachel were consistently finding an unusual amount of food items tucked into the clothing pockets and suitcases that they unpacked. They ate what they could on the job without being caught. Other times, the bread, dried fruit, or nuts were slipped into their pockets to eat later. Wretched memories of food poisoning reminded them to eat nothing that smelled rancid or toxic, even when they were racked with savage hunger.

The clothing and jewels Hinda unpacked held a new fascination for her. This interest added to her belief that the warehouse named Canada was a wonderland of sorts. Nevertheless, she found it disturbing that these innocent people, not knowing their destination, had packed valuables to trade for advantage, for food, or for their very lives. And now, they were dead, coerced and strong-armed into the gas chambers. Pushing aside such mournful thoughts, Hinda focused upon the details of the clothing. The garments that looked the correct size for Rachel and her captured her imagination. Visualizing complete outfits in her mind, she would then decide which ones would look more flattering on Rachel, or on her. This game soothed her.

The conditions in the camp were growing worse every week. Rations had diminished again. Sirens warning of nearby bombs were common, day and night. Hinda had overhead wardens saying that Crematorium One had been converted to an air-raid shelter for officers and staff. Throughout the camp, rumors claimed that Germany was losing the war.

Within Auschwitz, signs of the escalated attacks upon Germany and the regime's distress were ubiquitous. Maintenance of buildings had declined. Rigidly scheduled procedures such as shaving prisoner's heads on a monthly basis had been discarded. Fewer guards patrolled the workstations and other areas in the camp. German shepherds, trained to be vicious, accompanied the guards who were on duty. And those guards' emotional fuses were dangerously short. Quicker to behave even more maliciously, their excessive beatings and unwarranted mistreatment of prisoners had radically escalated.

Every day now, at morning roll call, the electric fence was lined with dead bodies where inmates had thrown themselves against it, committing suicide during the night. Oftentimes now, the guards did not bother to remove the carcasses. Other days, they made towering stacks of the corpses because only three crematoria were operational now, and they were overloaded, running twenty-four hours a day, seven days a week.

When Hinda had arrived at Auschwitz, there had been five crematoria on the property. One was now an air-raid shelter, and just last month, on October seventh, Crematorium Four was severely damaged and declared unusable. Hinda had reeled with the news: A large group of Jewish prisoners, two hundred fifty or more, who worked on the gas chamber and crematoria detail—a special work unit called the *Sonderkommando* in Auschwitz II-Birkenau—had used stolen explosives to set fire to Crematorium Four. Then, they had attacked the SS in the vicinity. While Hinda was glad about the destroyed crematorium, she was devastated to hear that all the prisoners had died fighting or were murdered by the SS. According to the reports, the SS lost three men and more than ten had been wounded.

Always checking for more camp changes that could signify that Germany was losing the war, Hinda had also noticed that, on the march from Block Eleven to Canada, the guards no longer shot the people who fell down. She overheard one guard say, "I'm not wasting these costly bullets on you animals." Instead, he had used his gun handle to beat the people who had fallen, whipping them lifeless.

Today, as Hinda's group marched to work, they passed a warehouse named Mexic. Its doors were normally closed, but this morning, the warehouse doors were pushed back. Hundreds of people were crammed inside. Just off the trains, the throng unknowingly awaited the gas chambers. There would be no Selection process for them as all categorizing procedures had been abandoned. Nowadays, every man, woman, and child coming into Auschwitz—whether or not they were capable of working—were gassed. And come they did. Multiple trains packed full of Jews from varying countries arrived daily. The Third Reich was in a mad rush, coordinating massive killings of European Jews. Extermination versus interment was the order.

That morning, when marching in front of the Mexic warehouse, Hinda and Rachel heard horrific screaming. The guard responsible for their group stopped and commanded them to halt. He asked a sentinel at the door to Mexic what was happening.

"The dentists are just harvesting all the gold teeth before we move these Judes into the gas houses," the Mexic guard reported.

Hinda shuddered, doubting that real dentists were onsite. Envisioning guards with pliers, she could easily imagine the horrendous pain the people were experiencing without anesthesia.

Inching closer to her sister, Rachel whispered, "Mexic is one *bad* place."

"Horrible," Hinda whispered in return. "And it worries me for our older brothers who are in Mexico City. Did they name this warehouse *Mexic* because Mexico is a bad place?"

"Could be," Rachel replied. "They named the warehouse Canada because that country is supposedly an abundant place." Not wanting to get in trouble with their guard, Rachel kept her face forward and spoke in a hushed tone. "I haven't thought of our older brothers in a long time. Do you think they even know we're imprisoned here?"

"Jack might," Hinda replied. "He's a journalist."

Sirens blared in the air. Their guard ceased conversing and commanded them onward.

Hinda sighed in deep relief when Rachel and she were safely inside Canada. The sirens stopped after five minutes, but she could not push thoughts of her older brothers and Mexico out of her mind. Especially when she thought of Jack, her favorite brother, she experienced rushes of goose bumps on her arms and legs. Knowing that it meant something significant, she pondered possibilities. Prayers for Jack leapt in her heart.

At twilight, on a Sunday evening, the night warden for Block Eleven stepped out for a smoke. She walked ten feet to stand under a tree, her favorite spot. Shortly afterwards, the warden from the adjacent Block joined her, and both women lit up cigarettes.

When the wardens were chatting and had turned their faces away from the buildings, a woman, who had been hiding in the shrubs, entered Block Eleven. Unfamiliar with the layout of the room, her eyes darted around as if in search of a specific person or thing. Standing in the front area, the woman called out, "Number 25305? Are you here?" Shifting her weight from one foot to another, she repeated, "25305." The woman cleared her throat and then said loudly, "Hinda, I believe is the actual name."

Hinda arose from her bunk, looking dubiously at the woman who was a stranger to her. Relieved to see that the woman was wearing a prisoner uniform, Hinda waved to her, and the woman proceeded down the aisle.

As she walked, the woman slid her right hand into her pocket. When she stepped close, she suddenly spun her neck around to look behind her to see if anyone approached. Satisfied that no one else was near, she inhaled deeply and plucked a small piece of paper from her pants pocket. Handing the paper to Hinda, she spoke in a hushed tone, "I work in the Central Pharmacy. Another person who also works there asked me to give this to you." Before Hinda could reply, the woman turned on her heel and quickly exited Block Eleven.

Taken aback and surprised, Hinda felt almost dizzy. Her hands trembling, she turned her back to the room and opened the paper. She strained in the dim light of dusk to read the sentence: *Soon, the dark clouds over the sky are going away, and you will see sunshine again.*

Her heart rate increased. Recognizing the handwriting, Hinda felt an exhilarating surge of energy. She wanted to joyously jump so high that she bounced her head on the ceiling.

Clutching the note to her chest in awe, Hinda whispered, "Walter. He's alive! He's here at Auschwitz, not in a coal mine."

95
Frostbite

On the second day of January, Hinda and Rachel no longer worked in paradise; they labored in hell.

The guard rolled back the doors to the no-name workstation. It was completely filled with corpses. Hundreds of decaying bodies lay there, oozing and polluting the space. "Here's the registry." He handed Hinda a black notebook. "Now, get to work matching the tattoo numbers to the serial numbers recorded in the book. Make a check mark next to the number when you have matched it."

"We are to work in here?" Hinda asked incredulously. The stench hit her in the face. Nausea roiled.

The sisters exchanged a look of disgust just before Rachel's face blanched pale. She gagged. Her head hanging inches from the snow, Rachel threw up the coffee and what bits of breakfast bread she had ingested.

The guard yelled, "You stupid Jude girl, if you don't stop retching, I will sic the dogs on you." He whistled, and two German shepherds ran to his side.

Phobic about the dogs, Rachel sidled around them and slipped through the doorway.

Hinda turned to see her sister ghostly white and wobbling, as if she were about to faint. She grabbed Rachel's arm to steady her. "Here, you take over the registry. I'll read the tattoo numbers to you. And try your best to not vomit. You can't afford to lose the fluid or nutrition. Neither of us can."

Bending over a cadaver, Hinda wrestled with the man's arm. It was so stiff, it felt impossible to maneuver it in such a way that she could see the inner forearm. Mustering all her might, she twisted the arm vigorously. At last, she was able to contort it just so. In sequence, she called out the numerals to Rachel, who matched the tattoo number to the registry.

After completing that area, Hinda shook her head in dismay. There was no avenue to get to the next section without stepping on dead bodies. Feeling her clogs digging into them, she said under her breath, "Excuse me, I'm sorry." To others, she whispered, "Thank you for being my stepping stones."

Riveted by the corpses' faces, Hinda chided herself for such irreverence. Nonetheless, she studied them. Old, middle-aged, and young, countless had died with their eyes wide open. She struggled to not look into their eyes as they stared coldly back at her.

When Hinda went into an area particularly dense with bodies, the guard saw her catch her breath and pinch her nose. He hooted and said, "These filthy Jews smell really bad, don't they?"

Rage swelled within Hinda; her cheeks reddened. She reached into her pocket and fingered Walter's note. Just knowing it was there engendered the willpower to remain composed, to not glare at the guard and rail him with scathing reprimands that his organs would decompose and stink the very same.

At the end of the grim day, Hinda's back ached from bending over. Her legs trembled and throbbed. Next to her, Rachel wept. In nervous shambles, she held her hand over her throat, striving to suppress the bile. Wounded birds with crippled wings, the sisters hobbled their way back to Block Eleven, to their bunk, their nest of hay.

Later that evening, before drifting into sleep, Rachel whispered, "What a disgusting job." Revulsion dripped from every syllable. "I don't understand why the Germans are even keeping those records. The people are dead."

Hinda yawned and stretched, her body aching. "The Germans always have systems, and they follow them rigidly. But you know these corpses were our camp mates. People who go straight to the gas chambers aren't tattooed." She turned on her side to face her sister. "No serial numbers or records are kept on them because the Nazis don't want the world to know just how many people they're murdering."

"How do you know this about no tattoo numbers for those going directly to the gas chambers?"

Hinda's heart clenched with guilt, remembering the day she lied about Sara and what the policewoman had said. Her eyes clouded with shadows, and she blinked repetitively as she added to the falsehood. "I overheard wardens talking together. That's what they said."

Rachel wrinkled her brow. "Are the cadavers in that warehouse from the fence?"

"Yes, oodles. Others were sick." Hinda flipped onto her back, unable to get comfortable. "I saw untold yellowed corpses there, jaundiced from malaria, typhus, or hepatitis. And scads of young people."

The night warden walked near; she shined her flashlight into their bunk. "Hey, 25305, 25306, stop that prattle and get to sleep." She moved the light down their bunk. "What has happened to this blanket?" She jerked up the end where the hem was jagged with pieces missing.

Wide-eyed, Hinda said, "Maybe the rats chewed into it."

The warden nodded and was about to walk away, but she tripped slightly on Hinda's clogs. She shined her light onto the floor. "The rats did it, you say? What are these?" She bent down and picked up pieces of the blanket that had slipped from Hinda's clog.

Swallowing hard, Hinda did not respond.

"I want an answer, 25305." She picked up Rachel's clogs and pieces of blanket fell from them, too. The warden shrieked, "Get up, both of you, right now."

Trembling, the sisters piled from the bunk. Hinda straightened her shoulders and said, "Warden, please let me explain. Our toes get so cold when we march to work in the early mornings. We used the blanket pieces to wrap them, so we didn't get frostbite."

The warden jeered, cackling in a mocking deriding tone, "Frostbite?" Her eyes hardened and her lips pursed together in righteous contempt. She snarled, "You've destroyed government property, you ungrateful tramp." She ripped the leather strap from her belt and began striking one sister and then the other. Alternating whipping Hinda and then Rachel, the warden walloped them until they both collapsed onto the floor and no longer screamed or cried. Blood spurted from their skin and jetted down their legs.

The warden's head held high, and her nose pointed upward in arrogance, she walked away. When she had retreated to her office and closed the door, two inmates slid from their bunks. In the darkness, the women picked up Rachel, who was limp like a rag doll, and tenderly placed her onto the hay. Then, they helped Hinda get up from the floor and into the bunk beside her sister.

Emotionally devastated, mentally demoralized, and physically destabilized to near unconsciousness, Hinda was uncertain if she and Rachel would live to awaken in the morning. Racked with excruciating throbbing and stinging, she could only hold one thought. *Escape. It is time.*

96
The Escape Plan
January 1945 | Oświecim, German-occupied Poland
Auschwitz Concentration Camp

In his private quarters, Walter sat in his leather wing chair, sipping a glass of brandy. Due to his diabetes, he did not typically have a nightcap. But tonight, he could not dissolve the lump in his throat or unwind the knot in his stomach. He sat there motionless, except for his eyes, which roved over every inch of the living room. The sofa had been moved slightly, its legs not aligned on the rug exactly the way he had placed them. The lamp next to him had also been shifted, but just slightly. The papers on his desk had been rifled through, and his desk chair turned in the opposite direction from how he had left it that morning. The housekeeper was not scheduled to come for two more days, and she would not have disturbed his papers. An unauthorized person or persons had entered and moved around his stuff. The question was *why*.

The phone ringing rattled his nerves even more. Walter stared at it, afraid to answer, afraid to not. When he did pick it up, he was relieved to hear the voice of his trusted friend, Dr. Hans Munch, a bacteriologist who had been brought to Auschwitz to research the growing cases of typhus and make recommendations on how to make the camp a healthier place. At one of their dinners together, Hans had lamented to Walter that not a single one of his suggestions had ever been implemented. He shared that it had soon become clear to him that camp officials were only interested in mistreating and killing off the prisoners.

"Dinner tomorrow sounds great," Walter replied to his friend's invitation. Scrutinizing his living quarters with suspicion, he offered, "I know it's my turn to have you here, but I just can't get excited about cooking anything these days. How about we go to the officers' club? My treat." Their plans set, Walter laid the phone receiver back in its cradle.

Rising from the chair, Walter went to his desk. Papers lay strewn across it, the way the intruder had left them. The mess was obvious, unlike the subtle rearrangement of the lamp and sofa. While wondering about the discrepancy, he straightened the papers and discovered that the first two pages of a letter to his parents were missing. If he were not spooked, he would have laughed. The letter to his parents contained nothing incriminating due to censorship of all mail. Mostly, he lied to them about how he was enjoying his work at Auschwitz. Thumbing through the other pages, he realized that more had been taken— additional pages containing his notes on hospital patients and some rare symptoms that he was researching.

Gathering his papers, he wondered what the intruder had been looking for. The inscribed rock that Rhino's mother had sent came to mind. Walter sighed. Thankfully, he had finally succeeded in shattering it, and had then scattered its tiny pieces in varying spots as he walked to work each day over the following week. If someone were looking for the rock, it was long gone.

While contemplating possibilities, Walter leaned his head back and closed his eyes. When the faces of his parents popped into his mind, he remembered how they had encouraged him to be a force for good at Auschwitz. In the midst of all the evil, he *had* been an agent of goodness, even though he had lied and used covert manipulations to do so. From the time that he and Soldier Rhino had joined forces, he had crossed the line of treasonous behavior, in particular giving Hinda curative medicine. And then, he had befriended Matija, and they had worked together to delay orders of Zyklon B. But now that the gas chambers were not operating, Zyklon B was no longer needed. While it was good news that Jews were no longer being gassed, Walter had been shocked last November when some of the facilities were destroyed. The explosions were deafening. Then, he learned that Himmler had ordered all gas chambers and crematoria to be partially dismantled, then blown up, using dynamite. Many prisoners, who were required to employ the explosives, had died in the fiery explosions. Walter grimaced. *Ah yes, Himmler didn't get his own hands dirty or risk his own life to destroy such incriminating evidence against the Nazis.*

Since that time, Walter and Matija had focused on getting restricted medicines to sick inmates. Now, connected to resistors of all ranks in the camp, Walter would persevere with his defiant, though altruistic, efforts.

Clenching his palm, Walter reflected upon how much he missed his parents. He had not been allowed to go home or see them since he arrived in October of 1942. Although he was not classified as a prisoner, in fact, he was one. No one, except the highest-ranking SS officers and regime officials, could leave once taking a post at Auschwitz. The intention was to minimize the risks of the outside world hearing accounts of the crimes and atrocious human abuse occurring throughout the camp.

The latest underground intelligence reports said British and American forces had freed France and invaded Germany. Yet, it could be months before they reached Auschwitz. Walter worried that he should not wait for their rescue, and neither should Hinda. Now, untold numbers of Jewish internees were slaughtered on a daily basis. Thousands more were being evacuated to subcamps within interior Germany. Forced to march long distances, most did not survive.

More urgently for him, underground reports stated that Russian troops were planning to storm Auschwitz in late January, sometime after the twentieth. Since Walter did not speak an iota of Russian, he feared Soviet forces would rush to kill him, presuming him to be a Nazi officer. Thus, he had devised an escape plan for the evening of January tenth. Matija would surprise Hinda and Rachel in the food hall and then escort them to the officers' hospital to meet up with Walter and Dr. Hans Munch. Garnering SS officer uniforms, Munch had hidden them in a storeroom in the basement of the hospital. The group would meet there, and the men would don the official uniforms over their regular clothing. Walter had secured nurses' uniforms for the women to wear after ditching their prisoner garb. Two SS officers, both defectors, had committed to be drivers and to have two vehicles, one military truck and one jeep, waiting on a side street. The women would hide under a tarp in the truck, and the two rebel officers would then drive the group through the south gates of Auschwitz and beyond to a safe area.

Draining his glass, Walter let the brandy slide down his throat. A sly, lopsided fleer curled his lips upward in wry amusement. *There may be a bug planted here in this room, but it cannot hear my thoughts. Hinda, my love, hang on. I'm coming for you soon.*

97

The Key

January 1945 | Oświecim, German-occupied Poland
Auschwitz Concentration Camp

Escape! Escape! If you're going to live to tell, you must escape! The words reverberated through her every cell as Hinda checked off the identity numbers of the foul-smelling corpses. Weak and bruised from the severe beating two nights ago, Hinda realized that her ability to stomach this disgusting work had been derailed—her coping capacity now a train wreck inside her. Choking back bile rising in her esophagus, she battled a constant and persistent urge to vomit. Her only weapon against it was to focus her mind upon an escape plot that had seeded and sprouted roots, which were germinating more deeply in her mind with each passing hour.

The corpse warehouse had become a breeding depot for dangerous bacteria. She feared that Rachel and she would become deathly ill from breathing in the fumes and touching the germ-laden cadavers. They were going to die, and soon, if they did not try to escape.

She was physically weak, but her mind felt clearer and stronger than it had in months, especially when she concentrated on the details of her escape strategy. Her every instinct poked and prodded her with urgency. Her mother's words of years ago had become a chorus of bells tolling in her heart: "Hinda, you have exceptionally good instincts. You must *always* trust them."

Nearing the end of the day, Hinda had completed an entire section of corpses. Before moving on to the next area, she yearned to go to the door for fresh air. Glancing to the doorway, she saw the guard standing just outside the warehouse. He puffed on a cigarette; billows of smoke surrounded him. There would be no fresh air. Moreover, he would not allow her to step out.

Signaling to Rachel to take the ledger to the back part of the room, Hinda made her way around the oozing carcasses. She stumbled on an extended foot and inadvertently turned to look. Instantly, tears sprang from her eyes. Color drained from her already pale face. She screamed, "No! Dear Lord, no, not my beautiful friend. Oh, Annie!" Crying uncontrollably, Hinda wailed. Her sorrowful mewls echoed throughout the warehouse.

Rushing to her sister's side, Rachel gasped. The corpse was, indeed, Annie. The sight of the young woman in death was woeful. Annie's vibrance had been stilled. Her once animated face was passionless; her bones were devoid of music.

From the doorway, the guard yelled, "What's all the commotion?" He chunked his cigarette stub on the pavement and stomped inside.

Hinda, in the throes of sobs, was rendered speechless. Rachel managed to say, "It's her childhood friend. She played violin in the orchestra here."

The guard shouted, "Like I care. And the orchestra is done with, anyway, shut down last November." He shifted his weight, one foot pawing the floor. He pointed his finger at Hinda. "You shut up, you lamebrained Jude girl, or in a few minutes, you're going to be lying there beside her in the same stinking shape. Get back to work right now, or I'm calling in the dogs."

At the end of the workday, the guard rolled down the door to the warehouse and hustled Hinda and Rachel down the path. At the corner, he motioned for them to stop. He lit up a cigarette.

Hinda's chin quivered as she choked back sobs. The sight of Annie's dead body had entwined one more garland into the wreath of grief buried in her heart. Yet her tears were expunged when she looked across a grassy area and saw a guard exit from the back of the warehouse named Canada. She watched intently as he locked the one-panel door, a back entrance and exit. Until recently, she had not known the door existed.

The Canada guard waved to their guard and then trotted across the grass to join him. They walked on together, the two guards in front, and Hinda and Rachel following behind. Soon, a third guard, plus a crew of workers from Canada, came up behind their group. That guard yelled, "Hey, wait up. You guys have an extra cig?" The two guards in front stopped to wait for him. The first one from Canada tugged a pack of cigarettes from his pocket. As he did, a key slipped from the same pocket and fell onto the ground.

Without a moment's hesitation, Hinda lifted her foot and placed her clog directly on top of the key. When the three guards all held fiery cigarettes in their hands and were chortling between puffs, she said, "A pebble is in my shoe." She bent down, fiddled with her clog, and scooped up the key. While sliding her foot back into the clog, she slipped the key into her pocket, the opposite one from the eating utensils so there was no sound of metal clanking against another when it tumbled into the deep pouch.

Later that night, Hinda dug her fingers into her pocket and fondled the key lying next to Walter's note that proclaimed there were sunnier days ahead. She whispered, "You're so right, my sweet Walter, if this key is what I think it is."

Astonished at her luck, Hinda deemed the key as a direct sign from heaven, from her Tatae, who had surely blessed her escape plan. She lay awake, going through all the details and the timing. As soon as everyone was asleep, including the warden, she would take Step One tonight. Tomorrow night, she would execute Step Two, and on Sunday, Step Three. The escape had to occur on a Sunday. It was the only day they had a significant slot of unsupervised time, hours unaccounted for, before they would be discovered missing.

The moonlight shimmering through the upper back window captured Hinda's attention. The soft glow of tonight's moon suffused her spirit, swaddling her in a tingly mantle. Hinda edged out of her bunk. She picked up her clogs, pressed them to her chest, and tiptoed to the front door. She turned the deadbolt, ever so slowly, and then the doorknob. Barely breathing, Hinda exited Block Eleven.

98
The Jeep

Sirens squalled, resounding in the warehouse with no name. The corpses remained unbothered. But for Hinda, the unnerving sounds spawned disquietude along with visions of Rachel and herself being struck with shrapnel or blown to bits, their body parts reduced to rubble.

Crouching down, Hinda covered her head protectively with her hands. Her fingertips instantly nestled into her newly grown tresses. It was almost seven months ago, in June, since her head had been shaved. At that time, she feared that she would be eternally bald as a result of extended malnutrition. A few months later, when the first hairs poked through her scalp, Hinda had squealed joyously. Without the continual shearing, her hair continued to grow, despite forced starvation and horrific living conditions. Now, she had short loose curls, while Rachel had several inches of ultra-straight strands.

The guard stepped to the doorway, surveying the sky. Explosive sounds boomed. "That's miles away," he proclaimed. "Get back to work, and don't take a break again."

Hinda suspected that Germany was losing the war. Ominous signs were everywhere in the camp. At roll call, strange things were happening. Significant numbers of Jews were selected every morning and then divided into two groups. One group went in the direction of the gas chambers, the other group was told to start marching toward the south gates. Block Eleven housed half the women it did just two weeks ago. It was clear she and Rachel would not survive another week if they remained at Auschwitz. She fully understood that they could die trying to escape. Yet she was filled with such a fervent desire to attempt escape that she felt strangely energized.

Surveying a new corpse and about to read the man's serial number, Hinda jumped backward. His skin was split open, and a repulsive stench arose from him. Averting her eyes, she couldn't bear to watch the maggots, all writhing in ecstasy while devouring his flesh. Fearing the larva or bacteria would enter her mouth, she held her breath while memorizing the numerals, then stepped aside to call out the tattoo number to Rachel. Hinda paused, watching Rachel tug at her uniform as though it hurt.

Remembering Rachel's upset last night, Hinda worried for her sister. It was just after midnight that Hinda had sneaked back into Block Eleven to find Rachel sleeping soundly. The warden had been snoring when Hinda entered, so it was the right time. She had to push through and awaken Rachel. In a dreamy state, at first Rachel did not object when Hinda instructed her to remove her uniform and put on civilian garments—a navy-blue skirt and gray angora sweater. Then, it had dawned on Rachel that Hinda was truly planning for them to escape. She had bawled, saying that Hinda was trying to kill her. Hinda grabbed her up, holding her tightly, straitjacket style, while also covering her sister's mouth with her hand. Her lips close to Rachel's ear, Hinda commanded that she stop crying and put her prisoner uniform back on over those clothes. They heard the warden's boots click on the floor, which meant she was leaving her office to start her rounds, checking all bunks. Rachel had quickly obeyed and was barely under the blanket when the warden shined her light in their direction. Afterward, the way Rachel had tossed her body this way, then that in the bunk, Hinda knew that she had continued to fret and cry silently. Rachel's first words to Hinda that morning were, "Tatae was right. You're *too* daring. Your boldness is what's going to kill us, not the Nazis."

Hinda blinked her eyes to focus on the present, then repeated the maggot man's serial number again. "Rachel, did you get it?"

"No, there's no such number here. You have it wrong."

Frustrated, Hinda leaned over the corpse again, trying to avoid the squirming larva. The number she had called out was accurate. "Here, let me see the registry."

Across the way, at the registry podium, Rachel glared, her eyes yowling silent complaints. She moved from behind the podium and handed the registry to Hinda. Sidling closer, Rachel whispered in a snappish tone, "Did you get these clothes from Canada? And where is your outfit? Your uniform hangs loose like normal."

Nodding yes, Hinda checked off the number, finding it out of sequence from the others. Sliding her eyes to the side, she checked the guard's location. Seeing that he had his back turned and was outside smoking a cigarette, she said, "I'll get my outfit tonight."

Rachel gasped. "You're sneaking out again?"

"Yes, Rachel, I couldn't get everything we needed in one night."

"Why didn't you just put an outfit on under your uniform while you were there?"

"I thought about it, but we need shoes too. I was afraid they would be discovered today if we tried to hide them in the hay. And if I can find hats or scarves, I'll get those too. Tonight."

Her lips trembling, Rachel sobbed, "You'll be captured. I just know it."

Glad for the soft light of the half moon, Hinda sneaked her way through the camp to the back door to Canada. She slipped the key into the lock and crept inside. The warehouse had been built with no windows. It had subtle security lighting that was left on at night.

Feeling more spooked tonight, she felt an urgency to hurry. Female youth garments had been moved since last evening, and outfits that she liked for herself then were not there now; they were already boxed. Bone thin, she and Rachel required clothing sized for adolescent girls. Digging through the piles, she found a white blouse and a dark maroon sweater. Thumbing through the skirts, she spotted a dark charcoal gray one. Taking it from the stack, she held the waist against hers. It was too big, but not drastically so. Rats scratching at her feet made the decision easy. She removed the pants to her uniform and donned the skirt. When she pulled her prisoner uniform pants on over it, she knew why Rachel had been so uncomfortable. The mid-calf length caused the fabric to bunch at the crotch and hip joints, blocked from sliding down into the legs of the pants. Next, Hinda removed her uniform jacket, slipped on the white cotton blouse, and topped it with the sweater. Her skin prickled happily to have regular clothing resting against it versus the slimy uniform. Yet a shiver ran through her as she thought of the now-dead girl who had previously packed the blouse.

Sliding the prisoner jacket over the maroon sweater, Hinda looked around for hats or scarves. Finding two gray beanie caps, she laid those aside. Then, when searching the shoes area, an array of warm boots captured her interest, but they were too cumbersome to carry and hide. After minutes of assessing shoe styles and estimating sizes, she found a pair of low-heeled pumps for herself and Mary Janes with a bow on the toe for Rachel. Both pairs were stylish but utilitarian.

Suddenly, an anxious feeling shot through her. It was impossible to know what terrain and circumstances they would encounter after the escape. Shaking off the worry, Hinda concluded that it was simply fear of the unknown. Yet the horror of the *known* circumstances at Auschwitz, she decided, was more dangerous. To stave off the fear, she repeated her father's words, *you will live, and you will tell,* to herself again and again.

She picked up the shoes she had selected for Rachel and stuffed one shoe into each pants pocket. Planning ahead, she had left her eating utensils with Rachel to create room. Next, she tucked the knit hats beside the shoes. Her pockets bulged. Ready to depart, she double-checked that she was leaving everything in order. In so doing, she espied a stack of wool scarves. She grabbed two, wrapped her pair of shoes in them, and tucked the roll into her uniform jacket.

Just then, Hinda heard the back door squeak. The sound of footsteps in the room took her breath. Her heart thumping wildly against her chest, she crouched down behind a stack of boxes. Peeking through the space between stacks, Hinda watched as a man entered. Even with the subtle, security lighting, she recognized him. It was the guard who had brought the cooked cat in exchange for the diamond. He shined his flashlight around the room, then circled the locked jewelry cases. Setting his flashlight aside, he fiddled with each case. He pounded on the locks and the lids, trying to release them, but nothing happened.

Crouched in an extremely uncomfortable squat, Hinda did not know how much longer she could hold the position. The shoes hidden in her uniform were digging into her abdomen, and Rachel's pair, poking through the pockets, were hurting her legs. Worse yet, rats surrounded her, nibbling at the soiled hems of her uniform pants.

Hinda watched as the man took a ring of keys from his pocket and tried every single key. None worked. In frustration, he slammed his fist on an ornate metal container, which sat separately atop the locked cases. The lid popped askew, even though a small padlock hung from a band that wrapped the circumference. Taking wire cutters from his pocket, he cut the band and opened the lid. Hinda held her breath as the man evaluated the jeweled treasures before slipping them into his pockets. He placed the band and lock into the metal box, closed it, and slid it inside his jacket. While buttoning up the jacket, he rushed to the back door and flipped the switch that controlled the nighttime security lighting before he stepped outside.

In blackness now, Hinda heard his key in the door, locking it from the outside. She lost her balance and fell onto her knees just as she heard a key in the door again. Within seconds, the security lighting flickered back on. The back door slammed shut. Listening for steps, and hearing none, she presumed that the man had returned to switch back on the nighttime lighting. But she was not certain.

Rising awkwardly, Hinda grabbed hold of box corners and pushed up to a standing position. In search of a better hiding spot, she crept to the men's clothing area and slipped behind an especially tall stack of crates. Waiting, scarcely breathing, Hinda tried to expel the time clock ticking in her head, issuing warnings to get back to Block Eleven soon. But she worried that the man could still be lurking nearby or on the pathway. After what seemed like ten minutes, Hinda decided to brave an exit.

She peeked around nooks and corners. At every step, she checked to see if the coast was clear. Deciding it was just the rats and her, Hinda dashed to the rear door. Taking a deep breath, she inched the door open just enough for her to slip through to the outside.

When rotating the key in the lock, she heard voices approaching from the pathway. With the stealth of an experienced filcher, Hinda skulked around the corner of the building. Cloaked by darkness, she peered around the edge of the warehouse and saw two guards sauntering along the main pathway, just feet from where she huddled. They stopped. One went to the door, checking to see that Canada was secured, its back door properly locked. When he returned to the pathway, both he and his comrade lit up cigarettes and started telling jokes.

Frustrated, Hinda felt trapped. The clock in her head was ticking loudly, urging her to get back to Block Eleven before the warden made rounds and discovered she was missing. Unconsciously, she sighed audibly, then clamped her hand over her mouth. Panic began to rise. The jewelry thief had caused a serious delay and now these guards. Looking along the exterior wall, Hinda surveyed the length of the warehouse in the opposite direction. She could go that route, but it would take her dangerously close to the watch tower, where she could easily be seen and shot down by the guards on duty there.

In the next instant, sirens blasted. Hinda heard the two guards hoot about taking cover. One said that he had a key to another warehouse in the area. Their boots clacked on the pathway as they ran. Amidst bombing sounds, she inhaled sharply and crept toward the main trail.

After an hour of slinking her way through shadows, Hinda came to the avenue where the Blocks for the women's camp were located. Inching out from the corner, she looked both ways on the street. From out of nowhere, a military jeep with its lights out whizzed past her. Hinda darted across the street, her heart racing. Hiding behind the first Block, she could hear the jeep's engine revving as it went in reverse. Its brakes screeched as it came to a halt nearby.

Strobes of light streaked through the spaces between buildings. Realizing that the jeep driver had a flashlight and was stalking her, Hinda made a run for it. At Block Five, she halted, leaning against the brick, gasping for breath. She straightened the bundle inside her uniform, then sneaked alongside two more Blocks. With four more to go, she shivered, not only from the wintry night air but also from the sheer fear of capture. In desperate need of fortitude, she recited her father's prophetic phrases, *you will live, you will tell,* until she reached the door to Block Eleven.

Arriving there, new waves of dread struck her. Possible scenarios chewed at her already raw nerves. The warden could be awake, and she could have already made rounds, and be waiting with a bullwhip. What's more, the warden may have locked the door. Behind her, Hinda heard the jeep's engine. Quickly, she twisted the doorknob, inched open the door, and stepped inside. As noiselessly as she could, she turned the deadbolt lock. Although the warden was snoring loudly, Hinda heard the jeep's engine idling.

Moving swiftly, Hinda tiptoed back to her bunk and was surprised to see hay piled up on her side. Underneath it, their one blanket had been rolled to look like a human body—hers. Curled into a ball, Rachel slept on the rock-hard bunk with only a little hay under her, and she was completely uncovered. Tears trickled down Hinda's cheeks.

Thunderous raps on the door rattled her senses. In one swift stroke, Hinda scattered the hay. She grabbed the blanket and jumped into the bunk. Like a robot on high speed, she unrolled the blanket over Rachel then pulled it across herself. Hinda curled against her sister, the bundle across her abdomen pushing against Rachel's back, the shoe in her side pocket digging into her leg. Commanding her body to stop shaking and be still, Hinda pretended to be asleep.

Yawning, the warden shuffled to the door and let the patrol guard inside. He traipsed up and down the aisle shining his flashlight into each bunk. Some prisoners, including Rachel, sat up, their eyes wide with terror. When Rachel saw that Hinda had safely returned and was asleep, she collapsed back into the bunk. Her silent tears streamed, puddling into the hay.

After a brief dialogue with the warden, the patrol guard clomped to the door and exited into the night. The warden locked the door, then trudged back and forth along the aisle, aiming her light into each and every bunk, counting all inmates. Satisfied, she returned to her office. Soon, a quiescent hush settled over Block Eleven.

Long before the first streak of dawn, Hinda slipped from her bunk. After thoroughly scoping out the room to make certain that she was not being observed, she removed the bundle from her jacket. Taking the two pair of shoes, hats, and scarves, she hid them amidst the hay near the end of the bunk. Returning to bed, she lay there wide-eyed, boldly beseeching the Almighty for protection, for fortitude, for blessing upon her daring scheme. In the next hour, before the wake-up whistles blared, Hinda Mondlak plotted, planned, and prayed.

99
Snowstorm

Sunday, January 7, 1945 | Oświęcim, German-occupied Poland
Auschwitz Concentration Camp

An arctic wind, tousling Hinda's russet tresses, whipped through the lines of prisoners at Sunday morning roll call. Snowflakes fell like powdered rain. Hinda shivered, yet an excited warmth burned inside her. This was the day she had planned with single-minded focus for weeks. The winter storm, if it lasted into the afternoon, was a heavenly gift.

Standing beside Hinda, Rachel had contrary thoughts. The frigid wind cut like glass through her skin. She fidgeted with the skirt rumpled at her waist. It had been a balancing act to hike it up high under her uniform jacket to use the latrine earlier. Rachel's eyes darted back and forth, looking for guards who might be coming for her if they had noticed the navy-blue fabric.

At the end of the hour, wardens strutted down the rows, selecting prisoners. When one came to Rachel, she paused. The warden's index finger came forth and pointed at Rachel, then suddenly, she withdrew it and pointed to the next woman in line.

Whistles pierced the air. The selected prisoners were told to step aside. All others were dismissed to clean their bunks and Blocks, the Sunday morning protocol before having the afternoon to rest.

Once they could walk away, Hinda clutched Rachel's arm. Leaning in close, she whispered, "My dear sister, you were almost taken."

"That might be better than what you're planning to do with me," Rachel huffed.

Rolling her eyes in exasperation, Hinda sighed. "Those selected people are going to the gas chambers or an unknown destination they have to march to, and wherever it is, you know it'll not be any better than this hellhole. Rachel, please, you have to let me try to get us out of here. Can't you see that things are changing for the worse every day?"

"I do see it, but I'm scared. I had rather just go and throw myself on the fence now."

"Only if I'm dead first, will you do that," Hinda exclaimed. "Let's go clean our bunk area as usual. Then, we'll take a stroll."

It was noon. Low snow clouds hugged the earth. Snowflakes swirling around them, the sisters walked briskly from Block Eleven to Block Three. At the corner, Hinda directed Rachel to turn into an alleyway where there was a collection of trash bins.

"You keep watch, Rachel. I'll go first. Cough if you see anyone coming from either direction." Hinda removed shoes from her pants pocket and set them on the ground. Then holding the beanie cap and scarf under her chin, she shed the prisoner pants. Her eyes widened as she remembered the eating utensils. Reaching inside the pants pocket, she pulled out the spoon and tucked it into the skirt pocket next to Walter's note. The prisoner jacket came off next. Taking the hated clogs, she wrapped them into the despised uniform. Gratified, she smiled and buried the bundle at the bottom of the nearest garbage container. Squiggling her feet into the pumps, she shook out her skirt and smoothed the maroon sweater. Next, she folded the wool scarf and placed it around her neck. After tugging on the beanie cap, she asked, "How do I look?"

"Quite smart, actually," Rachel replied. "Like you belong in an officer's family."

Ecstatic, Hinda grabbed up Rachel, hugging her close. "Your turn, now. And be sure to keep your spoon." Playing watchdog, Hinda turned, checking both directions while Rachel made her change. Seeing how chic Hinda looked inspired Rachel to hurry with her own transformation, though her brows were furrowed, and her mouth was puckered with tension. Struggling to fasten the buckles on the Mary Janes, she fell backwards against the building.

"They're not real buckles. They just slide on," Hinda chided. Nervousness was building inside her. "Try to hurry."

Obeying her sister, Rachel quickly pulled the second shoe on and slid its strap up on her foot. Straightening her skirt, she looked at Hinda. A question mark dominated her face.

"Ooh, Rachel, you look beautiful. But it's snowing even harder now. Put on your scarf and hat and then toss your uniform. Bury it next to mine."

Rachel dug down into the trash. She thrust her uniform bundle near Hinda's, and then spread loose garbage on top, covering it. "Oh no! My spoon." Rachel blurted out the words in an exasperated, but hushed, tone.

Just then, four women turned the corner, coming their direction. Immediately, Hinda hooked arms with Rachel and the sisters began to saunter forward. She leaned close to Rachel's ear and whispered, "Don't worry about the spoon. I have mine. We can share if we need to."

After they had passed the small cluster of female prisoners, who paid them no mind, Rachel said, "I feel weak. We missed lunch. That awful fish-eyeball broth is better than nothing."

"We would have had to wear our uniforms to the food hall," Hinda said. "And we couldn't leave our civilian shoes and stuff in the hay because that's when the warden conducts bunk inspections. I have an idea, though."

On their way to the main street, Hinda veered onto a side alley that ran along the back of the guards' kitchen. When they turned the corner, they heard the rear kitchen door slam closed. No one was in sight, so they forged ahead. Garbage overflowed from the receptacle.

"They just dumped the lunch trash," Hinda said excitedly, "Let's look for scraps." Providence prevailed. They each found sausage links and crusts of bread. Returning to a side street, they ate hungrily, savoring every morsel.

As the sisters walked on, Rachel said, "It's so cold. I wish you'd gotten us coats. Canada had all kinds of jackets, right?"

"Yes. But I couldn't think of any means to hide such bulky garments. We couldn't wear them until after we had ditched our uniforms."

The wind picked up when they turned onto the main street, which was off-limits to prisoners. Visibility was near zero. Hinda took Rachel's hand. "My dear sister, it's time for our stroll to freedom."

Rachel shivered. "What about Sara? Are you just going to abandon her, leave her here?"

Startled, Hinda's eyes widened. She gasped. "Sara? We can't possibly get her. Only camp staff or military personnel are allowed in that area. But I promise you, we'll come back for her or find her when the war is over, which according to Walter's note, could be soon."

"If that's true, then why try to escape now? And *what about* Dr. Walter?"

"As for Walter, I love him and will look for him, too, when the war is over. But Rachel, every ounce of my being says we must go now, today." Hinda swallowed hard. "Otherwise, I feel strongly that we're going to die in the next week."

A convoy of military trucks roared down the street, kicking up slush from their tires. Rachel lifted her skirt and jumped aside. "Okay, but why try it in this snowstorm? I'm freezing."

"Sunshine wouldn't cloak us like this low visibility does. My sweet sister, please take a minute. Fill your heart, your mind, and your soul with courage and fortitude, right now, before we take this next step. Almighty God and our Tatae are both looking upon us as we journey to freedom, but we must do our part." Hinda felt her blood streaming warm inside her; thoughts of liberty coursed through her every vein.

Careful that their posture remained casual, the sisters walked slowly through two intermediate exits, passing watchtowers with mammoth German shepherds and armed guards, who assumed the girls were officers' daughters acting juvenile, strolling outdoors without coats in such a winter storm. After passing through the third exit, a guard shouted, "*Sofort aufhören.*"

Although Hinda perfectly understood the German phrase, which meant to stop at once, she did not alter her pace. She urged Rachel to just keep moving forward. Suddenly, they heard growling and snarling. A German shepherd, who was almost as big as they were, lurched forward and sunk its sharp teeth into Hinda's leg. Blood spurted.

An SS officer, dressed in a black uniform topped with a black overcoat that hung to his ankles, rushed over and grabbed the dog by its leather collar. Pointing to the gash on Hinda's leg, he said, "Go the infirmary. Get that wound treated." Glancing back to the guard who had yelled and sent the dog, he gestured for him to return to his post. Turning to face Hinda, he said, "After the infirmary, you girls need to go home or at least put on proper coats for this blizzard." He pivoted and led the German shepherd in the opposite direction.

Hinda hooked arms with Rachel and limped away. Strangely, her leg did not hurt. At the corner, she scooped up clean snow that had collected around the street lamp and packed it inside the wound. She felt no pain but hoped to minimize swelling and sanitize any bacteria from the dog's mouth. They continued walking along the main street. Like a compass, Hinda's instinct pointed her in the direction they were going, but she could not see well enough in the snowy air to know if the main gates were ahead. Yet Hinda sensed this was the correct path.

"We're lost," Rachel grumbled.

"Keep moving forward. I believe we're on track." Just then, Hinda spotted a horse-drawn wagon with piles of hay in it. She yanked Rachel's arm, tugging her into the middle of the street. "This is our ticket. Jump on while it's still moving slowly." The dense snowfall their shield, they climbed into the back of the trailer without the driver seeing them. Acting quickly, Hinda first covered Rachel, then herself, with hay. The layers of straw warmed them; yet they shook and shivered from worry of being discovered.

Whispering into Rachel's ear, Hinda said, "As soon as we come to a town, we'll slip out and begin our new destiny." Rachel blinked but said nothing. The northern wind howled around them. The snow felt damper now, not as powdery as before.

After they had traveled several kilometers in the windy, wet conditions, the driver reined the horses to the side of the road and stopped. From his seat, he rotated his legs around to face the trailer. He swung them over the ledge and stepped into the wagon bed. Bending down, he rifled through the hay, searching for his coat, which he had covered with straw to keep it dry. His fingers gripping the coat's collar, he shook it vigorously to remove dust and the pieces of straw that had stuck to the wool. While dusting the coat, he accidentally stepped on Rachel's foot. The driver, who was wearing an Auschwitz contractor's badge, kicked the hay from her. Grabbing Rachel's hair, he jerked her up to standing. The man swung his arm back and struck her across the face, slapping so arduously that Rachel's right eye immediately swelled. Arising from the hay, Hinda leapt from the trailer onto the roadway.

"What are you girls doing in my wagon?" the man growled. In one swift move, he shoved Rachel out of the trailer and jumped down to the ground.

"We just wanted to hitch a ride into town," Hinda replied, trying not to cry. She helped Rachel to her feet.

"What town?" His face set in a stony scowl, he demanded the exact name.

"I don't know, sir."

"You're Polish Jews, aren't you? I can tell by the way you speak."

Hinda stared at him, her large eyes wide, appearing enormous, not blinking.

He grabbed Hinda's arm and jerked up the sleeve of her sweater, exposing her tattoo. "Auschwitz prisoner, you are. And now, caught trying to escape."

Hinda said, "Yes, sir, and it looks like we're not very lucky."

"You scum. You may have gotten through the gates today. But I'm taking you back to Auschwitz at the break of dawn tomorrow morning. And you know what will happen then."

Noting the man's hand on his gun holster, Hinda wished he would remove the pistol and shoot the two of them, right there. A more merciful and benign death than hanging.

He dropped his hand from the gun. "Get up there in front of those horses and start marching."

Unable to look at Rachel's face, Hinda's shoulders sagged, the weight of guilt and dismay dragging them downward. She tugged on Rachel's arm, and they took their places in front of the horses. The man climbed up into his seat, cracked a whip, and the horses clopped forward.

The sisters clopped forward too. Marching beside Hinda, Rachel sobbed. Mostly, she cried about the reality of being captured, but also because of her fear of the giant horses. She could feel their breath on her back, which chilled her spine. As she marched onward, the square at Auschwitz loomed in her mind's eye. Two readied nooses waited in the gallows, one for Hinda's neck and one for hers.

After marching for what seemed like hours, they came to a village called Oświęcim. A frigid darkness surrounded the sisters as if they were fossilized inside an ebony glacier. The driver stopped at a farmhouse on the edge of town. "We'll stay here tonight," he announced. "I have another job at Auschwitz early tomorrow morning. I'm taking you girls back and turning you in, first thing." He proceeded to unhitch the two horses and started walking toward the barn. "Hurry up. I'll not allow you stupid Jude girls to ruin my evening."

The man threw open the barn doors and led the horses to the water trough, where they drank thirstily. He put the horses in their stalls, and they immediately began munching on the hay, their enormous teeth crunching the straw. Pointing to an empty stall, the man commanded, "You two, sleep here. And don't get any ideas about escaping. This is wartime. There's a curfew in this town. You'll be arrested. Besides, there's no way out. I'm locking the doors." He tromped out of the barn, slammed the double doors shut, and engaged the exterior locks.

Hinda clasped Rachel against her. "My dear sister, I'm sorry. Please forgive me for dragging you into this. I was sure my instincts to escape were correct. But—"

Rachel broke away from Hinda's embrace. Her right eye bruised and swollen completely shut, she exclaimed, "I told you it wouldn't work. Now, we'll be hanged or worse."

Her face a solemn visage of shame, Hinda once again implored her sister to forgive her. Every syllable she uttered oozed with remorse.

Rachel plopped down into the hay and turned her face to the wall.

Her voice cracking, Hinda begged, "Please, Rachel, remember how hard I've worked to keep you safe and alive." Wringing her hands, Hinda paced back and forth in front of the horse stall. Abruptly, she came to a standstill. Stepping inside the crib, she crouched down in front of Rachel, who turned to look at her. Mirthless and resolute, Hinda said, "Tomorrow, back at Auschwitz, I *will* keep my promise to you. We'll die together. Holding hands."

A t four in the morning, Hinda's eyes popped open. The same dismal cloud of culpability descended upon her. She turned onto her side in the barn stall and was startled to see Rachel lying there, staring at her.

Anguish and desperation etched upon her face, Rachel groaned, "That Nazi driver takes us back to Auschwitz this morning."

Upon hearing those words, the dolorous fog in Hinda's mind instantly cleared, the doomsday cloud dispelled. Her father's words flashed before her: *You will live. You will tell.* Unexpectedly, an otherworldly strength surged through her entire body. Hinda leapt to her feet, wondering if it was God or Tatae. Whoever it was, the message streamed through her internal speaker system and without a trace of static.

In the dim light—one light bulb burned on low near the double doors—Hinda began searching the barn. Barefoot, she zoomed around examining walls. Her eyes focused like lasers, Hinda inspected the entire stable and found no openings. One of the horses neighed and tossed his head in her direction. She peered behind its stall. Lo and behold, there was a tiny door. It was latched on the inside with a lock. She questioned whether it was a storage bin or a door that opened to the outside. Hinda pushed past the horse and tugged on the latch. It did not budge.

Without intention or thought, Hinda reached out her hand and stroked the curve in the horse's back. It swished its tail and rubbed the side of its face against the front post. Afraid the enormous animal would squash her, she stepped backwards. Her foot thwacked against metal. Bending down, careful to avoid bumping the horse's rump, Hinda plucked an old horseshoe from the straw. She turned it in her hand, viewing it with wonderment.

"What is that?" Rachel asked. "And aren't you scared of the horse?"

"Yes, I'm afraid, but this horse is our friend. He led me here to this little door." At first, Hinda struck the latch with the horseshoe. Nothing happened. Trying a different approach, she fit one edge in between the wall and the latch. Using the horseshoe like a lever, she pushed and pried. Her arm ached but then, unexpectedly, surged with an uncanny energy as if her father's arm were helping her, as if his were pushing mightily against hers. She applied pressure, more than she thought ever possible, and the latch shifted, then popped. The little door swung wide to the outside world.

"Come on, Rachel, let's get out of here."

"Wait, Hinda, your shoes. And your scarf and hat." Rachel slid on her Mary Janes and leapt to her feet. She grabbed up Hinda's things. Holding her breath, she inched past the horse and followed her sister, crawling through the miniature doorway.

Hinda slid her feet into the pumps. Looking up into the dark sky, she proclaimed quietly, "Thank you, dear Lord, and my sweet Tatae." She wrapped the scarf tightly around her neck and slipped the beanie cap on her head. Taking Rachel's hand in hers, she crept around the side of the barn. The winter morning sky cast no light, though Hinda guessed it was nearing five o'clock, which meant the driver could be going to the barn soon. Intentionally, she turned in the opposite direction from the farmhouse. The sisters found their way along the roadway. After twenty yards, they crossed in a jogging stride to the other side.

A light glowed in the distance. Hinda pointed at it and said, "This way." Arm in arm, the sisters traversed a meadow, trudging approximately one kilometer. A two-story house with two lights shining inside came into view. As they got closer, they noticed a moving light in the yard. A young man, who carried an oil lantern, stepped up to a well and set the lamp on its ledge.

Hinda approached him. "Hello, sir. We're lost and very cold. Would it be possible for us to warm ourselves in your home until sunrise?"

"I'm just a worker here and was about to get water for the animals," he replied, his tenor kind, his face lavished with a gentle smile. "I'll go and ask my boss, though, on your behalf."

Her teeth chattering from the cold, Hinda answered, "We thank you kindly, sir." When the young man limped away, Hinda noticed that he walked on the side of his right shoe. While he looked stout, she decided that his impairment was why he hadn't been called to fight in the war.

Shortly, the young man returned with an extremely tall gentleman, who was wearing a heavy coat buttoned to his neck. The coat collar was turned upward in a handsome fashion, yet the coat was an outdoor insulated type. A well-to-do farmer's coat, Hinda guessed.

The man shot forth questions, interrogating them. "Who are you?" Where do you come from?"

Unwilling to confess the truth, Hinda said, "We got lost and are very cold. Would it be possible, sir, to come inside your house, just until daylight when we can see where we're going and regain our bearings?"

His eyes darted back and forth between Rachel and Hinda. Without another word to them, he directed his employee to take them through the side door into the kitchen.

Once inside, the young man asked the sisters to sit at the breakfast table. It was then that Hinda noticed that one of his arms was shorter than the other. Yet, quickly and efficiently, he lit the wood already stacked in the fireplace. Flames blazed, instantly throwing out surprising heat.

Nodding to them, the young man asked, "Would you like coffee?"

"Yes, please," Hinda replied, her tone enthusiastic.

Within ten minutes, he brought two mugs of steaming hot coffee. Seconds later, he delivered a plate heaped high with thickly sliced dark bread.

Hinda thanked him profusely, her eyes of azure glazing with tears. She and Rachel sipped their coffee and shyly took a piece of bread each. Ravenous, they wanted to smash multiple slices into their mouth all at one time but managed to maintain control.

Explaining that he needed to finish his work with the animals, the young man smiled sweetly at them and then exited the side door.

"Thank you, God, thank you," Hinda whispered, wishing this glimmer of safety could last an eternity.

"Where do you think we are?" Rachel asked, her voice barely audible.

"Germany or Poland, but I don't know which. The war changed many borders."

The sisters sat quietly, nibbling bread and sipping coffee. Warm now, but still anxious about what was to come next, they felt grateful for this brief respite and for such ample bread, a feast to them.

When sunrise streaked the sky and was peeking through the lace curtains, a heavyset woman came down the stairs. She introduced herself as Mrs. Melik, saying that her husband had said that the girls would be joining them for breakfast. At the stove, she poured milk into a pot. While stirring in the semolina, she told them about her son who had been forced to join the German army last year and was fighting in the trenches. *The Russians*, she explained in an exasperated tone fraught with fear. For five minutes or more, she stirred the concoction, whisking it vigorously. After removing the pot from the heat and covering it with a lid, she sat down at the table, coffee cup in hand. Blotting her tears with her apron, she relayed that months had passed since they had received any word from their boy, their only child.

Hearing that the woman's son was in the German army, Hinda presumed that the family belonged to the Nazi party. Feeling anxiety exploding inside her, Hinda held the coffee mug beside her face near her lips as if that would hide the terror that she desperately did not want to show.

Mr. Melik strode through an interior door and sat down at the table with them. He nodded to his wife, and without a word, she served him first. Then she set full bowls of steaming semolina pudding in front of the sisters. During breakfast, the couple was outwardly polite and kind. Yet Hinda noticed Mr. Melik casting suspicious, nervous glances at Rachel and her.

After eating, Hinda offered to help Mrs. Melik wash the dishes in return for their hospitality.

Frowning, Mr. Melik spoke sternly. "Girls, it's getting late. It's time for you to go."

Shuddering from the awareness that they belonged nowhere, had absolutely no one and nowhere to go, Hinda steeled her nerves. She asked if she could speak to Mr. Melik in private.

Clearing his throat gruffly and appearing quite annoyed, he instructed Rachel to help his wife. He seized Hinda by the arm, ushered her out the door, and led her inside the barn.

Speaking earnestly, Hinda confessed the entire truth to him, that she and her sister had escaped from Auschwitz. She showed him the serial number tattooed on her arm and voiced how scared they were. "All of our family has been killed and our home confiscated. We've been beaten and starved. And we're so very tired. My sister's life and mine belong to you now, Mr. Melik. Do as you wish with us."

He paced back and forth, his fists were clenched, and his entire face expressed distress. He turned toward Hinda. "I don't want yours or your sister's life. All I want is for you to leave my property as soon as possible. You girls are in extreme danger, and your very presence here places my family in grave peril."

"I'm incredibly sorry, sir," Hinda replied with sincerity.

Sighing angrily, he opened his mouth to speak, then closed it. Finally, he said, "I'm going to the house to talk to my wife. Don't leave this barn or even peek outside. Do you understand?"

"Yes, sir. You have my word. I promise to God."

His eyes cast downward, Mr. Melik exited the barn.

Immediately, Hinda began to tremble, and a rigor shook her. She presumed that he and his wife would return Rachel and her to Auschwitz or turn them in to the Gestapo. She paced, wringing her hands. In the stalls to the left, the horses whickered, as though they sensed Hinda's terror. Then, the sheep in the corner began baaing. Under her breath, she prayed, "Dearest Lord, these animals are noble. They're nothing like the cruel degenerate animals, pretending to be humans, at Auschwitz. Please, can Rachel and I stay here in this barn?"

After thirty minutes or more, Mr. Melik swung open the barn door. Hinda stopped pacing, her hands trembling, expecting the ax to fall.

His tone strident, Mr. Melik said, "I've spoken with my wife at length, going over the least dangerous options for us. We've had news that Russian troops are approaching near here. Our area is being patrolled heavily for the next five days. So, my wife has agreed for you and your sister to stay in our home for one week. One week only. Do you understand?"

"Yes, sir. I do."

"Today is Monday. One week from today, next Monday, you *must* leave. There'll be no bargaining. Do we understand each other?"

"Yes, sir." Relief and gratitude ashine on her face, Hinda grabbed his hand and kissed it.

Startled, Mr. Melik wiped that hand on his pants and tucked it inside a coat pocket. His jaw muscle twitching, he said, "In our attic, we have a storeroom where I keep my seeds. You and your sister will stay up there, and you're not allowed to step outside that room."

Inside the attic, Mrs. Melik gave the sisters two thick blankets and suggested they sleep atop the seed sacks. She pointed to the ones that were lying horizontal, not the upright bags.

After she left, Rachel flopped down on the bulging sacks and smiled. She actually smiled. Hinda looked at her sister in awe. The sight of Rachel's face with a genuine smile upon it was a distant memory. Indeed, it had been so long, Hinda scarcely recognized her.

With exuberance, Hinda squealed, "We have one full week of peace and safety. Can you believe it?"

"It's amazing," Rachel exclaimed. "Just what did you say to Mr. Melik in the barn? He seemed angry."

"I told him the truth, that we escaped from Auschwitz and had nowhere to go, with our family killed and our home and everything taken from us. He was quite annoyed and concerned that our presence here puts his family in danger. But overall, he was nice." Hinda plopped upon a stack of sacks. Her body relaxed into the top bag. "Ooh. This is the closest thing we've had to a mattress to sleep upon since we were taken from our home in Zieluń five years ago." She tossed one of the blankets over on Rachel, then pulled up the other one, covering herself up to her neck. Physically exhausted and emotionally drained, both sisters were asleep before a clock hand could have moved one tick.

In the afternoon, they awoke from their nap. There was one window up near the roof. It was located too high to see anything but the sky. Yet it helped them know the time of day. Hinda guessed that it was late afternoon, nearing five o'clock. She arose and explored the room. Cracking open a creaky door in the corner, she exclaimed, "It's a bathroom. Well, sort of one." She pushed down the handle on the toilet. It burbled, but no water ran in it. A bucket sat on the floor next to an old, stained basin. Hinda turned the sink faucet and cold water poured forth. "Okay, so I think we fill the bucket with water and pour it into the toilet bowl for it to flush."

"Hurry and try it. I need to go," Rachel disclosed.

"Then you go first," Hinda said. "Let me know if it works."

Just then, there was a rap on the door. Hinda approached and recognized the voice of the young man they had met that morning. He said, "Knock, knock, I have supper for you."

Hinda swung open the door to let him enter. He carried a large tray that had two plates of food, water glasses, and two small loaves of bread on it. Setting it down upon the seed sacks, he said, "When you're finished eating, set the tray outside your door, and I'll retrieve it later."

"How kind of you. Are you sure that we cannot help? We're excellent workers."

"My boss and his wife want you to stay in this storeroom, hidden away."

"Please tell them we said thank you for the food. It smells wonderful," Hinda exclaimed.

The young man nodded assent and said, "I'll bring breakfast early in the morning." Seeing the surprised look on Hinda's face, he added, "You can expect two meals a day."

Her eyes wet with tears and her lips quivering, Hinda stuttered, "We . . . we are beyond grateful."

101
The Long Drop

Light snowfall dusted the square. It was midday. Officers, guards, medical personnel, and prisoners gathered for the ceremony that they were mandated to attend. Dr. Hans Munch hung back among the crowd, his hands fisted in his coat pocket, his head down, his eyes closed.

On the stage, Chief Pharmacist Victor Capesius waited at the microphone. Dr. Josef Mengele and camp commandant, SS Major Richard Baer, stood at attention behind him. To their left, two nooses hung from the gallows.

A funereal hush came over the crowd when armed guards ushered Walter Zeilhofen onto the stage and placed his neck into the first noose. Following behind him, a guard wrestled a female prisoner, number 46139, Matija Banovic, onto the black box next to Walter and tightened the rope around her throat.

Capesius spoke into the microphone, his tenor voice booming throughout the square. "Traitors! These two despicable humans are rebel traitors of the worst kind. Take a good look at them. If you, too, have treasonous ideas about saving Jews or sabotaging the goals of the Nazi regime, death by hanging will be your fate as well."

Dressed in their most formal regalia, a troop of high-ranking SS officers stepped forward. Each one waved an oversized swastika flag. Stentorian whistles blared three times in succession.

"Walter Zeilhofen," Capesius spit out the name as if it tasted repugnant. "You have willingly, and with forethought, committed multiple acts of treason. Therefore, it is my great honor to command that You. Now. Be. Hanged."

If his hands had not been tied behind his back, Walter would have raised his fist in victorious defiance of the Nazi regime. *Abhorrent, malevolent evil,* he believed with all his heart. While there would be no physical escape as he had planned for tomorrow evening, shortly, his spirit would be free. Walter's one and only regret was not getting Hinda and Rachel through those wicked gates and to safety. Fully aware that his last words were upon his lips, Walter whispered, "My beautiful Hinda, I'm sorry."

The armed guard kicked the black box from under Walter. His body jolted and lurched in the air, jerking tight the noose and rope knot placed under his left jaw. The second his neck broke, dislocating the axis bone which severed his spinal column, his blood pressure plummeted to zero. Yet his brain flashed with images, beloved faces he had revered and adored—his mother, his father, and that of his one true love, Hinda Mondlak. Walter felt feathery angel wings brush against him. His brain darkened. His body went limp.

The troop of SS officers then shouted in unison, "Heil Hitler."

Underneath the gallows, the guard, who had operated the ropes, bowed his head in prayer, then crossed himself. In a reverent tone, he whispered, "You were a good man, Dr. Walter. I hope you approve of my hanging method of a long drop with a jerk of the rope to give you a quicker death. I was ordered to do a short drop where you would have suffered strangulation and excruciating pain. If Capesius and Mengele noticed the difference, I may be joining you soon."

102

Today Is . . .

The sky through the attic window appeared gray. Gusty winds whipped around the corners of the two-story house. Lying atop the seed sacks, Hinda clutched Walter's note to her chest. Turning on her side, she opened the fold and read it again.

Sitting on a seed sack, Rachel flipped through pages of an illustrated book that Mr. Melik had brought up the day before after learning that she was interested in art. He had explained that the collection of fables, *Der Edelstein*, was one of the first books ever illustrated, using wood print blocks, back in 1461. His copy was a new 1944 edition featuring enhanced drawings. While Rachel was entranced with the artwork, she read limited German. She glanced over at her sister, hoping she would read one of the fables aloud. Yet again, Hinda appeared to be in a trance, her index finger tracing over each letter of Walter's note. "You're obsessed with that," Rachel commented.

"I can't seem to get Walter out of my mind. Looking at his handwriting used to make me feel happy, but this week, it brings a heavy feeling to my heart. I don't know why."

Just then, there were footsteps on the stairway and then a rap on the door. Mr. Melik edged the door open. "I just wanted to check on you girls. How is today for you?"

"I'm enjoying the artwork in this book," Rachel said, her eyes brighter than they had been in years.

"Excellent," he replied. "And how about you and that wound on your leg?" he asked, directing his gaze at Hinda.

Sitting up, Hinda straightened her shoulders. "It's healing nicely, sir, thanks to the salve your wife provided."

"Good. Just remember that today is Friday. On Monday morning, you must be on your way."

"Yes, sir. We understand. Thank you for your kindness and generosity."

He nodded, his lips pressed tightly together. Ducking his head under the doorframe, Mr. Melik closed the door behind him and descended the attic stairs.

Inside the attic, Hinda said, "Every day, Mr. Melik comes up those stairs supposedly to check on us, but he is coming to remind us of what day it is." Hinda lowered her voice, trying to mimic his deep pitch. "This is Tuesday. This is Wednesday. This is Thursday. This is Friday."

In response, Rachel suppressed a laugh, then her brows furrowed, and her lips pursed with concern. "But he's been nice to us and seems kind overall. Do you think if we cry and beg him really hard on Monday morning, Mr. Melik will change his mind and let us stay just a bit longer?"

The sisters locked eyes. Rachel could see the wheels in Hinda's mind turning slowly, then spinning, then reeling.

103
White Doves

When dawn stretched and yawned across the Monday morning sky, the door to the attic storeroom unexpectedly opened. Unannounced, a Gestapo officer, who had a gun on his belt and a baton in his hand, stomped into the room. "You two come with me," he said, his guttural voice gruff and demanding.

Shocked, alarmed, and petrified, Hinda and Rachel leapt from the seed sacks and hurriedly grabbed their scarves and hats. Trembling, they slid their feet into their shoes.

The officer motioned them down the stairs, poking them in the back with his police baton. Downstairs, there was no sign of Mr. or Mrs. Melik, or the young man who worked for them. The entire house was strangely still and quiet. But to Hinda, it was not a mystery. She instantly understood that Mr. Melik had turned them in to the Gestapo. It had all been pre-planned.

Hurrying the sisters out the side door, the Gestapo officer tromped into the meadow. "March beside me and match my stride. I've no time for slowpokes this morning."

"Sir, may I ask where you're taking us?" Hinda inquired, her voice shaky.

"Just come with me," he snarled.

Marching in silence for ten minutes or more, Hinda grappled with the compelling feeling that he intended to kill them. Rebooting her mental strength, she primed all the valor she could muster. "Sir, Mr. Officer," Hinda spoke resolutely. "I beg you to let us live. You'll not be sorry. We've heard reports that Russian troops are approaching this area. All Germans are in danger of being captured or killed by them. My sister and I can save you and your family."

The officer shook his head in annoyance. In a haughty, condescending tone, he said, "And just how would *you* do that?"

"We're Polish Jews, escaped from Auschwitz. The Russian government opposes Hitler's Nazi regime and is invading with the intention of taking all of Germany." Hinda swallowed hard and explained further, "I can show them our

Auschwitz tattoos, proving the Nazis persecuted us. And then, I would say that you and your family acted humanely, protecting us, saving my sister and me. I believe they would then spare your life."

The officer offered no reply, trudging onward through the weeds and grass. Hinda wanted to say more but decided against it, not wanting to unduly anger him.

In about fifteen minutes, the officer stopped, and then he completely changed the course of his direction. After one hour of walking through pastoral country-side, he turned onto a lane that led to a village. Bells tolled seven times. Hinda assumed they were church bells and wondered if they denoted the time, as in seven o'clock in the morning, or if the peals were a call to prayer. They walked past a small grocery, and then, just two streets beyond the post office, the officer turned onto a gravel driveway that stretched up a slight hill to a two-story brick house. At the porch, he tucked his baton into the loop on his belt and said, "This is my house. I need to talk with my wife. Come on inside." He gestured toward the chairs in the kitchen for them to sit, and then disappeared through a doorway.

As instructed, the sisters sat down. Shivering, Rachel said, "He's going to kill us, isn't he?"

"Start praying and do not allow yourself to envision that."

"We could just run out the door. He didn't tie us to these chairs," Rachel implored.

"And go where?" Hinda protested. "I made a good point with him. He changed direction and brought us here. Let's wait and see. I'm inclined to leave our fate in his hands."

After what seemed an eternity, the officer tromped into the kitchen with his wife trailing behind him. She smiled reticently at the sisters sitting at her kitchen table.

Inhaling sharply, the officer announced, "After consulting with my wife, I've decided to give you refuge in our home." He leaned forward, close to Hinda's face. "But if the Russians come to our door, you must tell them that we have protected you, and saved your and your sister's lives."

Hinda looked directly into his eyes and proclaimed, "I promise to God, I will."

"It's settled then," the officer said. "Now, go with my wife."

The blonde-haired attractive woman, who was quite slender in comparison to Mrs. Melik, pointed to the stairway. "Please follow me."

On the second level, she ushered Hinda and Rachel into a room that had six bird cages with two doves in each one. They were white doves—the symbol of peace. Hinda blinked and double blinked. The entire scene appeared surreal.

"These birds are our son, John's," the officer's wife explained. "He's nine years old, and doves are his hobby, his pets."

"They're quite beautiful," Hinda commented.

Nodding to Hinda, the woman said, "The dove room is where you'll stay. Our servant, Victor, is bringing cots, one for each of you. He'll set them up with sheets, blankets, and pillows."

"Thank you. We so appreciate your kindness," Hinda replied, relief surging through her. Standing to the side of Hinda, Rachel smiled brightly. The very mention of pillows excited her. She nor Hinda had slept with a pillow under their head in years.

The woman explained, "Victor will cover all the windows." She brushed hair away from her face on the left side, then her fingers raked through her blonde strands like the teeth of a comb. Her soft voice changed to a serious timbre. "I need you both to understand that *under no circumstances* are you to look out the glass or to open the windows. And don't pull back the coverings, regardless of what's happening." She looked to each sister, eyeing them sternly.

Both Hinda and Rachel shook their heads vigorously in assent. Hinda expounded, "We understand and will do exactly as you say. We're immensely grateful for the refuge."

A young man with dark hair appeared in the hallway. Waving him inside the room, the officer's wife said, "This is Victor. He'll set up the beds for you and cover the windows. And what are your names?" After the sisters repeated their first names, the woman properly introduced them to Victor, adding that he would also bring meals to them.

Victor set the cots on the floor and promptly returned with armloads of bedding and extra fabric to cover the windows.

Hinda said, "We can help you. We're excellent workers."

Victor looked to his boss. She was already saying no, emphatically declaring that they were not to go near the windows. Then she smiled wryly. "But, if you'd like, you can put the sheets and such on the cots. And you can call me Mrs. Olmos." She started toward the door to leave, but then turned in her tracks and said, "We have a small facility here." She opened a side door, which Hinda had presumed was a closet, revealing a small lavatory and a toilet with a bucket sitting beside it. She explained, "The sink faucets don't work. Victor will bring you two buckets of fresh water every morning for your personal cleansing and for flushing the toilet."

Her every word imbued with sincerity, Hinda said, "Thank you, Mrs. Olmos. We so appreciate your thoughtfulness and kindness."

Walking to the main doorway, Mrs. Olmos spoke to Victor, "Please see to it that these girls have what they need to be comfortable."

"Yes, madam, I will."

While Victor covered all the windows, Hinda and Rachel made their beds, unable to hide their delighted smiles when they touched the plush pillows. The light in the room became dimmer, as Victor worked. When finished with the coverings, he bowed slightly to them. "I presume you didn't have breakfast. Could I bring you coffee, bread, and butter now?"

Unconsciously, Hinda placed her hand on her stomach, which rumbled with hunger. "That would be wonderful, indeed. Thank you."

When the door closed behind him, the sisters wrapped their arms around each other, giggling giddily. Tears of relief and happiness rushed down their cheeks. "Is this a dream? I can't believe our luck," Hinda shrilled.

Rachel dropped her head for a moment, then lifted it, looking into Hinda's eyes. "It's not all luck. It's your quick thinking and smart strategies, my dear sister."

Embracing Rachel tightly, Hinda avowed, "I feel Tatae's hand in this. Our father is helping us. And so is the great Lord Almighty."

104

Loose Tongues

Hinda watched the boy named John gently place the dove back in its cage. Innocence radiated from him. His clear, soft eyes spoke volumes, telling a halcyon tale of having never experienced tragedy, abuse, starvation, or incarceration, not for one single day in his entire life of nine years. Nor did he appear to have any cognizance of the monstrous persecution that had transpired in the last six years mere kilometers from his home.

Scooping up another dove to pet, little John turned to Hinda. "*You* know that I'm nine years old, so can I ask how old you are? My mother said not to, but I said you wouldn't mind."

"I'm glad you asked. I'm twenty-three right now and will be twenty-four in May."

John whistled as if that were old. "How about your sister?"

Rachel piped up, "I'm seventeen. Soon to be eighteen." She reclined on her cot, eyes closed, tracing designs in the air with her index finger.

His nose and forehead scrunched into wrinkles, little John asked incredulously, "Are you drawing in the air?"

"Yes, that, and painting pictures in my mind."

He looked at Rachel as if she were an intergalactic alien inhabiting the wrong planet. "Do you ever draw on paper?"

"If I had paper and pencils, yes, indeed, I would."

"Hmm," he muttered, tilting his head to the side. After feeding all the birds, John said, "I need to check in with my mother. I'll be right back."

Later, the boy named John raced down the hallway, a wide grin dimpling his rosy cheeks. He swung open the door to the dove room. He dashed over to Rachel and proudly set a sketch pad on her cot. He plunked down a box of colored pencils and a regular pencil with extra erasers. When Rachel squealed with delight, the boy's gray eyes danced and shimmered, spewing dazzling rays similar to freshly lit sparklers.

To Hinda, he said, "I forgot to ask if you like to draw."

Chuckling, Hinda replied, "No artist here. Even stick figures are hard for me. I like to write, though. If you have any spare paper—"

Before Hinda could finish her sentence, John interrupted. "I was right," he exclaimed with glee. He dug in the bag on his arm and proudly presented Hinda with a spiral-bound notebook and a pencil. "I wondered if you wanted to write in this like a diary. My mother does that. She fancies her own thoughts, I guess."

"How lovely. You're a perceptive and smart boy, John Olmos."

John ducked his head as if embarrassed, but his eyes were as radiant as an effulgent high-noon sun.

Feeling as if they were floating in a dream of tranquility, one they wished to not awaken from, Hinda and Rachel soothed their battered souls with the nourishing peace of the Olmoses' home. Resting deeply and eating regularly, the sisters began to feel a smidgen of well-being.

On a set schedule, Victor brought them three meals a day. He had apologized that lunch would be a light snack. The sisters had been flabbergasted to be served thick sandwiches or stews with crusty bread at midday. Lunch alone held more calories than they ingested in one month at Auschwitz. Victor dazzled them with hearty, nutritious food such as they had never tasted. They ate everything, and at times, lapped their plates with their tongues, savoring any dribbles of sauce or gravy.

The previous week, Mrs. Olmos had surprised them with soap and shampoo. Using the buckets of water that Victor delivered each day, the sisters relished having clean bodies and hair. Wanting to give back and to be of help, they had offered to clean the doves' cages, but Officer Olmos had declined, saying his son must be solely responsible for the birds.

Hinda found the cooing sounds of the doves strangely comforting. The soft, flute-like noises penetrated her psyche in such a way that her ever-present anxiety felt less daunting. Always aware that their circumstances could change for the worse at any time, she was certain that once she pressed the tip of the pencil onto paper, words about her constant fear would flow effortlessly onto the pages of the notebook, alongside phrases depicting the horrific cruelty and unjust abuses she had endured. Anxious queries would find their way onto the pages too: Have the Russians taken over? Are the Germans still in charge? When would this respite at the Olmoses' home end? What unknown would come next?

Opening the notebook, she had already crafted the first sentence in her mind: *My only crime is that I am a Jew.* Yet those words did not appear in the first chapter. Her spirit hijacked the pencil and wrote about freedom, what it would feel like to openly and freely walk in public . . . to amble along the main street of a city, town, or village and to unabashedly enjoy the breeze on her face . . . to have enough money to shop in a toy store and buy amusing things, such as a beautiful doll with golden hair that fell in long ringlets . . . to frolic in the rain and jump in the puddles like a carefree child . . . to polka, waltz, and foxtrot with euphoric elan . . . to have a real home again, a haven where she was cocooned in comfort and safety . . . to feel joy dance in her heart.

At the first blush of daybreak, Rachel awoke with her covers in a knot. Agitated, she jumped from her cot. Shaking her sister's shoulders, she exclaimed, "Hinda, wake up, wake up. I had a vivid dream. Tatae has sent us a warning."

One eye popped open, the other remained closed. Sleepily, Hinda asked, "About what?"

"A tall woman who has jet black hair. In my dream, Tatae spoke to me. He said that this woman is conniving and mean-spirited, that she's going to denounce us to the authorities."

"Rachel, how dare you wake me to tell such a story? Don't you think the torment and fear of our uncertain circumstances is enough? You've simply had a nightmare. Get ahold of yourself."

Looking at her sister in disbelief, Rachel threw herself onto her cot and yanked the blanket over her head. In about five minutes, with hot tears scalding her cheeks, she grabbed up her sketch pad and pencils, and began drawing furiously.

By late February, the sisters had been harbored in the Olmoses' home for six weeks, and the dove room had begun to feel like a safe place. They enjoyed daily conversations with little John and the family's servant, Victor. Otherwise, they had limited interaction with Mr. and Mrs. Olmos, and none with the outside world.

On the last Friday in February at ten o'clock in the evening, just as Hinda was drifting off to sleep, the doorknob rattled. Then, someone rapped their knuckles on the dove-room door in a vigorous rhythm. Fear tightening her every muscle, Hinda crept to the door and inched it open.

A tall woman, who had jet black hair, shoved Hinda backwards and stomped into the room. She put her fist in the air and shrieked, "You two Jew girls don't belong here. I'm going to turn you in to the authorities. I'll denounce you if it's the last thing I do." She kicked her heels together and extended her arm in a Nazi salute and screeched, "Heil Hitler." Her eyes ablaze, she slammed the door as she exited.

Scarcely breathing, her mouth agape, Hinda gawked at Rachel as if her sister were a ghostly revenant. She stammered, "This is exactly what you dreamed."

"I told you; it was real. Tatae sent us a warning." Rachel, whose skin had blanched to a pallid alabaster hue, cried as she spoke the question, "What are we going to do now?"

"I'm thinking that I must talk with Officer Olmos. Tonight." Hinda removed the nightgown that Mrs. Olmos had provided and proceeded to get dressed. Her face an austere portrait of angst, she rang the buzzer, calling for Victor, which she had never done.

Within five minutes, Victor knocked on their door. His hair was tousled as if he had been asleep and unexpectedly roused.

"I apologize for bothering you this late, Victor. Please forgive me. We had an intruder who threatened to denounce us. I feel I must speak with Officer Olmos. Is it possible for you to arrange an appointment for me?" Hinda gulped. "Tonight?"

His brows furrowed in consternation, Victor replied, "I can ask." He used his fingers like a comb, coaxing his wayward hair back into place. "That is, if Officer Olmos has not yet retired to his bedroom."

After a long ten minutes, Victor escorted Hinda down the stairs to the kitchen where Officer Olmos waited at the table. He arose in gentlemanly fashion when they entered and asked Hinda to be seated. Turning to Victor, he asked him to serve tea.

Hinda kept her hands in her lap, her fingers caressing each other in worry. Victor rattled two cups onto matching saucers. Soon, the teapot whistled, and Victor placed a cup of steaming tea in front of Hinda and Mr. Olmos, who then dismissed Victor.

"Officer Olmos, I deeply appreciate your meeting with me this late in the evening. We've had quite a scare."

Lifting his teacup to his mouth, the officer's lips puckered as he blew air onto the hot liquid. "Victor told me about an intruder. Describe this person and what happened."

"A tall woman with long, black hair knocked on the door to the dove room. She stormed in and screamed that, as Jews, my sister and I didn't belong here. She said she was going to turn us in to the authorities."

"That fits the description of Ursula, my best friend's wife. She and her husband were here visiting this evening, and she excused herself to go to the lavatory just as they were about to depart. But I had no idea that she went upstairs and spoke with you." He sighed heavily and looked at the ceiling. He stroked his chin as if deliberating. "I'm quite embarrassed to confess that, last week, I confided to my friend that I'm hiding you in exchange for your help with the Russians." He smiled shyly. "You and your sister are my insurance policy. Perhaps I bragged a little."

Blinking repetitively, Hinda thanked him again for giving them refuge.

"I promise you that nothing bad is going to happen to you in my home." Officer Olmos cleared his throat. "Just so you know, my friend enjoys drinking a few too many cocktails at socials. He and his wife hosted a party last weekend. That must have been when he told his wife our secret."

"I understand, sir, but are we safe here now that this woman knows about us?"

He sighed in a disgruntled way. "You are. I'm the highest-ranking Gestapo official in this area, and this woman's husband works for *me*." Abruptly, he stood up from the table. "I'll phone him now and put an end to this."

Hinda waited at the table. She could hear Mr. Olmos' voice from the other room, but she could not distinguish any words or the gist of what he was saying.

When Officer Olmos returned to the kitchen, his lips were slightly curved in a sly grin. "You have nothing to worry about. My friend owes me a favor, a significant one, and he swears on stacks of Bibles that his wife will be silent and will not go to the SS about this matter. He hopes in exchange for their cooperation that you'll also help his family, vouch for them, when the Russians come."

Hinda nodded, fully grasping the slippery situation. "But of course, I will, if that's what you want me to do, Officer Olmos."

"Then, it's settled," he said. Pushing his chair back, he stood, signaling that the meeting had ended.

Rising from her chair, Hinda said, "I noticed you said *when*, not *if*, the Russians come. May I ask if there is news on this front?"

"Soviet forces are prevailing. They've now taken Warsaw and other major cities in Poland. Germany appears to be losing the war." His earlier smile vanished, and his eyes darkened with dread. "The Red Army has encroached into this rural region. We expect them any day, any hour."

Inside the dove room, Rachel exclaimed, "What took so long? I've been so worried!"

"It's quite a tale," Hinda replied. "I'll give you the short version tonight because I'm exhausted." While explaining what Officer Olmos had told her, Hinda undressed and buttoned the nightgown for the second time that evening. Rachel fell asleep quickly, right after Hinda relayed that Officer Olmos had declared them safe in his home, that he would not let anything bad happen to them on his watch.

Crawling onto her cot, Hinda burrowed in and tugged the blanket up to her neck. As the clock ticked, troublesome thoughts began to gnaw at her, bedeviling her eyelids, denying sleep an entry. Her mind whirred. Mr. and Mrs. Olmos hosted gatherings and often attended social events where alcohol was served, as did Mr. Olmos' cohort and his wife, Ursula. Two distressing questions loomed: Just how loose did their tongues become when they imbibed? And was Officer Olmos, her Gestapo Guardian Angel, a fool to trust his friend and his mean-spirited wife?

105

Tents and Trenches

March 1945 | Silesian Rural Region | War-torn Poland

On the first day of March, Mrs. Olmos roared into the dove room. Agitated and obviously upset, she began smoothing the covers on one cot. "Please help me," she begged.

"What's wrong?" Hinda asked, her anxiety skyrocketing.

Mrs. Olmos pointed to the corner of the room. "Fold these cots and roll them over there. Gather all your things and go down the back way, the servants' stairs. Victor will meet you outside. Hurry. There's no time to even put on your shoes." She yanked a pillow out from its case and handed the pillowcase to Rachel. "Put all your personal items in here. Take the soap and shampoo too. All evidence of you must disappear."

Hinda folded the cots neatly and rolled them to the assigned place while Rachel frantically gathered their personal items. Once the sisters were at the back stairway, Mrs. Olmos whispered in a raspy urgent tone, "Two SS officers are downstairs demanding to inspect all the birds. You must leave at once or be captured. Please wait near the garage for Victor; he'll be there after he serves coffee to the officers." She followed them down the back stairs, locked the door behind them, and went into the kitchen to put sweet biscuits on a plate.

Outside, behind the garage, the sisters slipped on their shoes and wrapped their scarves around their necks. A chilling wind howled around the building. Rachel sobbed, "It's that black-haired woman. She denounced us just like Tatae warned she would."

"Mrs. Olmos said the SS officers were here to inspect the birds. Something feels off," Hinda replied. Cocking her ear to the side, she said, "I hear Victor coming."

A stricken look on his face, Victor approached. "Dear girls. Please hurry, you must get out of this region." He grabbed Rachel's arm in his and began walking at a fast clip on a rock-lined pathway that led into the woods.

Tree leaves brushed against their faces as they picked their way around large trunks and knots of roots. When they were out of sight and hearing range from the house, Hinda probed for information. "Victor, can you please explain what happened?"

"Two SS officers showed up unexpectedly, saying they had a report that the Olmoses were in possession of messenger birds, which is illegal in times of war. They demanded to inspect the doves. Mrs. Olmos almost fainted but kept her wits about her. Asking if they knew who her husband was, his rank in the Gestapo, she showed them to the living room and offered them coffee. Thankfully, they accepted."

"Are we going to hide in the woods and then go back when the SS have gone?" Rachel asked with a hopeful intonation.

Victor stopped in his tracks, and he took Rachel's hands in his. His dark eyes darting back and forth between the sisters, he said, "I'm sorry to tell you that you can never go back there now. The SS will be watching their house and the entire Olmos family. And SS officers can be vicious."

"We know about the SS. And we don't want any harm to come to you, Victor, or to anyone in the Olmos family. We're forever indebted to them," Hinda averred, her voice unsteady. "You can leave us now and get back to your duties. We'll keep moving in this direction."

"No! I'm not leaving you," Victor exclaimed. "I know this area. It's a long way through the woods, and you would get lost. There are quicker routes, but we can't take those and keep you hidden." Leading the way through the forest, Victor further explained that, according to the news he had heard, the sisters were close to complete freedom. "If Germany would only admit defeat and surrender," he lamented, "then Jews and others, who have been unfairly incarcerated, would be liberated."

Observing Victor closely, Hinda wondered why he, who spoke perfect German, seemed eager for Germany to surrender. Why would he use the words, *unfairly incarcerated*? Then, it struck her. Victor resembled the Gypsies, whom she had seen imprisoned at Auschwitz. Had Officer Olmos saved Victor from incarceration in exchange for his working as a servant in the Olmoses' home? Both Officer Olmos and his wife had called Victor their servant, whereas Mr. and Mrs. Melik had referred to the young man who worked for them as their employee. As they moved along, Hinda pondered the truth of Victor's work status.

After walking many kilometers, the trio emerged from the trees. The soft light of dusk hovered around them. Across a wide field, a small house with wisps of smoke wafting from a lone chimney beckoned.

Upon seeing the house, Hinda asked to see the pillowcase that Victor had been carrying for them. Exploring its contents, she was dismayed to find that her diary was absent. Sacred to her, the journal was her medicine. "My diary," she shrieked. "I left it under the mattress. It was folded up in my cot that we rolled into the corner."

"I'll look for it when I return. If possible, I'll get it to you tomorrow." Victor assured her. "For now, let's knock at this house and see if these folks will let you stay overnight."

An elderly woman answered the door. She bristled at the sight of them. Crossing her arms, she barked, "What do you want?"

Hinda sensed that the woman was frightened, but underneath all the defensiveness, there was a good person. Yet, the woman said no, categorically no, they could not stay in her home. She complained that her husband was not well, and she expected that the German or Russian army would show up soon. "My husband and I already fear for our lives," the woman protested. "Vagrant girls on the run would only put us in more danger."

Hinda's desperation unhinged, she began to cry—profusely. With Rachel already sobbing, the two were a duet of despair. Victor hung back, looking down at the ground.

"All right, all right! I'll take you in for tonight," the woman said angrily. "But I'll *not* provide you with any food, not one bite. And you have to sleep on the floor."

Humbly, Hinda thanked the woman, agreeing to her terms. She kissed Victor on the cheek and thanked him for his gallantry in seeing them safely through the woods. Rachel hugged Victor good-bye and praised his undue kindness.

The woman motioned the sisters inside the house. They traipsed through the warm kitchen, which had two small beds where the couple slept. A meager fire burned in the fireplace. The woman went to a cabinet and withdrew two thin blankets, and then showed them to a vacant room at the northernmost corner of the house. Icy air slapped their faces. The room was freezing cold.

The next afternoon, after a nearly sleepless night, there came a knock on the door. The elderly woman announced that the sisters had a visitor, the same young man who had escorted them yesterday. With a suspicious look in her eyes, the woman said to meet him outside.

Victor stood on the gravel path leading to the house, a wide grin adorning his face. The sisters dashed to his side, wrapping him in hugs. Hinda screeched with exuberance when he produced her treasured diary, all in one piece and not damaged in any way.

Thrusting a food basket in front of them, Victor said, "Surely, you're starving. Let's sit on the grass so you can eat properly." While they were getting settled, he explained that they should eat the sandwiches on top first. He pointed underneath to loaves of bread and cured meats. "These should keep for a while, if stored in cool temperatures."

Her eyes misty with tears, Hinda said, "You're a lifesaver, Victor. We can't begin to thank you enough." Then Hinda chuckled. "No need to worry about keeping the meat cool. Our room here is a freezer."

After the sisters had inhaled the sandwiches, Victor handed them each a small bag. "Mrs. Olmos wanted you to have these, and she hopes they fit."

"Shoes!" the sisters exclaimed at the same time.

"Mrs. Olmos said she noticed that yours were worn. And she feels badly about your abrupt departure and that you can no longer stay in their home. She thought these shoes might help you along in your journey."

Both girls slipped on their respective pairs, which were a surprisingly fair fit. They stood and danced a jig, showing off the styles to Victor, who grinned.

Glancing at the position of the sun, Victor said, "I must go now to be back in time to serve dinner."

"It's extremely far for you to walk a second time today," Hinda exclaimed sadly.

"Not really. It's just a bit over one kilometer each way because I can walk openly on the roads," Victor replied.

"Please give Mrs. Olmos our sincerest appreciation for the shoes and the food," Hinda implored, her voice quaking. "And, Victor, we'll never forget all that *you* have done for us."

The sisters watched as Victor, their friend and ally, strode away.

Her instinct raising its voice, Hinda understood the finality. She and Rachel would never see Victor again.

Late on their third night at the elderly couple's home, thunderous knocking on the front door jarred the sisters from sleep. Listening carefully through the wall, they heard the woman invite what sounded like two men into the kitchen where her husband was resting. Overhearing part of the ensuing conversation, Hinda deduced that two German army officers had entered and informed the couple that troops had taken over the field in front of their house, pitching camp there to prepare for battle with Russian forces. Already alarmed, the sisters panicked when they heard the old man telling the officers about the two runaway girls in the back room.

Within minutes, there was a knock on their door. Without waiting for a response, a tall officer opened the door. Shining his flashlight upon Hinda and then Rachel, he said, "I apologize for disturbing you, but I need to see your documentation." When there was no response from either sister, he declared, "In times of war, everyone must carry papers."

Indescribable anxiety shot through Hinda. She felt her throat tighten as if closing up and blocking her air passage. Unsure if she could breathe, she coughed, a whole string of expulsions of air, while praying for her face to remain neutral and to not reveal the truth—she and Rachel were Jews, and worse, escapees from Auschwitz.

At that moment, her instinct kicked in with an idea. "Officer, I'm sorry to report that we don't have our papers with us. Russians approached our home, and we had heard hair-raising stories of how brutal they are, and how they rape women and girls. Our mother is deceased, and our father was away at work. We were so frightened that we just decided to bolt out the door and run to safety. Hiding and scrambling in the woods, we became lost."

Paying rapt attention to what Hinda was saying, the young and quite good-looking officer replied, "Your fear may very well become real someday soon."

"Then, my sister and I must keep running."

"There's no need for immediate alarm. I promise you that my troops will protect you from those Russian savages. And, if the day comes, you'll leave here under the protection of my troops."

"We thank you immensely, sir," Hinda said earnestly.

In a respectful tone, he said, "Thank you for your time. Have a good night." He pivoted on his heel and closed the door behind him.

Before the light of dawn had awakened the night sky, Hinda paced the floor of the cold room. With a thin blanket draped around her shoulders, she prayed fervently. Movement across the way interrupted her behests to the Almighty.

Stretching and yawning, Rachel sat up. When she remembered last night's episode with the officer and saw Hinda pacing in distress, a torrent of tears flooded her cheeks. She exclaimed, "Hinda, we have to get out of here now."

"Impossible," Hinda chided. "An entire unit of the German army surrounds this house. We have no papers. If we're caught and interrogated, do you think we would be believed again?"

"So, what are we going to do? Just be sitting ducks to be shot or worse?" Rachel rolled into a ball on the hard floor. Her body began to shake.

"Let's pray for guidance," Hinda advised. Then, in a more demanding tone, she said, "Get up and stand with me. Let's say the Shema."

After completing the sacred prayer, Hinda embraced her sister. "My sweet Rachel, keep your mind open, and I will, too, so that God and Tatae can guide us as to what to do next. For now, let's get dressed and fix our hair."

When the first streak of sunlight glowed on the window, there was a light rap on the door. A German soldier said, "Officer Gorman has invited you girls to join us for breakfast."

Holding the door slightly ajar, Hinda said, "How lovely. May we have a few minutes?"

"Certainly. See you in the dining room shortly."

Hinda waited for his footsteps to trail away. "Rachel, we must adjust our sweaters far down onto our wrists and make certain that our tattoos don't show when we move our arms."

"I'm scared. Do I have to go?"

"Yes, you do. But we're changing your name. Rachel is *too* Jewish. Today, your name is Lena. And speak as little as possible."

The sisters slipped on their new shoes that Mrs. Olmos had given them, which were much cleaner and classier than their other ones. They smoothed their skirts and fluffed their hair, using each other's eyes as mirrors.

"Thank God we have hair and are looking healthier, and not so emaciated, after two months of eating real food. We're still thin, but now, we're even a bit pretty," Hinda proclaimed.

When they entered the dining room, the six officers who surrounded the raw-wood table stood and saluted the sisters. "Heil Hitler," they said in unison.

The young officer from the night before showed the girls to two empty chairs beside him. In the middle of the table was an enormous meat dish. The lead officer began forking pieces onto their plates.

When one of the officers asked their names, Hinda introduced herself, adding that her sister, Lena, was extremely timid, and to please forgive her silence. Then another officer asked about their surname. Politely, Hinda covered her mouth with her hand as if needing to swallow the food in her mouth before speaking, all the while she searched her brain for a German name that was not Jewish sounding. She was about to say Zeilhofen when Rachel, thinking of Soldier Rhino, blurted out the name, "Rhinehardt." She then repeated it, dividing it into two syllables with equal emphasis on each one like it was two separate names, "Rhine. Hardt."

The men chortled, encouraging the shy girl who had found spine to speak.

"Rhinehardt," one officer said, raising his coffee cup in salute. "A good German family."

Smiling brightly, Hinda patted her sister with pride. While quite impressed with Rachel's ingenuity, she was trembling in terror on the inside. Fearing more personal questions, Hinda quaked at the thought of geographical inquiries about where they came from; she had zero knowledge of the region. Every bite she took, she prayed for strength.

Her physical proximity to Nazi uniforms, decorated with blazing stripes and medals, had ripped off the scabs of traumatizing memories. Reliving monstrous atrocities, a reel of flashbacks paraded through Hinda's mind, striking a mighty blow upon her psyche. Her wounds bled freshly, filling her with immense dread. Sitting in such propinquity to the officers also increased the odds that they would identify Rachel and her as Jews. It took all the courage she could muster to remain seated at the table, to not grab her sister, and run from the house. To cope with the overwhelming apprehension, Hinda donned her inner armor—her father's sacred prophecy. Silently, she recited to herself the words, you will live; you will tell.

The soldiers' conversation turned to the savage Soviets. Intentionally, Hinda let her angst surface and be revealed in her facial expressions. The officers nodded in approval, with no thought that the distress revealed on her face was fear of them and the merciless cruelties she knew they were capable of committing, all in the name of Hitler and the Nazi regime.

When a lull in discussion occurred, the elderly man asked for war news, specifically, how near the Russians were. One of the officers offered a surprising tidbit when he spoke of Auschwitz.

Hinda struggled for composure as he conveyed that the Red Army had stormed Auschwitz in late January, liberating the prisoners and taking captive the surviving German staff and military. The old man appeared horrified, while the old woman shook her head in dismay.

Breakfast then ended with a signal from Officer Gorman. He stood and thanked the elderly couple for their generosity. Next, he turned to Hinda and Rachel and said, "Thank you, ladies, for gracing us with your beauty and good company this morning."

Immediately after his parting words, there were knocks, a sound Hinda recognized as the buttstock of a rifle striking against a wooden door. The officers clustered in the entry to address a young soldier who stepped inside. While clearing dishes from the table, Hinda overheard him reporting that his squadron had captured a group of Jews at the edge of the woods.

"Are they some of the freed prisoners from Auschwitz?" Officer Gorman inquired.

"Yes, sir. They all have serial numbers tattooed on their left arms. There's eight of them. Do you want us to jail them or shoot them?"

"Don't waste the ammo. Take them into the woods and hang them. Retrieve all the ropes."

"And the bodies, sir?"

"Leave them on the ground. Vultures will strip the carcasses clean."

Lingering in the dining room, while whisking crumbs from the table, Hinda heard the entire conversation. She tugged on her sweater sleeve, covering her tattoo. Chills snaked down her spine.

That night, when the sisters lay on the hard floor in the cold room, Rachel said, "Do you believe what the officer said this morning about the Russian army storming Auschwitz and freeing the prisoners?"

"Yes, I do. Did you hear the German soldier report that they had captured a group of Jews who had Auschwitz tattoos?"

"I heard, but what does this mean for Sara? She's fourteen years old now. Not a child."

Hinda blinked repeatedly. "Fourteen is still young. Surely, the Russian officers transported the children and younger teens to a place of safety."

Weeping, Rachel exclaimed, "How will we ever find her now?"

Hinda turned onto her side, away from her sister, too ashamed to look at her. The big lie about Sara closed in around her heart, trapping her in its ugly mire. She turned back toward Rachel and looked into her sister's eyes, which brimmed with agonized worry. "In actuality, we don't know if Sara is still alive. It was two years ago that I saw her playing. In that wicked place, who knows what evil happened to her after that. And we don't know what transpired as for violence when the Russian army invaded Auschwitz."

"You think Sara died?" Rachel asked. Fresh tears shot forth, and her chin quivered.

"Only God knows for certain," Hinda replied, and this time, she spoke the truth.

Late afternoon on a chilly March day, a young low-ranking officer appeared at the door of the elderly couple's home. He asked to speak with Hinda.

Taken aback, Hinda inquired indignantly, "How do you know my name?"

Removing his patrol-style hat, the soldier replied. "My superior officer told me to ask for you." The soldier focused his eyes intently upon Hinda's face, studying her features in an overt manner. "The officers who had breakfast with you and your sister last week were impressed with the young lady with the big blue eyes. I now see what they mean."

Hinda stiffened. "And you're here for what?"

"I need your help to kill a chicken. If you assist me, I'll give part of it to your family."

Comprehending that it was his way of giving notice that he was appropriating one of the chickens, and she had no choice in the matter, Hinda stepped into the yard, "Which one?"

Pointing at the plumpest chicken, he said, "That one."

"With all due respect, sir, that one is the only egg-producing hen in the entire lot. It's a significant food source for the elderly owners. *Please* choose a different chicken."

"Nope. I want that one." He aimed his gun and fired. Fluttering its wings, the chicken squawked. Surprisingly, it escaped the bullet. Staring directly at Hinda, the officer snarled, "Must be a Jew chicken."

Anger flared like explosives inside her, but Hinda managed to appear calm.

"Get over there, right now, and chase that Jew chicken in my direction." This time, he pointed his gun at *her*.

Walking briskly to the opposite side of the yard where the chosen chicken pecked at the gravel, Hinda glimpsed the elderly woman watching her through the window. Knots formed in her stomach. Hinda chased the hen toward the soldier. He fired. The bullet shot straight through its neck, ricocheted off the side of the house, and lodged into a tree trunk near where Hinda stood. Though dead, the chicken flopped around as if it were a freshly caught fish, its gills deprived of oxygen-giving water. In about thirty seconds, the hen lay still.

"Fetch that Jew chicken and ferry it over to that soldier waiting near the trench," the young officer commanded, scoping his rifle in Hinda's direction again.

Lifting the lifeless hen, Hinda delivered it to the soldier, who held the chicken away from his body. He then sprinted across the field to a campfire blazing near clusters of army-green tents.

On the return to the house, Hinda was forced to walk past the officer who had killed the chicken without dirtying his hands. Ogling her body with every step she took, the young officer stood on the porch, blocking her way. When she brushed past him, he winked at her, then sneered in an obviously menacing manner.

Hinda's face blanched. *He suspects that I am a Jew.*

Inside the elderly couple's house, Rachel scoured the kitchen sink, while Hinda applied a special wax to the dining-room floor in an effort to remove scuff marks. The woman had complained that the soldiers had damaged it with their boots. On the day of the breakfast with the officers, the sisters had helped the woman clean all the dishes. Surprisingly, the usually disgruntled woman complimented them on being industrious and efficient workers.

Seizing opportunity, Hinda proposed that Rachel and she have daily household chores in exchange for food and a roof over their heads. The woman had squinted her eyes and rubbed her chin as if deep in thought—doubtful thoughts—but then, she nodded her head up and down, as if saying yes in slow motion. In her next breath, she qualified that she would provide only two meals a day *if* their work proved satisfactory. Pleased, Hinda readily agreed. In the days that followed, the woman seemed content with their work. Yet, at times, mood swings clouded her judgment. Although she watched the sisters toil and complete every assigned task, she did not always keep to her agreement. On her bad days, she provided only breakfast.

Anticipating trouble after the loss of the lone egg-laying chicken, Hinda had expected the woman to blame her and then beat her or oust Rachel and her from the house into the wilds. After a full week, the woman had not said one word about it. Hinda concluded that the woman, like her, was afraid of the soldiers and what they might demand next.

In the following weeks, through to the end of March, Hinda and Rachel did the woman's bidding, performing cleaning and organizing jobs. For the sisters, the work was a welcome relief. It guaranteed food—breakfast, at least—and it busied their hands while their minds strained to keep fear at bay. Hinda worried that the irascible chicken soldier would return and demand to see their arms, exposing their tattoos, then drag them off to the woods to be hanged. Inwardly, she harangued that valuable bullets could be used to kill a chicken that could have just as easily had its neck wrung, but not to execute captured Jews. While she worked, she wondered about the Jewish prisoners who the Russians had freed from Auschwitz. She fretted that, if they had fled into territory still under German control, there was no freedom for them, just recapture and death.

Each afternoon, the woman allowed the sisters to take a short break and go into the yard for fresh air. The field in front of the house looked dramatically different with military tents pitched across it in zigzag formations. And now, wide deep trenches had been dug around the entire perimeter of the field.

Bombing and artillery noises blasted the air. Sonorous sounds of war. No longer far in the distance, the vibrations rattled the windows of the elderly couple's humble abode.

His eyes feral, his face gaunt, his pelvic bones poking through his tattered uniform, Wolf Yoskowitz leaned over his brother, who was lying in their bunk nearly unconscious. Dangling a fat worm over Joseph's closed mouth, Wolf urged, "Open up and swallow this."

"Can't," Joseph muttered, his voice faint and weak.

"You can, and you *will*, or you're going to die." Wolf placed his fingers against the side of Joseph's neck. His brother's pulse was slow, dangerously slow. Near the breaking point himself, Wolf felt desperation crawl into his heart. "Joseph, I need you to hang on, to fight to live. We've suffered through too many heinous hells for you to give up now."

Joseph's eyelashes fluttered. He opened his eyes halfway and murmured, "Why *now*?"

"Officers, guards, and staff are fleeing this place in droves every day," Wolf explained. "Word from the underground is that Germany is losing the war and that foreign military is approaching. Bombing sounds are closer now. But, Joseph, you have to eat to survive until sympathetic forces arrive and can get medical help."

"Meat. Supervisor," Joseph mumbled, his words barely audible.

The dim light in Wolf's eyes clouded, the reality of Joseph's condition eclipsing his hope. His brother was too sick to remember that their quarry supervisor disappeared in November of last year. Wolf debated with himself. He wanted to remind Joseph of that and that he had not had any additional protein since the previous October, when their supervisor had been caught giving extra food to his best quarry workers. Instead, Wolf simply said, "Our supervisor is gone. There's no food, except for these critters I scavenged."

Joseph turned his head to the side and made a burbling sound, conveying his disgust.

"You don't have to chew. Just let the thing slide down your throat. You won't even taste it, but you'll absorb some protein."

Joseph's breathing changed to longer intervals between inhales. After a while, he whispered, "Mother is here. She has soup."

While wanting to declare his brother delirious, Wolf calmly replied, "I'll help her feed you. Open your mouth."

Joseph obeyed, appearing as helpless as a baby bird.

Wolf inserted a worm. "Swallow this good soup our mother has made." After Joseph gulped, Wolf placed another worm at the back of his throat, saying, "Here's another spoonful."

When Joseph had ingested three bugs and five worms, Wolf prayed, thanking God, their provider, for the sustenance. Soon after Joseph fell asleep, Wolf stepped outside. Immediately, he wanted to vomit. The stacks of corpses had grown exponentially from just yesterday. The stench in the square had become as onerous as the horrific odor inside the barrack.

Say a Jewish Prayer

A blustery Sunday, the first day of April heralded the arrival of the Red Cross. Nurses and volunteer workers carried injured German soldiers into the elderly couple's home. The small four-room house morphed into an infirmary within the hour.

Assigned to kitchen duties, Rachel made coffee and warmed the bread and soup the Red Cross organization had brought. Hinda was put to work cleaning the wounds of German soldiers. *Hitler's Hit Men,* she called them to herself. She wanted to gouge their wounds, rendering their injuries more serious. Yet Hinda gently cleansed their assaulted areas while a barrage of painful memories of Nazi soldiers strutted through her mind. Many had gravely wounded, even murdered, her loved ones; many had harmed her.

From behind Hinda, a nurse approached. "Oh no! You must remove your sweater. The sleeve is dragging against the wounds. It could spread bacteria."

Near panic, Hinda gaped at the nurse. Her sweater sleeve sheathed her secret. Placing her palm to her forehead as if checking for fever, Hinda replied, "I must tell you that I'm not feeling well. I've had congestion and frequent chills for two days now. The sweater keeps me warm. Is there another job I can do?"

The nurse squinted at Hinda, her head tilted back on her neck, as if not believing her. But then, she said, "You can wash bandages."

Throughout the afternoon, Hinda soaked, scrubbed, and boiled soiled bandages in batches. A volunteer would then take the clean ones to the outdoor clothesline for drying. The little house overflowed with patients, nurses, and Red Cross staff who chattered about the war. Listening closely, Hinda learned that Russian troops were only six miles away and were expected to arrive at their exact location by Monday evening, less than twenty-four hours away.

Thinking of the German troops camped in the field in front of the house, which would soon be a battleground, Hinda began to pray, "Dear Lord Almighty and Tatae, I desperately need your guidance again. What should Rachel and I do next and when? Do we run tonight or stay put? Please protect and shield us from harm. My mind and heart are open, awaiting your direction."

That night, Hinda did not feel a strong impulse to leave, nor did she feel completely comfortable staying. Her experience, though, with this gift called *good instincts,* was that if there was not a compelling urge or continuous gnawing of thought, it was best to not take any action.

Monday brought an inferno. In the dusk of late afternoon, bombs and mortars lit up the sky. Nearby towns and villages, which were not visible during the day, were now showcased in flames. In every which direction, mortars and grenades exploded. Scattered fires blazed and crackled in the adjacent woods.

The elderly woman clutched her purse and her husband's walking cane. To Hinda, she shrieked, "We're going to run. Do you and your sister want to come?"

The four of them bustled from the rear door of the house. The old man pointed the way to what he considered the safest direction. When the terrain became more rugged with uneven ground and tall weeds, the man had difficulty keeping pace. He urged, "You girls run ahead. Veer to the right when there's a choice of direction. If you come upon friendly help, please wait for us."

The sisters trudged onward, making their way through the field, until they came to a gravel road. Picking up their pace, they walked briskly at a near jog for almost one kilometer. After a sharp turn in the road, they came to a complete stop. An enormous army tank, parked horizontally across the road, blocked all passage. A soldier, wearing a military-green uniform with red strips of fabric stitched on the collar, sat on a ledge near the top of the tank. He craned his neck in all directions, surveying the area. Upon seeing the sisters, he clambered down to the ground, while yelling at them in a threatening manner.

Noting the red collar, Hinda surmised he was Russian. While not understanding his language, she knew his words were vile. His mouth twisted perversely, and his eyes spewed viciousness.

Using the butt of his rifle, the soldier began striking both sisters on their heads. Within seconds, Rachel's skull gushed blood, streaking down her face, while Hinda's forehead sported a gaping wound. He shoved them onto the ground, kicking at them both.

Hinda belted out a distressed scream with such grittiness that an officer poked his head out of the tank's interior. "What's going on down there?"

The soldier answered that the girls were scouts for the Germans and had discovered the location of their campsite.

Employing an authoritative tone, the officer ordered the soldier to back off until he could interrogate the women. He then proceeded to climb from the tank. His black uniform, which also had a red collar, appeared more formal, depicting a higher rank. He helped the sisters to their feet.

Hinda explained that they were on the run from the Germans and the soldier had started beating them without any cause. Sensing her father's spirit standing beside her, encouraging her, Hinda pushed her sweater sleeve upward to reveal her tattoo. She motioned for Rachel to do the same. "Sir, we're *not* Germans. We're Polish Jews. We escaped from Auschwitz."

Eyeing them skeptically, he commanded, "Say a Jewish prayer."

Hinda recited the first few words of the sacred Shema but then burst into sobs. Overcome with emotion, her shoulders jerked, and her chest heaved. Watching Hinda cry so distraughtly ripped holes in Rachel's already fragile coping net. She began to weep, too, her hands trembling.

The officer pressed his lips firmly together, and his boot kicked at the grass. Suddenly, he broke down. Big tears rolled onto his round cheeks. "I am also a Jew. From what used to be Czechoslovakia, now Bohemia-Moravia. I lost *all* of my family at Auschwitz." He wiped his eyes. "I so hate Hitler and the Nazi regime that I joined the Russian army."

"Then you understand, sir," Hinda said, her voice quavering as she tried to quash the intense emotion that had overwhelmed her. "I beg you to help us. Can you *please* take my sister and me to the nearest, safest town? We'll be grateful to you forever."

By this time, more soldiers had surrounded them. The officer dismissed them to return to their duties. He then led Hinda and Rachel behind the tank to a field where hundreds of tents and artillery equipment sprawled across the land, an acre or more. Leading them to a well, the officer reeled up a bucket of fresh water. "Use this to freshen up and cleanse the blood from your faces."

While splashing water on her face, Hinda inhaled deeply, breathing in relief that she and Rachel had survived another close call. Sidling close to Hinda, Rachel cried as though she were in severe pain. Hinda turned to observe Rachel's wounds, and her mouth fell agape. A steady stream of blood trickled from Rachel's ear. Stifling a scream, Hinda called out to the officer, who then hurriedly guided them to a makeshift infirmary inside a tent.

After examining Rachel, the army doctor, who had wild, bushy eyebrows, asserted that it was the close-range mortar explosions that had caused a rupture in her inner ear. To halt the bleeding, he tucked medicated cotton gauze inside the ear canal, while instructing Rachel to not remove it until the next morning. His eyebrows jiggled when he explained that she could experience temporary hearing loss in that ear, and if it had not returned to normal in three weeks, she should see a doctor. Before dismissing them, the doctor applied antiseptic to their head lacerations and covered their wounds with bandages.

The sisters exited the infirmary to find the camp filled with thousands of Russian soldiers roaming about in all directions. As young women, they caught attention. Hinda inhaled sharply as soldiers ogled her in an intimidating manner. Feeling vulnerable and scared, Hinda leaned in close to her sister's good ear and whispered, "Don't look at these men. Don't make eye contact. They could easily overtake us, drag us to their tent, and violate us."

Elbowing his way through the soldiers, the Jewish officer spotted the sisters. "I was just coming to meet you at the infirmary." He escorted them to a clear space near the well. "What else can I do for you girls?"

Reiterating her original request of him, Hinda implored, "Could you please help us get to the nearest town or village that is safe?"

The officer was silent, then called out to a nearby soldier, who was young and quite tall. "Take these ladies to safety, to the nearest village that our army has secured and occupied."

In Yiddish, Hinda gushed profuse thanks, and lightly hugged the Jewish officer. Hearing the beloved Yiddish of his childhood, he smiled at her personalized expression of gratitude. Before walking away, Hinda said, "Sir, there was an elderly couple coming behind us. They're German, but they let us stay in their house. Please show them mercy if they arrive here."

"Did they feed you?"

"Not at first, but then later, they did, in exchange for work."

The officer grimaced. To the young soldier waiting to escort the sisters, he gave instructions about the location of the nearest town under Soviet rule. As they talked, the rabid soldier, who had hit Hinda and Rachel with his gun, trotted over to the officer and talked in a muffled voice. After casting a sideways leer at the sisters, he sprinted away.

The officer motioned to Hinda. "My mercy will do no good for the elderly couple you mentioned. Their bodies were just found in the pasture that you must have traveled through too. Both had suffered fatal wounds from mortars. You girls were lucky to have gone ahead of them."

Walking in complete silence, Hinda and Rachel followed the young, tall soldier through multiple fields and, finally, to a roadway. Though frightened, they matched his pace, shadowing every step he took. As night enclosed around them and it became even darker, they came to a village. The soldier checked his compass and then nodded at the sisters. Pointing toward the main street, he made odd gestures with his hands.

Deducing that he only spoke Russian, Hinda interpreted his attempts at sign language to convey that this village was under Soviet rule and safe. Nodding her assent, Hinda waved good-bye. The Soviet soldier promptly trotted off in the same direction they had come.

Rachel asked, "Where are we? I didn't see a name for this place." Stroking her fingers through her hair, she picked at strands, placing them to cover her bloody ear.

Bells tolled. Hinda counted. "It must be nine o'clock." A thought struck her, a memory of hearing such bells in the dove room at the Olmoses' home. Pivoting around, she spotted a small grocery store. And just two streets away from it, she saw a post office. Hinda declared, "I believe this is the village where the Olmoses live."

"It does seem familiar," Rachel replied. "We're free now, but some freedom this is," she lamented. "We have no money to buy food or rent a room. What are we going to do?"

A few yards away, a lone street lantern flickered, seeming to beckon to Hinda. It seemed ominous, for it was the only street lantern lit for blocks, due to the war. Believing it to be a sign, Hinda said, "Let's go this way and see if we can find the Olmoses' house. If they've not been captured, perhaps they would let us spend *one* night."

Before long, the sisters trudged up the slight hill on the gravel driveway. Even though the Soviets had taken the town, the exterior of the two-story red-brick house appeared undamaged. Surprisingly, the front door to the house was wide open. After knocking, Hinda peeked around the corner and saw no one. She and Rachel stepped inside and, right there, standing in the opposite cranny of the vestibule was Gestapo Officer Olmos. Dressed in full Nazi uniform, swastikas on both sleeves, he appeared frozen, all rigid like a statue. When he saw them, his eyes flickered briefly with recognition, then went flat and dull. He shouted, "Heil Hitler." In a robotic manner, he repeated the same stiff movements while saying, again and again, "Heil Hitler."

Rage whirled through Hinda, chilling her heart that already brimmed with loathing for anything of Nazism. Yet, this Nazi had been good to Rachel and her, had kept them in his home for seven weeks, and fed them extraordinarily well, all without any labor requirements. Conflicting emotions—gratitude served on a platter of hatred—ate at her nerves.

"Sir, are Mrs. Olmos and little John here?" Hinda asked politely, suppressing her inner seesaw of turmoil. Officer Olmos offered no reply, continuing with his Nazi salute ritual as if he did not hear her or see her.

Since he had not asked them to leave, the sisters went to the kitchen. Ravenous and excruciatingly thirsty, they hoped to refresh themselves from the traumas of an evening on the run: traveling lengthy distances on rough terrain, surviving a beating from a vicious Russian soldier, and breathing intense smoke from mortars and grenades that had burst all around them.

After gulping down two glasses of water each, they went to Victor's quarters behind the back stairwell. The door was fully open, and the room was entirely vacant as if Victor had never resided there. Puzzled, they returned to the kitchen to find bread or something of substance to eat. Just then blood-curdling screams invaded the space.

"Yikes," Rachel exclaimed, "That sounds like Mrs. Olmos."

The unnerving cacophony—Mrs. Olmos' screams pleading for help coalescing with the sounds of Officer Olmos shouting Heil Hitler—moved Hinda to action. She stepped to the doorway and saw that Mr. Olmos remained in the exact same place in the foyer. Seemingly catatonic, he saluted Hitler repetitively.

Unnoticed by Mr. Olmos, the sisters tiptoed through the living area to the master bedroom. The door was ajar. Hinda peered inside and beheld a nightmarish scene. One Russian soldier had the slim and pretty Mrs. Olmos pinned down on the bed while another burly one raped her violently. Without making a sound, Hinda took Rachel firmly by the arm. Quietly, they climbed the stairs. In the second-floor hallway, they noticed that the door to little John's room was open. The space was completely empty. Not a single remnant of furniture, bedding, or toys remained.

Moving on tiptoe, the sisters entered the dove room. It, too, was vacant, except for the cots, which were sitting in the corner where Hinda had rolled them a month ago. No white-dove coos graced the room. The birds were gone, as were the cages. Once the sisters had folded down the beds, Hinda began to tremble and shake.

"What did you see in that bedroom?" Rachel asked in a whisper.

"The unspeakable, what we fear most. Russian soldiers are absolute beasts."

"What should we do? It's dangerous here."

"We stay. This is a roof over our heads, and it's too risky to try and leave tonight. There could be more soldiers at the rear of the house or on their way, yet to arrive."

"Should we try and blockade the door with these mattresses?"

"These flimsy things wouldn't stop those brutes. Neither would the cot frames. Besides, we shouldn't make any noise."

"I wish I had hearing loss in both ears. I can't bear to hear Mrs. Olmos scream. How long will this last?" Rachel whispered, her voice anxious and breathy.

"There were two men in that room, probably taking turns having their way with her. Let's pull the covers up and lie as still as possible and not make another sound. Pray, Rachel, pray, with all your heart and all your soul that those savage animals don't find us."

Soon after midnight, Hinda slipped out of bed. The Olmoses' house was quiet now. An hour earlier, she had heard a ruckus downstairs and then nothing more after the door slammed two times in succession.

A crescent moon glimmered through the windows, which still had the fabric coverings that Victor had nailed to the wood casings when they had first arrived. Pushing back the makeshift curtain, she peeked out, peering down into the backyard. Nothing moved except for tree leaves swaying slightly from a soft breeze.

Hinda's gaze went to Rachel, who was sleeping soundly, exhausted from the traumatic day. Hinda, also exhausted, wished sleep would come so easily to her. She fretted, wondering if they would ever find real safety. She reclined on her cot. Hunger pains throttled her stomach. Pondering options, Hinda decided it was too risky to tread down the stairs in the dark and riskier still to turn on a light that could draw attention.

Morning would reveal the nature of their circumstances. And then, just who or what would they find? Dead bodies downstairs? Injured bodies? Soviet soldiers?

When dawn's first light streaked through the window, Hinda's eyes popped open. She arose and checked the backyard. From her limited viewpoint through the small glass panes, she did not see any soldiers, civilians, or animals. Her fears slightly assuaged, she went to the door and turned the knob ever so slowly. Rustling sounds behind her stopped her in her tracks. Turning, she saw Rachel flopping on her cot and then bounding up as if it were a trampoline.

"Don't leave me alone!" Rachel implored.

The sisters crept down the stairs together. The living room was in its usual order. In the kitchen, the two glasses they had drunk from the previous evening sat on the counter in the exact spot where they had left them when Mrs. Olmos had begun screaming. All else in the kitchen appeared to be in order, nothing rearranged from the previous night.

"Let's check the master bedroom. We have to know if anyone is here."

Rachel gulped. "I'm too scared. I'm staying in the kitchen."

Sighing heavily, Hinda tiptoed across the living room to the master bedroom, where she found the door wide open. The bed had been stripped; the mattress lay bare. An eerie sensation swept over her as frightful visions invaded her psyche, images of the Soviet soldiers killing Mrs. Olmos and rolling up her body in the covers. An urge to know if anyone—dead or alive—was in the house overcame her. Stepping softly, she explored the bedroom and bathroom. Towels were folded neatly, and the shower curtain was drawn back, revealing a clean bathtub. No one was there. Nor was anyone hiding in the closet.

In the foyer, Hinda checked the front door and found it shut tightly but not locked. After double locking the door, she drew the cords to the draperies in the living room and watched the fabric panels unfold across the windows. She then adjusted each corner for fuller coverage. Returning to the kitchen, she found Rachel devouring a piece of ham.

"Looks as if we have the house to ourselves, at least for this morning," Hinda reported. "Let's make coffee. Then take it and some food upstairs." Tugging at the curtains, she pulled the lace panels across the kitchen window. "These are see-through; stay away from this window."

Once they were situated in the dove room, the sisters hungrily ate two sandwiches each. While sipping on coffee, they discussed the mysteries abounding under the Olmoses' roof. For starters, why were John's room and Victor's quarters vacant of all belongings and furniture? Tossing out ideas, they decided on the least disturbing answer. Perhaps Victor had moved the little boy to a safer place, to his grandparents' or another relative's home. Since Officer Olmos felt that the Russians' arrival was imminent, even a month ago, this seemed a likely scenario. Yet the doves were a different matter. They would not have been easy for Victor to transport. The sisters concluded that the SS had seized all the birds and their cages the first of March, the same day they had been forced to flee.

Next, they hypothesized about what had happened to Officer and Mrs. Olmos. They both were perplexed as to why Officer Olmos did not put up a fight and remained in the foyer when Russians were raping his wife in the bedroom. Furrowing her brow, Hinda said, "In actual fact, we don't know what transpired before we arrived. The Russians may have threatened to kill Officer Olmos if he didn't remain in the foyer and make a lot of noise so they could hear him and know where he was." Hinda shrugged. "It doesn't make sense why they didn't tie him up or handcuff him. We just can't know the truth of it. But I do know that when I went into the Olmoses' bedroom this morning, the bed had been stripped of the bedspread and all sheets and covers." Rachel's face turned to chalk. Potential answers about what had happened to Mrs. Olmos after the soldiers were done with her were too nefarious for either sister to conjecture in spoken words.

"Do you really think we should stay here?" Rachel entreated.

"I don't know what to do," Hinda lamented. "We've nowhere to go and no money for a train ticket if we did. It's not safe for Jews out there. We're still in a war zone. Just listen to all the bombing sounds." Hinda wrung her hands together in fretful worry. "For now, let's take it a day at a time and see what happens. Let's only go downstairs twice a day for food and water, at dawn and at dusk. It's imperative that we stay away from all windows."

108
Siberia

Ten days later, Hinda and Rachel were catnapping when loud knocking jarred them awake. Hinda whispered, "That's the front door. Let's don't answer." The knocking persisted and soon morphed to thunderous pounding. The sisters crept to the top of the stairway, scarcely breathing.

Suddenly, the door swung open, revealing two men. One, who was older with a shiny bald pate and was dressed in civilian attire, grasped an iron tool he had used to open the door. The other man, a Soviet military officer, who had a full head of wooly hair, clutched papers. The Russian officer yelled foreign words. The bald man shouted at them, "Get down here, now!"

Striving to steel their nerves and not show their terror, the two sisters descended the stairs, with Hinda going first. In a respectful manner, they approached the men.

"We have orders for your apprehension. The both of you," the civilian man explained.

"May I ask why?" Hinda inquired.

"You are spies. German spies!" The Russian officer spit out his accusation with acerbic authority, though his enunciation was barely understandable. "You spies. Going to jail in Siberia." He held up the documents, Orders of Apprehension, and shook them in Hinda's face.

"Siberia?" Hinda gasped. The threatening look on the officer's face stopped her from asking him more questions. His woolly hair reminded her of one of the brutes who had attacked Mrs. Olmos. She decided to pose her inquiry to the civilian man. "Sir, may I ask what names are listed on the Apprehension Orders?"

"No names, but the document specifies two females who fit your descriptions and reside at this location." The bald man pointed his iron rod at Hinda and commanded, "Gather your personal things now. Then you must come with us. You have no choice in this matter."

Motioning for Rachel to remain at the door, Hinda raced up the stairs and grabbed the pillowcase that held their nightclothes, Rachel's sketch pad, and her journal. She removed her journal, then went to little John's bathroom, and took two towels. Fearing they would confiscate her journal since they had accused her of being a spy, she wrapped it in the towels and carried it separately.

At the door, the Soviet officer jerked the pillowcase from her hands and inspected the contents. He flipped through Rachel's sketch pad and raised his eyebrows in appreciation of the artwork. Nodding acknowledgement, he appeared momentarily disarmed.

Hinda explained to the civilian man that the towels carried supplies for when Rachel and she had their menses. The man ducked his bald head in outright embarrassment. He made gestures to the officer to not bother with the towels; they had passed his inspection.

In silence, the sisters trailed the Soviet officer. The civilian man, gripping his iron tool, followed behind them. After walking about ten blocks, they came to a building that heralded a temporary sign printed in bold letters: SOVIET COMMAND.

Inside the building, the wooly-haired officer escorted the sisters down to the basement. There, he pushed them into a small cell—disgustingly dirty and rat-infested. A bench was the only seating, and it was covered in nasty, putrid grime. The officer grinned broadly, his yellow teeth glinting in the dark. He jangled keys and slammed shut the cell door. After securing the lock, he clomped up the stairs.

Scared of, and disgusted by, the gargantuan rats that scampered all across the floor, Hinda spread one of the towels across the feculent bench. She and Rachel sat atop the towel and tucked their feet up under their legs. Worrying that officers or guards could see into the cell, Hinda kept her journal wrapped in the second towel.

In the darkened room with nothing to do but think, Hinda became obsessed with thoughts of her mother and how she died. Longing to visit her grave in Mława, Hinda visualized standing over the grave, begging her mother for forgiveness. For killing her. The stark truth was a sharp thorn stabbing her heart. Admittedly, she was careless that day. If she hadn't been jailed, her mother would not have been on the street looking for her, would not have fainted, and fallen upon her breastbone, not have died, at that time. On the second day of circuitous self-accusations tumbling in her mind, she opened up to Rachel, venturing to speak of her burdensome guilt.

"Hinda!" Rachel said through gritted teeth. "If you hadn't gone outside the gate and worked for that Polish woman, Mrs. Kowalski, in exchange for food, all five of us, living in that ghastly mill with no kitchen, would have died of starvation." Rachel rose from the bench and stomped her foot in exclamation. "Remember what Tatae said. Mommy was *privileged* to die the way she did. It was quick and *not* at the hands of the Nazis."

Listening to Rachel's perspective, void of condemnation, Hinda felt her guilt shrink to a manageable size. Yet the grisly gremlin, placing blame upon her, still breathed deep inside her.

For forty-eight hours, the sisters experienced Soviet hostage hospitality—feisty rats, filth, a horrid stench, one bucket to urinate and defecate into that was already half-filled when they arrived, continuous darkness, and no place to lie down for sleeping. Twice a day, a guard brought cold coffee and one slice of stale bread for each of them.

Late morning on the third day, a Soviet guard stomped down the stairs to the basement and unlocked the cell. He gestured for Hinda and Rachel to go up the stairs. Following them, he pushed their backs, urging them to hurry. At the building's front entrance, he shoved them through the main doorway.

Once outdoors, Hinda immediately noticed a travel bus parked on the street. It was already almost filled to capacity with men. Catching bits of conversations around her, she understood that the soldiers on the bus were Ukrainian. They had been accused of treason and were being transported to a jail in Siberia.

The guard, who had unlocked their cell, hustled the sisters over to a Soviet soldier, who ordered them to board the bus.

Hinda bowed her head, petitioning the Almighty and her father, Tatae, for help. The soldier allowed her a moment of prayer, then began prodding her with his baton.

"Sir! Sir! Please wait," Hinda yelled. "We're not German. And we're not Russian. There has to be a mistake. I beg you for an interview with the commander or the highest-ranking officer on these premises."

The soldier's beady eyes bore into her for what seemed like hours. At last, he said, "Just a minute. Don't move from this spot." Before going inside, he asked another soldier to stand watch over them. When the soldier returned, he pointed to a second-floor window where the commander, a tall man dressed in a formal uniform, motioned for the sisters to come upstairs. Two Soviet soldiers escorted them inside the building.

At the top of the second-floor stairway, the threshold opened to one large room. The commander sat behind a massive desk spread with maps and papers. Trepidation beating their hearts, the sisters approached him. He gestured for them to sit in the two chairs opposite his desk.

The tall and burly commander wore a menacing frown along with an official jacket that was copiously decorated with medals and ribbons. The two soldiers stood behind the sisters' chairs, their guns drawn. It was an intimidating scene.

Inhaling sharply, Hinda said, "Thank you, sir, for taking your valuable time to speak with us. We need to understand why we've been ordered to board the bus to Siberia."

His lips twisting into a scowl, the commander barked, "Because you're German spies."

Grabbing Rachel's arm, Hinda pushed up her sister's sleeve, revealing the Auschwitz tattoo. Then she extended her own inner arm and showed the commander the serial number tattooed there. "Sir, we're Polish Jews and have been incarcerated, and treated cruelly, at Auschwitz for over two years. We despise Hitler and the Nazi regime. We would *never* become German spies. Would you please allow me to tell our story?"

Leaning back in his chair, the commander nodded his assent.

Hinda launched into the saga of their home and property in Zieluń being confiscated in March of 1940, and the family then forcibly moved to the Mława ghetto, where they were confined. She told of the devastating loss of their parents and then their imprisonment in Auschwitz in December of 1942.

The commander listened intently as Hinda unfolded the horrors of their suffering and tribulations at the hands of the Nazis in the concentration camp named Auschwitz.

After a long while, the Soviet commander interrupted. "Do you know what our father, Stalin, says?"

"I do not, sir. I apologize," Hinda replied.

Using his closed fist like a gavel, the commander knocked his hand against his desk multiple times. He upped his voice volume dramatically while reciting Stalin's quote: "See everything. Believe nothing."

Her hopes for freedom dashed, Hinda fought back a surge of tears and began silently praying. Begging for Divine intervention, she supplicated for a miracle, beseeching the Almighty to save Rachel and her from imprisonment in Siberia. Not feeling a sense of peace, she then entreated the spirit of her father, Tatae, asking him to appeal to God on her behalf.

The commander rocked forward in his chair and tapped a small bell on his desk. A woman wearing a military uniform entered the room. The commander roared to her, "Frisk and search their bodies thoroughly and then return them to this room."

The woman directed the sisters to a side door. Once inside the small room, she demanded they remove all their clothing and empty the contents of the pillowcase onto her desk. They did as she instructed. Her fingers were nimble and efficient as she explored all their bodily cavities. Next, the woman searched through their personal items, the nightclothes, Rachel's sketch pad, and Hinda's diary. Placing everything but Hinda's journal back into the pillowcase, she ordered them to get dressed.

Two hours later, the woman returned the sisters to the commander's office. She rendered her report to him in Russian. Then she placed the spiral-bound notebook on his desk. His forehead furrowed when he flipped its pages. "What is this?" he asked in a threatening tone.

"My diary, sir. It's written in Polish. I can translate for you," Hinda offered.

His tone gruff, the commander snarled, "I have my own interpreter." He tapped the bell again, this time three rings in succession. A young soldier entered the room. He proceeded to read and translate Hinda's journal. After the third chapter, the commander boomed, "Enough."

Arising from his chair, the commander signaled the meeting had ended. Hinda and Rachel both sprang from their chairs and stood erect, awaiting their sentence.

Stepping around to the front of his desk, the Soviet commander extended his arms and placed his palms on Hinda's shoulders. He looked into her eyes and declared, "You and your sister are free to go. However, your diary will be sent to the Kremlin. The details in your written accounts are valuable to us."

A tsunami of relief washed over Hinda upon hearing the announcement of their freedom. Yet her heart shattered at the news that her cherished diary was officially seized. Quashing waves of emotion, Hinda bowed slightly to him. "Sir, thank you. My sister and I sincerely thank you."

Free—narrowly escaping an edict for life-long incarceration in Siberia— the sisters walked arm in arm into the night. Although they had entered the commander's office at noon, the sun had already slipped past the horizon and the moon was now rising.

"I can't believe he let us go." Rachel exhaled audibly, a deep, slow sigh. "But what do we *do* now?" she asked, walking as if in a daze, holding tightly to her sister's arm.

"Go back to the Olmoses' house and clean this filth from us," Hinda replied, her voice shaky from deep fatigue and the vortex of emotion still churning inside her.

"I want to burn my clothes," Rachel said.

"Yes, our clothes are going in the garbage. We'll find new outfits in Mrs. Olmos's closet."

"We're not spies, but we've become thieves," Rachel exclaimed.

"Where Mrs. Olmos is now, she has no need for clothes. Plus, we won't take anything of value." Hinda sighed heavily, "And, dear sister, tomorrow morning, we're leaving this town and putting this dreadful experience behind us."

109

The Supreme Commander

April 11–12, 1945 | Weimar, US-occupied Germany
Buchenwald Concentration Camp

Stars and stripes rippled in the breeze. A convoy of army tanks, military trucks, and jeeps—all displaying American flags—rumbled down the gravel road to the Nazi concentration camp named Buchenwald, located twelve kilometers from the town of Weimar, Germany. The arrival of the US Sixth Armored Division, led by Major General Robert W. Grow of the American Third Army, which was commanded by General George S. Patton, heralded hope for the unjustly persecuted imprisoned there.

Yet, the American forces would not arrive in time that afternoon to liberate *all* the remaining Buchenwald inmates. Hundreds would die in the next hours.

Inside the camp's SS office, the phone buzzed. Surveying the guard tower through the window, Tobias, the tall man sitting at the desk, lifted the receiver on the third ring. "Buchenwald," he barked.

"This is Gestapo headquarters in Weimar. Beware. American forces have been sighted in the area. We're sending explosives on the train." The Gestapo officer raised his volume, yelling into the phone. "Blow up the entire camp. Destroy everything—all inmates and barracks. Heil Hitler."

A wry smile parted Tobias' lips. Energizing his voice, Tobias spoke with authority into the phone, "The camp is already blown up. Don't bother sending explosives. Except for this building, SS Headquarters, everything is totally destroyed, including all remaining inmates. Received?" After hearing confirmation and another Heil Hitler from the Gestapo, which ended the conversation, Tobias jostled the receiver back into its cradle and peered through the window, his prisoner uniform reflecting in the glass.

"Blow up the camp before the Americans can witness the horrors perpetuated here? Not happening. Damn Nazis. They say Heil Hitler. I say, *Hell to Hitler,*"

Tobias exclaimed. He turned to look at the dead SS officer lying on the floor and pondered what heinous acts against humanity the man had personally committed in the name of Hitler.

Tobias closed the desk drawers he had rifled through and then pushed the chair back. When he stood up, his long legs, excessively lank and emaciated, appeared as stilts made of bone. Clutching the dead officer's canteen, he drank thirstily. Valued as highly as liquid gold to him, the fresh water tasted sublime. He forced himself to save a fair amount and began searching the office for food. Having already hunted through all the desks and found nothing, Tobias explored the storage areas. And there, in an open locker, was a sausage sandwich wrapped in paper. He squeezed one end. The bread was soft. "Don't think you'll be eating this for lunch today," he said to the corpse. Tobias gobbled half the sandwich, rewrapped it, and tucked it into his pants pocket.

Lifting the pistol and an extra clip of ammunition from the lifeless officer, Tobias checked that the gun's safety was engaged and then carefully placed it inside his shirt. From the desktop, he grabbed the canteen and the gun that a resistor group had given him early that morning after they had stormed the guard tower. He had then used it to kill three SS officers, including the one in that office. Holding the pistol cocked and ready to fire, Tobias limped to the door and exited. His energy flagging, he nixed his next plot and decided to return to his barrack in the main camp for a quick rest.

The lives of Wolf and Joseph Yoskowitz hung in the balance. Both breathed shallowly. Their bodies were weak and near death from starvation and disease.

Wolf, lying in his wooden bin, could hear the roar of airplanes flying low overhead and the shouts of other inmates clamoring that it was either the Americans or the British. He struggled and strained with all his might to arise, but he could not move from his bin.

Extreme weakness had invaded Wolf's muscles. Immobile, he could no longer walk or even stand on his own power. Joseph, semi-unconscious and burning hot with fever, lay next to him. Wolf surmised that his brother had typhus, whereas he didn't know what disease plagued him. Helpless, Wolf feared that the German guards and SS officers, the few who still worked, would shoot both Joseph and him if they saw their condition. At random, the remaining camp officials blitzed barracks and shot inmates who appeared ill. Later, they dragged the dead to the square, stacking them in piles.

Suddenly, gunfire rattled the room. An SS officer, whose eyes darted with wild panic, ran down the rows, shooting into the bins where prisoners were sleeping or reclining.

Wolf watched as the officer neared the bunk he shared with Joseph. The officer paused to reload his gun. Then he continued to aim directly at inmates and fire all along the row. A fearsome realization exploded in Wolf's mind: The officer was killing everyone in there, sick or not.

When the officer pointed his gun at Wolf, the barrel abruptly jerked upward, and his bullet hit the ceiling. The officer's body crumpled to the floor. Shot in the back, the bullet lodged in his heart, he writhed an instant and then lay lifeless.

His pistol drawn, a man named Tobias, a prisoner who could barely walk himself, stood mere paces away. He nabbed the gun from the dead officer and handed it to his pal from the quarry—Wolf Yoskowitz, who had once saved his life, hiding him and feeding him when he was ill. The loaded weapon tumbled to the floor. Wolf did not have the strength to hold it.

"Wolf man, you're even weaker than yesterday," Tobias lamented. He retrieved the gun from the floor, placing it beside Wolf. Then he held the canteen to his friend's mouth.

Wolf's hands trembling, he grasped the canteen and drank fresh water, his first liquid in days. "Thank you, Tobias. For this and for saving my life just now, and my brother's."

"I owe you that and more. Fight to hang on, just a few more hours. American military is nearby. I heard the good news in the SS office where I stole lunch." Tobias pulled out the remaining part of the sausage sandwich and held it to Wolf's mouth. "Eat what you can."

An hour later, Wolf held the pistol in his lap, his finger poised on the trigger. He strove to remain calm. Sounds of battle ricocheted. He listened intently. Mortars and grenades were exploding in the main camp near his barrack. Gunfire was incessant.

After another hour or more, there was silence except for men's voices intermittently yelling orders. But the language was not German; it was English. Looking to his brother, Wolf could see Joseph's chest rising and falling with short, labored breaths. He whispered, "Lord, please let the Americans find us in time."

April 12, 1945

Wolf jerked awake. From the crack in the wall, he noted the sun's midday position in the sky. The worrisome rattle in Joseph's chest was now obviously louder. Wolf's ears perked up when he heard men talking outside the door. He strained, endeavoring to get up and go to them for help, all to no avail. Just then, he heard a voice he recognized.

"In here. This barrack. Please check out these guys," Wolf's friend, Tobias, pleaded.

American soldiers entered Wolf's barrack. Seeing no German military or guards there, they motioned in a man who wore a highly decorated US Army uniform.

"General Eisenhower, look at this." One of the soldiers pointed to the bullet-riddled corpses in the wooden bins.

Wolf called out, "Help us, my brother and me, please." He strove to call out louder. "Help!"

Two soldiers made their way down the row. One hollered, "Two live ones here."

The general followed closely behind them, his interpreter alongside. He stepped up to Wolf's bunk. Bobbling his head in dismay, the general's blue eyes clouded as he surveyed the young men's condition—emaciated, diseased, bruised, feeble, and lying in their own excrement.

"Son, are you able to walk?" General Eisenhower directed the question to Wolf. The interpreter translated the ensuing conversation between the two.

"No, sir, I cannot." Wolf replied. "And my brother here is near death. Typhus, I think."

Turning to his soldiers, the American general issued orders, "Contact the medics. Get these two boys to our nearest field hospital."

General Dwight D. Eisenhower reached out and touched Wolf Yoskowitz on the shoulder. "How long have you been here?"

"Since June of 1941, sir."

"Four years at Buchenwald." Shaking his head in awe, General Eisenhower said, "Then you are tough. Keep holding on, son. Medical help is on the way." Holding his fingers together and horizontal, he raised his hand upward in a crisp gesture. The five-star general saluted Wolf Yoskowitz and proclaimed, "You are now a free man."

After completing a tour of the grim atrocities found throughout the camp, General Eisenhower, who served as Supreme Commander of the Allied Expeditionary Forces in Europe, issued orders to his chief communications officer. "Contact the United States Congress and the British Parliament. Demand that official delegations from both governments visit Buchenwald Concentration Camp as fast as possible. In addition, notify all Allied War correspondents to get in here immediately and document these atrocities." Pausing, he rubbed his chin. "And I want the German people living in this area to be brought in on buses and required to see, firsthand, the barbarous cruelty their Nazi government has perpetuated upon innocent people. The brutality is unconscionable and the most shocking, inhumane sight I have ever witnessed. The world *must* know. The world must *never* forget."

110

The Road to Puławy

Early May 1945 | Southern Silesian Region | War-torn Poland

Blistered and oozing blood, Rachel's feet throbbed. The sisters had walked in slushy sludge since leaving the Olmoses' house early that morning. Deciding their course on the wings of prayers for guidance, Hinda had selected one of the roadways, not knowing where it led.

Wearing fresh outfits, they each carried a pillowcase stuffed with essentials gleaned from the Olmoses' home. The cotton sacks bulged on their backs as they trod in the mire of melting snow. Slipping and sliding, they removed their slick-soled shoes and walked barefoot. The muddy muck—chunky with gravel and bits of ice—cut into their feet, especially Rachel's. After five hours of trudging along, Rachel groaned audibly with every step.

"Let's take a breather," Hinda said as she spotted a good-sized tree that had low branches. She waded through the snow in the ditch. Rachel followed, stepping in Hinda's exact footprints. At the tree, Hinda hung her pillowcase on a sturdy limb and placed Rachel's sack in a wide fork of the main trunk. She then helped Rachel recline upon a substantial branch.

"Oh no! My poor Rachel," Hinda wailed when she examined her sister's feet, which were peppered with swollen lacerations and oozing bloody blisters. Alarmed, Hinda took two small towels from her supplies and filled them with snow. Intent upon reducing the swelling and pain, she wrapped Rachel's feet in the makeshift ice packs.

Their backs resting against the trunk, the sisters lounged on tree branches while munching on smoked sausage and stale soda crackers from the Olmoses' larders. Selecting carefully that morning, they had packed boxed crackers, lightweight canned goods, and preserved meats. Fresh foods, like bread and vegetables, were long gone.

"Maybe we should have opened a can of sardines," Hinda commented, the dry crackers catching in her throat. When the word sardines passed through her lips, a memory of being in Mława sprang to life. She remembered the time when she had sneaked through the ghetto gates and walked to the train station, trading her sweater for sardines. Afterwards, her legs had ached terribly. That night, she had dreamt of walking on a country roadway with Rachel, whose feet were blistered and bleeding. And now, three years later, they were living that very scene.

Resting on her branch, Rachel choked down a piece of aged, smoked sausage. She exclaimed, "Sardines would've been moister, for sure. And they wouldn't stink up this open space in the middle of nowhere. Hinda, we haven't seen a single vehicle or any signs pointing to villages or towns ahead. I'm beginning to wish we'd stayed at the Olmoses' home."

Shaking her head vehemently in dissent, Hinda said, "Not prudent. Someone in that town or neighborhood had turned us in as spies and listed that exact address. That's what was written on the apprehension order. Whoever did that was aware we were staying in that house."

Rachel shrugged her shoulders and yawned, too tired to blame the black-haired woman.

Hinda stood from her branch. "We stayed there, this last time, without permission, because we were desperate, with nowhere to go, delaying the very situation we're in today." Raising her eyes skyward, Hinda added, "Furthermore, I feel that it's not long before members of the Olmoses' family show up to find out what happened to them. Or to claim the property if Officer and Mrs. Olmos are dead. And I believe they are. Brutal Russian hands took their lives. I just know it."

In the late afternoon, having walked for nearly nine hours, the sisters came to the town of Wilków. Beyond exhausted, they struggled to hold themselves erect. Finding the main square in the center of town, Hinda strategized, looking in all directions for clues of where to go or what person to ask for help. The square was buzzing with activity. Troops of Soviet soldiers patrolled the square and roamed about the nearby streets.

Spotting a young woman who was near to her age and carried a baby in her arms, Hinda decided to approach her and ask her simple questions about the town, hoping to engage her. At first the woman eyed the sisters suspiciously, but the longer Hinda conversed with her about town trivia, the more she seemed to relax, patting her baby girl on the back and smiling. Rachel, who leaned against

Hinda's shoulder, barely able to stand, cooed at the baby, playing peek-a-boo. The baby suddenly flung out its arm, offering Rachel its teething ring, and then just as quickly, tossed it on the pavement.

"Now we have to sterilize it," the woman grumbled. When she reached down to retrieve the teething toy, she saw Rachel's feet and screeched, "Yikes. What happened to you?"

Hinda explained their plight, saying they had walked through sludge all day.

The woman tilted her head sideways for a moment, then said, "Would you like to come to my home? You could have tea and relax for a bit before you journey on."

"How kind. Thank you. Yes, we would be immensely grateful," Hinda replied, with Rachel leaning so firmly against her shoulder that she thought she would surely topple over.

An elderly woman, a color-blocked knitted throw across her lap, greeted the sisters. Rocking to and fro in an antique chair, she introduced herself as the grandmother. The young mother explained to Hinda and Rachel that the baby and she had come to live with her grandmother when her husband, the baby's father, had been killed in the war fighting the Russians.

While sorrowful pangs for the young woman, already a widow, leapt in Hinda's heart, her stomach instantly tightened. The woman's husband had died fighting Russians, which meant these people were German.

After getting the baby situated atop a quilt on the floor, the young mother brought a pan of warm salt water for Rachel to soak her feet in. Then, she served tea and buttered biscuits filled with blackberry jam.

Delighted to have company, the elderly woman proved to be a genial conversationalist and, surprisingly, the sisters' oracle. As they sipped their tea, she soon invited Hinda and Rachel to spend one night, if they did not mind sleeping on the floor. Considering Rachel's condition, Hinda put her anxiety of Germans aside and accepted the gracious offer.

The savvy grandmother, perceiving the sisters' predicament, spoke about a nearby municipality named Puławy, which she said was only twenty-five kilometers from Wilków. She emphasized that it had a large population of Polish people who would likely welcome them and provide refuge.

The moment the woman mentioned the town's name, Puławy, Hinda's stomach lurched, but in a positive, familiar manner. Her hand pressing on her lower abdomen, Hinda interpreted the sensation as a prophetic signpost, an arrow pointing the way.

Early the next morning, when the sun was barely poking its nose above the horizon, the sisters trod on the road to Puławy. After an hour of walking in silence, seeing no people or vehicles, Rachel, who limped along with her feet wrapped, said, "I know those women were German, but they were so nice to us, especially to me, giving me salve and these bandages."

"Yes, I think God is trying to show me that not all Germans are bad people."

"I thought you learned that with Dr. Walter and Soldier Rhino."

At the mention of Walter, tears unexpectedly sprang from Hinda's eyes. "I did, but then we repeatedly suffered such horror at the hands of many Nazis, all Germans."

"Why are you crying?" Rachel asked.

"Honestly, I don't know. Whenever I think of Walter nowadays, I feel sad. Probably because I never told him that I love him. If this war will ever truly end and we can get settled, I intend to find him."

After walking in mud approximately twenty-five kilometers, crossing through numerous villages, and stopping frequently to rest Rachel's feet, the sisters arrived in Puławy. A full moon overhead cast its bright glow, aiding their search for the center of town.

Aghast at the destruction that they had already witnessed while walking into town, homes destroyed from bombs dropped in air strikes, Hinda looked all around the square, which was lit with street lamps. Every direction she turned, she saw devastation. Buildings wrecked from bombings lined one side of the square. Other structures were reduced to rubble and ash, totally destroyed. What's more, she saw no civilians, only Russian soldiers.

In the far corner of the square, Hinda noticed a cluster of buildings, damaged but standing. Lights shone from the inside. She helped Rachel across the street to what looked like a makeshift police station or offices for local authorities. Hinda pushed on one of the doors. It opened easily. She went inside with Rachel hobbling behind her.

Standing behind the main counter, a man, who was up in years and sported a ragged, handlebar mustache, frowned upon seeing them enter. He gruffly asked, "What do you want?"

Encouraged that he was speaking Polish, Hinda explained their predicament.

In a hostile tone, he then embarked on a lengthy interrogation of her. After asking countless questions, he suddenly snapped, "Get on now, you homeless girls. It's way past closing time. I'm shutting down this place."

"With all due respect, sir, I've answered your every question. We've walked for hours, the entire day, all the way from Wilków. And my sister's feet are bleeding." Eyeing a row of chairs against the wall, Hinda inquired, "Could we possibly sit down for a minute before we go?"

"All right. One minute," the man snapped. He cast his eyes downward to Rachel's feet. His scowl seemed to soften when he surveyed her blood-soaked bandages. Uncrossing his arms, he nabbed keys from a drawer. "After I lock up, I reckon you can come with me. There's a neighborhood not too far from here where a lot of Polish people reside. I will only escort you to the edge of that area. It's up to you to find a welcome mat there."

111
Out of Order

"Adolph Hitler is dead?" Hinda squealed.

The Polish couple, who had readily taken in the sisters, sat at their kitchen table, both bobbing their heads up and down, indicating it was true.

"Who? What? Where?" Hinda asked excitedly.

"On April 30, the Soviets closed in on the bunker where Hitler was hiding," the husband explained. "He shot himself before *they* could get him."

Leaning forward with intensity, Hinda asked, "Does his death mean that the war is over?"

"Not yet. Though it could happen soon. Even this week." The husband dunked bread crust into his coffee. "Germany hasn't officially surrendered, but it's rumored that they're getting so trounced that Hitler's replacement, Admiral Doenitz, and Army General Jodl have engaged in talks with the Allied forces' commander, General Eisenhower."

"Allied forces?" Rachel inquired. She scooped up the last bit of cabbage from her second bowl of soup.

"You girls haven't had much war news, have you, now?" The man's eyes blinked repetitively, thinking of their isolated years of being imprisoned at Auschwitz, and then, their life of hiding, on the run, after their escape. "The Allied forces include numerous countries, France, Canada, etc." he explained. "The big three, though, are the United States of America, the United Kingdom, and the Soviet Union."

Elbowing her husband, the wife said, "He's obsessed with politics and current events. He follows every scrap of news we get, which isn't much with our city in ruins. We've seen dark days of war here too. But what might interest you girls most is that now all the central roads in Poland are declared freed. You wouldn't be arrested if you travel on the main roads."

"That's true. And, also, our local municipality recently announced that it is providing rail passes to qualifying survivors of internment camps. To destinations within Poland, that is. You may want to investigate that possibility with the authorities tomorrow."

Hinda's eyes popped wide upon hearing that tidbit. She placed her spoon into the empty bowl. "This vegetable soup was delicious, and so was the fresh bread. We can't begin to thank you both enough. I know it's late in the evening."

"We are delighted you knocked on our door," the wife replied. "You have quite a riveting story. All that you've been through is heartbreaking. We hope you find a smidgen of peace here in our home." She briefly tucked her chin onto her chest. "I must warn you, though, that for breakfast tomorrow, all I have to offer is bread and Polish headcheese. But you girls don't eat pork, right?"

Hinda chuckled, fully aware that headcheese, before the war, was considered undesirable, one of the lowest-quality cured meats. She replied, "These days, we eat everything. After surviving forced starvation for five years, and living on the run, we are grateful for any and all sustenance."

The sun held court in the midmorning sky, shining brightly with nary a cloud in sight. Hinda helped Rachel, her feet freshly bandaged, walk through the rail station. Finding the correct platform, they boarded the train bound for Katowice, which was a larger town than Puławy or Wilków, or any of the municipalities where they had been since escaping. The sisters settled into their seats, placing their pillowcase sacks underneath. Hinda's head swiveled gracefully on her swan-like neck as she looked around the passenger car. The sight was not a welcome one. Her stomach tightened, and her throat knotted.

Russian soldiers occupied almost all the seats. Then, an entire platoon boarded, rowdy and raucous while loading their hefty satchels into the luggage bins. Once they sat down, no seats were vacant. The sisters were the only civilians and the only females traveling in that car, and their passes restricted them to that specific one.

Memories overwhelmed Hinda, vivid flashbacks of seeing Soviet soldiers brutally rape the pretty Mrs. Olmos. Her heart began to thump loudly in her chest. Leaning in close to Rachel, Hinda whispered, "I'm terrified of these Russian men. We're surrounded."

Covering her mouth with her hand, Rachel replied in hushed tones. "I feel hundreds of hungry eyes checking me out, like I'm a steak on a plate. Their dinner."

"As soon as the conductor takes our tickets, we're going to the bathroom. And we're *not* coming out," Hinda averred. She whispered softly, but her tone was determined and willful.

Locked inside the bathroom, Hinda lay on the floor curled atop a towel. Rachel sat on the commode lid.

"Why are we going to Katowice?" Rachel asked. "We don't know anyone there."

Hinda sighed heavily. "After the man at the city agency finally agreed to give me two rail passes, I had to choose a town. I looked at the map of Poland on the wall, and Katowice just jumped out at me. It lit up for a split second. I decided it was Tatae's spirit casting his light, guiding me."

"Wonder what will happen to us there?" Her eyes watery, Rachel began to weep. "Will we ever have a place to call home?"

Too weary to offer comfort, Hinda replied in a curt tone, "Do you think I like living this way? Do you think I planned for it to be this hard after our escape?"

"Are you mad at me?" Rachel asked, her chin trembling.

"No. It's not *you*, Rachel. Truth is, I'm still enraged, absolutely furious, at the haughty man at the city office who, at first, categorically denied us travel passes."

Just then, there was a knock on the bathroom door. Hinda made the sign for Rachel to flush the toilet. The person banged loudly. Hinda jumped up and held her hand on the inside latch, afraid the hard knocks would jar it open. After a while, the person went away.

"There's another bathroom, right?" Rachel whispered.

"Yes, at the front of the cabin, but their attempts will continue. Let's try to rest a bit." Hinda curled back on the towel and pretended to doze. Visions of the arrogant agent continued to disturb her. The condescending tone and manner in which he declared that Rachel and she did not qualify for train passes without legal documentation proving they were Polish citizens had felt Nazi-esque. Reflecting back, Hinda did not know if it was God or Satan that had possessed her and caused the eruption. Typically, she kept her wits, resorting to crying and begging in those situations. But this morning, she had unexpectedly gone ballistic, screeching in a mad rage. Intense anger churning inside her, she shoved up her sleeve and showed him her Auschwitz tattoo. Shouting at full throttle, she asked, "How can my sister and I have legal papers when the Nazis took everything from us? They confiscated our home in Zieluń, put us in the Mława ghetto, killed our parents, and then hauled us to Auschwitz, where they seized *all* our remaining personal belongings." When the man did not respond, she railed, "Our names were erased. The Nazis branded us like animals with *their* documentation—a serial number." Her every word burning with rage, Hinda felt surely flames were forking from her mouth.

The man had backed away from her, his eyes wide with apprehension. He gaped at her as if she were a demonic dragon primed to annihilate him. Abruptly, he picked up a yardstick and pointed to the map of Poland on the wall, asking which city she chose for her rail passes.

Lying on the bathroom floor with her eyes closed, Hinda watched the scene replay in her mind. Finally, the anger began to abate, and her heart rate slowed. She mused, *I'm completely worn out. That fiery fit of fury drained my energy, but it worked.*

The second day on the train, the sisters remained locked in the small bathroom. They took turns lying on the towel and sitting on the commode lid. Frequently, they endured the soldiers pounding on the door, all the while fearing that they would rip the door from its hinges and sexually assault them.

Ravenous, they checked the contents of their pillowcase bags for food items and found one can of sardines. Hinda said no. The strong odor of sardines would draw attention to the fact that they were camping out in the bathroom. Instead, they drank water from the sink faucet, filling their stomachs with liquid, striving to manage their hunger.

From the commode lid, Rachel complained, "This trip is taking forever." She arose and stretched, arching her body this way, then that. "Tell me again. How far did the man say?"

"Three hundred kilometers, a full two-day trip," Hinda replied.

Outside the door, they heard the sound of heavy boots and then a metal object rapping against the door. Rachel flushed the commode. Hinda turned the water faucet to run full blast.

A male voice thundered, "I'm the train conductor. And I order you to open this door now. Other passengers need to use this bathroom." Keys jangled next to the doorknob.

Hinda turned the water off and made hand signs to Rachel to start gagging as if she were retching. Lifting the latch, Hinda opened the door slightly. "Sir,

I'm sorry. My sister is extremely ill. One minute she is vomiting; the next, she has diarrhea. I don't think you want that mess in the seats or aisles."

Hearing Rachel gagging, the conductor backed away. "I do not. Keep it as clean as you can in there. I'll place an *Out of Order* sign on this door."

As the conductor's boots clomped away, Hinda whispered, "Yikes, Rachel. You're as good as Soldier Rhino at that." The retching sounds had turned Hinda's stomach. Nausea rising in her, she exclaimed, "Stop now. Please!"

Rachel's skin a greenish pale, she vomited bile into the toilet, her gag reflex fully triggered.

112

The Bearded Old Man

May 1945 | Katowice, War-torn Poland

Near to seven-thirty in the evening, the sisters—beleaguered and hungry—departed the train. As they slogged their way through the rail station, they noted signs warning of the strict wartime curfew in Katowice: No civilians allowed on the streets after 8:00 p.m.

Her shoulders slumping in distress, Hinda presumed this meant that Germany had not surrendered. Even still, they were free in this part of Poland. With tears welling in her eyes, she struggled to retain composure, questioning why she felt so miserable when she had fought so hard to get here. The answers roiled inside her: she was mentally and physically worn down; she had no money, and she was totally lost as to where to go or how to take care of Rachel and herself in this unfamiliar city.

Abruptly, Rachel erupted into sobs. "What are we going to do?"

Pretending to be confident, Hinda took Rachel's arm in hers and began walking hurriedly, as though she had a plan. Just ahead, she saw a trio of folks, lugging suitcases. They strode briskly, as if certain of their direction. She followed them.

After walking four blocks, those three entered a small hotel. Exasperated, Hinda looked around for signs of residential neighborhoods. Seeing nothing, she urged Rachel onward. A young man, dressed in waiter's attire, dashed past them on the sidewalk. He called out, "Ladies, you've less than five minutes to get inside. Curfew!"

Feeling panic rising, Hinda pulled her sister into a jogging pace. With every step, Rachel yelped, her feet bleeding again. At the corner, Hinda spotted a short, narrow street lined with shabby row houses. Lights shone from some; others were dark. Hinda ran ahead and knocked on doors. Rachel limped behind her.

Getting no response at the first five homes, Hinda muttered, "People are just too scared to open their doors after curfew." Edging near her breaking point, Hinda repeated her father's promise, *You will live; you will tell.* Her spirit struggling, she continued to knock on doors.

Towards the end of the street, a man cracked opened his door. He greeted them but did not invite them inside. His door slightly ajar, he listened as Hinda told him about their need of refuge. Pulling the door closed behind him, he stepped outside onto the porch. "You girls should go to the International Red Cross building. It's not that far from here, and they have a makeshift shelter for the homeless."

"Can you give us directions? We've never been to Katowice before."

"I can," he said. Turning his head to the side, the man coughed and then spit phlegm onto the grass. After lighting a cigarette, he said, "But I'll do better than that. I'll escort you there."

"Sir, we thank you. But what about the curfew? Will we be arrested?"

From his pocket, he dug out a badge with a policeman's crest on it. "I'm retired, but with this, the authorities will let us pass."

Women, all dressed in crisp white uniforms, manned the main desk in the Red Cross building, which resembled a sprawling warehouse on the inside. One of the women led Hinda to the registration table. "Please write your name, birthdate, birthplace—both the town and the country—and, lastly, where you've come from most recently," the woman instructed.

Hinda nodded. "First, I need to help my sister." She went back for Rachel, who was near to fainting, and helped her to the table and into a chair. To the woman, Hinda said, "My sister's feet are injured, and she's extremely weak. May I register her information for her?"

"Yes, and I'll get a nurse to look at her feet," the woman replied, pursing her lips in a purposeful manner. Turning to walk away, she said, "Wait for me at this table."

Shortly, the woman returned with a wheelchair. To Rachel, she said, "Maybe this will help." She then gestured for Hinda to assist Rachel into the wheelchair as though she did not want to touch her. Once Hinda had completed their registry, the woman directed them to a cafeteria-type room. Servers brought hot soup—a thin beef stew with diced carrots and potatoes—along with two slices of bread and glasses of water.

To Hinda and Rachel, after not eating solids in two days, the simple meal tasted like a feast. When they had scraped their bowls clean, a new volunteer came to their table. She had a bright smile, yet her news was not sunny. "You can sleep here one night. Tomorrow morning, you must be on your way soon after the morning meal. Are we clear?"

Hinda nodded assent though disappointment shook her soul. Outwardly calm, she said, "Yes, we understand, and we're truly grateful for the food and safe shelter this evening."

This volunteer led them to a side area where she gave the sisters each a blanket and a thin mattress. Pointing to a different section, the woman said, "Find a place over there to sleep." She plucked a tube of salve from her apron pocket and instructed Hinda to apply an ample amount of the ointment on Rachel's feet. Before walking away, the volunteer explained, "The nurse is swamped tonight. She said this salve should help, if applied regularly."

After piling the bedding on Rachel's lap, Hinda pushed the wheelchair to the sleeping section. At every turn of the wheel, she felt a heaviness descending upon her. Weary of living like nomads, she had hoped for more than one night there. Her hopes now dashed, her heart ached, and her spirits plummeted.

During the night, Hinda awoke with a start, a dampness on her neck. Then she realized the cause: wet tears. She had been crying in her sleep. When Hinda closed her eyes again, painful scenes of the last five years flowed through her mind like a river carrying hazardous debris atop its currents. *I've just turned twenty-four, and I feel like I'm eighty-four. I've been robbed of my youth and so has Rachel, who is just now eighteen years old.*

Hinda sat up on the thin mattress. In the dim light, she could see Rachel's slim oval face as she slept. Her sister's brows were furrowed even in sleep. *She, too, is depressed. I must shield her from my sadness and this desperation that erodes my spirit.*

At breakfast, the sisters learned that the Soviets now ruled Katowice. The previous local government had been dissolved and all currency declared valueless, both the Polish *zloty* and the German *mark*. Seizing total economic control, the Soviets had closed all banks and financial institutions, confiscating those funds. Similar to Nazism, the Russian motto was NO WORK: NO FOOD. Compensation for work was restricted to coupons, which were under strict control of the local Soviet governing powers. To obtain coupons, people toiled, cleaning the war-ravaged ruins in the city.

No currency, Hinda grumbled to herself. Fingering the two items in her pocket, Walter's note and her Auschwitz spoon, Hinda felt more despair creep into her heart as more of her hopes were dashed. During the night, she had thought of the spoon, which had markings that claimed it to be rust free. Today, she had planned to seek out a merchant who would buy it from her. Swallowing her disappointment, Hinda asked for news of the war ending, the status of Germany's surrender.

One of the female volunteers raised her voice to mega decibels and shrieked, "The war still rages. Just look at all these victims seeking shelter."

The women running the facility that morning were encouraging the people who had spent their one allotted night to leave the shelter immediately after breakfast. While Hinda understood the organization's service and the sheer volume of people they were helping, she—not ready to brave the streets—felt rushed to the door.

As the sisters approached the exit, another volunteer, a cheery blonde, hurried over with a small bag of bandages for Rachel's feet. "Take these with you and use that salve two times a day," she instructed. Waving good-bye, she wished them well in their journeys, and then she promptly turned her attention to a disheveled-looking man who carried two screaming toddlers.

Possessing no maps and having no plans, the sisters exited the International Red Cross building. Walking at a snail's pace, they trod through varying districts. Observing a trio of young Jewish people walking on the same street, Hinda experienced a pang of sentiment, a wave of homesickness for life before the war. Caught up in a nostalgic moment, she began speaking Yiddish to Rachel.

Suddenly, an elderly man, who had a white wooly beard that trailed past his waist onto his thighs, yelled, "Stop." He approached the sisters, speaking Yiddish to them. His voice sounded strangely powerful. A host of questions poured forth: "Where are you from? What happened to you during the war? How did you survive years of persecution?"

Hinda looked at the old Jewish man in awe, wondering how he had avoided the gas chambers in his elderly feeble state. And how had he kept the Nazis from shaving that bizarre beard? Although tired of telling her tragic story, Hinda politely gave a brief rendition of their woes. Respect was due him, she concluded.

He paid rapt attention to Hinda's every word, eager to hear the details of Rachel's and her unjust treatment by the Nazis. Yet he would tell the sisters nothing about what had happened to him, where he was incarcerated, or how he had survived. Pointing to a narrow walkway between buildings where a bed-roll was spread, he said, "That's my home today. All I possess is my own solitude."

Standing beside Hinda, Rachel gazed at the man as if she were in a hypnotic trance. Her inner paintbrush was at work depicting the man's spellbinding appearance: his deeply wrinkled face with intricate grooved lines—matrixes of artful patterns—paired with his preposterously lengthy, tousled, and matted beard, so coarsely knotted that it resembled stalagmites growing from a cave ceiling. To her, he was a museum piece, a rare antiquity that merited enshrining.

Nudging Rachel from her reverie, Hinda announced to the man, "It's been such a pleasure to talk with you, sir, especially in our childhood language. It's time, though, that we continue our search for refuge."

The man's eyes fluttered as he blinked in the sunlight. "Katowice has nothing to offer you. But in the next city, Sosnowiec, just ten kilometers northeast of here, a town committee was formed to help the refugees and survivors of the war. You should go there and ask for assistance."

"That's an excellent idea, sir, but I'm quite concerned for my sister's feet," Hinda replied. She pointed to Rachel's bandages. "Her feet are gammy and sore from our walking long distances, going from town to town."

He shook a bony finger at her, "Nah, nah, girl, you don't walk. You hitch a ride."

113
A Seraph
May 1945 | Sosnowiec, War-torn Poland

Climbing out of the old jalopy, Hinda flashed a bright smile. She profusely thanked the driver and his wife for the ride to Sosnowiec. Buses and all sorts of vehicles had passed by the sisters as they stood on the Katowice highway, feeling apprehensive about the mode of travel called hitchhiking—getting into a car controlled by a complete stranger. Providence graced them when a kind couple stopped and asked their destination. The husband agreed to take them to the entrance of the city, which was a bit out of his way. Joyously grateful, Hinda and Rachel waved heartily to the couple as they made a U-turn and drove away.

Having memorized the directions that the man with the ridiculously long beard had provided in detail, Hinda searched out specific landmarks as they trod deeper into the city of Sosnowiec. After almost an hour of plodding along, they came to the War Refugee Headquarters.

At the entry desk, male attendants greeted them. The head agent, who had military-style buzzed hair, instructed the sisters to register their information in a notebook. Afterward, the deputy assistant escorted them into a spacious room, where he asked them to be seated.

Peering around the room, Hinda gawked. Thinking she would faint, she clutched Rachel's arm. The people sitting in that room did not look like people; they looked like living skeletons with just a skerrick of skin stretched tightly across their bones. Concentration camp survivors, just recently freed, some of them were barely alive; all were dirty, ragged, smelly, and diseased.

Dearest Lord, have mercy on these poor people. Hinda sighed heavily. "Rachel, this one room holds evidence of flat-out evil. It bears testimony to the criminal, immoral, and wicked works of the beastly Nazis."

"My eyes weep to look at them. So heartbreaking," Rachel whispered.

"Take a good clear look at them, Rachel, and then at us. We look like royalty in comparison. This is proof that we did the right thing, escaping Auschwitz when we did."

The people gaped at the pretty sisters, who wore decent clothing, had hair and combed tresses at that, and who did not appear to be suffering complete starvation. One woman reached out her grimy hand to them and croaked out the words, "Can I touch your hair?"

Hinda's heart twisted into knots. She twirled Rachel toward the door. "Not for another minute are we staying in this room."

Back inside the office, where the people looked clean, well-dressed, well-rested, and healthy, Hinda spoke to the attendants at the front desk. "Dear gentlemen, my sister and I cannot stay in that room. Not because we don't deserve it, and not because we're better than them. On the contrary, we are the same. But after suffering the horrors of Auschwitz and the terrible journey after our escape, we're totally demoralized. Can you please just grant us a tiny corner where we can be by ourselves?"

The agent in charge twisted his mouth to the side. His tone imbued with surprise, he exclaimed, "Auschwitz? No one has shown themselves from there."

"Sir, I don't blame you for your disbelief," Hinda replied. She pulled up the sleeve of her sweater to reveal her Auschwitz serial number. Rachel yanked her sleeve upward and held up her tattooed arm too.

The man appeared genuinely shocked. Clearing his throat vociferously as if that also unblocked his mind, he spoke in a solemn tone. "Up until now, not a single person has come to us from there. I didn't know if there were *any* survivors of that hell pit, let alone young female escapees." Turning to his deputy, the man said in a commanding tone, "Please ask Golda to come here. Now."

Soon, a middle-aged woman, who sported copper-red hair and a white apron, appeared. Grumbling to herself, she hurried to the desk while brushing bread crumbs from her lips.

The lead agent said, "Golda, may these two girls stay at your place for a few days?"

Golda frowned, then proceeded to thoroughly eyeball each sister up and down. Directing her gaze back to the agent, she hesitated, then nodded in the affirmative. Snapping her fingers at the sisters, she commanded them in a strident tone, "Come. You can help me with my duties."

Once they were in the kitchen, Golda pointed to a door labeled *Workers Only*. "Go to the lavatory, both of you, and do your business. Then wash your hands, and I mean scrub them, using heaps of soap and *hot* water." She stomped over to a small table where a half-eaten bowl of soup sat atop a plate with part of a sandwich to the side. "I was in the middle of lunch when they called me." She plopped down in the chair. Within a second, the spoon was in her mouth.

When the sisters returned from the lavatory, Golda's mood had improved. Nodding toward the stove, she said, "Help yourself to a bowl of stew. And don't be shy. Fill it to the rim. You look hungry. Plus, you're both awfully skinny."

At four o'clock in the afternoon, Golda declared, "Sakes alive, you girls are good workers." Her red curls bobbled as she nodded enthusiastically.

Whatever chores Golda assigned to the sisters, both Hinda and Rachel had executed them not only perfectly, but with gusto. Far ahead of schedule with preparations for the refugees' evening meal, Golda broke out into song. After warbling multiple verses, she hummed happily.

Later, close to eight in the evening, after the staff and refugee dinners had been served and the kitchen was spotless and ready for the next day, Golda pointed toward the stairs. Tired, the three of them slowly climbed four flights of narrow, steep stairs to her studio apartment, which had two rooms—one large living area with one bathroom.

Once inside, Golda invited the girls to sit at the dining table for tea and cookies. The sweet butter shortbread melted deliciously upon Hinda's tongue. In that one splendid second, Hinda decided that the woman named Golda was a seraph, a real-life, red-haired angel.

As they chatted, the sisters learned that the Sosnowiec refugee operation was just one arm of a major attempt across Poland to help war victims. This local agency, Golda remarked, was quite large, taking up the entire first floor of the building. It had shower facilities, and a wardrobe room with gently used clothing, plus sleeping areas, dining rooms, and even a makeshift synagogue. If they were not hospitalized, the refugees could stay for three days. Typically, they left feeling stronger and enabled to go in search of their families.

Confused, Hinda said, "But the people we saw today were dirty and diseased. Do all who come here have the opportunity to clean up?"

"That was a particularly sad group that came in this morning. It'll be tomorrow before all of them are bathed, dressed anew, and diagnosed. The office was short staffed today."

Staring off into the ethers, Hinda sensed the Divine hand upon the timing of her and Rachel's arrival. If not for that dreadful, depressing group in the holding room this morning, she and Rachel would not have recoiled. Consequently, they would not have eaten so well and not be staying in private quarters with Golda. Silently, Hinda offered up prayers of gratitude. Then a string of odd thoughts struck her. *Was the homeless man with the crazy beard otherworldly? He had appeared out of nowhere and had spoken eloquently, as though he were a rhetorician, telling of the refugee center in Sosnowiec. Had heaven, at the bidding of her sweet Tatae, materialized a mouthpiece on planet Earth to speed Rachel and her along to this safe destination?* A knock on the door startled Hinda from her contemplations.

Appearing to be expecting someone, Golda readily opened the door to a janitor carrying a thick mattress and two pillows. Pointing to the opposite end of the room from her bed, she asked the man to place everything on the floor there. After seeing him to the door, Golda stretched and yawned. "It's getting late. How about if you girls take a hot shower and get ready for bed?"

Their eyes wide, the sisters exclaimed simultaneously, "A *hot* shower?"

"It's been awhile, huh?" Golda asked.

"In five years, we've only had one warm bath, and that was after the escape. We've washed up out of buckets, but we've not had a *hot shower* since we were forced from our family home in Zieluń," Hinda reported sorrowfully. Yet her emotional switch swiftly flipped. Grinning in anticipation, she eagerly asked, "May I go first?"

Golda chuckled, "Jump in. There's soap, shampoo, and towels in the bathroom. But let's get you nightclothes first." Within minutes, she returned with clean nightgowns, panties, and bras for both sisters. "Tomorrow, we'll go to wardrobing and get you fresh clothes and shoes—several outfits, at least. A shipment arrived from Warsaw today."

Overcome with a feeling of profound appreciation, Hinda gushed, "Golda, you *are* an angel, a beautiful one. I'll carry the image of you and your immense kindness in my heart forever. What you're doing for my sister and me cannot be measured in gold."

Dabbing at the corners of her eyes with an embroidered handkerchief, Golda replied, "You girls are good people." Her lips tugged to the side as she quelled rising despair. "I'm all alone. I lost my husband, all my family, in this terrible war." Golda bowed her head briefly. Copper tresses fell across her tear-dappled cheeks. "I'm quite grateful for your company."

114

Make Us Cakes

May 14, 1945 | Sosnowiec, War-torn Poland

On Monday, May 14, when the matutinal sun cast reddish-orange hues across the horizon of Earth's northern hemisphere, the newspaper landed with a loud thump on the front desk at the refugee center. One headline dominated the front page: **GERMANY HAS SURRENDERED!** The feature article stated that German Army Chief of Staff, General Jodl, had signed the official surrender document on May 7, 1945 at Supreme Headquarters of the Allied Expeditionary Forces, located in Reims, France.

"Unconditional surrender" described the terms. The commentary asserted that General Jodl had initially restricted Germany's surrender to the West while continuing the war in the East. Yet the supreme commander of the Allied Expeditionary Forces, General Eisenhower, demanded total surrender in both areas. The journalist lauded the American general, Dwight D. Eisenhower, as formidable when he warned Jodl that he was prepared to seal off the Western Front, which would place the failing German forces in the hands of the Soviets. Eisenhower disallowed further communication with Jodl and other High-Command members of the Third Reich. He refused to be present at the May 7 meeting, saying he would not occupy the same room as Nazi leaders until unconditional surrender was accomplished. The article reported further that General Jodl radioed Hitler's successor, Grand Admiral Donitz, with Eisenhower's final terms. Donitz ordered Jodl to sign the instrument of surrender. Eisenhower's Chief of Staff, General Bedell Smith, presided over the May 7 meeting and signed the document as an agent for Allied forces. The article went on to name the top brass who signed as official witnesses: Russian General Susloparov and French General Sevez. Additionally, the piece stated that Jodl signed other surrender documents, one each, for Great Britain, France, and Russia.

The refugee center's director read and reread the three words of the headline and then the ensuing article. Soon, he was jumping joyously and shouting gleefully. "Germany has surrendered, unconditional surrender in the East and the West." Employing his full-lung capacity while zealously emphasizing one potent phrase, he yelled, "Nazi Germany is defeated!" Tears stained his cheeks when he cried out, "Did you hear me? Nazi Germany is officially defeated!" His feet stomped in jig-like patterns. "The news has come to Sosnowiec a week late, but that doesn't change the glorious truth."

When Hinda and Rachel came down the stairs that morning, they walked into a surprising euphoric commotion. The staff was whooping triumphantly, dancing, and sweeping each other up in hugs. Her copper curls bouncing, Golda was in the middle of it all, hooting riotously.

Exhilarated, the director boomed, "Golda, make us cakes. Celebration cakes!"

Exhausted from his brief excursion outdoors, Wolf Yoskowitz gazed at the sunset reflected in the window near his hospital bed. At a mere twenty-eight years old, he pondered whether or not he had already reached the sunset of his life. Despairing thoughts plagued him: *Am I so physically damaged that I can never walk again? Is it even possible for me to feel young, virile, and energetic?*

Extreme weakness still held his muscles captive. From his critical condition two weeks ago when he was admitted to the Allied forces' hospital, Wolf felt noticeably stronger due to the consistent intake of fluids and nutrition. Yet the strange muscle weakness persisted.

Two of the hospital's doctors appeared disinterested in his case now. Noting the dull expression in their eyes and their hurried manner, Wolf believed both had assessed him as hopeless. Yet, this morning, the chief physician, Dr. Stephens, had sat on Wolf's bed and spoken about his diagnosis: myositis, inflammation of the skeletal muscles, which move the body.

"Mr. Yoskowitz, you told me that you endured harsh, forced labor in the quarry at Buchenwald," Dr. Stephens paraphrased from an earlier conversation with Wolf. The doctor's rosy-brown eyes emitting compassion, he continued, "I understand that the work was excessively strenuous, especially considering you were malnourished. Typically, though, with myositis, severe injury occurs at a specific time or times. It's possible that it happened with such long hours of strenuous toiling day after day, but do you remember any events beyond that?"

Wolf closed his eyes. He knew exactly when it happened, but he never wanted those words to cross his lips.

Dr. Stephens watched as Wolf lay there, stone-faced. Yet his eyelashes fluttered, and his eyelids twitched. The doctor surmised that Wolf was accessing memory. Gently prompting his patient further, Dr. Stephens spoke softly. "This may ignite painful memories for you. Nonetheless, it's beneficial to your treatment for me to know the kinds of injury your muscles sustained."

Wolf's eyes remained closed, his lids clamped tightly, trying to shut out the recollection. Finally, he answered, "At gunpoint, I was often harnessed like an animal, along with five other men, to a utility wagon piled high with heavy stone and then forced to pull it. For miles. Many men passed out; many died trying." Wolf sighed then inhaled deeply. "It was a game for the guards. We were commanded to sing German marching songs, loudly, while straining to move along the load. They called us *Singing Horses.*"

"Good God, man. That's barbaric." Bewildered, Dr. Stephens waggled his cupped hands up and down in the air. He then made a fist and pounded it in his palm. His rosy-brown eyes turned thorny with rage, their color no longer velvety. His voice tense, the doctor inquired, "And afterward, did you experience *severe* muscle cramps and aching?"

Wolf opened his eyes and looked directly at Dr. Stephens. "Yes, for days and nights afterward. Especially in my legs."

"It's incredible that you even survived this mockery of human life. I've no doubt, your skeletal muscle tissue suffered severe injury."

"Can muscles heal? Will I ever walk again?"

The doctor briefly bowed his head, attempting to construe a hopeful response. "Time will tell. You also have a viral infection due to the hideously unsanitary conditions at Buchenwald. You'll need rest and solid nutrition for a lengthy time."

Wolf watched Dr. Stephens walk away, his white lab coat swaying as he strode briskly down the hall. In the afternoon, the doctor returned and instructed the nurse to take Wolf outside to bask in the fresh air.

Although Wolf had only sat up in a wheelchair, he was appalled at how the one-half hour session outdoors had totally worn him out. Even still, the tall trees, their leaves rustling in the breeze, had buoyed his spirit. He imagined the trees whispering to him of better days ahead. But then, when he returned to the grim inside—full of chaos and pain, where hundreds of soldiers and war victims fought for their lives—his hope for the future was erased and instantly replaced with outrage. Overwhelming anger consumed him. The Nazis had burglarized his physical strength. They had confiscated his determination and zest for life, stealing his very essence.

Piercing laughter and chatter from the next room turned Wolf's gaze away from the window. The sounds heralded the arrival of the night shift. Wolf felt a stirring of feelings as he thought of a particular night nurse called Bernie, who had been off duty the past three nights. Bernadette was her real name, and the one he preferred. Closing his eyes, he envisioned her face, so alluring and full of light. A chandelier in a dusky room.

Bernadette had not once looked at Wolf with pity the way the other nurses did. Instead, her high-wattage smile would light up her yellow-green eyes as she told him that she saw a strong, handsome, and remarkable young man when she had the privilege to be in his presence. Her touch was strangely calming to Wolf, even though he found it electric. Others must have experienced her sparks. The army doctors and nurses, who worked with her, would laughingly warn, "Watch out. Don't get burned by Bernie."

Wolf rolled on his side, and there she was, the lovely Bernadette, buzzing around the patient in the bed next to him. Wolf would be her next subject, and he knew just what to expect. She would take his vitals, flash one of her wide smiles, wink at him, and then comment that his pulse and blood pressure were higher, more elevated, than the earlier entry.

Try as he might, he could not rein in his physical response. In mere anticipation of her nearness to him, of her touch, his heart rate accelerated.

Down the hallway, Joseph Yoskowitz plucked at stray threads on the army blanket on his bed as if they held answers to how his brother was faring. Late last week, when the nurse had taken him in a wheelchair to Wolf's bedside, Joseph had cracked, had broken down, and sobbed uncontrollably, distraught about his brother's weakness and inability to walk.

Joseph was fortunate, his doctor had said. He was blessed to not have typhus, and lucky to not have died as the medics believed he would when he arrived unconscious. Within thirty minutes of his admission, his condition had been diagnosed—a pervasive bacterial infection that had turned septic and gone into pneumonia. Both were life-threatening conditions, and treatment had been quickly initiated. The nurse on duty that day later relayed to him that one of the doctors had said to a comatose Joseph, "Due to the wonder of sulfonamides, you will get well, young man."

Now on the second round of sulfa drug treatment, Joseph could breathe without experiencing excruciating pain. Walking was another issue, although he could stand on his own now. The nurses said that mobility would come in time, as he regained strength.

Turning to face what he believed to be east, Joseph mumbled, "Thank you, God, for today's blessings, tomorrow's hope, and for your abiding love. Amen." Burrowing his head in his pillow, Joseph thought of Wolf. A knot instantly formed in his throat. Clenching his fists to box back rising anguish, Joseph launched into beseeching the Almighty. Quietly, he mumbled, "My brother. Dear Lord, please help him. I would not have lived to be in this hospital and receive what the docs here call wonder drugs without Wolf's protection. I would have died my first year at Buchenwald but for his determination, his strategizing, and his persistent care of me. Have mercy upon my brother, Lord. He's a good man; he truly deserves for his health and full mobility to be restored."

Late that evening, the registered nurse named Bernadette was summoned to the staff break room to meet with Dr. Stephens—the chief physician for the Allied forces' hospital, which occupied a war-battered office building near Weimar. When she entered the room, he gestured toward the refreshment counter. Understanding the cue, she happily filled a mug with black coffee before joining the doctor at the table in the far corner.

Arising from his chair, Dr. Stephens stood while Bernadette slid into her seat. "Thanks for joining me on short notice."

"Sure. What's going on?"

Dr. Stephens looked closely at the nurse who he found sultry and wholesome at the same time. Clearing his throat, he said, "I want to discuss a project that goes beyond the scope of field-hospital protocol. But before I explain, how's my patient in bed thirty-two, Wolf Yoskowitz, tonight?"

Upon hearing Wolf's name, she crossed her legs, then uncrossed them in the next second. "Totally exhausted from his outing today," Bernie reported in a crisp tone. "He could barely choke down dinner before succumbing to deep slumber."

"His fatigue is concerning, but I've heard that he perks up when *you* are around."

Bernadette's yellow-green eyes lit up with a sparkle. "I do my best to rally his spirits. I sense a fighter in there, and that's the personality we must resurrect for him to make real progress."

"I agree. That's precisely why I want you to take a lead role in my special mission. Would you consider switching to the day shift to have contact with him during waking hours?"

She tilted her head to the side. "Me? Work the day shift?"

Dr. Stephens nodded in the affirmative and then explained, "The inflammation of the patient's muscles, the myositis, is quite serious, a condition the young man may never recover from, especially since it stems from severe injuries and a viral infection. He needs help beyond the usual treatment."

"You're certain that it's not bacterial?"

"It's definitely not bacterial. His white cell count was elevated when he first arrived but is normal now. He showed no muscular improvement whatsoever after receiving sulfa drugs." Dr. Stephens sighed heavily. "The other doctors on the team say there's nothing else we can do for him, that we should release him to a nursing facility."

"They're giving up on him. Already?" Bernie retorted, her nostrils flaring, her nails digging into the flesh of her palm, aghast at the implication.

"They are, but I'm not ready to toss in the towel. Not yet. The patient named Wolf haunts me in an inspiring way. My hunch is that with specialized treatment, he can improve enough to walk with assistance."

Squinting her eyes disparagingly at Dr. Stephens, Bernie responded, "I'd hoped for more than *that* for him." She swallowed hard. "And you think *I* can make a difference?"

"I've no doubt, Bernie. *You* can."

"What do you have in mind?"

"Should you choose to participate, I would assign you to two patients on the day shift, with most of your time spent rehabilitating Mr. Yoskowitz." The doctor tapped the table with his index finger for emphasis. "My plan for him includes a mix of daily testosterone injections, physical therapy, intermittent rest, high-protein nutrition, therapeutic time outdoors, and salutary conversation with you."

"Testosterone injections? That's controversial. I didn't know we had access to such."

"Thanks to General Eisenhower for enlisting the pharmacy in Weimar to function as our supplier, we can get atypical medications. The steroid was delivered late this afternoon. My goal in using it is to build muscle mass, increase energy, and suppress inflammation."

"Daily doses will likely change his mild temperament."

"Don't be fooled by his good manners. The guy is intense. He survived Buchenwald. And, frankly, I prefer for him to feel angry rather than apathetic, with no will to live."

"I understand. Anger ranks far higher on the *I'm Alive* scale than apathy does. But Dr. Stephens, there's an issue about which you should know." She squirmed in her chair and gulped down half the mug of coffee. Glancing furtively around the room, she inhaled sharply before divulging her secret. "I'm personally attracted to the patient, Wolf Yoskowitz." She paused, watching the doctor's eyes dim and his long eyelashes flutter as he blinked upon hearing her declaration. Sighing, Bernie added, "I took a few nights off to get away and clear my mind, only to find the same feelings when I returned tonight. Ethically speaking, my physical attraction to the patient prohibits me from working so closely with him."

"In a regular hospital, yes. In this case, though, I feel that your personal interest in him is exactly what he needs." Shifting his weight in the chair, Dr. Stephens exclaimed, "Hell, Bernie, this poor guy has been enslaved, severely abused, tortured, and experimented upon. Not to mention overworked and deprived of life-sustaining liquids and nutrition for four years. Damn Nazis." He drummed the table with his knuckles. "Wolf deserves a chance, at least to walk again. He's not even thirty years old yet."

"But you're playing God with my heart. And his."

"Only *you* can do that," Dr. Stephens stated with emphatic firmness. His hand uncurled, flattening out on the table. "Speaking of God, after this war and seeing such unjust brutality and tragedy, I must say that I'm not sure what I believe anymore." He sighed and momentarily gazed upward to the ceiling. "Yet I feel *something*, a presence bigger than me, urging me to pull out all the stops to help this particular young man."

Bernie lowered her head and spoke in a barely audible whisper. "Wolf *is* special."

Dr. Stephens leaned across the table and took her hand in his. "Bernie, dear Bernie, I've watched your expert nursing work in varying field hospitals for almost a year now. And I've experienced firsthand how your infatuations come and go, sizzling and fizzling." Stephens attempted a laugh, but his mouth twisted into a wry bittersweet smile. He ducked his head briefly and then gazed directly into her eyes. "More importantly, though, I've observed that when *you* focus your attention upon a patient you like and with whom you have a rapport, miracles occur. Odds are beaten." He leaned back in his chair. "What do you say? Are you on board?"

116
Orphans

Hinda wore defeat like a surrender flag across her slumped shoulders. A vow to herself remained unfulfilled. She sighed heavily and leaned her head against the small window, as the train departed the Mława station.

It would be midnight before she arrived back at the Sosnowiec refugee center. Golda, who had secured the rail ticket for her, would be disappointed to learn that the entire trip had been in vain. Rachel had warned her sister, saying Hinda's plan was not only ill-founded but would result in wasted time. Nevertheless, Hinda had remained obsessed, thinking that if she could sit beside her mother's grave and beg for forgiveness, then the burdensome guilt and belief that she had caused her mother's death would disappear.

Almost fainting, Hinda was utterly shocked when the truth was verified: her mother's grave was no more. Now, tall healthy wheat grew abundantly in the field where the small cemetery had existed, just three years ago. Seeing zero evidence of any mounds or markers in the entire area, Hinda concluded that her mother's grave had not been moved. She surmised that it had been plowed up when the field was planted with wheat. Even in death, there was no peace for her mother's body. Her remains had been enslaved as fodder and fertilizer.

Hinda was certain she had found the right spot, even though the old mill had been torn down and the other changes in that part of Mława had proved confusing. Fortunately, an older woman, who worked in a bakery, extended sympathy to Hinda when she showed up distraught about not finding her mother's grave. After giving her tea and warm bread, the woman had then walked with Hinda through the neighborhood that was once the ghetto, pointing out what used to be where. For Hinda, every street corner, every crack in the sidewalk, and every pebble stimulated memories. Most were revolting.

Now, there were no towering walls, no gates, and no Gestapo. Yet there were still sounds of war, echoes of gunfire and mortars in the distance. The Polish Resistance Army was vigorously fighting the Russians to regain their territory.

Sadness was in the air, obvious on people's faces, due to the Red Booth, the Soviet occupation. Stores were open, but merchandise was minimal. Factories remained closed; industry was paralyzed. On the streets, conversation involved questions of how to kick the Russians out of their beloved Poland.

Conversely, Hinda wanted to *flee* the country of Poland.

As the train rumbled along in the night hours, Hinda's mind ticked with thoughts of what was to come next. Although Rachel and she were comfortable and well fed at the refugee center in Sosnowiec, they could not stay indefinitely. A temporary organization, it could be closing its doors in the next few months.

Like a drumroll announcing it in her mind and heart, a notable realization struck her core. She whispered the word, "Orphans." She and Rachel were war orphans, alone and floundering in an upside-down, postwar Europe.

Her brain churning with cogitations that led to dead ends, Hinda decided that it was time to contact her brothers in Mexico City. They should know that Rachel and she were alive and desperately needed help. Yet the phone service throughout Poland was still limited. Plus, navigating the challenges of international communication stumped her. Tomorrow, she decided, she would ask the director of the center for assistance with sending such a message. Her nerves bristled as she realized that it could take months to receive a reply. She worried further that her older brothers had forged such a grand new life for themselves that they didn't care a whit about Rachel and her, anymore. It was possible that they wouldn't even respond to a message from her.

Her older sister, Fanny, who now lived in New York, popped into her mind as an option. Immediately, her gut wrenched at the idea of contacting her older sister. Whirring with memories of Fanny's problematic temperament, Hinda concluded that it was prudent to contact her older brothers first. All of them were kind and had pleasant temperaments, but Hinda placed her highest hopes on her brother Jack. If he were still working as a journalist, he would likely have the ability to respond to her and in a timely manner. Jack was a strong communicator and had written copious letters to their parents after he immigrated to Mexico City. In the last letter the family received from him, Jack mentioned that he had moved to a different news organization, and that he now held a higher position as a *lead* journalist, specializing in politics. Soon after that, the Nazis shut down all mail services in Poland.

Suddenly, the train's wheels seemed to vibrate differently on the tracks, making screeching sounds every few minutes. As Hinda was jostled in her seat, she felt her heart surge, reminding her of another promise she had made to herself: Find Dr. Walter Zeilhofen. But finding him presented a minefield of obstacles. It was still dangerous for Jews to travel in the central part of Germany where Walter's hometown was located.

Unexpectedly, a memory surfaced in her mind. At Auschwitz, when she had malaria and had been hidden in the infirmary, Walter had talked about his parents, who lived in Bavaria—the town of Gunzberg, to be exact. He told her of their backup plan to meet in Breslau when the war ended. He explained that his father had tons of relatives there. If Bavaria were ravaged, his parents would seek refuge with them. Walter had chuckled, claiming that Breslau's robust Germanic population was half Zeilhofen folk.

That settled it. She and Rachel were going to Breslau. And soon.

For the rest of the train ride back to Sosnowiec, she thought of nothing but Walter. Although she was fully aware that her father, even from his other-worldly perch, adamantly disapproved since Walter was a gentile, Hinda did not dissuade the love she felt for the good doctor from filling her heart.

Leaning into the seat, Hinda imagined what it would be like to see Walter again—to throw her arms around him and hold him tightly. Excitement and joy swelled within. Arduous feelings of love swirled and tingled through her body. Although Walter and she had never kissed, the mere thought of his lips pressed upon hers incited passionate emotions, enlivening her muliebrity, and making her feel like a complete woman—an alien feeling to her, yet a surprisingly satisfying one.

Sosnowiec

The next morning, the refugee center bustled with people seeking help. Hinda had gone about her usual tasks, which she enjoyed, finding the work noble. Her mind had buzzed with questions for the director. By midafternoon, a lull in activity brought quiet to the main desk. Deciding it was a suitable time to approach the director, Hinda inquired about how to send a message to her brothers in Mexico City. Disillusionment deluged her when he replied that international calls were not yet possible due to downed and damaged phone lines. Telegrams, he had explained, were controlled by the military and restricted to their use.

"Patience, Hinda. Patience," he encouraged. Sighing loudly, the director added, "We are still digging ourselves out of the destruction of this terrible and lengthy war."

"Do you have an idea of how long I must wait?"

He scratched his head. "A couple of months, probably."

"That's hard to hear. Will this center still be open then?"

"Most likely, but I'm not sure how much longer after that, as more war victims get settled and refugee traffic slows."

"Then, I think it's time for my sister and me to move on."

"Good grief, Hinda. It's still dangerous out there with the Polish Resistance Army fighting the Soviets." He pointed to the ceiling. "This is a roof over your head. Temporary, but you're safe and well fed here. Food is still scarce in many parts. Don't act rashly." He shuffled his feet, as if troubled. "Golda told me that she's glad for your company and hopes you will stay longer with her. As for me, I know that you and your sister are valuable workers. You're both welcome here, as long as we have funds to continue operating."

"Thank you, sir, that's truly kind and generous of you. It means a lot." Hinda ducked her head. Russet strands fell against her cheeks when she lifted her neck. Her azure eyes misted with tears. "But I feel an urgency to find a dear friend who is connected to Breslau."

"Breslau? Wrocław?" The director exclaimed, "What's the right name for that city today?"

Hinda cracked a thin smile. "Is it Wrocław now?"

"Depends on whom you talk to. I did read, though, that at the meeting of the Big Three at the Yalta Conference this past February, Poland's borders were shifted westward, absorbing Breslau. Stalin allowed Polish officials to rename it Wrocław now that it's under Soviet occupation." The director leaned across the desk, nearing his face to hers. His eyes squinted dubiously. "Hinda, are you aware of the population there? The city is still *ninety-five percent* German."

117

The Star of David

Late June 1945 | Wrocław/Breslau, War-torn Poland

Onboard the late afternoon train bound for Breslau, now renamed Wrocław, Hinda thrilled with the excitement bubbling inside her. At last, she was on her way to find Walter. And, this time, she traveled in style. No more tattered pillowcases stuffed with essentials, Rachel and she each had a real suitcase packed full of lovely clothing, thanks to Golda, who had also gifted them with food bags containing sandwiches and goodies galore.

Noting Rachel's posture and pout, Hinda felt a bit of guilt creep into her exuberance. It was obvious that her sister, whose eyes were red from crying, did not share her excitement. While Rachel was fond of Walter and wished Hinda the best with him, she was profoundly upset to leave the safety of the refugee center and Golda, who had become like a mother to her. It had been a heart-wrenching good-bye.

The train had departed Sosnowiec at precisely five o'clock in the afternoon. The sisters had settled in and slept through a good part of the night, although the train had stopped along the way at every town that had a depot, or even a small platform, including those in the middle of nowhere. Often, there were prolonged delays before the train moved forward again.

Now, seconds past six o'clock, the sunrise illuminated the sky. Hinda stretched and yawned, looking out the window at the countryside. In the seat beside her, Rachel, wide-eyed, munched on one of Golda's shortbread cookies.

The train rumbled smoothly around a curve and then, suddenly, braked hard, jerking and screeching to a sharp stop. Passengers were abruptly thrown forward, then backwards, jostled, bounced, and knocked about. A baby wailed, while other passengers screamed and yelled expletives. Hinda rubbed her neck, fearing she had a whiplash. Next to her, Rachel coughed and gagged, a chunk of cookie lodged in her throat.

An older male hobbled down the aisle, gripping the back of seats for stability. Peering out windows on both sides of the train, he called out, "There's no town or station in sight. What the heck is going on?"

Abruptly, four armed soldiers, all dressed in the brown uniforms of the Polish Resistance Army, burst into the car. Blocking the doors, one stood at the back and one at the front. Both had their guns drawn. The third, his rifle cocked to fire, accompanied the captain, who began methodically going from seat to seat asking for identification of nationality. When passengers' papers revealed Soviet citizenship or heritage, they were handcuffed to their seats.

The captain's eyes widened when he came to Hinda. Looking terrified, her blue eyes bulging, she admitted they had no papers, though they were Polish Jews born in Zieluń. She and Rachel exposed their only documentation: Auschwitz tattoos.

"Depart the train. You girls get out now, or your lives will be in jeopardy." The captain's command to them boomeranged throughout the passenger car.

The sisters grabbed their suitcases and food bags and scrambled to the doors and down the steps into a grassy pasture. A large convoy of soldiers, dressed in the same brown uniforms and headgear as the ones inside the train, stood near an enormous barricade that had been constructed across the tracks. The barricade had been placed strategically on the tracks, just past a major curve. The train conductor had no warning. He was forced to suddenly stop or cause a serious wreck.

"Start walking," a Polish soldier yelled. He jerked his gun in the direction the train had been traveling. "Wrocław is that way. Follow the railroad tracks."

Clinging to Hinda's arm, Rachel quibbled, "I knew this was a bad idea."

"Stop the *I told you so*. It's unproductive. We've no choice now but to deal with this situation. Besides, it's just a temporary setback. My instincts are pointing us in the right direction."

Letting go of Hinda's arm, Rachel wanted to argue that Hinda was so obsessed with Walter that she was irrational. But she held her tongue. Her sister's face was already scrunched into an expression of serious distress.

Other passengers departed the train and joined the sisters in the field beside the tracks. One woman said, "They told us we're the lucky ones, being Polish."

The woman's teenage son spoke up. "We have to walk. That's not lucky." He turned to the soldiers and shouted angrily at them, "Polish or not, you're *not* our friends."

"The cause, young man, the cause," a soldier yelled in reply. "Walking for a day or so is a small sacrifice to help us oust the Soviets from our country. How about some appreciation?"

The boy grumbled inaudibly. He bent over and picked up a rock. "I'll show you my appreciation. Take this in your stupid head." He coiled his arm back, glaring at the soldier. His mother did nothing, said nothing.

Hinda stepped near and grabbed the boy's arm. "Just who is the ignorant one? Drop the rock now, or your insolence will get us all killed or handcuffed to our seats."

The boy turned his glare toward Hinda, but he loosened his fist. The rock fell to the ground.

Moving in a knot, the evicted passengers trudged along the railroad tracks. After about an hour, a highway came into view. The group dispersed quickly. The young and unencumbered sprinted toward the road, hoping to be the first to hitch a ride.

Mostly cargo trucks poked along the highway. After countless ones had passed, a truck stopped for Hinda and Rachel. The driver invited them to ride inside the cab with him, saying he could take them only to where the highway split, which was approximately fifty kilometers ahead. To get to Wrocław, he instructed, they would need to catch a new ride or walk.

Ride, they did, but in the back of a flour truck. Once they arrived in Wrocław, at nearly eight o'clock in the evening, they looked like ghouls. White flour dusted their hair, faces, and clothes.

Stores were already closed, and few civilians were outdoors. Russian soldiers patrolled the streets. Buildings were damaged from bombs, but it was still evident that Breslau/Wrocław was a beautiful city. Once again, Hinda found herself in an unfamiliar municipality at night with no specific destination.

The sisters walked aimlessly, though Hinda held her shoulders back with purpose as if she knew where she was going. Crossing a wide avenue, she spotted two policemen on the next corner. Approaching them cautiously, she asked if there were any shelters or facilities that took in refugees. The tallest of the two tossed his cigarette down on the sidewalk and ground out the sparks, using the heel of his boot. A whimsical set to his mouth, he told them of one such shelter. He then gave general directions. As they were walking away, he called out, "What's the white stuff? Are you trying to be ghosts or mummies?"

Hinda turned back to face him, "No costume, sir. The white stuff is flour. We rode here in a truck transporting flour, and it was windy."

"A bit of advice. Shake it off before you get to the shelter."

"Yes, sir. Thank you for your help." The sisters immediately dusted off as much of the flour as they could from their clothing. They both bent double, shaking the flour from their hair.

Following his directions, the sisters walked for forty-five minutes, going deeper and deeper into the city. And still, there was no sign of the facility. Storm clouds were building. Thunder rumbled. Rain fell.

Frightened, Rachel suddenly grabbed Hinda's arm. "Stop! Are you going mad?"

"What do you mean? I'm just following the policeman's directions. We must hurry to get to the shelter before it rains harder."

"And what if it's still a long way from here? We're young females. Walking the streets this late at night is asking for trouble." Rachel sighed heavily, her lower lip trembling.

Hinda looked up at the inky starless sky. A shiver came over her. She took her sister's hand and declared, "You're right. Let's go one street over. I saw houses with lights on inside. Maybe someone will take pity on us."

Hand in hand, the sisters started to cross the street, but Hinda hesitated, sensing an odd prickling on her shoulder, as if a force tugged on her from behind. She turned and looked upward. There, near the roofline at the topmost part of the war-riddled building that they happened to be standing directly in front of, was a Star of David. Barely visible with the dim light of the street lamp, the sacred Jewish symbol was damaged but still recognizable.

"Rachel, look up there," Hinda exclaimed. "See the Star of David? This building used to be, or still is, a synagogue. Let's see if it's open."

Hinda knocked on the ornately carved door. When there was no answer, she turned the handle. The door was unlocked. Pushing it partway open, she looked inside and saw an empty sanctuary. Hinda motioned to Rachel, and they tiptoed into the foyer and set down their bags. As her eyes roved over the vast interior, Hinda heard voices. She inched forward, and there, in a long hallway, she saw three people, a middle-aged woman and two men, who stood together, talking and laughing. Hinda recognized German and Yiddish words. Heartened to hear Yiddish being spoken and the trio's apparent merriment, she started walking toward them. Rachel followed her.

Startled to see strange young women inside the building at that hour, the female of the group in the hallway rushed toward the sisters. She shouted in a stern tone, "What are you two doing in here? Get out! You don't belong here." Appearing ready to forcibly escort the sisters to the door, the two men quickly circled around them. One of the men appeared especially menacing. Reddish purple scars puckered the left side of his face, spanning from his ear to his chin.

Taken aback by the trio's hostility, Hinda spoke in Yiddish. "I apologize for intruding like this. We're Jewish and saw the Star of David on the building. The door was unlocked, so we thought it would be okay to come inside."

"Unlocked?" the woman shrieked.

The man with the scarred face sighed heavily. With a stricken, alarmed look in his eyes, he apologized to the woman, explaining that he must have forgotten to lock the door. She rushed away to go lock it.

Hefting his shoulders upward, as if he were asserting his authority, he turned to Hinda and asked in a gruff tone, "Where do you come from, and what do you want?"

"We've just arrived from Sosnowiec, the refugee center there." Hinda swallowed, choking back the tears congesting her throat. "We're looking for a dear friend but need help, especially a place to sleep tonight."

At that moment, the woman returned to the group. Staring intently at Hinda, she stood with her arms crossed defensively.

In a sinister tone, the other man said, "Prove that you're Jewish. Lots of folks can speak a fair amount of Yiddish."

"Our surname is Mondlak, but we have no identity papers, sir." Hinda pushed up her sleeve to reveal her tattoo. Like a puppet on cue, Rachel bared her arm. Hinda explained, "Auschwitz tattoos are our only documentation. My sister and I were incarcerated precisely because we're Jews." Hinda paused, noticing a flicker of sympathy on their faces. When there was no verbal response, she continued her attempts to prove her Jewishness. "I can say the Shema, if you would like, or other sacred prayers. My father, Salomon Mondlak, was a *Talmudic* scholar. He was a professor at the yeshiva in Zieluń before the Nazis seized our home and took our family to the Mława ghetto. My mother died there. The Gestapo killed my father. Then my sister and I were imprisoned at Auschwitz for twenty-six months."

The men's posture morphed to a friendlier demeanor. The woman reached out her hand and stroked Rachel's forearm, tracing the inked numerals. "You poor girls. I'm sorry I was so harsh with you earlier."

Probing further, the men inquired about the family story, and how the sisters had survived such persecution. Accustomed to interrogations, Hinda obliged and answered eloquently.

After a while, the woman interrupted and said, "It's getting quite late, but you should know that we have young men, about your age, housed in adjacent buildings. Many have the same Auschwitz tattoos as you. Would you like us to put you in touch with them?"

"Yes, please," Hinda said emphatically. Hope leapt inside her.

Out into the night they went. The man with the facial disfigurement escorted Hinda and Rachel to a nearby building and then to its second floor. Striding confidently to a particular door, he rang the buzzer, then rapped rhythmically three times. Surprisingly, the man pulled a key from his pocket and unlocked the door. He instructed Hinda and Rachel to leave their bags in the entry hall and to follow him.

In the main room, eight young men sat around a table playing cards. Ten or so others lounged on the sofas and chairs reading books. Everyone rose to their feet when the man announced the arrival of guests.

From the far corner of the room, a male voice whooped excitedly, "Hinda Mondlak! Rachel Mondlak!" He rushed toward the sisters, scooping them into a hug. "It's Aizik, your cousin."

Hinda gasped. A deep sob arose inside her. She cried, "Aizik, I thought you were dead, sent to the gas chambers after Dr. Mengele cut on you." In awe, she patted his cheeks and peered into his green eyes.

"You survived. Thank God." Aizik shook his head in disbelief. "I came to the women's camp and looked everywhere for you in January when the Red Army freed us. A woman from Block Eleven said you were both dead."

"We escaped in early January," Hinda explained.

"Escaped?" Aizik screeched incredulously. He spelled out the letters, "E-S-C-A-P-E-D?"

The sisters nodded their heads enthusiastically.

"Boys, Uncle Haim, did you hear that?" Aizik yelled out with wonderment and pride, "My petite girl cousins achieved the impossible. Escaped Auschwitz. Amazing."

All applauding, the young men in the room crowded around the sisters. Aizik's close friend, Leo, reached out and pumped Hinda's hand, then Rachel's. "I feel like you're my cousins too."

The man, who had escorted the sisters there, beamed. Known to the boys who lived there as Uncle Haim, he appeared delighted with this serendipitous turn to the evening. Chuckling happily, Haim said, "Mighty fine. It's quite gratifying to see a family reunited here tonight." He dug his fingers into his pocket and withdrew multiple keys. After sorting through them, Haim winked and tossed a particular key to Aizik. "You take it from here, Aizik. Please help your cousins get settled into Unit Four downstairs. I believe that small studio will do for these two." Haim turned toward the door but immediately pivoted around and saluted Hinda and Rachel. "Congratulations, and welcome to our Jewish compound. Please call me Uncle Haim." Yawning briefly, he added, "It's past bedtime now, so *please* save your escape story until tomorrow evening. We'll celebrate your victory with a special dinner." Smiling broadly, Haim added, "*All* of us are eager to hear the exciting details."

118
Separated
June 1945 | Weimar, US-occupied Germany

Sitting erect on the edge of his hospital bed and grasping the metal bars of a medical walker, Wolf Yoskowitz pulled himself up to a standing position. He was on his feet—the first time since early March. Even though his legs wobbled, Wolf's ebullient smile and the golden sheen in his eyes rivaled the luminosity of a full moon lighting up a night sky.

"Great job, Hercules," Nurse Bernadette encouraged, her eyes dancing with delight. "How does that feel?"

"Amazing," Wolf replied. In the next second, he abruptly sat down on the bed, his leg muscles trembling.

Soon after Wolf awakened from his afternoon nap, he watched his brother limp down the hallway using a cane for support. Arriving to Wolf's bedside, Joseph said excitedly, "Nurse Bernie said you stood up today, pulled yourself up."

"Yeah, I did." Wolf flashed a wide smile, radiating with pride. "I'm stronger every day now. How about you?"

Joseph tilted his head to the side and swallowed hard. Tears spilled from his eyes. "Tomorrow morning, the doctors are releasing me from this hospital."

"Man, that's great!" Wolf grasped his brother's hand enthusiastically. "This calls for celebration, not tears."

"I don't want to leave *you*." Joseph choked out the words. "But now that I can walk and don't require medication, they say I have to go. Plus, they need the bed."

"Where will you go?" Wolf asked, his voice laden with concern, the reality sinking in.

"Allied forces are providing rail passes to Wrocław, the closest city across Poland's borders. There's an International Red Cross there that will help connect me with surviving family and friends."

"Wrocław? You mean Breslau?" Wolf's forehead wrinkled in confusion.

"The army officer who talked to me this afternoon said the borders were recently redrawn. The city is now back in Poland and was renamed Wrocław."

"That's good for Poland, but whatever it's called, the city is heavily Germanic. I would prefer you go somewhere else."

"Sorry, brother. I have no resources to do otherwise. At least, they're helping me."

Wolf nodded. "Once there, you'll try to find Mother, Erna, and Alexander?"

"Yes, but it's possible that none of them survived this wicked mess." Joseph's lips twisted against each other as he grappled with facing such a painful reality. "Brother, we need each other now more than ever, and we *must* stay together. Wolf, please. Promise me you'll fight with all your might, with all you've got, to walk again, so you can join me in Wrocław."

119
Four Days

Bolts of lightning streaked the starless sky when Aizik turned the key in the door to the first-floor apartment. "Be prepared. It's a small studio, tiny like a closet," Aizik warned. He swung the door wide for the sisters to enter. They gasped.

Rachel dashed from room to room, squealing with delight at every turn. Returning to the living room, she plopped onto the sofa. Then she instantly jumped up and spun around, twirling in circles as if she were a frenzied ballerina. She shrilled, "A closet? It's a palace!"

Hinda gawked at the living room that had a plush sofa and two plump chairs, lamps, end tables, and bookshelves. She threw her arms around Aizik, hugging him with euphoric gratitude.

"Explore the rest," he encouraged, his green eyes—emerald orbs resembling irises of a rare Nebelung cat—brimmed with pride. He pointed to the hallway.

Hinda pinched her cheek, thinking she was dreaming, when she saw two full bathrooms and two bedrooms each furnished with a dresser, a full-size bed, side tables, and lamps. "Ooh," she exclaimed. "It's beautiful, and it even has thick mattresses and pillows."

"And clean sheets," Aizik interjected. "Clean and crisp."

From across the apartment, Rachel cried out, "Hinda, come see. It has a *big* kitchen with a table and chairs."

Sprinting to the kitchen, with Aizik close on her heels, Hinda asked in awe, "Who does this belong to?"

"Uncle Haim. He owns this building, and the one next to it. He runs the entire compound. Hey, I bet you didn't have any dinner." Retrieving a platter of roasted chicken from the refrigerator, Aizik set it and a jar of mustard on the table. "There are fresh loaves of rye in the bread box."

"You must have been expecting someone. Have we intruded?" Hinda asked, holding her breath, scared this would all disappear in the morning.

"We had some business associates due to arrive tonight, but they were delayed, now arriving tomorrow. But don't worry, Uncle Haim designated this one for you. There are more apartments in the next building where they can stay. Come, sit down, and have a sandwich."

Rachel, who was exploring cabinets and finding pots and pans along with spices, flour, matzo meal, sugar, and canned goods, asked in a choked voice, "Can we stay more than one night?"

"Yep, you can." Aizik said, aglow with a wide smile. "You're part of the great family now. Uncle Haim said welcome to our Jewish compound. Those words mean you can stay until you have a definite plan, somewhere solid to go, even if that's a long time from now."

"Please tell me this is real, not a dream," Rachel squeaked, tears tumbling down her cheeks.

"As Tatae would say, praise God," Hinda exclaimed. "We owe you big time, Aizik. Uncle Haim took us in because we're your cousins."

"Praise God is right, to be united with you two, the only blood family I have left now." Aizik moved to the window and closed the curtains. Lightning flashed and thunder roared. "That's quite a storm out there. God was smiling upon all of us tonight, especially getting you to safe shelter before the severe weather hit. How was it that you found the compound?"

A sheepish smile crept onto Hinda's face. "Actually, it was Rachel who deserves the credit. She chided me for walking on the street so late at night. Stopped me right in front of the building with the Star of David."

Rachel beamed. "But Hinda, it was your instinct to go inside. And that's where we met Uncle Haim."

Aizik sliced chicken while Rachel spread the bread with mustard. Nodding in appreciation, Aizik remarked, "Ah yes, Hinda's golden instincts."

"Speaking of Uncle Haim," Hinda said. "Is the scarring on his face burns or birthmarks?"

Sighing heavily, Aizik replied, "Burns. Another heartbreaking saga. Prior to the war, Haim owned commercial properties. When the Germans first occupied Wrocław, he resisted leasing his apartments and retail spaces to declared Nazis. One day, the Nazi regime confiscated those buildings. Later that night when the family was sleeping, the Gestapo doused his home with gasoline, then set fire to it. Haim was trying to get everyone out when a main wall and part of the roof fell, crushing his family, but not him. Realizing that his wife, daughter, and son had perished, and that the Gestapo would be watching the house from the street, he crawled to the kitchen. His clothing and hair were in flames, but he managed to get to the side yard and roll in the grass. Barely alive, he found his way to the home of a trusted employee, non-Jewish, whose family was connected to the Polish Underground. They nursed him back to health and kept him in hiding."

"How devastating for him to witness his family in flames," Rachel murmured sorrowfully.

"For sure," Aizik said. "Haim knows people are curious about his scars, but he despises talking about it. That all happened five years ago, but it's still too emotionally painful for him. Please don't give him your sympathies."

"Understand," Hinda replied emphatically. "Neither Rachel nor I will mention it. But speaking of fires, how did the synagogue here in this compound escape the Nazi decree to burn them all?"

"The locals say that because this synagogue was part of dense development, a complex with buildings attached for more than one city block, the Nazis decided it was too risky to torch it. The Germans confiscated the building though, and used it as a warehouse and housing for militia. It was only recently that it became an active synagogue again, after Germany lost the war and the Soviets booted the Nazis out."

"That's incredible. And to think, we stumbled upon it tonight," Hinda replied.

Nodding, Aizik asked, "So, dear cousin, what brought you to Wrocław? It's quite dangerous and very Germanic here."

"Yes, we know," Hinda replied. "I'm hoping to find information about the whereabouts of Dr. Walter from Auschwitz. Do you remember him? Walter Zeilhofen? He has family here in Breslau. I mean Wrocław."

Aizik's face crumpled. He turned to the side and coughed. He covered his nose and mouth, while making sneezing sounds. "I'm sorry. It's the mustard. Sometimes makes me sneeze."

"What Hinda didn't say," Rachel announced, "is that she's in love with Dr. Walter. He saved her life when she had malaria. He wrote her love letters."

"Rachel, shame on you. That's *my* story to tell," Hinda chided.

"And another one that will have to wait." Aizik checked his watch nervously. "I didn't realize it was so late. I report to work early tomorrow, so I need to scram." He kissed Hinda, then Rachel, on the cheek. "I'll see you tomorrow evening for the celebration dinner."

At the door, Hinda said, "Just quickly, before you go, may I ask what you do, and why there were so many guns and so much ammo in the room upstairs?"

"Yep, and I think you'll like the reason—the irony, anyway," Aizik said, appearing to have regained his composure. "We work for the SSP, the Soviet Secret Police. Our job is to apprehend Nazis, who are then bussed to labor camps in Siberia, never to return. You two could join us in the fight by spying for us. The job pays extremely well. And it's quite gratifying."

"Work as Soviet spies?" Hinda wrinkled her nose and waved goodnight to her cousin. When the door was locked, she turned to Rachel. "As much as I would love to see Nazis captured, I will *not* work for the scary Russians."

The massive table in the dining hall was set with a feast. Hinda sat at the head of the table with Rachel to her right.

"Clothes? You accomplished this amazing feat, escaping the heavily guarded, fenced, and gated Auschwitz, using civilian clothing?" Uncle Haim asked incredulously.

"Yes, to be fair, deceased Jews' clothing that I took from Canada, the warehouse. As I said, the blizzard helped cloak us. But our faces were our own and uncovered. All dressed up in stylish outfits, we appeared as officers' daughters out for a stroll, enjoying the snow."

From the opposite end of the table, Leo, Aizik's best friend, whistled admiringly. "A simple but absolutely brilliant escape plan."

The young men cheered and whooped. Everyone toasted the sisters, especially Hinda for her ingenious plot and her bravery in executing it. For the remainder of the evening, the sisters shared the travails and tribulations of what had happened to them after their escape.

At ten o'clock, Uncle Haim arose from the table. "We've all been blessed by hearing your astonishing story tonight. The Lord was with you every step, no doubt." He nodded to the sisters. "We hope you'll find peace here. Let us know if we can be of assistance as you settle in, no matter too small." Turning to the group, Haim said, "Good night, everyone. Tomorrow is a new day to capture Nazis. There's still far too many of the hateful monsters out there."

"Aizik, please come in and stay for a while," Hinda pleaded. "I feel wound up after sharing our escape story. And there's so much I want to ask you about. Plus, we never discussed ideas for finding Dr. Walter."

Averting his eyes and looking down at the floor, Aizik declined. "Hinda, I'm just too tired tonight. Enjoy this moment; keep basking in the glow of our celebration of you and Rachel. I promise I'll spend tomorrow evening with you. All subjects fair game then. Okay?"

Kissing him on the cheek, Hinda let Aizik go, locking the door behind him. She turned to see Rachel waltzing around the living room, a dreamy look in her eye. Rachel squealed, "I'm so happy. We have a safe and cozy home. We have comfortable places to sit, to sleep, to eat, and even a real kitchen. What more could you want?"

Hinda wanted to say, "Walter, I want Walter." Instead, she replied, "Let's cook dinner for Aizik tomorrow evening. There are ample choices in the refrigerator. And, perhaps, I can sweet-talk you into making Golda's famous apple strudel for dessert."

The following evening, Aizik smacked his lips. "Superb strudel. Some of the best I've ever tasted. Rachel, where did you learn to bake like that?"

"Golda, the cook at the Sosnowiec Refugee Center, taught me. I was her main helper."

"Well then, here's to Golda." Aizik raised his glass. Turning to Hinda, he said, "I know you had seven brothers and have lost Joel. So how many live in Mexico City?"

"All six, but I had rather discuss Walter now. Can you help me locate a Zeilhofen family here in Breslau? I'm hoping one of them will know where Walter is living and help me contact him."

Carefully folding his napkin, stalling, Aizik replied, "Let's go into the living room to talk about this. Then we can tackle the dishes."

"You two go ahead. I'll do the dishes," Rachel urged.

"No, I insist. The queen of strudel deserves to put her feet up for a minute." Aizik gave Rachel an eerie look, his eyes so extremely narrowed that they were spooky. A shiver came over her. Rachel promptly followed him into the living room.

When they were settled, Aizik and Hinda on the sofa and Rachel in a lounge chair, Hinda crossed her arms tightly against her chest. "Okay, cousin, get on with the lecture. I know you disapprove since Walter is not Jewish."

Aizik cleared his throat. "I don't know how to say this except to say it outright." He reached for Hinda's hand. "About two weeks before the Red Army liberated Auschwitz, Dr. Walter was hanged for treason in the square. I saw it with my own eyes, watched the entire atrocity. I'm sorry, Hinda, but Walter is dead."

Recoiling backward, Hinda slumped against the sofa. Feeling a dagger stab her heart and flames engulf her whole being, she screamed, "Nooooooo." Deep inside, she felt her spirit come undone, completely unhinged. Another person she loved killed by the Nazis. Another dream gone, her singular hope for true love taken away. Chills and rigors shook her body. In a torrent of tears and wails, she bolted from the room and threw herself into her bed, pulling the covers over her head. And that is where she stayed for four days.

Her hair matted, Hinda sipped coffee at the kitchen table. Her entire face appeared puffy from crying, and her eyelids were so swollen, she could barely see.

Gripping her hand, Aizik said, "I came as soon as I could after getting Rachel's message that you wanted to speak with me."

Her chin quivered. "Thank you. I know I must move on from grieving, but first, I need to hear details. What can you tell me about the hanging?"

Disturbed to see Hinda still in such a distraught, grief-stricken state, Aizik bowed his head for a moment, collecting his thoughts. Speaking softly, he said, "The square was packed, all of us forced to watch, and this time, all medical staff too. From what I could see, Walter was calm, and it was over quickly, surprisingly fast. He did not dangle in obvious agony the way most did when hanged in the square. We heard that the guard in charge of the gallows was a resistor and that he set up the rope for instant death even though he had been ordered otherwise."

"Thank God it was as merciful as possible." Sighing, Hinda asked, "Who spoke, condemning him?"

"The head pharmacist, Capesius, was at the microphone. He cited multiple counts of treason and acted exceptionally contemptuous of Walter. A female prisoner, who worked in the pharmacy, was also hanged for treason immediately after Walter."

Hinda raised her head in surprise. "A woman brought me an encouraging note from Walter." Hinda pulled the now tattered paper from her pocket and spread it on the table. The ink was faded, but still readable: *Soon, the dark clouds over the sky are going away, and you will see sunshine again.*

Aizik leaned in to read the note. "That's nice. And may I suggest you take Walter's words to heart right now, today. Hinda, your life is far from over. You *will* see sunshine again."

Hinda nodded. "I am a survivor." Fresh tears slipped from her eyes. Stroking the note, she said, "The woman who delivered this said she worked in the pharmacy."

"Then, probably, she's the one who hanged that day. She and Walter had been cancelling chemical orders for the gas chambers and giving Jews unauthorized medications. Hinda, it's clear, Walter was not an anti-Semite."

"Indeed, I wouldn't be alive today without his help," she said, blotting her eyes with a napkin. "He risked his life for me when I had malaria." Staring off into space, as if imagining the scene in the square at Auschwitz, Hinda probed further, "Was the evil Dr. Mengele there?"

"Ah, yes. Satan himself, the devil who castrated me, was there, standing on stage, dressed in full Nazi regalia," Aizik replied. His nose bridge wrinkled, his upper lip raised in disgust, his tone sardonic, Aizik added, "And the beast appeared positively pleased to watch Walter hang."

120

Palestine

"Almost ready for a marathon, Hercules. You're making amazing progress," Nurse Bernadette praised Wolf as he took steps on his own, all without the use of a cane or walker.

Applause was heard from down the hallway. Dr. Stephens, smiling brightly, clapped enthusiastically. "See if you can make it over here," he encouraged.

One slow step at a time, Wolf maintained his balance. Although his leg muscles trembled slightly, he kept going. When he reached Dr. Stephens, he grinned playfully, mischievous as a Cheshire cat, and walked ten more steps before he stopped and plopped down in a wheelchair parked to the side.

"Yoskowitz, that was outstanding. When did you start walking without assistance?"

"Just yesterday, sir. But I've been visualizing it in my head for over a month now."

"And I cannot take any credit for that," Bernie said. "It was his idea, and clearly, this man has some super mental powers."

"May I walk back now?" Wolf asked, his blue eyes blazing and a shy smile enhancing his chiseled features.

"Do you mind if I examine you first?" Dr. Stephens had his stethoscope on Wolf's chest before he could reply. Placing his hands upon his thigh muscles, the doctor nodded. "Only slight tremors. Okay then, you have the green light to start the trek back to bed."

With the doctor on one side of him and nurse Bernie on the other, Wolf walked the entire course back to his bed.

"This is a red-letter day," Dr. Stephens proclaimed. "I'm exceptionally pleased with your progress. Keep this up every day for a full month, and we'll consider releasing you."

"Speaking of a red-letter day," Bernie said, picking up an envelope on Wolf's bedside table. "Mail from the International Red Cross. It's a letter for you, Wolf."

Later, after a rest, Wolf sat in the hospital bed fingering the letter. A knot had formed in his stomach. He felt certain it was from Joseph, but he feared the news it probably contained about the rest of the family. With a series of deep sighs, he ripped open the envelope.

> *Dear brother, Erna is here with me. She's a skeleton but alive. She reports that Mother, Alexander, and she were all imprisoned at Dachau in Germany. Upon their arrival, Mother and Alexander were taken to a different part of the camp. She never saw them again and fears they were sent to the gas chamber. But we're still actively searching all records with the help of the Red Cross. Before being reunited with me, Erna applied for passage to Cyprus, in hopes of getting to Palestine from there. I have now submitted my formal request too. I tried to apply for you, but you must be present and have your signature witnessed. All mail must go through the military or the International Red Cross. So, if allowed, I'll notify you should we depart before you arrive here. Erna sends her love to you and is praying for you to join us soon. We miss you. Blessings, Joseph*

Awash with mixed emotions, Wolf reread the letter. Seven times. The knot in his stomach unwound itself with the news that his sister, Erna, was alive and reunited with Joseph. The segment citing his mother and youngest brother, Alexander, as unaccounted for produced tears and angst. The last time he saw them in the woods, it had been sheer agony to see German soldiers haul them away. And now, try as he might to feel optimistic, Wolf could not conjure one shred of hope for them. His spirit whispered that they were both dead, that only their dusty remains were present on planet Earth.

The issue of passage to Cyprus then Palestine hastened Wolf's heartbeat. When Wolf was at Buchenwald, he had prayed—day after day and night after night—for the war to end and for doors to open wide, allowing him to immigrate to Palestine, the only Jewish National Homeland in the world. In 1922, Wolf was only five years old, yet the memory of the celebration was still vivid. His father had trumpeted the news: The League of Nations unanimously approved Palestine as the Jewish National Homeland and had issued the British Mandate to oversee it. Frequently discussing it for years afterward, his parents had planned to move the family there if they could ever get out of Poland. Their yearning to live in Palestine had been so contagious that Wolf had never forgotten. And obviously his sister, Erna, had not either.

Today, though, Wolf's desire for Palestine was met with a grisly vision—a narrow bridge that collapsed when he was halfway across. Although he strained to push such pessimism away, the image returned a second time. Wolf speculated what it could mean. He could be released from the hospital in a month, at the earliest. But even that might be too late. Joseph and Erna could have already departed by then. Or it could mean that he made the trip to Cyprus alone, but then the British denied him entrance to Palestine. He leaned his head into the pillow. The bridge appeared a third time. Wolf asked one last question of himself: When the time came to leave the hospital, could he bear to part from Bernadette? His pulse rate skyrocketed. His heart split apart.

121

The Telegram

August 1945 | Wrocław, War-torn Poland

Hinda bounced through the door to the apartment. "Rachel, I got it. I got the job!"

Wearing an apron, Rachel ran to the living room. "That's wonderful. Which one?"

"The Polish Magistrate. I'll work in the Registration Department. My salary is piddly, paid in coupons. But it's something." Hinda sniffed the air. "What smells so good?"

"Aizik had groceries delivered this morning. More than we requested." Rachel's eyes danced with delight. "Two bags of apples were an obvious hint. So, I'm making a double strudel for dinner tonight with the guys. Come sit in the kitchen. I'll make tea."

"The boys will love it, *if* Aizik lets them have any." Hinda chuckled, then the corners of her mouth turned decidedly downward. She plopped down in the chair. "I'm afraid I've disappointed Aizik. He worked so hard, obtaining multiple offers for me when I asked for his help in finding a job. But each one involved working for, and with, the Soviets."

"Have you told him how *truly terrified* you are of the Russians?"

Hinda rotated her head on her neck as if it ached. "I tried, but he doesn't get it. The Red Army liberated Auschwitz, freeing him, so he's enamored."

Rachel sighed, "I think Aizik will be relieved about your job. He's been worried about your depression over Walter. All the boys have been. Several mentioned it to me."

Bowing her head, Hinda muttered under her breath, "I'm entitled to feel how I feel." Shifting her gaze to the ceiling, she lamented, "I'm weary of hearing Aizik and the boys advising me to move on. I've wanted to rail at them, but they've been so good to us, so generous, I couldn't."

Rachel brought tea for both of them. "I'm sorry if they've upset you. But seriously, Hinda, they're fantastic to us. Aizik supplies our daily food and other needs. Uncle Haim provides dinner and the roof over our heads. And I feel safe here with all those guys upstairs."

"Yes, but we're *too* dependent. It was okay, at first, but now that I have a job, it's time to start paying for groceries. It's important to me that I pull my own weight and not be a burden."

Scrunching her nose at the aroma, Rachel leapt from her chair. She grabbed potholders and pulled the pastry from the oven. "Hinda, you worry too much. Aizik openly says he makes a ton of money, is saving for university, *and* is tickled to be helping us."

Going to the stove, Hinda eyed the strudel. She crooned, "Mmm. A masterpiece." Moving to the window, she peered at the cloudless sky. "Was David one of the guys who mentioned my depression to you?"

Rachel suddenly looked as if the sun had risen on her face. Her eyes sparkling, she said, "Yes, David did. He used the word *grief*, though, not depression. Why do you ask?"

"I'm not blind. There's bounteous flirting going on between the two of you."

After working at the magistrate's office for three weeks, Hinda regained her emotional equilibrium. No longer obsessing over Walter or lost love, she focused on stability and security, which engendered concern about their current situation. Unlike Rachel, who she had assessed as naïve about the apartment and how long they could stay there, Hinda's every instinct warned that they were not truly settled yet. And now Aizik was talking about starting classes at the University of London in January. She had to find a way to communicate with her brothers in Mexico City.

The registrar at the Polish Magistrate had suggested that Hinda go to the Soviet Command Center and request help for how to send a telegram to her brothers via the Russian military. That evening, she discussed it with Aizik. He provided a contact name, though he warned it was nothing more than a name for the appropriate person to approach. The following day after work, Hinda braved the trek to the main Soviet office. Due to Aizik's connection with the SSP, she had expected a friendly reception. But the woman sitting behind the desk had rudely scowled at her, saying absolutely not. Steeling herself, Hinda boldly asked to speak to a supervisor. Disgruntled, the burly Russian man led her to his office, where he interrogated her for two hours. As the sun was setting, he agreed to send a short telegram to Jack Mondlak in Mexico City:

> Hinda & Rachel are alive, residing at this address: 609 AltbüBerstrafBe, Unit 4, Breslau/Wrocław.

Ecstatic but weary, Hinda embarked upon the journey home. The streets remained dangerous with the Polish army and resistor groups fighting the Soviet occupation. Sounds of gunfire and shouting stalked her every step. By the time she neared the building with the Star of David, other worries pestered her: How could the telegram reach her brother, Jack, when she had no official address for him? She had only noted that he worked for a major newspaper as a political journalist. And if he did receive it, would he respond?

122
A Bridge

Wolf Yoskowitz boarded the train bound for Gliwice, his hometown, though he had no one there to receive him. Once he was settled into his seat, he pulled two letters from his bag. Postmarked the twentieth of August, one letter was from the International Red Cross notifying him that both Erna and Joseph had received permits for passage to Cyprus and had departed Wrocław. The organization also offered condolences that efforts to locate other surviving Yoskowitz family members had proved unsuccessful.

Wolf had read the letter a dozen times already. But, today, he reread it again, attempting to make peace with his decision to go to Gliwice instead of Wrocław, where the International Red Cross would have facilitated his application for passage to Palestine via Cyprus. His stomach knotted and his chest tightened; he had been unable to shake the angst ignited by the unnerving vision of a bridge collapsing under him when making that trip. Shocking to him, he was now averse to pursuing that route in the immediate future.

The Allied forces agent, who secured his rail pass, had disagreed with his choice of cities. Yet Wolf had convinced the agent to defy protocol and allow him to return to his hometown, where he was more likely to find help and potentially connect with surviving friends. The army agent had acquiesced due to a Displaced Persons Center located in Gliwice where he knew for certain that Wolf could find temporary refuge.

Not confident that he had made the right decision, Wolf pondered the distressing unknowns. Yet the knowns offered no comfort: his mother and Alexander were dead. Joseph and Erna were thousands of miles away. Aloneness engulfed him. He closed his eyes, deciding to read the second letter later, although he clutched it tightly as though it were etched in gold.

Jolted awake by the passenger behind him, who was snoring like a bear in hibernation, Wolf fumbled in his bag for his medication. Sipping the orange soda he had bought prior to boarding, he swallowed his daily steroid tablet. On the day of Wolf's release from the hospital, Dr. Stephens had prescribed daily exercise, and provided a three-month supply of testosterone supplements to be taken once a day and pain pills to be taken as needed. To Wolf's surprise, the Allied forces agent supplied clothing and a stack of coupons for purchasing basic needs.

After engaging in a series of leg lifts, flexing and raising one leg at a time up and down, Wolf relaxed into the seat. He opened the second letter, although he had already perused it multiple times. The scrawl was difficult to decipher, hurriedly penned at three in the morning. First, he looked at the signature: *Love you forever, Bernadette.* At that moment, he felt he could read those four words every hour for a lifetime. In the text of the letter, Bernadette explained that she had to return home to London. Her mother had suffered a massive stroke.

Wolf gazed out the train window. He did not see the forest and lush foliage; he saw Dr. Stephens' haggard face the morning he delivered Bernadette's letter. The doctor had described the turmoil of the previous night when Bernie had received alarming news. The team had scrambled to get her onboard an Allied forces' truck departing for Paris, where she would catch a flight to London, or worse case, take a ship. While sharing details of Bernie's sudden departure, Dr. Stephens emphasized how, amidst it all, she had insisted upon writing a note to Wolf.

Returning his gaze to Bernadette's note, Wolf read and reread the sentence where she invited him to come to London when he was released from the hospital and could apply for a visa to Great Britain. To Wolf, the invitation did not seem to be just a polite gesture. She *urged* him to come. Moreover, she provided an exact address and telephone number.

Suddenly, the narrow bridge appeared in his mind's eye. Wolf blinked and double blinked, trying to clear the image. Yet the bridge loomed large. He stepped onto it. When he was halfway across, the bridge collapsed. He plummeted.

Wolf audibly gasped, "What is going on?"

123

Her Soul Danced

Late October 1945 | Wrocław, War-torn Poland

With the artistry of a professional caterer, Rachel arranged freshly baked cookies on a tray. The corners of her mouth curled upward in anticipation of how delighted the guys who lived upstairs would be with the assortment of shortbread, ginger, and oatmeal cookies.

The group of men had changed significantly since Hinda and she had arrived. Frequently, residents departed to live more normal lives, and then—like a revolving door—new residents swiftly moved in. The three constants so far were Aizik, Leo, and David. No matter that the group changed often, everyone begged Rachel to bake goodies.

In the back bedroom, Hinda brushed her hair, readying to go upstairs for the compound's nightly dinner hosted by Uncle Haim. As the brush glided through her russet tresses, her mind whirred with thoughts about the young men who Rachel and she dined with most evenings. Not a single one held any attraction for her, whereas Rachel appeared to be falling in love with David.

The notion caused her hand to jerk, and strands of hair tangled in the bristles. While unwinding the knot, she thought: *My heart is numb and too tangled to feel anything as for romantic relationships.*

Suddenly, her reflection caught her by surprise. Gazing into the mirror, Hinda remembered her shaved, bald head, then the dry, brittle straw-like hair that had first grown back. Tonight, she realized that her hair had now regained its youthful sheen and was thick with waves. It was actually healthy and quite pretty. Yet all vanity vanished when she heard a knock on the front door. Tossing the hairbrush aside, she strode to the living room.

"Who's there?" Hinda inquired with the door closed and locked.

"The International Red Cross," a female voice answered. "A telegram for Hinda and Rachel Mondlak."

Hinda jerked opened the door. After a brief exchange, the statuesque woman handed over an envelope and promptly exited.

Calling out to her sister, Hinda yelled excitedly, "Rachel, come quick. We have a telegram." When Rachel was by her side, Hinda displayed the official envelope addressed to them.

Hinda & Rachel Mondlak 609 AltbüBerstrafBe, Unit 4, Breslau/ Wrocław

Waves of excitement paired with anxiety rushed over her. She caught her breath and ripped open the envelope. She proceeded to read the short message aloud:

Ecstatic to hear that you two are alive. Working on ways to be reunited. Your brothers love you. Jack Mondlak

Relief coursed through Hinda. It had really happened. Jack had responded and with alacrity. She had succeeded in making a connection with her brothers, who lived worlds away in Mexico City. Her soul danced. Hope burgeoned.

124
Running
November 1945 | Gliwice, War-torn Poland

Diligent with his daily strength-building exercises, Wolf Yoskowitz walked briskly along the avenue in downtown Gliwice. Counting the storefronts that he recognized, he was astonished at what a small number it was. War had changed the city dramatically.

When he had first arrived in Gliwice, he had gone to the Dutka bakery only to find it nonexistent. Rubble and ashes, it was. Businesses on either side of it had burned too. Devastated, Wolf inquired along that street as to what had happened. One man reported: Nazis burned it down in February last year. The fire was so explosive, the entire block was in jeopardy. An older woman, who owned a nearby grocery, relayed more horrific news: The day the bakery burned, the entire Dutka family, who had been harboring Jews, was killed on their farm, their property seized by the Nazi regime. Returning to the rubble, Wolf had sat on the curb, his hands tightly fisted, stifling screams and sobs. Tidal waves of anger, anguish, and sorrow washed over him, battering his very soul.

Today, as he neared that street, he turned in the opposite direction and unconsciously broke into a jog. Five minutes later, he realized he was running. His legs pumping, his feet slapping against the pavement, he ran from the heartbreak as if it were a predator chasing him.

Suddenly, he burst into laughter. He was not just walking on his own, he was running. And he had no pain. He bowed his head and proclaimed with quiet reverence, "Praise God. I am healed. I am strong again."

That evening, Wolf perused the bookcase in the den area of the home where he was staying. Glancing at the fire burning in the fireplace and taking in the coziness of the room, Wolf still couldn't believe his good fortune. On the train from Weimar to Gliwice, he had sat next to two brothers, Daniel and Noah Ehrlich, who were also concentration camp survivors. As the train rattled on the track for hours on end, the three enjoyed camaraderie. Near the end of the trip, Daniel invited Wolf to go with them to a center for young men, which was run by the Polish Underground State. Surprisingly, the place was an attractive two-story home. A philanthropic businessman, who was ex-military, funded the project to help male war victims rebuild their lives. The man's secondary goal was to recruit members to join the underground fight to oust the Soviets from Poland. Yet enlisting was not compulsory to live at the center temporarily; a concentration-camp survivor could stay up to six months.

Tugging on a tome of world maps, Wolf took the heavy book to the round table beside the fireplace. There, a previously selected volume awaited him. Holding a hefty book in each hand, he lifted one at a time above his head, stretching his arm upward. After twenty-five repetitions, he lifted both books at the same time. On the twentieth repetition, voices in the hallway caught his attention. Daniel and Noah stomped into the room, grumbling at each other, both in an obvious huff.

"Hey, guys, what's going on?" Wolf asked.

Noah chortled, trying to lighten the mood. "Wolf man, you're obsessed with exercising. But smart idea using books as weights."

Daniel made a beeline to the fire, warmed his hands, then thrust them into his pockets. "Noah has enlisted with the Polish Underground State. And he didn't discuss it with me first."

"Come now, big brother, we had many conversations," Noah replied. "Besides, we've been apart for years—you incarcerated in Auschwitz, and me in Bergen-Belsen camp."

"Exactly my point. We should stay together now." Daniel gripped the iron poker beside the fireplace and jabbed at the blazing logs. "And honestly, Noah, though I don't like the Soviet occupation tactics, the Red Army saved me from the Nazis. Freed all of us at Auschwitz. I just can't find it in me to be so mad at them that I want to fight them or kill them."

"Then, you need to go to Breslau, Wrocław, or whatever that city's name is these days," Noah advised. "I've heard that the Secret Soviet Police there pays people well to kill or capture Nazis. Bet you'd find that satisfying."

Daniel nodded. "Some of the boys were talking about that last night. Said there's a Jewish compound there that takes in young men who are willing to work for the SSP." Turning to Wolf, Daniel said, "I may go check it out. Want to come with me? You hate the Nazis too."

Squinting his eyes as if trying to see the future, Wolf said, "I don't know, man. I don't want to participate in violence of any kind. I want to work in business. But I must admit that making decent money is appealing."

Before going to sleep that night, Wolf acknowledged his amazing progress that day: he had run one-half kilometer without muscle tremors or pain, during or afterward. He so wished that Dr. Stephens and Bernadette could know; he would write letters to them, but the postal service was still in turmoil and unreliable. Furthermore, the Allied forces hospital in Weimar could be in the process of shutting down by now. Thinking of Dr. Stephens, the one doc who had cared, who had gone out on a limb for him, Wolf bowed his head and said a prayer of beholden appreciation.

His body temperature warmed with thoughts of Bernadette. He could hear her cheery voice saying, "You've done it, Hercules. Defied the odds." While he yearned to see her, he would not make the trip to London anytime soon. The eerie bridge vision had nixed that idea.

No longer intimidated by the vision of the collapsing bridge, Wolf had come to look at it as a compass. Gliwice had proven to be a safe choice. He had made new friends and could stay at the center through the end of January without enlisting. Now that he was physically strong again, it was time to get a reasonable job. He was in the process of connecting with business owners who had been on his flour-delivery route before the war. What's more, new options were surfacing each day.

Turning on his side, Wolf burrowed his head into the pillow and pondered going to Wrocław with Daniel. The bridge did not appear. Moments passed. He strained to conjure it in his mind's eye. No bridge.

125

University of London
December 1945 | Wrocław, War-torn Poland

"Does your leaving require Rachel and me to move out of this apartment?" Hinda asked, her hands nervously twisting against the other.

Aizik took her hands in his, calming their fit of worry. "I spoke with Uncle Haim, and he wants you and Rachel to stay here until you have somewhere solid to go. And he knows you're in the process of connecting with your brothers in Mexico City. He has tapped our friend, Leo, to be in charge of you when I depart."

"We like Leo, but why do we need someone in charge of us?"

"Because Uncle Haim is old-school protective. You and Rachel are the only females in the group. He wants to be sure you're safe and that you have a pal to go to if there's an issue."

Hinda nodded. Her eyes suddenly widened. "Gracious sakes, Aizik, I didn't congratulate you. Please forgive me." She patted him heartily on the knee. "I'm so proud of you, our only family member to attend the University of London."

"It's a dream come true for me." Aizik drew in a long breath. "I'm excited *and* anxious."

"When do you leave?"

"Classes start on the fourteenth of January. So, I want to be settled in by the first of the year. If all my paperwork comes through, my plan is to depart late next week."

"I'm certainly going to miss you." Tears sprang from Hinda's eyes.

"No good-bye tears today. I'm still here." Aizik stood to leave. At the door, he asked, "Do you remember Daniel Ehrlich from our shtetl in Zieluń?"

"Of course, I do. And his younger brother, Noah."

"Uncle Haim told me this morning that he recently heard from Daniel, inquiring about working with us here. He said he's coming to visit next week or the next."

Hinda's eyes of azure, shining a brighter blue, lit up at the news. "That's wonderful. Did Noah survive the war? Is he coming too?"

"I don't know. Uncle Haim just said that Daniel might bring a friend, a man who survived Buchenwald. Daniel was at Auschwitz, he said, but I never encountered him there."

"Buchenwald? Where was that camp?"

"Germany, near Weimar. Uncle Haim hopes this guy comes since we've never hosted anyone from there. Different stories for us to hear." A jaunty grin spreading across his face, Aizik turned and playfully knocked Hinda on the arm. "If I remember correctly from our years at synagogue together, Daniel Ehrlich had a serious crush on you."

A rosy flush crept up Hinda's neck and tinged her cheeks. Returning Aizik's gesture, she teasingly punched Aizik on his arm. Looking over her shoulder to check on Rachel's proximity, Hinda stepped into the hallway and closed the door. "On another note, I've been meaning to ask you about David Sochaczewski. My hunch is that Rachel is falling in love with him. Is he a good person?"

"David was at Auschwitz with me and Leo. From what I've observed, he's a fine man. And I've noted Rachel's fondness, which appears mutual. *But.* Encourage her to take it slow."

126

Secret Beacons

Mid-December 1945 | Wrocław, War-torn Poland

"Everyone, please give a warm welcome to Daniel Ehrlich and Wolf Yoskowitz." Uncle Haim introduced his guests to the group of young men who had gathered for the nightly dinner. "They're joining us today from Gliwice. Previously, though, Daniel endured Auschwitz and Wolf, Buchenwald." Greetings and handshakes ensued. A cluster of guys immediately surrounded Wolf, peppering him with questions about Buchenwald.

Moving away from that cluster, Aizik went to greet Daniel, who he had known from childhood, attending yeshiva and synagogue with him. The two had a joyous reunion, slapping each other on the back. "I believe you have a surprising treat in store for you, my friend," Aizik said, his green eyes aglow.

"How so?" Daniel inquired. "Looks like I already have. I'm happily shocked to see *you*. Didn't know that anyone from Zieluń was part of this compound."

"I've been here since February, soon after the Soviets freed Auschwitz. It's been amazing for me; it's truly a great place to heal and reclaim yourself. And earn money. But I must tell you that I'm leaving for London tomorrow. Starting university there next month."

"Wow. Congratulations." With his eyebrows furrowed, Daniel said, "May I ask about your family? Your cousin, Hinda Mondlak. Did she survive the persecution?"

Aizik turned as the door opened and Hinda and Rachel entered. "See for yourself," Aizik exclaimed, his lips curling into his signature jaunty grin.

Daniel's jaw dropped.

Across the room, Wolf's eyes widened in surprise at the sight of the two young women. His breath caught in his throat; a soft gasp escaped his mouth. The instant he beheld Hinda's face, he felt as if planet Earth shifted on its axis, plunging him into a gravitational tide that propelled him toward her. He found himself caught in such a forceful undertow that it commanded his mightiest mental mastery to withstand it, to resist rushing to her, and wrapping her up in his arms. Stunned, Wolf watched as his friend, Daniel, did exactly that, holding her in a tight embrace. The ensuing onslaught of jealousy almost buckled his knees.

Uncle Haim rang a small bell. "Time to proceed to the dining room for our celebration dinner honoring Aizik Shatz, who will preside at the head of the table." The group trailed into the stately dining room.

Pointing to the chair next to him at the main table, Uncle Haim said, "Mr. Yoskowitz, please sit here by me. Mr. Ehrlich, please sit with your hometown friends since you haven't seen them for many years during this horrific time of war."

Beaming, Daniel pulled out Hinda's chair for her and helped her to be seated to the right of Aizik and next to him. The warm sensation of hugging Hinda still coursed through him. Admittedly, he had held her a bit too tightly and too long for what was considered appropriate. Noticing the disapproving glance from Aizik, he worked on reining in his desire for physical contact with her, particularly the compulsion to drape his arm around her shoulder or to enfold her hand into his. As dinner progressed, Daniel could not help himself. Frequently, he reached over and affectionately fondled Hinda's arm or hand.

When dessert was served, Uncle Haim arose from his chair and tapped his glass with a spoon. When he had everyone's attention, he boomed, "Let's all raise our glasses in salute to Aizik, who is leaving us to attend the University of London." The Jewish toast to life, *L'chaim*, echoed across the room. Clearing his throat, Uncle Haim proceeded, "Aizik, you've been an exemplary resident and worker here. You epitomize what we strive for with your recovery from perilous persecution and then moving forward with a solid plan for your life. We wish you the best and would like to give you a token of our love and respect." Haim nodded to Leo, who stood and presented Aizik with a shiny gift box.

Surprised and delighted, Aizik lifted the lid and held up an elegant fountain pen. "This is perfect for all the essays I'll be writing. Thank you." His green eyes foggy with mist, Aizik continued, "I'll never forget what you've done for me, Uncle Haim." His gaze moving around the room, Aizik said, "I hope that all of you will truly soak up this opportunity, the benefits that come with living here, and the leadership offered by our generous Uncle Haim." The room burst into applause.

Uncle Haim bowed, taking in the moment. Then he said, "On another note, I've learned tonight that my interesting dinner companion, Mr. Wolf Yoskowitz, had the honor of meeting the illustrious General Dwight Eisenhower, *in person*, when the USA freed Buchenwald. Mr. Yoskowitz is modest but ask him, anyway, about how the general saved his brother and him when they were near death. It's quite a story."

In his chair, Wolf shyly ducked his head, his jaw set with indignation. The last thing he wanted was to talk about Buchenwald. He wanted to lock that dark door and *never* reopen it. Tonight, what he wanted most was to look upon the young Jewish woman at the opposite end of the table. Russet-colored hair that fell in thick waves paired with enormous sky-blue eyes made for a unique and compelling beauty. A magnet that pulled him. Strategizing ways to meet this stunning woman, who also exuded regal inner strength, Wolf decided on a plan. The very second dinner was adjourned, he would join Daniel.

Later that night, Hinda tossed this way and then that. Sleep eluded her. It had been heartwarming to see Daniel Ehrich again, to know that he and his little brother had survived the war. But his overly affectionate manner with her had quickly become annoying. Even his initial hug was inordinately close, almost crushing, making her want to recoil.

But if that other new guy hugged me that way, I might like it. Hinda bolted upright in the bed, astounded that she would have such a thought. Remembering when she first glimpsed the man named Wolf Yoskowitz across the room, she had instantly deemed him quite handsome. Then, after dinner, when Daniel had introduced her and the three of them talked briefly, she found Wolf's resonant voice, broad shoulders, and strong physique extremely appealing. Yet it was his bright blue eyes, such strength and intensity shining forth, that moved her. When he had greeted her, and their eyes met and lingered, a preternatural heat flared inside her, as if her bones closeted secret beacons that suddenly switched on.

Reclining into the pillow, the realization struck her: *I am seriously attracted to the man named Wolf. Dearest Lord, I pray, please make this go away. It feels too scary.*

The following morning, Rachel waltzed into the kitchen humming happily. "How long have you been up?"

"Long enough to be on my third cup of coffee," Hinda replied.

"You look upset. I thought you would be smiling this morning, reveling in all the attention Daniel Ehrlich showered upon you last night. And what about that guy with him? Whew, he is handsome."

"Enough to turn your head from David?" Hinda inquired, a sharpness to her tone.

"Heavens, no," Rachel exclaimed.

Hinda leaned across the table. "Rachel, are you in love with David?"

"I believe I am," Rachel clutched her chest and bowed her head. After a moment, she lifted it. Looking her sister square in the eyes, she said, "After the loss and torture that we've endured, I sometimes wonder if I know what love for a man is. Love beyond attraction."

Hinda placed a hand on her stomach, which churned with too much coffee acid and the implications of Rachel's statement. "Attraction is a place to start. Possibly, as good as it gets for those of us who've had our hearts desecrated and lives ripped apart by Nazism."

Tilting her head to the side, Rachel eyed her sister. "So, are you attracted to Daniel?"

"At first, I thought I was, but then I found him maddening." Hinda arose from the table. "I need to get dressed for work."

"What about that Wolf guy? I caught him staring at you."

"He's intriguing. But a man with that kind of looks and confident presence surely has a girlfriend, if not several."

"But Hinda, he came here to the compound. He's considering moving in and working here." Rachel sighed heavily. "Uncle Haim's rule is that the men living here must be unattached."

Hinda stopped in her tracks. "I didn't know. Is that impeding your relationship with David?"

Upstairs in the library, Uncle Haim laid out the rules for living in the Jewish compound, plus the types of jobs available with the Secret Soviet Police, and the salaries and commissions associated with each. Daniel and Wolf listened intently.

At the end of the hour, Daniel announced, "I'm in. All of the jobs sound appealing to me, especially the capture of Nazis."

"Excellent, Daniel. You can replace Aizik, starting tomorrow." Turning to Wolf, he asked, "And you, Mr. Yoskowitz?"

Wolf peered at his hands, his fingers spread. "My ideal is to work in business. But I want to give this a go. Is there an office job or spying spot open?"

Flipping through his notepad, Uncle Haim paused on a particular page. "One spy spot is available. No office jobs right now."

"Yes, sir, spying it is. I accept. Thank you for this incredible opportunity." Wolf stood and offered his hand to Uncle Haim. "I won't let you down, sir," Wolf said as the two engaged in a firm handshake.

"Welcome to our great family. And call me Uncle Haim. Everyone does." He chuckled. "Training begins later this morning. Before we sign contracts, let me be clear. No wives or fiancées are hiding in the wings, are they?"

"No, sir," Daniel and Wolf spoke at the same time.

A shadow darkened Daniel's face. "May I ask, sir, what happens if we meet someone here? Someone we want to marry?"

"Romantic relationships are not encouraged here; our underground involvement is dangerous work. Yet true love versus infatuation is a rare thing. If that should come along, we can discuss your options."

Just then, there was a light knock on the door. Leo pushed it open and said, "Uncle Haim, I apologize for interrupting, but Aizik is ready to depart."

Haim nodded. "Let's all go down and give Mr. Shatz a proper send off."

On the street, the driver loaded luggage into the car owned by the compound. Aizik, looking dapper in a trench coat, checked his tickets: train to Paris and ship passage to London.

Hinda exited the building and rushed over to Aizik. "I'm on my way to work but wanted to say good-bye." Embracing her cousin, she exclaimed, "How can I ever repay you for all you've done for me and Rachel?"

"Be happy, Hinda. You and Rachel living happy and prosperous lives are my rewards. And the greatest revenge we can get on the Nazis."

Wolf, Daniel, and Uncle Haim joined the group gathering on the street. Wolf watched as Hinda patted and kissed Aizik's cheeks. He witnessed the love pouring from her. *She would be a wonderful mother,* he thought.

"Aizik, I've asked Daniel to ride with you to the train station," Uncle Haim announced. "He's taking your position with the SSP. Please brief him on the details of the job."

Just then, explosives and gunfire erupted on the next street over from them. Leo and the guys, who had come to say good-bye to Aizik, dashed away, moving toward the commotion.

Uncle Haim rubbed the side of his face, the scarred side. "I don't like the sound of things out here this morning. Wolf, would you escort Hinda to the magistrate's office where she works? You can get your prescribed exercise, and I'll breathe easier about her being on the streets. We can start your training when you return."

"Absolutely, sir," Wolf quickly replied. "I would be honored."

Concerned that police would soon blockade the streets, Uncle Haim hurried Aizik and Daniel into the car. He motioned the driver onward. With no more fanfare, the car pulled from the curb.

Tears clouding her eyes, Hinda waved one last time to her cousin, then steered Wolf in the direction of her workplace.

Standing in the compound's doorway, Uncle Haim watched the pair walking down the street together, already chatting. Although his mouth was set with a practiced grimace, inwardly, Haim smiled.

127

The Cinema

Hinda exited the government building where the magistrate's office was located. She bounded down the steps, expecting to see her new friend, Wolf Yoskowitz, waiting by the lamppost. For the past three weeks, Wolf had escorted her to work each morning, and he had been there waiting for her when she got off at three o'clock in the afternoon.

Walking daily together had engendered conversation that she found inspiring. Wolf openly shared what he wanted in life and how he intentionally held a distinct vision of it in his mind. His ambition, confidence, and clarity impressed her. Plus, he espoused a reverse philosophy from what she was accustomed to hearing from concentration camp survivors. Wolf acknowledged that, yes, he had been severely victimized by the Nazis, but he adamantly refused to be a victim for the rest of his life. He intended to be successful and enjoy every day.

Hinda relished their discussions to and from work. Yet at three o'clock this afternoon, Wolf was nowhere in sight. *He's delayed in a spy sting*, Hinda surmised. *Or he's bored with walking me home every day.* Surprised at the level of disappointment she felt, she headed in the direction of home. When she turned the corner to the next street, gunfire exploded. A knot of men fought each other just a hundred feet from her. Posthaste, Hinda turned back, racewalking the opposite way. Feelings of worry for Wolf surfaced. *What if he was caught in that, was one of those men?* Anxiety gripped her. She jolted into a jog. Soon, she was back in front of the government building. Sitting down on the steps, Hinda fought back tears. *I don't want to care about that man. Dear God, I cannot withstand any more hurt.* She gripped her arms, hugging herself. *Enough of the self-pity. I must find a different route home.* She stood and looked around at the intersection of streets, deciding which way to go. Just then, she heard her name.

Clutching ribbons of paper in his hand, Wolf loped toward her, shouting, "Hinda, wait." Breathy from running, he paused at the bottom step. "Whew, I was afraid you'd already left. I apologize for being late; I was stuck in line trying to purchase these." He held up two tickets.

"What are those?" Hinda asked, noticing the profound relief that surged through her upon seeing him.

His intense blue eyes sparkling especially bright, Wolf took her hand in his. "These, beautiful lady, are movie tickets. The cinema on the square is reopening tomorrow evening, the first postwar show, a French film. May I have the pleasure of your company? Would you please join me?"

Stunned, Hinda sputtered, "You mean go out, like a date?"

"I mean exactly that." Wolf squeezed her hand. "I'm asking you out. What do you say?"

Hinda's eyes widened to an enormous size. Having never been on a real date, she felt as if a kaleidoscope of butterflies, their wings fluttering wildly, had invaded her stomach. She smiled shyly and replied, "I say yes."

128
Jealousy

Uncle Haim leaned back in his desk chair while listening to the complaints of the young man who sat opposite him. Interrupting, Haim said, "Daniel, what you're asking is preposterous. I'll have no part of it."

Shocked and rattled, Daniel Ehrlich almost bit his tongue when spitting out the words. "But Yoskowitz is stealing *my* girl."

"The Hinda Mondlak that I've come to know would not permit such nonsense." Uncle Haim narrowed his eyes. "You grew up with Hinda. But Daniel, how well do you know her as an adult woman?"

"Better than Wolf Yoskowitz does," Daniel shrieked. "Sir, are you aware that he escorts her to and from work *every* day?"

"Yes, and I've blessed it. We've had an escalation in resistor attacks on the Soviets that often involve innocent civilians who happen to be on the street. A woman and her baby were killed last week, just two blocks from here."

"Then why do you allow Hinda to work outside this building?"

Leaning across the desk, Uncle Haim replied emphatically, "She's fiercely independent and not a freeloader, which I admire. And, I believe, the work at the magistrate's office is healing for her. We've all been through hell with the persecution of us Jews; yet, in the face of that, and at a young age, she displayed extraordinary acumen and stamina."

Crossing his arms, Daniel huffed. "So, you will not tell Wolf to back off?"

"Absolutely not. And I'll not tolerate conflict of this nature in this compound. What's more, I was clear when you signed your contract. I do not encourage romance here."

"But I've known since I was an adolescent that I wanted to marry Hinda Mondlak. She was always the most beautiful and sweetest girl in our shtetl."

"She's a beauty, but there is far more to her than meets the eye. For starters, a bold and courageous spirit. Do you know that Hinda *escaped* Auschwitz and got Rachel out with her?"

"No, sir, I was not aware of that." Daniel squirmed in his chair.

"You're viewing this through a one-way lens that's focused only on you. What about *her* feelings? Has she encouraged a personal relationship with you?"

"She's pushing me back, but that's because of Wolf's attention to her."

"Have you considered that Hinda is pushing you away because of a *lack* of romantic feelings for you?" Uncle Haim stood, gesturing to Daniel that it was time for him to leave. "Because you have conflict with another resident, namely Wolf Yoskowitz, and are hyper-focused on a relationship with Hinda Mondlak, I want you to go back to Gliwice and visit your brother. Take two weeks off. Give yourself some distance from this."

"With all due respect, sir, I don't want to do that."

"It was not a suggestion. Leo will book your rail passes. You leave tomorrow."

129

The Full Moon

January 1946 | Wrocław, War-torn Poland

"Hinda Mondlak, will you marry me?" Wolf Yoskowitz, his resonant voice steady and sure, suddenly posed the question as they walked in the square after the movie. Glancing upward to the brilliant full moon shining overhead, he stopped at what seemed like the exact center of its luminosity. Facing her, Wolf wrapped his arms around Hinda, holding her in a gentle embrace. His eyes locked onto hers as he awaited her reply.

"Marry? This is our first date." Hinda squeaked the words, her mouth instantly dry upon hearing his shocking proposal.

"Yes, our first date, and I never want it to end." He caressed her cheek. "You are *the* beautiful, strong, and intelligent Jewish girl I've dreamed of my entire life. I knew it the very moment I saw your face. Weeks ago."

Her mind spinning, she stared into his eyes. Seconds turned to minutes. Words would not come forth.

After a long silence, Wolf entreated, "Hinda, please, let's spend our lives together. Let's be a real family. With God as my witness, I promise to protect you and take care of your every need. Marry me and be my queen."

"This hurts to say, but I don't know if I *love* you. I care and am attracted to you, but love . . . love feels beyond me, right now. I worry that Nazism and the persecution so battered and shattered my heart that I'm incapable."

Wolf placed one finger across Hinda's lips, "Shh, let's don't speak of that right now. Though I believe I love you, what I *know* for sure is that we belong together." He pulled her closer, pressing his body against hers.

She leaned into him, surrendering to the exquisite feeling of the warmth he emanated. With his strong and muscular arms holding her so tightly, she felt safe. At that moment, she realized that, for weeks now, as she had walked alongside him on the streets, the overall safety she felt with him was unparalleled. And now, the expression radiating from his eyes, so caring and kind, engendered the perception that she was treasured and protected—a rarity she valued.

Gently lifting her chin, tilting her face upward to his, Wolf implored, "Darling Hinda, let me take care of you. Be my wife. I vow, with all my heart and soul, to honor and cherish you as long as I live." His lips found hers.

Her lips embraced his, sought them out for more, matching his passion. The intensity of her response surprised her—and him.

Breathless, Wolf said, "Was that a yes?"

Somewhere in that long first kiss, it felt to Hinda as if a smattering of the broken shards of her heart pieced themselves together again. With hope for wholeness, she gently stroked his face and declared, "Yes, Mr. Wolf Yoskowitz. I will marry you."

Beaming with elation, Wolf lifted Hinda up and swung her around in euphoric glee. "Let's celebrate. With chocolate." Taking her arm, he strode to the one kiosk still open on the square. "Would you like coffee?"

"I want to share our news with my sister. I can make coffee at the apartment."

"Wonderful idea," Wolf exclaimed. "I presume that David will be with Rachel?"

Hinda nodded, her heart fluttering with a flurry of sentiments.

Turning to the kiosk attendant, Wolf pulled a wad of coupons from his pocket and purchased four of the largest chocolate bars on the cart.

Holding hands, they embarked along the sidewalk. After a mere three steps, Wolf stopped and shoved the chocolate bars into his pocket. He gently grasped Hinda's shoulders and pulled her close to him. With the full moon lighting their entwined silhouette, he kissed her—again and again.

130
Betrayed

At seven-thirty the following morning, there came a knock on the door of Unit Four. Hinda, who had dressed early and had just poured her first cup of coffee, waltzed to the door with a dreamy look in her eyes. Expecting Wolf, she readily opened the door without asking who was there. To her chagrin, it was Daniel Ehrlich, who barely resembled himself. Dark circles under his puffy, red eyes, Daniel looked as if a fitful night fraught with crying jags had foiled any rest. He plunked down a travel bag near the doorway and stepped inside without invitation.

Uncomfortable with Daniel's proximity to her, Hinda stepped back from him, "Are you going somewhere?"

"Gliwice for a couple of weeks to see Noah, my brother. Uncle Haim's orders." She raised her eyebrows. "Is Noah okay?"

Daniel dropped onto one knee. "Hinda Mondlak, will you marry me?" Reaching out to her, he gripped her hand. "I've always loved you, Hinda, *always* wanted to marry you, as long as I can remember." Tears slid down his cheeks. "Please, honor our history together. Say yes and become my wife."

"Daniel, I . . . I can't."

He stood and lunged toward her, grabbing her roughly. "You must. You will."

His face millimeters from hers, his breath felt hot on her neck. Hinda tried to wriggle free from his grasp. Daniel tightened his hold on her. Hinda screeched, "Let go of me."

"Not until you agree to marry me," he exclaimed angrily.

Wrestling one hand free, Hinda drew it back and slapped Daniel across the face. She shrilled, "I will *not* marry you. Wouldn't now, even if you were the last man on Earth."

His lips contorting in a vile sneer, Daniel snarled, "You don't mean that. You love me." He seized her hand and muscled her arm behind her back, twisting it sharply.

Hinda let out a blood-curdling howl, which awakened Rachel.

Scrambling from her bed and throwing on her robe, Rachel reeled into the living room. Assessing the scene and the crazed look in Daniel's eyes plus his forceful hold on Hinda, she quickly decided she was too petite and slight to have any physical impact on the guy. Stepping to the side, she darted through the doorway.

"Rachel, wait! Help me," Hinda squealed.

"Hang on," Rachel yelled as she sprinted down the hallway. On the stairway, she took two steps at a time. At the door to the men's quarters, Rachel rang the buzzer six times in succession, the code to communicate an urgent problem. At the same time, she pounded on the door, shouting, "Help! Help!"

Leo yanked open the door. "What's happened?" he asked just as David and Uncle Haim raced up behind him.

"It's Hinda. Daniel Ehrlich is attacking her."

In Unit Four, Daniel continued to hold Hinda in a tight vise. He ranted, "It's that *shmendrik*, Wolf Yoskowitz. He has turned your attention from me. But you're mine." He thrust his pelvis against hers. "I'm taking you now. Then, you'll have no choice but to marry *me*."

Fearing for her life and virginity, Hinda attempted to knee his groin, but she could not move her legs, as he had wrapped one of his around hers, locking her to him. Her small frame was no match for his bulk. Outrage flared like a roaring furnace inside her. She shrieked, "I survived and escaped the Nazis. You, one of my own people, will *not* ravage me." Wriggling free her other hand, Hinda dug her nails into his neck, clawing the sensitive area of his throat. Inflamed and crazed, Daniel pushed Hinda against the wall, pressing his body against her. He clamped his lips upon hers. Hinda's fingers found the natural protrusion on his neck. She squeezed, pinched, and twisted his Adam's apple. Daniel yelped and shoved her onto the floor. Mounting her, he clasped her wrists tightly above her head. Hinda screamed and screeched. His mouth quickly covered hers, stifling her pleas for help. Pinning her under him, Daniel writhed atop her.

Suddenly, four strong hands, those of Leo and David, wrestled Daniel off Hinda and yanked him onto his knees. In the doorway, Uncle Haim and Rachel appeared shaken and shocked by the scene, their rapid breath catching in their throats. Appraising the ugly situation, Haim fingered the safety on the small pistol that he always carried in his right pocket. Then he stuffed the handcuffs that he had grabbed upon hearing Rachel's cry for help into his left pocket. Part of the pair stuck out the top and rested on his belt.

Dashing over to her sister, Rachel helped Hinda scramble up from the floor just as Wolf rushed into the room. Quickly assessing the scenario, Wolf went to Hinda, who was trembling and whimpering audibly while straightening her clothing. Wrapping his arms around her, Wolf exclaimed, "What just happened here? My darling, are you okay?"

Hinda fell against Wolf, allowing him to nestle her in his arms.

Daniel bristled, fisting his hands, though Leo and David still restrained him. His face reddened and his mouth twisted as he tried to break free. He yelled at Wolf, "You idiot thief, stay away from her. She's mine."

Grasping Daniel's wrist, Uncle Haim slid on handcuffs and then jerked him into a standing position. Haim bellowed, "You've lost your mind, man. Clearly lost it. And she's not *yours*. She belongs to no man, only to God." Turning to Hinda, his tone urgent, Haim inquired, "Hinda, are you okay?"

Glaring at Daniel, Hinda nodded and choked out the words, "I will be, sir, though he almost—"

Gently rocking Hinda in his arms, Wolf, who had shunned violence, struggled with the compulsion to flatten Daniel, smash his face, and wring every ounce of life from him. If Hinda were not safely in his arms, he would have done just that.

Uncle Haim shifted his weight and hefted up his shoulders. His voice tight and menacing, his nose inches from Daniel's, Haim spat out a warning, "Soviet spies will be watching you, tracking your every move, Daniel Ehrlich. If you return here or approach Hinda Mondlak ever again, I'll have you arrested by the SSP and shipped to Siberia."

Daniel stared strangely ahead. The color had drained from his face, and his eyes appeared vacant, as if he were not seeing anything or anyone. Yet, he repeated three phrases in the same sequence: *Hinda Mondlak. She is mine, my wife.*

In a commanding tone, Uncle Haim spoke over Daniel, issuing orders to Leo and David. "You two escort this *meshuggener* to the train station. Book him a *one-way* ticket back to Gliwice. At boarding, remove the handcuffs, then guard both doors to that car until the train has departed."

Abruptly, Wolf called out in a piercing tone, "Search his bag, sir."

Surprised at the suggestion, Uncle Haim tilted his head in puzzlement, then promptly reached for Daniel's bag. Unlatching the suitcase, he lifted the edges of the clothing packed on top, exposing two guns and a box of bullets underneath. Haim turned the guns in his hands, examining them. His left ear and the scars on his cheek suddenly turned a deep carmine color. "These are mine from upstairs. He stole them."

Placing his hand on Haim's shoulder, Leo asked, "Shall we arrest him, sir?"

"No, Daniel is one of ours. He's betrayed us, but we'll not betray him, not in this condition. He needs medical and psychological help."

Daniel stared straight ahead, mumbling the same three phrases, "*Hinda Mondlak. She is mine, my wife.*"

"A change of plans, Leo," Uncle Haim announced, his face set in a sharp grimace. "You and David go with him on the train. Keep him handcuffed and don't let him out of your sight. I'll contact my comrade, who runs the Polish Underground Men's Center in Gliwice, and inform him that Daniel is a danger to himself and to others, and request that medics meet the train." Haim motioned to Leo and David, who then strong-armed Daniel from the room and down the hallway to the street exit.

Uncle Haim watched from the hallway until they had exited. Then he stepped back inside the apartment. "I need to go upstairs and make this communication to Gliwice. Should take about fifteen minutes. Wolf, please stay here. We have important matters to discuss." As he exited, he said, "I'll be back shortly."

After returning to Unit Four, Uncle Haim's head bobbled in disbelief. He directed his gaze at Hinda. "I pray that you are truly okay. In retrospect, I should have forced Daniel to leave the compound yesterday, considering his preposterous request."

"What request, sir?" Wolf asked.

"He asked me to intervene and prohibit you from seeing Hinda. His conflict with you was concerning, and then it became clear that Daniel was abnormally obsessed. I ordered him to take two weeks off and to leave for Gliwice this morning. But it never occurred to me that he would attack the woman he claimed to love."

"A far cry from love, it was an act of sheer madness," Wolf declared emphatically.

Rachel, who sat in a side chair, chimed in, "Rage, not love, from what I saw."

Uncle Haim rubbed his chin, as if puzzled. "Wolf, what on earth gave you the idea to search his bag?"

"Well, sir, images of the guns on the table upstairs kept coming to mind. Then, like a lightning bolt, it hit me. Daniel planned to shoot me on the street this morning."

"Heaven help us. You're most likely correct." Haim bowed his head, then snapped it upward. Looking from Hinda to Wolf, searching their faces, he said, "I had planned to say no, that it's too soon, but after this upsetting episode, I say yes. You two go forward with your wedding plans."

Wolf's jaw dropped. "Sir, how did you know? I only proposed last evening. I had planned on speaking to you about it first thing this morning."

"I have multiple eyes and many ears." Uncle Haim chuckled, then his expression turned serious again. "You two have my blessing, but I must inform you, Wolf Yoskowitz, that your employment with the SSP has ended. You've violated the contract. You're officially fired."

Without flinching, Wolf calmly replied, "Yes, sir. I expected that. The terms of the contract were clear: no wives or fiancées allowed due to the dangerous nature of the work. I'll begin immediately arranging new employment and living accommodations. Do you prefer that I move from the compound today?"

Sniffing at the air, Uncle Haim said, "Do I smell coffee? I could sure use a cup."

Her eyes wide with worry, Hinda arose from the sofa.

Jumping up from her chair, Rachel said, "Sit down, dear sister. I'll serve coffee."

"How about we go into the kitchen, and all four of us sit around the table there?" Uncle Haim spoke in a more pleasant tone than he had in his recent, intense proclamation to Wolf.

"Certainly, sir," Hinda said, though her stomach churned, and her heart rate accelerated. She worried: Was he about to evict her and Rachel too?

Once the four were inside the kitchen, Haim was struck by its immaculate condition. It looked as pristine as it did when the sisters had arrived, and he knew they cooked copiously. "The place looks fantastic," he announced.

Setting a plate of homemade shortbread cookies on the table, Rachel said, "My sister runs an ultra-clean and tidy household."

"I can see that, and I sincerely appreciate it."

"Speaking of appreciation," Hinda said, her lips trembling, "Rachel and I are eternally grateful for your benevolence, Uncle Haim, allowing us to live here all these months. And now, it sounds like we need to—" Sobs broke the sentence. She squeaked the last word, "leave."

"Whoa, whoa, Hinda. I'm sorry. I'm the one who has lost my mind, given what you've been through this morning." Uncle Haim leapt from the chair and took Hinda's hands in his. "I should have spoken to Wolf in private about the SSP contract. And, hey, no one in this room is moving from the compound by my request." He pointed to Wolf. "Not him. Nor you, nor Rachel. I've not allowed females to live in the compound before you. Too many complications, such as today. But you girls are now like daughters to me."

Hinda gazed into Uncle Haim's eyes. Observing honest sincerity, she wiped at her tears. "Your words of assurance mean a lot, sir." Her hands shaking, she attempted a smile. "Let's sit down and enjoy coffee and this delicious shortbread."

While returning to his chair, Uncle Haim averred, "I have multiple ideas on how all this can work." Laying his palms atop the table, he spread his fingers fanlike and lightly tapped the table as if each fingertip represented a different idea. "I've been mulling this over, sensing the direction your relationship was headed." Haim sipped his coffee, then continued, "So, Wolf, while your engagement to Hinda did terminate your SSP contract, I could use assistance in running this complicated compound. If you're amenable to that sort of office work, your salary will remain the same. You can continue living in the men's quarters upstairs until you are married, then you can move in here with your bride, in Unit Four. What do you think? Is it a deal?"

Wolf beamed. He extended his hand for a confirmation handshake. "Yes, sir!"

Uncle Haim dipped shortbread into his coffee. While savoring it, he gurgled approving noises. Looking toward the ceiling as if double-checking his offer, he said, "On another note, I've had my eye on a vacant storefront nearby. Wolf, you expressed interest in working in business when you first arrived here. How would you feel about trading in the underground market?"

"Sounds intriguing, sir. How would that work?" Wolf inquired.

"It's simple, really. We put the word out to folks in the underground, then they bring goods to the store that they believe are valuable, such as art, frames, fur coats, crystal, silver, etc. You buy them at a low rate in exchange for coupons, and sometimes rubles, then you resell them for a profit."

"Are these goods stolen?' Wolf asked, his jaw set. "I would not be a part of such."

"Nor would I," Haim exclaimed. "During the persecution, valuables were buried and hidden in odd places. I'm referring to these now-salvaged goods, found and unclaimed."

Wolf glanced at Hinda, covering her hand with his. "Interesting, but with all due respect, sir, while I have a bit of savings, I don't have that kind of capital to lease a storefront and purchase inventory to resell. My first priority is to buy this beautiful lady a wedding ring."

"Ahh yes, a ring." Haim raised his coffee cup in salute to Wolf then dunked a larger-than-polite piece of shortbread into his cup. Eating the entire chunk in one bite, he swallowed hard. Ducking his head briefly, he replied, "I didn't expect you to fund the enterprise alone. The Soviets have compensated me extraordinarily well for operating this compound on my property. I can get you started, be a partner of sorts. We can discuss the details later, along with office duties. Think about it."

Wolf nodded, feeling as if the Almighty had unexpectedly breathed favor in his direction.

Not feeling as certain as Wolf, Hinda asked, "Is the underground trade business safe?"

"Everything has its risks today. But this work would be far safer than spying for the SSP, as he's been doing." Uncle Haim sighed. Rubbing his scarred jaw, he said, "Hinda, it's as safe as any business can be with the Soviets and Polish armies engaging in daily battle for the territory of Poland. War still rages. And at our very doorstep."

Standing in the doorway to Unit Four, Wolf gently cupped Hinda's cheek. His blue eyes twinkling with delight, he announced excitedly, "We're all set for the twenty-fourth. I just met with the rabbi."

"Sunday, the twenty-fourth of February? That's big news. Come and sit down." Hinda motioned to the sofa.

Disappointed that she did not dance with joy and cover his face with kisses, Wolf's wide smile dimmed.

Once they were settled on the sofa, Hinda reached for his hand. "Wolf, I feel that before we proceed with marriage, I must confess my heart." She dropped her eyes to the floor, his gaze too intense to hold, considering what she was about to tell him.

"That sounds ominous," Wolf replied. "But, my darling, I don't wish for you to carry burdens." The room suddenly felt as if the walls had moved close, crushing in on him.

Regaining her courage and conviction, Hinda looked directly into his eyes. "When you proposed, I told you that I didn't know if I was capable of love, so it's only fair that you know." She straightened her shoulders, bracing them. "I carry love in my heart for another man."

"Who *is* this man?" Wolf asked, his face flushed and set like stone. He pulled his hand away from hers and curled his fingers into his palm.

"Walter Zeilhofen, a doctor at Auschwitz, who treated me for malaria. He saved my life."

"Well, then, I'm grateful to him." Sighing deeply, Wolf asked, "Did you have relations with him?"

"No, Walter never laid a hand on me in that way. And, just so you know, though I had scary close calls with Nazi men in the ghetto and Auschwitz, at twenty-five, I'm still a virgin. But *if* I could have found Walter after the war, I'm not sure that would be the case."

"You looked for him?"

"Yes, that's what brought me here to Breslau as he had relatives here. He was German, though not a Nazi, clearly not. And obviously not Jewish; he worked at Auschwitz."

Squinting, as if searching an obscure map, Wolf inquired, "Where is this Walter now?"

"Heaven, I assume." Hinda's eyes brimmed with tears. "He was such a good man."

"Heaven? I'm confused. Is he missing or deceased?"

Tears spilled in rivulets down Hinda's cheeks. "After I escaped, Walter was hanged for treason, for helping Jews and for participating in Resistance efforts. My cousin, Aizik, witnessed his death, so I know it's true."

Slumping against the sofa, Wolf clasped his hand over his chest. "I was near a heart attack, and now, you say this man you love is dead?"

"I felt I had to be honest with you. Love is love, dead or not."

"Yes, but can you build a life with a ghost?"

A flicker of a smile graced her lips. "No. I cannot." Hinda placed her hand on Wolf's knee. "I want to marry *you,* if you'll still have me, and enjoy life together, but my heart has felt heavy. I needed to tell you about Walter."

"Hinda, Hinda, Hinda. Your honesty is admirable, though hard to hear." Wolf put his arm around her and snuggled her close to him. They sat that way in silence as he stroked her hair, his mind twirling, and his fingertips nesting in her russet tresses. Abruptly, he said, "Well, I guess it's my turn now."

Hinda bolted upright. "You love another woman?" Disengaging from his arms, she rearranged her hair as if releasing the effects of his touch. "Is she dead or alive?"

"Alive," Wolf replied. "I wouldn't say I *love* her; that's a potent word. Though, I once thought I did. To be perfectly honest, I did feel a strong physical attraction. And, still today, I have a sincere fondness for her."

"Who is she? What's her name?" Hinda rattled off the questions, her tone terse.

"Bernadette. Nurse Bernie is what the doctors and nurses at the field hospital called her. I wouldn't be walking today without her and Dr. Stephens' help. And the Lord's mercy."

Hinda's mouth fell open. "You couldn't walk? You're so incredibly strong now."

"I could not. And I never want to speak of it again. Nor anything to do with the horrors of Buchenwald." His chiseled features appeared as a statue, though his jaw muscle flinched.

"This . . . this . . . this nurse," Hinda sputtered. "Did you have relations with her?"

"Not even a kiss. She was exceptionally warm to me but always professional."

"Was she *in love* with you?"

"Her mother had a stroke, and she was called away in the middle of the night. Before she departed, she wrote a letter to me where she professed her love. She invited me to come to her home in London when I was released from the hospital."

"Did you go?"

"No. I went to Gliwice. Met Daniel and Noah on that train, then ended up here."

"Do you regret not going? Do you dream of her?"

"Not for a minute. That is, after I met *you*."

Hinda searched his eyes. "We both carry affection for medical professionals who helped us at critical times. But now that the other-relationship shoe is on *my* foot, I admit, I'm jealous."

Wolf stood from the sofa and pulled Hinda into his arms. "My darling Hinda, you must know that my world shifted on its axis the night I saw your face for the first time. I've never experienced such a rush of attraction and deep feeling for a woman. Not in my entire life."

"I felt something, too, a definite attraction, when I first saw you." She stroked his face, her fingertips lingering on his strong jawline. "And then, something else quite powerful and moving when I looked into your eyes."

Breathing easier, Wolf exclaimed, "You, Hinda Mondlak, are the woman I dream of now. Actually, I've dreamed of you for many moons. To survive the persecution, I envisioned a beautiful, strong, Jewish woman to share the wonders of life with. You *are* her in every way, and more. So, on the twenty-fourth of this month, will you marry me? Be my beloved queen?"

132

White Gold

Wintry clouds, mixed with patches of sunshine, hovered over the old war-battered synagogue. Inside, young men wearing yarmulkes atop their heads sat in small groups on both sides of the main aisle. At the front, four men—two of whom were Leo and David—held wooden posts of the *chuppah*, the canopy under which the ceremony would soon occur.

Earlier, Leo and Uncle Haim had visited Wolf in a small side room. The two were there as friends, offering the groom support. But, also, they were present in an official capacity: to witness the signing of the *ketubah*, the marriage contract.

Wolf—debonair, dressed in an ivory vest, black jacket, and dress trousers—read the document multiple times. Satisfied with the terms outlining all that he was to provide for Hinda and her rights in the marriage, Wolf took up the pen and signed the sacred contract. The rabbi then instructed Haim and Leo to sign their full formal names as authorized witnesses.

Grinning broadly, Uncle Haim slapped Wolf on the shoulders in congratulations, saying what an honor it was to witness this special signing. Leo shook Wolf's hand heartily.

On the opposite side of the synagogue, Rachel pinned a small corsage, two white rose buds bound in white tulle, onto the shawl-collar lapel of Hinda's wedding suit. She kissed her sister's cheek. "I'm so disappointed that Aizik couldn't come. I'm all you have to escort you to the chuppah."

"And you are better than *just enough*, my precious sister. I'm extraordinarily grateful to have *you* alive and here with me at this turning point in my life, my wedding. Besides, I feel that Tatae and Mommy are hovering over us. Earlier, I experienced an ethereal touch—Mommy's hand helping me as I placed the veil's comb in my hair. And when I awoke this morning, it felt as if Tatae were stroking my face and praying over me. I sensed his blessing."

"Tatae would definitely approve of Wolf, a man of strong faith and principles."

Hinda nodded in agreement, "It's about time for the *bedecken*, right? Wolf could be knocking any minute." She smoothed the fabric of the peplum flaring outward from the cinched waist of the suit jacket, while remembering her desire to wear a traditional wedding dress. On her meager salary, a secondhand one was all she could afford, and those were rare. The one time she had found a used dress that would fit her small frame, she had stroked the satin bodice and tenderly grasped a swath of the lace. Unexpectedly, her fingers instantly recoiled. A prescient vision overcame her: the young bride, who had worn that dress, had married a hateful, abusive man. Hinda had rushed from the shop. That evening at dinner, she discussed the dilemma with Rachel, lamenting that she wanted a *new dress*, not a used one with negativity saturating its threads.

Overhearing the conversation, Uncle Haim leaned across the table. He gently chided Hinda, explaining that new clothing, particularly dressy attire, was not readily available for purchase in postwar Poland. While watching an expression of deep disappointment followed by sad acceptance seep into the features of Hinda's face, Haim stroked the scars along his jawline. Suddenly, his eyes sparkled, and he declared that he would commission a seamstress, whom he knew from the synagogue community, to make Hinda a new dress and veil. His gift, he announced with pride. The next day, the woman came to Unit Four and took Hinda's measurements.

Two weeks later, a package arrived. Hinda opened the box to find a two-piece suit, not a tailored style but a dressy design with an ankle-length skirt. Its mauve color surprised her. When she slipped on the jacket and peered into the mirror, she was pleased with her reflection and what the unusual hue did for her pale skin, russet hair, and blue eyes.

The sound of Rachel's voice returned Hinda to the present moment. "I know I've already told you," Rachel exclaimed. "But glory be, Hinda, you look amazingly beautiful. And the mauve suit is a masterpiece. Fits you perfectly. And your veil is exquisite too. Here, let me check it." Standing on tiptoe, Rachel reached up to the fancy embellished comb from which the veil flowed. "It's secure. Are you nervous?"

"Just excited, I think." Hinda placed her hand over her chest. "Though my heart is beating faster than normal."

A soft knock on the door turned the heads of both sisters. Rachel opened the door and then stepped back for the groom to have a full view of his bride.

Wolf's eyes bulged, his breath caught in his throat. Hinda looked even more stunning than he had imagined she would. Ever so gently, Wolf pulled the veil down over her head and face, honoring the tradition, called *bedecken*, where the groom checks to be sure that the bride is the correct person—based upon the biblical story of Jacob, who was tricked by a heavy veil and married Leah instead of his intended Rachel. The veiling ritual was also symbolic of reminding the groom that it was the bride's inner beauty by which he was most attracted. Contemplating this, Wolf believed it to be true for him, though it had taken all his willpower to resist kissing Hinda before he covered her exquisite face.

Watching from the doorway, Uncle Haim admired the lovely bride. A tear blurred his vision momentarily as he thought of how Hinda reminded him of his daughter who had perished in the fire when he was burned. Looking to Wolf, who slightly resembled his son, his firstborn gone in the same blaze, Haim's chest tightened. His voice rich with emotion, he said to Wolf, "Son, it's time for our walk to the chuppah."

Distinctive and unique in style, this chuppah had ivory lace sides, twelve inches in length dropping from the white silk top, which was adorned with a royal-blue Star of David in its center. Originally, the lace had been white too. But over time, it had turned to an ecru hue, which added to its antique mystique—begging the question of how many hundreds of couples had stood under this canopy and become man and wife, had become one, a singular home unto themselves.

Dressed in formal robes, the rabbi took his place under the sacred covering, signaling for the processional to begin. Wolf, escorted by Uncle Haim, strode confidently down the center aisle. As was tradition, Wolf and Haim stepped to the left side underneath the chuppah.

Turning in their seats to view the bride, the guests watched Hinda, accompanied by Rachel, proceed toward the canopy. The guests, all young men from the compound, grinned joyfully and nodded approval. Some inwardly whistled, their kind of silent applause for such beauty.

Arriving to the canopy, Rachel steered Hinda to the right, and they took their places. Hinda stepped forward and walked slowly around her groom, circling Wolf seven times. Following tradition, she thought of how the circles in the eyes of God were creating a protective wall around Wolf, while also being symbolic of intertwining their lives and creating a new home.

During the circling ritual, Rachel smiled coyly at David, who held the chuppah post on the front left corner. David had chosen that particular spot to have a direct view of Rachel throughout the ceremony. He reeled with hope that Rachel and he would soon be married under this very canopy. Surprised at Uncle Haim's encouragement of Wolf and Hinda's romance, David felt optimistic whereas before he had feared Haim's wrath. And then, there had been Rachel's concern that she, being younger, could not marry before Hinda did. Months ago, those prospects were depressing. Hinda Mondlak never acted attracted to anyone, and hundreds of young men were in and out of the compound every few weeks. Then, out of nowhere in mid-December, along came the distinguished Wolf Yoskowitz.

After the rabbi recited the blessing on the first cup of wine, a blessing of thanksgiving for this special moment, he gave the cup to Wolf, who passed it to Hinda. The couple sipped happily, as wine symbolized the joy they would have in their marriage.

At that moment sounds of nearby gunshots penetrated the air, disturbing the peaceful ambience of the synagogue. Uncle Haim pivoted to face the main entrance, double doors that now rattled. A vexed scowl puckered the skin folds of his scarred jaw. He gestured to the guys sitting in the back pew. Without a word, seven young men strode to the entrance, their guns drawn. Three veered to a side door and quietly exited onto the street. The remaining four flanked the main double doors, guarding them. Satisfied, Haim turned to the rabbi and motioned for him to proceed with the ceremony.

On cue, Wolf presented the ring, a fourteen-karat white-gold band. With the rabbi's guidance, he spoke the words: "Behold, with this ring, you are betrothed unto me, according to the laws of Moses and of Israel." A radiant smile lighting his face, Wolf then placed the band on Hinda's right index finger, the finger considered closest to the heart.

Due to the veil, Wolf did not see the tear that slipped down Hinda's cheek. She had expected the ring to be sterling silver, an affordable metal. Yet the weight of it, the way it felt on her skin, her instinct told her this ring was either platinum or white gold. Pondering the unique man, who was now officially her husband, her heart leapt with a distinct sensation. Realizing its profound meaning, Hinda whispered, "Dearest Wolf, I *do* love you."

Singing in Hebrew, the rabbi's tenor voice pierced even the rafters of the synagogue as he showered the married couple with seven blessings, *sheva b'rochot*. He gave thanks for the joys of love, intimacy, and marriage, for the creation of humanity, and for the community's happiness. Taking the second cup of wine, the rabbi blessed it, giving thanks for the delight of reaching this wonderful moment. He invited Wolf and Hinda to sip and receive the blessing.

Signaling the end of the ceremony, the rabbi nodded to Wolf, while discreetly gesturing to the floor where a glass lay wrapped in fabric. A dazzling smile lighting his face, Wolf clasped Hinda's hand and stomped the glass with his right foot, shattering it. The young men in the pews went wild, enthusiastically shouting *mazel tov*: congratulations, good luck, and good fortune.

The elated couple blazed down the aisle.

Once inside the small room designated especially for *Yichud*, the sacred alone time immediately following the ceremony, Wolf wrapped Hinda into his arms. After gently lifting the veil from her face, he ravished her with kisses—short ones, long ones, deep ones. Not having seen each other for a full week prior to the wedding, they eagerly embraced, ravenous for the touch of the other.

Each had fasted before the ceremony, and soon another kind of hunger made itself known as savory aromas vied for their attention. Selecting canapés from previously prepared trays, they fed each other delectable bites.

Blotting her lips with a napkin, Hinda said, "I was told that a feast awaits us."

"Yes, Uncle Haim and the guys have gone all out," Wolf replied. "It'll be quite the party, a grand reception." His eyes twinkling with pride, Wolf kissed her right hand. "Before we go, may I have the honor of moving your ring for you?"

Lightly stroking her index finger, caressing the wedding band, Hinda exclaimed, "It's beautiful. My finger tells me it's not silver. I hope you didn't break the bank."

Removing the band, Wolf slid it onto Hinda's left ring finger where she would now wear it. "It's white gold, fourteen-karat. Only the best for Hinda Mondlak Yoskowitz, my regal, beautiful queen." He drew her to him. Cupping her face, he peered into her eyes, mysterious azure oceans that he wanted eons to explore. "My darling Hinda, this is absolutely the happiest day of my life. God willing, I intend for us to have thousands more enchanted days together."

133

The Diagnosis

Early May 1946 | Wrocław, War-torn Poland

At the storefront, Wolf prepared the shop for closing. Writing in a ledger, he completed the documentation of goods traded and sold for the day. His pencil paused on the marked-off entry of a sapphire necklace. At the last minute, he had decided to decline the trade. He could not authenticate it. Plus, if it were genuine, he worried who would buy such an expensive piece. Yet the delicate necklace set with blue stones and diamonds had stirred his imagination; he had envisioned how exquisite it would look on Hinda with her long neck and eyes of azure. *Someday,* he mused, *I'll be able to afford beautiful jewels for her.*

After double locking the door, he headed home. His steps were quicker than normal; he was excited to surprise Hinda with a rare evening out—dinner and a movie. When he got to Unit Four, his soaring spirits plummeted.

"Another bad day, my darling? You were ill on your birthday earlier in the week." Wolf leaned across the bed and kissed her cheek. "I'd planned for us to go out and finally celebrate."

"I can't." Hinda groaned. She turned her head to face Wolf more directly, then winced from the movement. Her voice weak, she moaned, "I can't even wiggle a finger or lift my head a half inch from this pillow without feeling horribly nauseated."

"You had this last weekend and just two days ago. Along with sporadic vomiting." He sat down on the edge of the bed and stroked her arm. "I wish I had taken you to the doctor then."

"It's probably just a bug."

Wolf's brows furrowed, making the crease in his forehead more evident. "Maybe. But you've been feeling exhausted and looking quite pale for more than two weeks now. And your appetite is zero." He stood from the bed. "Perhaps, you simply need deep rest to get over this. Close your eyes and try to snooze for a bit. I'll be in the next room, reading the newspaper. If you need anything, just call out." Wolf tiptoed from the room, leaving the door slightly ajar.

In the living room, Wolf switched on the lamp by the chair and sat down to read. The words blurred, not capturing his interest. He tossed the paper aside. *I can't bear seeing Hinda like this. What if something serious is wrong with her?*

Stepping lightly, he went to the kitchen where Rachel was cleaning art brushes. A small canvas lay on the table, still wet with paint.

Whistling softly, Wolf commented on the painting. "That's impressive, Rachel. The roses look incredibly real. But do they have thorns *that* big?" Wolf asked.

"I intentionally exaggerated them. Poetic license. By the way, I made Hinda soup for lunch, but she couldn't keep it down. Not even a sip of water. How's she feeling now?"

"Poorly. Miserable, in fact. I've decided to go upstairs and talk to Uncle Haim and see if he knows a doctor who would be willing to come here. While I'm gone, can you sit in the living room, in case she needs something and calls out?"

"Sure. But Wolf, it's already dusk," Rachel asserted. She spread the clean brushes on a dish towel. "Do you really think you can get a doctor to make a house call this evening?"

"I cannot, but Uncle Haim can."

Wolf paced back and forth the length of the living room. Rachel and David sat nestled together on the sofa.

"Hinda has to get well," Rachel fretted. "Our wedding is ten days from now." David took Rachel's hand and squeezed it.

Wolf checked his watch. "The doctor has been in there for almost an hour now. That's too long for it be something simple, like a bug."

"He has to answer to Uncle Haim, so I'm betting he's just doing an extra thorough examination," David offered.

The bedroom door opened, and the doctor, who wore thick-rimmed glasses that dominated his face, motioned to Wolf. "Mr. Yoskowitz, you can come in now."

In the bedroom, Hinda's head was propped up on a stack of pillows. Her skin ashen, she looked as if she were acutely ill.

The doctor said, "I have reached a diagnosis and confirmed it with physical examination. Your wife has something to tell you."

Wolf stepped to the bed, his heart thumping against his chest.

Hinda reached out her hand to Wolf, who clasped it in his. "My dear husband, I'm not dying. I'm pregnant."

His eyes bulged and suddenly, his entire face appeared as if a light bulb were inside it. Gently, he placed his hand on her abdomen and whispered reverently, "A baby, our child, is growing in there?"

"Yes, sir," the doctor proclaimed. "Sometime next November, your little one should arrive. I'll know more about timing as the pregnancy advances."

His neck tilted back on his neck, and Wolf let out an ecstatic whoop. "We're having a baby! Praise God." Tenderly kissing Hinda on the forehead and both cheeks, he beamed. "You'll be a wonderful mother, the best ever." His head rocked back and forth in complete awe. "My darling Hinda, can you believe it? I'm going to be a tatae."

134
Doctor's Orders
Late July 1946 | Wrocław, War-torn Poland

Queasiness still her frequent companion, Hinda remained at her desk during lunch break. While nibbling on a sandwich, she reviewed the copy of the telegram message she had sent to her brother, Jack, in May: *Expecting baby, due in November. Rachel married David Sochazewski. Immigration papers needed for him.* She had yet to hear back from Jack. In early March, she had informed him of her marriage and provided Wolf's name. He had promptly sent congratulations and explained that he was encountering delays with obtaining papers. Be patient, were the last words on that telegram. She shifted her hand to her slightly rounded abdomen and briefly bowed her head. *Dearest Lord Almighty, please accelerate this immigration process. I'm close to five months along now. Let us be settled in Mexico City long before the baby comes.*

Placing the thickest half of the sandwich back in its wrapper, Hinda decided she would *try* to snack on it later. Wolf had packed her lunch and had stuffed the roll with extra chicken, far more than she could consume at one time without upchucking. Thinking of Wolf, she smiled, amused at how sincerely happy he was to be married and starting a family. Frequently, she overheard him boasting in wonderment, even to strangers, "I'm going to be a tatae."

Gratitude swelled inside her, particularly for Wolf's strong family values. The level at which he had embraced her sister was heartwarming. And then, after Rachel and David were married and David moved into Unit Four, Wolf's friendliness to David was impressive. Hinda chuckled at the memory of Wolf saying the apartment had suddenly shrunk, but in a good way. Even more surprising, Wolf had invited David to join him in the underground trade business when David was no longer allowed to work for the SSP. Entranced by her musings, Hinda wiggled her wedding band, rotating it on her finger. *Indeed, I am blessed.*

Her lunch break soon to end, Hinda eyed the sandwich wrapper, wishing she could eat the remaining half to boost her nutrition. She worried about the baby's health, considering her years of starvation combined with the disease and abuse she had endured. Once again, her hand flew to the swell in her abdomen, nesting there like a hen warming eggs yet to hatch. *Dear God, please let my baby be okay; let him be perfect, healthy, and strong.* Startled that she had used the male pronoun to refer to the baby, she arose from her chair too quickly, which brought on a wave of billowing nausea. Lightheaded, Hinda rushed to the lavatory.

Inside the shop, the underground trader leaned across the counter, his hand folded. He opened his palm to reveal a green gem. David squinted his eyes. "I'll get my brother-in-law."

In the back office, Wolf munched on a sandwich. He chewed slowly to make it last longer. The chicken slices were skimpy and not filling for a man of his size, but Hinda's nutrition was his priority. He gazed at the wall, envisioning his wife devouring the nourishing sandwich he had prepared for her. He imagined her body absorbing all the nutrients, which then flowed through the umbilical cord to the baby.

The curtain rustled with movement. David stuck his head through the fabric. "Wolf, a trader has something you must see. A gemstone."

Grabbing his coffee thermos, Wolf joined David in the main room. While Wolf was examining the stone, the front door opened. Uncle Haim rushed inside the store. He appeared agitated and anxious.

"Wolf. David. May I see you both in private?" Haim asked brusquely.

"Yes, sir," Wolf replied. Pointing to the gem, he said, "Would you take a quick look at this first?"

"I have urgent business. Won't take long." Haim headed to the back room, but as he neared the counter, his eyes widened at the sight of the green stone. Unable to resist the urge to view it closely, he stopped and hunched over the counter, his eyes inches from the gem. Sure enough, he spotted a mossy *jardin* in the center. French for garden, jardin is the name for the crystalline structure inside most emeralds. Exceptions, truly flawless emeralds, have no such inclusions, but they are extraordinarily rare. While Haim had not studied jewelry, he did know emeralds. It was his wife's birthstone, and he had purchased numerous ones for her before the war. He instantly recognized that the deep color of this stone and its jardin in the center denoted authenticity. Although the gem was not flawless, it was not inferior beryl or colored glass either. It was genuine emerald.

Haim nodded to the trader. "How much you offering?" When the trader named a surprisingly low amount, Haim's jaw dropped, but not outwardly. Controlling his expression, he intentionally displayed a practiced grimace. "Sounds high, but that's between you and him," Haim replied, pointing to Wolf. To the trader, he apologized for intruding. "I must speak with these gentlemen. Would you mind waiting a few minutes?"

The man shuffled his weight from foot to foot. "I'll give you five. Then I have to scoot."

In the backroom, Haim whispered. "Buy that stone at his asking price. He has no idea what he has."

Wolf nodded, "Yes, sir, and what's so urgent?"

"We've just received verified reports that the Polish Army is staging attacks against the Soviets, a twelve-hour blitz in this area. They're surrounding this neighborhood as we speak. Thirty minutes from now, these streets will be a war zone."

Wolf rubbed his chin. "What do you want us to do?"

"Buy that stone. Secure the store, and then you and David immediately head for home. Bring the emerald with you. I'll put it in my safe." Haim turned toward the curtain, then pivoted back. "I've dispatched Leo and his team to retrieve Hinda from work early and escort her home. Rachel is at the apartment and has been instructed to stay inside." Referring to Wolf as son, which he did frequently now, he urged, "Son, please don't tarry and get caught in the crossfire."

Walking hunched over, Hinda limped back to her desk. She stuffed the half sandwich into her purse and gathered her things. Scribbling on a notepad, she wrote to her supervisor saying she was ill and leaving for the day. A note left atop her desk would have to suffice. Walking ignited cramping.

In the restroom, a warm liquid had soaked her underwear. Not just any liquid, blood, bright red blood. And now, along with cramping, occasional sharp pains shot through her abdomen. In attempts to not panic, she remembered that this had happened to her mother when she was pregnant with little Sara. The doctor had ordered her mother to bed. *Lord help me, I just need to get home and lie down.*

In Unit Four, Rachel rolled out strudel dough. Her stomach in knots, she had difficulty focusing. Uncle Haim had been curt and rather menacing when he told her to remain inside the apartment, explaining that there was upcoming trouble on the streets. From the apartment door, watching Haim jog down the hallway, she had yelled, "What about David? Hinda and Wolf?" He had not heard her, or had pretended not to, and rushed out the exit door.

With the rolling pin pressing lightly on the dough, Rachel silently prayed. *Today, I'm married two months, just two short months. I'm so happy. Lord, please protect David. And Lord, you know that Hinda is my everything. I can't do without my sister. Please, God, may she return safely to this apartment.*

Wiping her hands on her apron, Rachel moved to the window, though Uncle Haim had issued strict instructions to stay away from windows and keep all curtains drawn. Nervously, she parted the panels and peered down to the street. Transported to a different time, she saw her mother hobbling down the rocky street of the Mława ghetto, toddling to her death when looking for Hinda. "Mommy," Rachel whispered, placing her fingertips against the glass pane. Then, her mother disappeared, and her vision cleared. Viewing the street below in real time, she gasped audibly at the scene. Running like a thoroughbred, Leo cantered down the sidewalk. He carried Hinda. She lay horizontal across his arms. Her head flopped back as if she had fainted.

Uncle Haim's face dour, he knocked lightly on the door marked Unit Four. Rachel swung the door wide for him to enter. Upon seeing David reclined on the sofa with his hands steepled in prayer mode, Haim stuck out his thumb, pointing toward the kitchen. Rachel tiptoed, and he quietly followed. Speaking in a muffled voice, Haim said, "I assume that Wolf is in with Hinda."

"Yes, sir. Did you get through to the doctor?"

Sighing in frustration, Uncle Haim replied, "I did, but he can't come until tomorrow afternoon. It's too dangerous for him to be on the streets now."

Rachel nodded. "David said that army tanks already dominated the streets. He and Wolf dodged bullets on the way here, and it was just all starting. Did the doctor have any advice about what we can do for Hinda?"

"He ordered strict bed rest and said to keep her feet elevated. Plus, he recommended plenty of fluids and eating small amounts every few hours."

"Medication?" Rachel inquired.

"He didn't mention any. As soon as the streets are safe, I'll send a car for him."

"Thank you, sir. We appreciate your help. Please say prayers for us."

Uncle Haim looked down to the kitchen floor, awkwardly pawing a tile with his shoe. "The doctor said one more thing." He shook his head sorrowfully. Exhaling sharply, he struggled to utter such words aloud, those of such an intimate female nature. Leaning in close to Rachel's ear, Haim forced himself to whisper the doctor's final instruction: "If she miscarries, save clots or tissue for examination."

Rachel's face blanched, turning multiple shades of ash gray. She collapsed against Uncle Haim and broke into sobs.

Embracing her, Uncle Haim stroked Rachel's hair. "We all pray that doesn't happen. Be strong, sweet girl. Your sister needs you."

Bracing her shoulders, Rachel blotted tears with the back of her hand. "I assure you, sir, I will be there for her in every way possible."

"I've no doubt, you will." Haim started to the door, then said, "Did you get the message that we've cancelled the group dinner tonight? The guys and I must stand guard in case of direct attacks on the compound."

"Leo informed me, and I've already started our dinner." She grasped his hand. "Uncle Haim, please be careful."

Creaking open the door to the bedroom, Rachel found Hinda looking ultra pale but resting comfortably with her feet propped up on pillows. Wolf sat in a chair beside the bed. "Am I interrupting?" Rachel asked.

"We were just talking about me quitting my job," Hinda said. "That is, if the doctor orders bed rest."

"And I say quit anyway, even if he doesn't," Wolf averred. Rubbing his chin, he added, "Not only for the baby, but also because of the escalating violence between the Soviets and the Polish Army."

Her hand moving in slow circles on her tummy, Hinda said, "But we need to save money for when we travel to Mexico. Train tickets to Paris plus intercontinental ship passage or airfare are going to cost a hefty sum."

"Let's not worry about all that right now. You need rest." Turning to Rachel, Wolf inquired, "Heard anything from the doctor yet?"

"Uncle Haim just left. He gave me the report. The doctor can't come until tomorrow. Streets are barricaded and perilous. But look at this, your feet are already elevated, which the doctor said to do. How did you know?"

"Wolf insisted that I prop them up," Hinda explained. "What else did the doctor say?"

"Strict bed rest until he can examine you." Rachel proceeded to relay the doctor's instructions to eat small amounts every few hours and to drink plenty of fluids.

His brows furrowed, Wolf asked, "Are her feet elevated enough?"

"Hmm, maybe not," Rachel replied, "I'll get throw pillows from the sofa."

"I'll grab them. And a glass of apple juice for my beautiful wife."

When Wolf had closed the door, Rachel gently stroked Hinda's foot. "So, how are you feeling? Still cramping?"

"Cramping, yes. But the sharp pains and spotting have subsided."

"That's good news. Hopefully, this is just an incident that bed rest will handle." Grappling with how to tell her sister what else the doctor had said to do, Rachel decided in favor of showing optimism. She would not tell Hinda or Wolf what else the doctor had said to do, not right now. She would only if it was necessary.

The door to the bedroom inched open; Wolf pushed it with his foot. His hands full, he carried two small throw pillows in one hand and a tray in the other. Rachel quickly took the pillows from him and placed them under Hinda's feet.

With the agility of an experienced waiter, Wolf set the tray on the bed next to Hinda. Proudly presenting a tall glass of apple juice and a plate containing saltines heaped with peanut butter, Wolf said, "Okay, my love, doctor's orders. Liquid and food."

"Rachel, what am I going to do with him? Just look at that huge glass filled to the brim." Hinda sighed. "And the peanut butter is mounded like mountains. Lord have mercy."

Before Rachel could reply, Wolf said, "Okay, let's go through the doctor's checklist. One: You're resting in bed and will continue to do so until he says otherwise. Two: Feet definitely elevated now. Three: You're about to have a snack with fluids and solids. So, Rachel, are we missing anything? Did the doctor say anything else?"

Without warning, Hinda cried out in pain. Moaning audibly, she groaned, "That was a sharp one." Her face twisted in distress, she jerked with another pang and another. The bedsheet under her suddenly felt wet.

Hateful Claws

Early August 1946 | Wrocław, War-torn Poland

His thick eyeglasses perched halfway down his nose, the doctor knocked lightly on the door and entered the patient room. Nodding hello to Wolf, he said, "Mrs. Yoskowitz, how are you feeling?"

"Tired. I have no energy. Can barely get out of bed."

"That's understandable. Your body has suffered an ordeal the past few weeks. How are your spirits?"

"Depressed. I cry—a lot. I worry I did something that caused the . . . the . . . miscarriage."

"Mrs. Yoskowitz, please understand it's nothing *you* did. My opinion is that, with all you endured at Auschwitz, as well as before and after, your body was just not strong enough to carry a child full-term." The doctor paused and pushed his glasses upward. "You mentioned that you had no menstruation cycles while at Auschwitz, and then just an occasional one here and there afterward all the way to when you became pregnant."

"Yes, that's correct. Stress and starvation, I assume."

"Yes, your entire reproductive system was ultra stressed by the extreme malnutrition you endured. That alone would halt menstruation." The doctor glanced over to Wolf. "There are rumors floating around in the medical community that chemicals may have also been used. The latest one I heard said that bromide was intentionally administered to stop women's menses and reduce men's sexual urges." The doctor shook his head in disgust.

Wolf placed his head in his hands. *Lord have mercy.*

"They didn't give us shots. How did I get this poison, if it was bromide?"

"Some say that it was dispensed in daily coffee."

"Coffee was our only liquid. They didn't give us any water, so I drank every drop of the bitter stuff. My sister too. Doctor, what does this mean?" Hinda turned her head away from Wolf. "Will I ever be able to have a baby? And, if I do, will it be deformed?"

A grim look on his face, the doctor sighed heavily. "I cannot answer that with any certainty, but you should be aware that it may not be possible for you to have children, based solely on suffering multiple years of significant malnutrition. As for bromide causing birth defects, we do not have enough information on its side effects. Please remember, these are rumors only. I've seen no documentation that bromide was used. The International Military Tribunal in Nuremberg is still ongoing, conducting investigations into such Nazi criminal behavior. Before drawing definite conclusions, let's wait and see if evidence on the use of bromide is found and documented."

Surprisingly stoic, Hinda simply nodded.

"On a positive note, you did conceive," the doctor encouraged. "That's a good sign."

Wolf interjected, "Considering her weakened condition, should she not get pregnant again anytime soon?"

"Her body needs time. I recommend waiting—maybe even a year." The doctor tugged at his glasses, sliding them up his nose again. "Both of you have lived in hellacious situations for multiple years. I want you to focus on nutrition, your overall health. Enjoy this time in your relationship. My nurse will give you a pamphlet on natural birth control methods."

Hinda cleared her throat. "One more thing, doctor, if I may ask. When you were there that dreadful day, I was woozy from pain medication. Did I dream that you said it was a boy?"

"It's not often with a miscarriage that we have such clear indication of the fetus's gender at that stage, but in this case, it was readily revealing. Yes, your baby was a boy."

In the lobby of the building where the doctor's office was located, Hinda collapsed against Wolf. No longer stoic, she broke down. Grief erupting, a volcano inside her, tears exploded from her eyes, soaking her husband's shirtfront and jacket lapel.

She slid her arms from around his neck, her hands curling with fury. Leaning into Wolf, she pounded and pummeled his upper back with her fist, screeching, "The Nazis. They starved me, and may have poisoned me, weakening, if not destroying, my entire reproductive system. And now, their hateful claws still find me. They trounced on my womb and killed our baby boy, our son."

Wolf held her closely. "Hinda, my darling Hinda. Yes, the Nazis did all that and more. But we *will* have children. Healthy, smart, beautiful children. I just *know* it. I feel it. In my gut. In my heart. And deep in my soul."

Hinda's fists unfurled. Her arms wound their way around his neck. She rested her head on his shoulder.

"My darling wife, we *will* have babies someday." Wolf closed his eyes. "I see them in my mind. There's more than one."

*A*dolph Hitler has climbed from his grave. Bone-chilling words. Wolf winced at the memory of Uncle Haim recently speaking that exact sentence. Struggling to focus on the numbers in the ledger, Wolf placed the register on the desk and succumbed to what was demanding his attention: flashbacks of that mid-July morning. Haim's face a portrait of panic, his burn scars inflamed as if fresh, he had paced the floor while telling Wolf of the daunting report from the underground.

On July 4, a mob—made up of Polish soldiers, police officers, and civilians — murdered forty-two Jews and seriously injured over forty others in the southeastern Polish town of Kielce.

Learning of the massacre through the underground, Haim told Wolf of the tragedy even before it hit the news outlets. Deeply disturbed, Haim also shared that the informants said the Kielce pogrom was *not* an isolated incident. They issued warnings about renewed activism in the many towns across Poland and Europe that had entrenched histories of anti-Semitism.

Stomping his foot, Haim ranted with fervor, "Those Kielce Jews—who had already lost everything, been brutally persecuted, and unjustly jailed in internment camps—were simply trying to reclaim their lives. For heaven's sake, Nazi Germany was defeated. In these postwar times, European Jews should be rejoicing in sunnier skies, not ambushed by hailstorms."

Catching his breath, Haim waggled his finger at Wolf and declared, "The war against us is far from over, son." Still pacing back and forth—long strides, short strides, shuffling baby steps—Haim had raged. "These regional mobs—Hitler-loving, anti-Semitic bloodhounds—are working together with one goal: zero population of Jews in the country of Poland."

Uncle Haim hefted his shoulders upward and stepped close to Wolf. Employing a strident tone, he urged, "You and David must get Hinda and Rachel out of Poland. And soon." An odd expression settled over Haim's face. Swallowing hard, he confided that he had decided to stay in Wrocław and continue the fight against Nazis. "I've nothing to lose now. The battle is worth the risks." Haim put his hand on Wolf's shoulder. "I hope you know that you can stay as long as I'm alive and running the compound. But, son, you're young. You deserve a *real* life in a location where you can prosper and thrive. A place where it's safe to raise a family."

Silent for fifteen seconds or more, Haim stared at the floor as if analyzing the grain patterns in the wood planks. When he lifted his head, his eyes revealed an edginess regarding what he was about to say. "To be frank, I'm worried that Hinda's brother has yet to attain immigration papers for you all. These matters take time, but it's been over a year now since their initial communication. And, truthfully, I just don't know about Mexico. Have you considered immigrating somewhere else, like Palestine, the United States, or Britain? I believe those countries would be safer, with Palestine being the safest of all for Jews."

Wolf fidgeted with the pencil. Haim's counsel continued to haunt him. With the miscarriage, he had lost mental focus, but now, the gravity of their situation pressed upon him. His body shuddered thinking of the dangers they faced every day. The clashes between the Polish Army and the Soviets had become feverishly violent and in their very neighborhood. And to know that Jews were being targeted anew in Poland and other towns across Europe twisted his gut, tying triple knots.

While cogitating on Uncle Haim's caution about Mexico, Wolf realized that Hinda had not heard from her brother, Jack, since early May. And here it was September. But did he dare approach Hinda with his concern? She fully expected Jack to come through any week now. She was set on joining her six older brothers and their families in Mexico City. She envisaged great support and family camaraderie with the Mondlak clan who resided there.

Questions plagued Wolf, boomeranging in an endless circle: *What if Mexico has denied immigration for us? What if Jack is reticent to tell Hinda? Or what if something bad has happened to him? What if time continues to tick on without hearing from him, months turning to years? Haim said it was urgent for us to get out of Poland.* Sighing heavily, Wolf tapped the table with the pencil. Distress escaped his lips in a whispered, "God help us."

An hour later, Wolf stood in line at the International Red Cross. When it came his turn, he asked to apply for immigration to Palestine, which was under the British mandate. Taking the papers across the room to an empty table, he filled in Hinda's and his information. As he wrote, he thought of his brother and his sister who both resided in Palestine. Although he was blissfully happy with Hinda, the ache to see his family had not gone away.

Wolf reviewed the document, an official application to the British government asking for Wolf Yoskowitz and Hinda Mondlak Yoskowitz, husband and wife, to be permitted entry to Palestine. Relieved that the image of the collapsing bridge had not appeared, he signed his name.

Tonight, he decided, *I'll tell Hinda.* He had yet to tell her of the pogrom in Kielce. She was so depressed about losing the baby, he had not wanted to upset her more or to frighten her. But now, it was time to tell her the truth. Their homeland of Poland was now a hostile hot pot.

"Palestine?" Hinda shrilled, raising her voice to Wolf for the first time ever. "I will *not* be separated from Rachel." She clutched her chest. "I *can't* leave my sister." Hinda choked out the words, breathing rapidly, nearly hyperventilating.

"I've spoken to David," Wolf calmly replied. "He said that if we're accepted, he would then apply to Palestine."

"That sounds risky. It could take years, or they could be denied entry and never arrive." Desperation swept over her. "Wolf, please try to understand. I promised my tatae before he died that I would do my best to be both mother *and* father to my younger sisters. I failed Sara, but not Rachel, so far. At Auschwitz, Rachel wanted to throw herself on the fence every day. She would not be alive without me. I . . . I . . . I cannot be apart from Rachel. Not even for a week."

"My darling Hinda, please—"

Before Wolf could say another word, Hinda stormed from the room.

Lying on the far edge of the bed, her back to Wolf, Hinda didn't move a muscle. Her body lay perfectly still. Her mind, though, squirmed frenetically between contemplations and petitions.

Wolf is a wonderful husband, my anchor during the miscarriage, Hinda reflected. *At this moment, though, I'm livid with him. I feel that he has gone against me by applying for entry to Palestine without talking to me first. It's such a shock, especially on the heels of losing our baby.*

Hinda prayed: *Dearest Lord, we're in crisis. You know I cannot bear to be separated from Rachel. Please intervene. Praises to you. Amen.*

Then, her brain twisted in another direction: *My brother, Jack, is working on getting immigration papers for us. But it's been months since I've heard from him, and the calendar is advancing. If we're accepted to Palestine before Jack attains permits from Mexico, I would have to go with my husband, leaving Rachel here.*

Turning back to God, she prayed: *Dearest Lord Almighty, I'm in agony. Do something that keeps Rachel and me together. Praises to you. Amen.*

Flipping back to thoughts of her husband, she reasoned: *Wolf's brother and sister live in Palestine. I'm sure he misses them. He, too, has lost most of his family to Hitler's insanity and Nazi cruelty. I understand him wanting to be with the two who survived, But when I think of not living in the same town as Rachel, let alone not in the same country, it feels like a sharp blade is stabbing my heart.*

Bowing her head, Hinda prayed: *Dearest Lord Almighty, please intercede and deny our entry to Palestine. Praises to you. Amen.*

Her mind reeling, she realized: *I've lived half my life without seeing my older brothers. I was thirteen when they left Poland. Now, I'm twenty-six. I don't really know them. Yet they're my blood family, part of Tatae and Mommy. Deep in my bones, I feel it's the right choice for us to go to them.*

Pivoting toward the throne of God, she pleaded: *Dearest Lord Almighty, my heavenly Father, touch Jack and enable him to attain immigration papers for all four of us—Rachel, David, Wolf, and me. Make it happen soon, really soon. Praises to you. Amen.*

Shifting her focus, she called out to the spirit of her earthly father: *Dearest Tatae, I beg you, please, do whatever you can there in heaven to ensure that Rachel and I stay together.*

Before drifting off to sleep, Hinda offered one last petition: *Dear God, forgive my strong will. I'm unable to surrender, for I know that it would devastate my spirit to go to Palestine without Rachel. And it could destroy my marriage, as I fear I would resent Wolf. He and I both have been tortured enough. Please shred our application to Palestine. Praises to you. Amen.*

As sleep descended, Hinda suddenly jerked. Her eyelids flew open, unveiling her short-sightedness. *I've prayed wrongly,* she lamented to herself. *Dear Lord, please hear this plea above all my others tonight. While I don't want to be apart from Rachel, I don't want to be separated from Wolf, either—not mentally, emotionally, or physically. All I'm really asking is that Wolf and I immigrate to the best place for us, and that Rachel and David immigrate to the exact same location at the same time as we do. Praises to you. Amen.*

The impact of her first disagreement with Wolf had caused a chilling ache in her heart. Hinda turned and gingerly scooted next to her husband. Wolf extended his arm back and pulled her closer to him. The heat radiating from his body enfolded her, warming her very soul.

137
Fate

Hinda reached to the far back corner of her lingerie drawer. Her fingers grasped a linen handkerchief. She withdrew it and sat down on the bed. Unfolding the material, her hand began to tremble. She had not looked at it in over a year since they had moved into the apartment at the compound. There it was, in all its glorious horror: the spoon.

While at Auschwitz, she had fiercely protected the eating utensil, although its handle, underneath, bore a symbol—an upright eagle sitting atop a crown—which was the official emblem of the German government under Hitler's reign. The one and only spoon issued to her had come with a warning: no others would be provided, even if lost or stolen. Used to dribble gruel into her mouth, the spoon had helped keep her alive in its own wicked way.

The sound of a key in the front door startled her. Recognizing Wolf's distinct footsteps, she hastily wrapped the spoon in the handkerchief and shoved it back into its hiding place.

Wolf hung his coat. The apartment was exceptionally quiet today. After the miscarriage, Hinda had not returned to work at the magistrate's office. Yet, always industrious, she was usually busy with an organizing or cleaning project when he arrived. Yesterday, he had come home to her defrosting the freezer section of the refrigerator, though she had only done it a few weeks ago, and the ice build-up was less than an inch.

Just as he was about to call out for his wife, there was a knock on the door. A young man, who wore a shirt bearing the International Red Cross logo, asked for confirmation of Wolf's full name. He then handed Wolf a manila-colored envelope, turned, and sprinted down the hallway.

"You're home early," Hinda commented as she waltzed into the living room. "Who was at the door, and what is *that*?" Hinda asked, pointing to the envelope.

"The International Red Cross," Wolf replied. Turning the envelope in his hand, he spotted the official seal of the British government. Instantly, his eyes widened. Showing the seal to Hinda, he said, "This contains our fate."

A stricken expression pinched Hinda's mouth. Her heart thumped wildly.

Wolf pulled a single paper from the envelope, a copy of his application for immigration into Palestine. His bright eyes dimmed, clouding with dewy fog. He threw his hands up in the air and cast his teary eyes heavenward. The question of *why* reverberated in his head.

The document floated through the air, as if powered by wings, finally landing on the floor near Hinda's feet. She gulped. Stamped in large, bold, red letters across the front was one word: **DENIED**. Relief gushed through Hinda. Her skin prickled. Another miracle had found her. Crisis had been averted. Prayers answered. Tinges of guilt engendered wonder: Was it my strong will? Was it God? Was it Tatae? Was it destiny?

Standing there, Wolf's disappointment was evident in his doleful expression and posture. His hopes of living in Palestine and seeing his family were dashed with one six-letter word: denied. No explanation accompanied the refusal; no argument could be made. No choice but to accept it. Steeling his resolve, Wolf drew Hinda into his arms and declared, "My darling Hinda, you're my main priority in life. I promised to take care of you. That is all that matters. Eventually, I'll see my brother and sister again."

"My dear Wolf." Hinda kissed him softly.

His forehead creasing with distress, Wolf proclaimed, "We can't continue like this, just coasting in time."

"What do you mean?" Hinda asked.

A feeling of alarm roiling inside him, Wolf averred, "Poland, once again, is dangerously unsafe for us Jews. And we have zero plans to get out. Hinda, we both barely survived years of unspeakable torture. We cannot risk being subjected to such monstrous treatment again."

Her voice rising to a higher pitch, Hinda exclaimed, "Jack is working on a way to get us to Mexico City."

"And that candle of hope was lit well over a year ago," Wolf retorted. "We need a clear strategy for how to exit *now*."

"Please try to be patient," Hinda coaxed. "Jack will come through. I just know it."

Wolf sighed, his frustration exposed by the length of his jagged exhale. "Send a telegram to your brother first thing tomorrow. Mark it urgent. If we don't hear from him soon with a solid plan, I'm applying for immigration to the United Sates."

Uncle Haim flipped through the pages. "You're keeping excellent records, son. But you haven't factored in the emerald that's kept in my safe. Perhaps you've forgotten it."

Taking the ledger, Wolf turned to a particular page. "The entry is here, sir." He pointed to a specific line, tracing underneath it with his finger. "This is the initial trade price. There's the sum you paid when you purchased the stone. The difference is shown as a profit here in the third column." Wolf set the ledger in front of Haim. "The emerald belongs to you, sir. You said you wanted it in memorial of your wife. In honor of her birthstone."

The blank look on Haim's face quickly morphed into one of horror. He tilted his head and squinted his eyes. "Well, Lord have mercy." Wearing a fretful frown, he grumbled, "I am the one who forgot."

Gunfire erupted on the street below. Haim shoved his chair back, went to the window, and jerked the curtain back. "This time it's the Soviets initiating the conflict."

Perplexed, Wolf asserted, "I don't understand, sir, why the Russians are still occupying this region. Wrocław is not part of their annexed territory. The lines were officially redrawn, placing this city in Poland."

"The answer is simple. STALIN. And his lustful quest for power."

139

The Yellow Envelope

Hinda burst into the storefront, the door banging behind her.

David, who stood behind the counter talking with a trader, appeared shocked to see her. His thick eyebrows furrowed, making the brows appear as one spanning across the bridge of his nose. "Is Rachel okay?" he asked. The sisters were not supposed to be out on the hazardous streets unless there was an emergency.

"Rachel is better than okay," Hinda replied. "Is Wolf here?"

David pointed to the curtain that shielded the back room from the sight of customers.

Slipping through the drapery, Hinda surprised her husband, who jumped from his desk chair when seeing her.

"What's wrong?" Wolf asked.

Throwing herself against her husband, Hinda jostled Wolf into a dance. "It's what's right, not what's wrong." From her purse, Hinda retrieved a yellow envelope. A telegram. She handed it to her husband, then tossed her head back and whooped, "Praise God."

> Take train to Paris; arrive December 12, Reservations at Hotel Henri IV, 50 rue des Bernardins. I'll meet you there & stay with you until visas & travel to Mexico City are arranged for you four. Love, your brother, Jack

140

Speechless

The light in Haim's office appeared as hazy as the dusky evening sky. Lamps were off. Draperies were drawn. Wolf entered at the appointed time to find his boss reclining on the sofa.

"Uncle Haim, are you okay?" Wolf asked, his tone laden with concern.

"No, I'm not. But there's nothing to be done, according to the doctors."

Wolf lifted a side chair and sat down beside the sofa. "This sounds serious."

"I don't want to talk about it. I want to talk business."

"Business can wait, if you're ill."

"You're leaving for Paris on Monday. We need to close out the books for your part of the trade business."

"Yes, sir. I have the ledger here. All columns are balanced. What's due to David and me are listed at the bottom of this page. I went over it all with Leo yesterday."

"Leo and I went to the bank today." Reaching behind a pillow on the sofa, Haim withdrew two envelopes. "This one is for David. Please give it to him. And this one is yours."

Taking the envelopes of cash, Wolf noted that his envelope was thicker. While he was due more money than David, the bulk of his was startling.

"Indulge an old man who is struggling with memory. Count yours here and now."

"Certainly, sir. Are you concerned that there's a mistake?"

Haim's eyes, which had appeared dull earlier, suddenly brightened. "Let's check to be sure," he replied.

As Wolf counted his share, his eyes bulged. "There's far more here than my number in the ledger. Definitely a mistake, sir."

Chuckling, Haim said. "No, son. I watched Leo count it three times. It's exactly what I asked him to pay you. I just wanted the pleasure of seeing your surprise."

Dumbfounded, Wolf stuttered. "I'm…I'm speechless."

"Thanks to all your hard work, we've all made some money on the trade enterprise. Consider the extra a bonus."

Unexpected tears sprang to Wolf's eyes. "I'm shocked and don't know what to say."

Haim chuckled again, "Wolf Yoskowitz, you deserve this more than anyone I know. It blesses me to give it to you. A simple *thank you* will do just fine."

Leaning over the sofa, Wolf took Haim's hand and squeezed it firmly, "Thank you, with all my heart and soul. I'm forever grateful. Now, what can I do for *you*?"

"Nothing you can do but pray for God's mercy to be upon me. I have Alzheimer's."

141

The Giant Eraser

Monday, December 9, 1946 | Wrocław, War-torn Poland

Seated on the train, Hinda blew kisses to Leo, who stood on the station platform waving good-bye. Through the window, Leo appeared golden, his skin glowing as if his entire body had been dipped into a vat of liquid gold. Behind him, the vibrant sunset on the horizon encircled the young man in its fiery aura.

When the whistle sounded and the train began to inch away from the station, Wolf saluted Leo. Then he took Hinda's hand in his. He leaned across his seat and kissed his wife on the cheek. "I wasn't supposed to tell you until we departed, but Leo and the guys chipped in together and bought our rail tickets to Paris. A parting gift, they said."

Hinda's large eyes doubled their size. Their azure color sparkled like moonlight twinkling upon ocean water. "For all four of us? Glory be, that's a big present."

"Sure is. They insisted, though. Remember, David was with Leo at Auschwitz and part of the core group long before I was. And the guys absolutely adored you and Rachel, and the feminine touch you brought to the compound. Frankly, I think Leo had a secret crush on you."

"He's a good man and will take exceptional care of Uncle Haim. Leo told me that he was staying with him until the end."

"And that may be years. The diagnosis is mid-stage Alzheimer's. By the way, Uncle Haim was adamant that I send our mailing address when we get settled in Mexico City." Wolf bowed his head briefly. "The man has become like a father to me. I'm glad to be leaving Poland, but it hurt to say good-bye to him, especially when he's feeling so devastated about his future."

"It's all so incredibly sad," Hinda sympathized. "I have horrific memories that I wish I could completely wipe from my mind. But he has no choice. A giant eraser is scrubbing his brain, removing the ugly memories right along with the cherished ones."

Leaning her head against the seat back, Hinda closed her eyes, reflecting upon previous train trips when she had been terrified and felt desperately anxious. This time, when she arrived at the new destination, a place where she had never been, she would not be incarcerated in hell. She would not have to forage for food in a foreign city, and she would not have to beg for a place to sleep. Plus, now she had Wolf, her loving and ardent protector, sitting beside her. They had ample food for the first leg of the trip to Paris, and they had money to buy food after that. She pinched the skin on her arm as a reality test. It tingled, chirping it was all true; she was not dreaming.

Opening her eyes, Hinda looked across the aisle to where Rachel and David sat. Rachel, who was happily munching on a cookie, smiled and waved to her. *My dear sister*, Hinda thought, *we have done it. Escaped to real freedom. We are now embarking on the long-awaited journey to our new life. Moreover, we are together.*

142

Familial Markings

Thursday, December 12, 1946 | Paris, France

The European rail system, disrupted by the war, was yet to be normalized. The journey from Wrocław to Paris took sixty-four hours—three different trains, lengthy delays, and innumerable stops. Cross-eyed from weariness, Hinda's muscles ached. Yet excitement coursed through her. Rachel, David, Wolf, and she were now safely out of perilous Poland and in France, a country rebounding from war in a more peaceful fashion.

Departing the train, the two couples trod into the massive station, Gare d' Austerlitz. In awe of the vastness and ornate architecture, they gawked as they navigated the labyrinth. While searching for signs to the main exit, Wolf found a currency office where he exchanged rubles for French francs.

Near the exit, Wolf spotted an information booth. Capable of speaking the most French of the four, Wolf approached the attendant to inquire about the location of their hotel. When Hinda showed the man the address, he gushed with enthusiasm, exclaiming how fortunate they were to have booked a hotel situated on the elegant left bank of the Seine. Moreover, he said that their hotel was located in the southeastern part of the city near Gare d' Austerlitz. Marking the points on a map, he explained that Hotel Henri IV was less than three kilometers away. He recommended walking and enjoying the sights, if they were not too tired.

It was straight up noon when the foursome departed Gare d' Austerlitz. An overcast sky served as their greeter to the bustling streets of Paris. Not one streak of sunlight pierced through the low gray clouds. The frigid air bit at their lungs as they walked. Even still, they were mesmerized by the beauty of the elegant architecture and the intact pristine buildings.

Although Paris was occupied by German forces for four years, 1940–1944, the City of Light had been protected from bombings and destruction due, initially, to the wishes of Adolph Hitler, who held an affection for the city: its magnificent museums, cuisine, and fine-art culture. Yet when Allied forces approached in August of 1944 with the intention of liberating France, Hitler made the decision to bomb Paris—a retaliatory mandate, as Allied forces were bombing historical cities across Germany. It was Nazi officer, General Dietrich van Choltitz, who boldly defied Hitler's orders and preserved the City of Light. Choltitz's largesse to humanity.

Stopping often to gape at the majestic beauty of the buildings and parks, the two couples took their time basking in the peace.

At last, they came to rue des Bernardins. Midway down the avenue, an awning sporting the name, Henri IV, caught Hinda's eye. Her pulse quickened. A mix of feelings washed over her. Her youth disrupted by Nazism, she had never stayed in a hotel before. A flitter-flutter in the pit of her stomach reminded her that she was ill-informed on proper protocol. More importantly though, within minutes, she would be reunited with her brother, Jack, for the first time in over thirteen years. Would she even recognize him?

Inside the lobby, it was soon evident that Jack was not there waiting for them. Hinda, with Wolf close by her side, approached the registration desk. Her stomach knotted with unknowns. Without documentation and Jack, what would happen with their reservation? Without him, would they be allowed to check in? And the price! They had no idea what the hotel rates were. How much would even one night cost?

The desk clerk finally found their names on the reservation list. When Hinda inquired about payment, he squinted at the ledger. His finger traced across multiple lines. Replying tersely, he reported that both rooms had been prepaid for three nights by Monsieur Mondlak, who had yet to arrive. Then, he turned to a bulletin board mounted on the side wall. The board was dotted with notes thumbtacked to it. He unpinned a small yellow envelope. "For you, Madam Mondlak Yoskowitz."

Handing the room keys to Wolf, Hinda ripped open the telegram.

> Delayed in Switzerland. Notify me when you've arrived & received this message. New plan: meet you at the hotel tomorrow, Friday, Dec 13th, 4:00 p.m. Get some rest and enjoy Paris. Your brother, Jack

Friday, December 13, 1946

Hinda pored over the hotel brochure touting its location in the heart of Saint-Germain-de-Prés and the historically significant Latin Quarter. It boasted that within walking distance were sights such as the Notre Dame Cathedral and the

River Seine. That morning, she and Wolf had enjoyed a long walk beside the banks of the famous river. Rachel and David had slept in but then joined Wolf and her for lunch. Afterward, they all strolled in the tranquil park across the street from the hotel. Yet, Hinda could not relax. She was too wound up about seeing Jack again.

At exactly half past three, Hinda entered the hotel lobby, primed for the arrival of her brother. Closer to four o'clock, Wolf, Rachel, and David joined her. They watched as taxis raced up and down rue des Bernardins, some stopping at the hotel, most not.

Around four-fifteen, a man climbed out of a taxi and headed up the hotel steps. When he entered the lobby, he totally ignored the foursome watching him attentively. Not Jack.

An hour later, a dapper gentleman emerged from a taxi. A wool scarf flowing from his neck, he wore a trench coat along with a short-brimmed fedora. Hinda could not see his face. But something about the way he carried himself, dignified and elegant like her father, made her heart skip beats. "It's him," she whispered. A knot swelled in her throat. Her eyes surged with tears.

The man removed his hat just before opening the door to the lobby. The slope of his head, his wide forehead and longish face, his black hair, and his gray-blue eyes were beyond familiar; they were familial markings. Hinda lunged toward him. The man set down his luggage and threw open his arms, wrapping his sister into a warm embrace. Cupping her chin, he exclaimed, "Hinda, our little Hinda, you're all grown up. Just look at you. A beautiful woman now."

From the side, Rachel stepped forward. Jack choked out the words, "Glory be, is this our Rachel? You were just a tiny girl when I last saw you." Jack kissed Rachel on one cheek, then the other. Embracing both sisters, he shook his head in disbelief. "You're both so petite. How on Earth did you survive the horrors? I'm utterly amazed that Hitler and his evil claws didn't obliterate you."

143

Signature of Evil

Late January 1947 | Paris, France

Days in Paris had turned into weeks. It was now nearing the end of January in the new year. Soon after arriving, in mid-December, Jack had negotiated with the hotel manager for a lower rate, one in line with a long-term stay.

While Jack worked on immigration documents, the foursome roamed the streets, enjoying the sights of Paris. The Eiffel Tower, Notre Dame Cathedral, the Arc De Triomphe, the shops and cafes on Avenue des Champs-Élysées and Boulevard Saint-Germain, all captivated their interest. Due to postwar complexities, many of the city's establishments had limited hours of operation, merchandise, and food service. Yet the war's aftereffects were especially evident in art museums; collections and antiquities had been crated at the beginning of the war with Germany. Only the collections recently unpacked were available for viewing. Even still, Rachel found her heaven at the Louvre as well as at Montmartre, the famous art district. And Hinda found hers when walking the Parisian streets, as she admired the fashions and flair with which French women dressed.

Jack joined them for dinner each evening. He interpreted the menus, ordered for them in perfect French, and picked up the tab. He pointed out menu words, explaining what they meant and would then teach them the Spanish equivalent. During these times together, he explained the reasons why it had taken over a year to arrange his trip. For starters, his job as a political journalist had been demanding with postwar news. It was only recently that he could take time off and work remotely, as he was doing part-time while in Paris. Secondly, transatlantic passenger flights to and from Europe were suspended during the war. When they resumed, schedule challenges abounded. There were few intercontinental passenger flights available, and those were to and from limited cities. Thirdly, there was the issue of finances—the hefty sums required to get the four of them from Europe to Mexico. Fortunately, he explained, the other five older brothers wanted to help with the costs.

"We knew you had lost everything," Jack said. "So, we created a special bank account, a *Little Sisters' Fund*." He explained that even with all six brothers making monthly contributions, it wasn't until November of last year that they had accrued enough funds for the stay in Paris and then the ensuing intercontinental travel to Mexico City.

Hinda exclaimed, "Dear brother, I am stunned and so incredibly grateful. Just so you know, I did work for a while and managed to save a bit, as did Wolf and David."

"Yes, sir," Wolf interjected. "We're not completely destitute thanks to some fine people in Wrocław who helped David and me establish work with the Soviet Secret Police and in the underground trade business."

"Interesting," Jack replied. "This process is slower than I expected, but I believe the funds we accrued are adequate until we can get you home. Hang onto the bulk of what you have. Starting a new life will be plenty costly."

At dinner one night in late January, Wolf inquired, "Jack, is Mexico City safe for Jews?"

"I believe it is, at least, in the Jewish community where we all reside, which has quite a large population of Jews, about fifty thousand—its own town within the city," Jack replied. "I have a more public profile outside of there than my brothers do, and I've not encountered any issues."

"Good to hear," Wolf said. "How much longer to obtain our travel permits?"

Jack tilted his head. "Hard to say. There's a lot of red tape. And none of you have birth certificates or nationality papers." Looking to Hinda, Jack said, "It's too bad Mommy didn't pack those when you were taken to Mława."

Instantly, Hinda's cheeks reddened, her entire face appearing as if a bonfire roared inside her head. "An axe came through our door that morning. No warning. We packed with guns pointing at us. And the Nazi soldier set a timer; we had under fifteen minutes. One bag per person."

Jack bowed his head, "Hinda, I'm incredibly sorry. Please forgive my naiveté."

Still quaking, Hinda said, "Even if Mommy had packed them, it mattered not a whit. When Joel, Rachel, Sara, and I were taken to Auschwitz and crossed through the gates, our suitcases were confiscated. Everything was taken from us. The Nazis wanted *this* to be our only identifying documentation." She pulled up her sweater sleeve and showed Jack her tattoo, the numerals 25305 running up her forearm.

Jack yanked down Hinda's sleeve. He looked around nervously to see if anyone at nearby tables had noticed. Perspiration beaded across his forehead. In a low voice, he said, "Do *not* show that here in Paris or anywhere. When you're settled in Mexico City, I know people who can remove that ghastly signature of evil."

144

Samuel Goldman

March 1947 | Paris, France–Le Havre, France

Early one morning, Jack Mondlak knocked on Hinda and Wolf's hotel-room door.

Wolf, who was fully dressed, opened the door and invited Jack inside. "I'm heading downstairs to get a coffee tray for us. May I get a cup for you?"

"None for me, Wolf, and please wait. I have urgent matters to discuss."

Yawning, Hinda entered from the lavatory. She said, "Good morning, brother. What's going on?"

"I'm excited to announce that I've obtained documentation papers and travel visas for you, Rachel, and David."

"Not for Wolf?" Hinda asked. Her large eyes widened in alarm.

"No." Jack winced. "After two months of trying, the highest levels of my government contacts cannot obtain *any* documentation for Wolf. Unknown reasons. Nonetheless, I was notified early this morning that a travel visa is available for a man named Samuel Goldman. No one has shown up to claim the papers. The six-month waiting period expired at midnight."

"What are you implying?" Wolf inquired.

"Would you be willing to become Samuel Goldman? If you take his name and his documentation, both legally and publicly, you could never be Wolf Yoskowitz again."

"Take on another man's identity? Not be Wolf Yoskowitz?" Aghast at the thought, Wolf stammered, I . . . I . . . I—" He thrust his hands into his pockets. In the next second, he flung them out and fidgeted his fingers through his hair, tugging at the roots. His neck flushed beet red. He paced.

"I wish I could say that you have time to think about it," Jack prompted, his gaze fixated intently upon Wolf. "But I need an answer now, or the offer will pass to someone else. If I can square it up this morning with the embassy officials, we can all leave Paris tomorrow."

Bowing his head, Wolf closed his eyes. Hot tears spotted his cheeks. He swallowed hard. Turning to Hinda, he brought her into a gentle embrace. "My darling, Wolf Yoskowitz is no more. I'm now Samuel Goldman. In our private time, though, would you please still call me *Wolf*?"

"My dear husband, I will, indeed." Her eyes brimming with tears, Hinda reeled with renewed understanding: *This man will take care of me, whatever life brings our way.* Tenderly, she stroked his face. "I'm so glad I married remarkable *you*. I love you with all my heart."

Three days later, Jack and the two couples departed a train in Le Havre, a port city in the Normandy region of northwestern France. Jack, who spoke numerous languages, had navigated the group through days of rail travel, multiple terminals, and complex changes of trains.

After a brief touring of the historic harbor in the town of Le Havre, founded by King Francis I in 1517, the group of five boarded a passenger liner. One week later, this oceangoing vessel would arrive to the east coast of the United States of America—specifically New York City.

On a side deck of the ship, Hinda and Rachel, who both wore Parisian scarves tied on their heads, watched waves crest against the ship's bow. The silk scarves, purchased in a swank shop on Boulevard Saint-Germain, were a gift from Jack. He had declared that his amazing younger sisters deserved a fashionable souvenir from beautiful Paris.

Standing beside their wives, Wolf and David appeared animated, excited to be on a ship. They discussed the waters of the English Channel upon which they floated, a channel that connected the southern part of the North Sea to the Atlantic Ocean.

Wearing a scarf knotted under his chin, ascot style, Jack joined the foursome on the ship's deck. "Beautiful, isn't it? he exclaimed, nodding to the expanse of water. Their faces dewy with sea mist, everyone agreed the view was awe inspiring.

Jack cleared his throat in an obvious manner. "On another note, did I mention that when we're in New York, we'll see our sister, Fanny?"

"My memories of Fanny are not all pleasant," Hinda remarked. "I hope she has changed."

Jack pursed his lips. "Fanny has not changed, not one iota."

"Will she be glad to see us?" Rachel inquired.

"Good question. One I cannot answer," Jack retorted. He took Wolf's arm in a gesture of affectionate respect. "But while we're all here together, I must emphasize that this fine man be called by his new legal name, Samuel Goldman, at all times. I'm overhearing a lot of slipups."

Rachel and David nodded their assent, although Wolf's identity change was shocking to them. They felt overwhelmed with the effort it took to consistently call him the name, Samuel.

"Hinda," Jack said, a sharp edge to his voice. "It's imperative that you introduce your husband to Fanny and all who you meet in New York as Samuel Goldman. Understand?"

"Yes, Jack, I do. And I'm grateful to be here together and on our way to a new life. Yet it's disconcerting that my husband suddenly has a different name. I'm doing the best I can."

"No more slipups," Jack chided. "And none from Rachel and David either."

"Yes, sir." David raised his hand crisply to his head and saluted Jack.

"Moreover, the same is true for when we arrive in Mexico City."

A light flashed in Hinda's eyes. She asserted with fervor, "You know, Jack, tons of people have nicknames. Why can't his nickname be Wolf? After all, he is my fierce protector."

"That he is," Jack declared. "No doubt." Then, with exasperation creeping into his tone, Jack said, "All right, then. To the family, he can be Wolf Goldman. But none of you are to ever address him with the surname of Yoskowitz. Understand?"

145

New York City

Speechless, Hinda and Rachel stood stock-still in the Fifth Avenue apartment that overlooked Central Park. Shockingly, their older sister, Fanny, slapped at their clothing.

Fanny screeched, "This may have been fashionable in dreary Poland ten years ago, but it's certainly not today, here in Manhattan. And take off those shoes. They're going in the trash."

Sipping a martini, Jack said, "Then, I guess they each will get prime pickings from your wardrobe, Fanny. I cannot allow you to send them out barefoot."

Fanny sniffed at the air, her nose pointing upward. "I have nothing that will fit them."

"Then fork over some money for them to buy new ones tomorrow," Jack suggested. Setting down his cocktail glass, he added, "Your older brothers have contributed significant sums for their travel expenses. We're grateful our little sisters are alive. By the way, did you know that Hinda orchestrated and executed a successful escape from formidable Auschwitz?"

Vigorously shaking her index finger in Jack's face, Fanny said in a scalding tone, "Do not speak of such, not to me nor to Izzie."

Rubbing his chin as if clarifying his thoughts, Jack said, "You know, Fanny, there's sophistication and then there's snobbery. It seems to me that you now fall into the latter category. Where's your empathy? Or do you save it all for societal charities that cater to your status?"

Just then, Fanny's husband, Izzie, who was a professional chef, appeared in the doorway. He directed them to the dining room where the table was formally set with place cards. Fanny, who sat at the head of the table, had seated her sisters at the opposite end from her. Jack sat on her right with Izzie on her left.

Izzie had prepared an elaborate five-course dinner that began with smoked rainbow trout. After the fish, the valet brought a small footed dish of icy sorbet. "An *intermezzo*," Izzie explained, when Hinda and Rachel appeared surprised, "to cleanse your palate."

Next came a small ramekin of French onion soup followed by white-asparagus salad. The main entrée of leg of lamb with mint sauce was served with parsnips and glazed carrots garnished with fresh dill. Dessert was a stunning chocolate mousse swirled in a stemmed glass. A thick layer of whipped cream and fresh raspberries topped the dish.

While every bite was sumptuous, one of the most delicious dinners Hinda had ever tasted, she seethed on the inside. Hinda felt like she was the awkward ten-year-old who Fanny used to taunt, telling her how ugly she was. At the time, she had not known what it meant, but Jack would whisper to her, "She's just jealous of your bones." But now, Hinda could see that, although Fanny was short in stature, she had largish bones—a sharp contrast to her own tiny wrists and ankles.

When enjoying a snifter of brandy after the meal, Fanny addressed Wolf. She leaned toward him. "So, Wolf, where is your family from?"

"I grew up in Gliwice, a town in southern Poland."

Tilting her head, Fanny replied "Hmph. Goldman doesn't sound like a typical Polish surname for that southern area. Gliwice is in the Silesia region, right?"

"Come now, Fanny, there are Goldmans in many parts of the world," Jack scoffed. "Just as there are Mondlaks."

The following morning, Jack took the two couples on a tour of the Empire State Building. He purported that it was currently the tallest building in the world, taller than the Eiffel Tower.

At lunch, while noshing on pizzas at a sidewalk cafe, they discussed the exquisite cuisine that Izzie had prepared for them. Jack said, "The guy is seriously frugal. He and Fanny went to a great deal of expense for that dinner. In that way, they honored us, and Fanny showed her love."

Hinda wanted to argue the point of love. To her, Fanny had acted unabashedly ashamed of Rachel and her. The love and honor were for Jack, who was a sophisticated man. Unable to contain her feelings, Hinda said, "I wonder what Fanny would be like if she had suffered persecution, had walked in my shoes through the war."

"Fanny has totally lost perspective," Jack replied. "She had the fortune of leaving Poland before the war and has turned her back on the horrors."

"More like a cold shoulder," Rachel said.

"Touché." Jack smiled wryly. "Speaking of Fanny and shoes." He withdrew an envelope from his jacket. "She slipped this to me as we were leaving last evening. There's substantial cash here for new shoes for you girls. Now, the question becomes, do you spend it here in New York or in Mexico City? Here, you could each buy one quality pair, maybe two. There, you could each buy an entire shoe wardrobe, or one fine outfit and two-to-three pairs of shoes. Have I mentioned that Mexico City is quite sophisticated with superb shopping?"

Hinda almost stuttered. She was shocked that her arrogant older sister had given them anything. She crossed her arms. "But when we see Fanny tomorrow, she will expect us to be wearing stylish shoes."

"We'll not be seeing Fanny tomorrow. She called this morning and canceled. And for whatever it's worth, my opinion is that your shoes are fine, quite appropriate for travel." Jack reached across the table and squeezed Hinda's hand, then Rachel's. "My little sisters are exceptionally clever and beautiful women. You both have every reason to be proud."

After lunch, they strolled down Fifth Avenue admiring the displays in the windows of the luxury shops. As they walked, Hinda began to regain her emotional equilibrium. All around her, diverse kinds of people bustled. Within steps, she heard three different languages, none of which she recognized. Although people looked at her, she did not see prejudice or judgment in their eyes. Her Jewishness did not matter. The wind ruffling her hair, Hinda felt *free*, freer than she had felt since childhood. Hooking her arm into Rachel's, she leaned close and whispered, "At last, we're free, truly liberated from Nazi tyranny. And, my dear sister, we're still together."

During a layover in the Chicago Midway airport, Hinda experienced the same kind of freedom she had felt on the streets of New York. She commented to Wolf that, if she didn't have family in Mexico City, she wouldn't mind living in the United States. He wholeheartedly agreed.

Responding to an announcement on the loudspeaker, Jack shepherded the group into the boarding area. "Almost home," he declared in a tired, yet enthusiastic, tone.

Once on the plane bound for Mexico City, Hinda leaned her head back on the seat. *We've come so far from when the four of us left Wrocław last December.* Her lips twitched into a smile, thinking of how accustomed to train travel they had become. But then, to be onboard a passenger ship crossing the Atlantic had been thrilling, a first, as was the airplane from New York to Chicago. She reflected back to Paris. Their two months in the City of Light had been refreshing and culturally exciting. Such an education. Then, except for the interactions with Fanny, the days in New York had been exhilarating. While she loved the tour of the Metropolitan Museum of Art, her favorite experience was seeing the Statue of Liberty. When Hinda closed her eyes, a vivid vision of Lady Liberty appeared. There it was again, the same intense feeling that she had experienced when the boat neared the banks of Liberty Island, and the enormous statue came into detailed view. To her, the lady's crown and the torch reaching heavenward extolling world enlightenment were beyond magnificent. Yet, it was the overall symbol, artfully expressing *freedom* for those who had been enslaved, so encompassing and powerful, that had touched her deeply, had brought her to tears. Just as Lady Liberty grasped her torch tightly, Hinda felt that she, after being enslaved by the Nazi regime, now fully grasped the immense value of personal freedom.

The reverie ended, and Hinda's eyes flew open when a baby across the aisle began to wail. Sadness exploded inside her. Hinda leaned across the seat barrier. She placed her mouth against Wolf's ear and whispered, "Will *we* ever have a baby?"

"Yes, my darling, we will. Be patient," he said softly. Taking her hand and gently massaging it, he said, "Give your body more time to heal. After we're settled into a place of our own and find our groove in Mexico, a new country to us, we'll try again."

Abruptly, the mother of the infant rose from her seat and stepped into the narrow aisle. She began jostling her baby boy up and down on her shoulder. The movement did not soothe him. He screamed louder.

Suddenly, the mother turned to Wolf. "Please, can you hold him?" An exasperated expression on her face, she pleaded, "The bathroom. I really need to go. I'm alone and can't manage him in that cramped space. And it's so unsanitary in there."

Cradling the infant, Wolf rocked his own body back and forth in the seat. The baby momentarily quieted down but then howled again. Hinda reached out her finger, placing it in the baby's hand. His tiny fingers curled tightly around her pinkie. She motioned for Wolf to keep up the rocking motion. Hinda crooned softly to the baby. His cries became fewer with longer gaps in between. By the time the mother returned, the baby was sleeping soundly. Carefully, Wolf eased the baby into the woman's arms without disruption.

Hinda rubbed her pinkie finger, missing the baby's warmth. She feared that the pressure from the void inside her womb would cause her heart to implode. Tears welled in her eyes.

Wolf kissed her on the cheek, whispering, "You'll be such a wonderful mother."

But will I even have the chance? she wondered. *Am I such damaged goods that I'm physically unable to birth a child?*

Hours later, when the wheels of the airplane touched down on Mexican soil, Hinda's skin prickled with goose bumps. Unexpected tranquility descended over her. She raised her window shield and looked out at the terrain. As if she viewed the land from the belly of a dove, a deep sense of peace took root in her soul.

When they deplaned, Hinda gasped in surprise. Two colorful signs waved in the air: WELCOME HOME, HINDA & WOLF and WELCOME HOME, RACHEL & DAVID. Five of her older brothers, all dressed in suits and ties, smiled broadly and waved heartily. Their wives blew kisses and looked elegant, wearing fashionable hats and gloves. The children, Hinda's very own nieces and nephews, cheered and jumped joyously.

My family, Hinda thought. *I am home.* In the breeze, a white feather floated in front of her. She plucked it from the air. It felt warm in her hand. An other-worldly sensation of wings whooshed across her face. Hinda looked skyward. Her eyes lit up like blazing flames of column candles. She smiled. *It's Tatae and Mommy. They're happy.*

Counting Fingers and Toes
September 1949 | Mexico City, Mexico

S itting up in a hospital bed, Hinda's russet hair fell across her shoulders, splaying across the pillows. Wolf sat on the bed aside her, his arm around her.

Hinda unfolded the blue blanket. In awe, they both peered down at the newborn, their baby boy just hours old. She spoke softly. "Just look at him. He's perfect."

"Yes, I see five fingers on each hand and five toes on each foot." Wolf reached out and stroked the baby's tiny foot. "It's a miracle. I have a son. I'm really a tatae now." Ecstatic, Wolf beamed, his eyes shining like stars twinkling in a midnight sky.

Hinda placed her little finger into the baby's hand. His tiny fingers curled around her pinkie. Tears spilled onto her cheeks. She thought her heart would burst with the reality. *I'm a mother. His mother. I want to give him everything.* Exuding wonderment, she exclaimed, "My dear husband, we are so incredibly blessed and lucky to have this healthy baby."

"Indeed, we are. Praises to our Lord Almighty," Wolf replied, his head bowed.

A nurse bustled into the room. "Your time is up. I must return him to the nursery."

Hinda's heart plummeted to the floor. Fresh tears flowed. She swaddled the blanket around the infant and held him closely against her bosom. Intentionally, she placed his cheek against her bare skin. "Do you *have* to take him now?"

"Mrs. Goldman, it's hospital rules. Get some rest, and later you and your husband can take a walk to the nursery. I'll place his basinet by the window." She lifted the baby from Hinda's arm. At the doorway, she turned and said, "The supervisor will be by soon for birth certificate information. Have you considered names?"

"Yes, we have." Wolf pressed Hinda's hand into his and proudly proclaimed, "Our son's name is Moises Julian Goldman."

148
Birthstone

Hinda bounced little Moises, now two and one-half years old, on her knee. Her enlarged abdomen pushed him to the edge of her lap. Expecting her second child, she was due to give birth next month in early June.

Pointing at the door, Moises giggled. "Papa. I hear Papa coming."

A cluster of balloons in his hand, Wolf came through the door, singing, "Happy birthday!" He had a radiant glow about him as he set down a grocery bag.

"What's that?" Hinda asked. "We're dining out tonight."

"A surprise. One you would never guess." Lifting Moises into his arms, Wolf kissed his son on both cheeks. "How's my little man doing today?"

"Fine, Papa," the toddler replied. Early to walk and early to talk, Moises was considered a precocious child. His voice lilted with happiness as he reached for a balloon.

Wolf let Moises down onto the rug by his abacus, the child's favorite toy. He unraveled a red balloon from the cluster and gave it to the boy. After securing the festive helium bouquet to the back of Hinda's chair, he kissed his wife, then placed his hand on her tummy. "How's our Lovie in here behaving today?"

"Active. Kicking my insides out."

Wolf withdrew a letter from his suit jacket's inner pocket. He pulled up a chair beside his wife. He took her hand. "This letter from Leo was delivered to my office." Wolf paused, bowing his head. "Uncle Haim passed away in March."

"God rest his soul. He was our angel, so incredibly good to all of us," Hinda eulogized.

"Indeed, he was. And there's more." Wolf checked his watch. The Mondlak family party to celebrate Hinda's thirty-first birthday started at six. Since the restaurant was nearby, Wolf said, "We have a few minutes. How about you read Leo's letter now?"

Hinda's eyes moved quickly across the page from left to right, reading the lines. Her mouth fell open in surprise. "Is it true?" she asked, searching her husband's face.

From the shopping bag, Wolf removed a cardboard box that sported multiple government customs stamps and seals. It was postmarked Wrocław, Poland. Reaching into the box, Wolf withdrew a black velvet jewelry case. He opened the top flap and presented the case to Hinda.

"Glory be," Hinda gasped. "An emerald. Is this the same one you bought from a trader?"

"That's the one," Wolf replied. "Uncle Haim then purchased it for himself in memory of his wife and the birthstone emeralds he had bought for her before the war. All lost in the fire."

"I'd forgotten that part," Hinda said.

"It's interesting that he finalized his last Will and Testament when he still had mental capacity, soon after we left Wrocław," Wolf commented. "I'm touched that Uncle Haim wanted *you* to have the emerald, your birthstone too."

"I'm deeply moved. And I think it's for you, too, Wolf. He called you *son*. Uncle Haim repeatedly said that I reminded him of his daughter, but I never dreamed he would bequeath me, us, such an exquisite gem." Hinda extended her hand upward, displaying a ring, a solitaire diamond, that Wolf had given her in February in honor of their sixth wedding anniversary. "I have this beautiful ring that I love. What should we do with the emerald?"

"I'm thinking a necklace. We'll take it to the same jeweler who designed your ring," Wolf replied. "And maybe it will be ready in time for you to wear it to the Ambassadors' Ball in November. Jack said he arranged our invitation."

Hinda turned the emerald in her hand and gazed into its center, the stone's garden. "What a birthday present!" She shrilled with excitement, "I can't wait to tell Rachel."

149
Baby Sara

Hinda rolled out an architectural blueprint across the breakfast room table. Gratitude welled up inside her. The four-bedroom condominium was a definite step up from their current two-bedroom apartment. Starting from nothing, Wolf had labored diligently building a garment manufacturing business. He had proven to be talented with all operations—production, business development, and management. After five years, the company was thriving. What's more, Wolf had now started a second business in construction.

Tugging at Hinda's skirt, little Moises pointed to the blueprint. "What's that, Mommy?"

Her heart pinged with delight. *Dear Lord, thank you. I will never tire of hearing that beautiful word, Mommy.* To Moises, she explained, "That's our new house."

The child looked quizzically at her. "Not house," he said, making three-dimensional shapes with his hands.

Hinda lifted up her young son to better view the architectural plan. She clarified, "It's a flat *drawing* of a condominium home." She flipped the pages to one that showed the roofline of the complex. Turning again, she said, "This page shows the layout of our specific unit, the rooms and their dimensions. See the numbers in each space. They indicate how big those rooms are."

The boy's eyes widened and seemed to spin with fascination. "Why you look at this?"

Hinda set Moises down. "Whew, you're getting heavy. I have it ready for Aunt Rachel. She's coming over to help me measure and place furniture so moving day isn't so chaotic."

The child clapped with delight, hopping from one leg to the other. "Aunt Rachel. Yah!" He licked his lips. "Strudel?" he asked.

"Not today. Aunt Rachel is too busy with her gallery showing plus helping me with interior design for our new home."

"Aunt Rachel. Artist." Little Moises declared. He then wrinkled his brow and cocked his ear to the side. "Uh oh. Baby Sara's awake. I hear her." The faintest cry could be heard from the other room. But in the next moment, loud screeches penetrated the walls.

Hinda called out, "Mommy's coming." Once in the nursery area, a space in Moises' room, Hinda changed the baby's diaper, then lifted the four-month-old into her arms. Cuddling her little girl, Hinda repeatedly kissed the baby's forehead, cheeks, nose, and chin. "My precious little Sara, my beautiful Zurele."

As Hinda was departing the room, she stopped and winked whimsically at the beautiful doll sitting atop the dresser. The doll's golden hair fell in ringlets past her shoulders; her startlingly lifelike blue eyes seemed to stare directly at Hinda. Memories, of yearning for such an alluring doll when she was just a girl gazing into a storefront window, flashed through her mind. Visions of the cloth doll that her parents had made for her unfurled, which triggered thoughts of her youngest sister, Sara. Hinda pressed her baby daughter, Sara, to her bosom and whispered, "Your namesake was robbed of her childhood, but *you*, I pray, will enjoy a splendid one."

150

The Spoon

November 1952 | Mexico City, Mexico

Hinda stood in front of the full-length mirror, adjusting the ruffles on the strapless neckline of her black taffeta evening gown. Her bare arms glistened with freshly applied lotion. She extended her left forearm, examining it closely. The 25305 tattoo that had screamed she once was owned by the Nazis was forever gone. Although its removal had been excruciating, now her skin was healed and perfectly smooth.

Whistling a lyrical tune, Wolf, who looked dashingly handsome in his tuxedo, came up behind her. From the dresser table, he picked up the necklace. "May I have the honor, my love?"

"Yes, I was waiting for you. I'm so excited, I can hardly stand it."

Ever so carefully, Wolf placed the jewels around Hinda's neck and double-checked the security of the clasp. Stepping back, he gaped in awe. The emerald pendant set with diamond accents made for a stunning piece.

Later, while dancing at the Ambassadors' Ball, Wolf whispered in his wife's ear, "You're the most beautiful woman here."

"That's what an emerald and diamond necklace will do for a girl."

Wolf chuckled, then his face turned serious. "No, my darling. You must know that you're stunning without jewels." The music changed to a Vienna-style waltz. He pulled her close. They danced gracefully, cheek to cheek. His throat knotted as he remembered the person he used to be: Wolf Yoskowitz, lying in a hard, wooden bunk incarcerated at Buchenwald, starving to death, barely alive, but employing his mental strength to envision a beautiful Jewish girl, and then, conjuring the feeling of holding her as they waltzed. A survival strategy then, but now, here she was—for real—in his arms. His dreams had come true.

Abruptly Jack cut in. "Sorry to bother you two lovebirds, but the Israeli ambassador requests to speak with Hinda."

"Absolutely not. I just can't agree to you going to Israel to give depositions," Wolf exclaimed once they were home.

"But, Wolf, my statement will help convict the monster Mengele, if they ever find and arrest him. With my own two eyes, I witnessed his savage butchery. That's not hearsay. And the evil doctor also castrated my cousin, Aizik, who then could never father children. I must go to Israel and help them build their case."

"According to the ambassador, Mossad operatives are expending extraordinary effort to find the guy, but they haven't yet. Your witness statement is a moot point until they arrest him. My darling, you know that you still suffer nightmares and flashbacks that send you to bed on some days. Giving a deposition would be traumatic, bringing all the horrors back to the front of your mind. Your information would be beneficial for archives or if Mengele ever comes to trial, but at what price to you? To us? You said I'm your fierce protector, and to be that person for you, I just cannot support you doing this."

Hinda stomped her foot and turned away. She stood, tensely, her hands fisted.

"Hinda, my darling Hinda," Wolf stepped close behind her and gently ran his hands up and down her arms. "Of course, it's your decision. But please know, I couldn't bear to lose you, not even a tiny psychological piece of you. We have a wonderful life now. My darling, I need you. And more importantly, our beautiful little ones, Moises and Sara, need you."

The following morning, Hinda placed the phone back in its cradle. The transatlantic call to London had taken twenty minutes to get connected. Finally, Aizik had answered, and he had been delighted to hear from her. When she told him that the government of Israel was seeking to connect with Jews who had been damaged by Josef Mengele, Hinda thought Aizik would jump right through the phone. While disappointed that the evil madman was yet to be captured, Aizik had reeled with excitement at the chance to tell his story and strengthen the case against the wicked doctor. "Gladly," Aizik had proclaimed, giving his permission for Hinda to submit his name and for the Israeli ambassador to contact him.

Believing she had contributed after all, Hinda felt a deep satisfaction settle over her. She looked around the spacious kitchen-den area in their new home.

The cat was curled in the corner, and three-year old Moises sat on their new comfy sofa looking through books.

In the playpen, little Sara squealed, her newest noise. Hinda gazed adoringly at her tiny-boned little beauty, now five months old. Checking the time, Hinda removed two baby food jars from a pan of hot water. Then, reaching behind a row of cookbooks, she withdrew a linen handkerchief. Unfolding the fabric, she removed her Auschwitz spoon. After washing it, she placed it on the tray.

Little Moises climbed down from the sofa and ran to the playpen. He pushed his fingers through the netting to entertain baby Sara, who now fussed and gnawed on her fists. "My sister is hungry," he announced.

Scooping up Sara, Hinda strapped her into the highchair. Motioning to Moises, she urged, "Get your abacus. Count for her while she eats." Hinda knew he would. It was their ritual.

Hinda dipped the spoon into the Gerber jar, the most nutritious and expensive baby food she could buy. When she put the Auschwitz spoon mounded with pureed plums into Sara's mouth, Hinda's mind filled with declarations: *Sara Goldman, my beautiful daughter, you will never starve. You will never be forced to eat gruel. You'll not be imprisoned and beaten bloody simply because you're a Jew. You'll always be free to be you. You'll have the best of life, all that your father and I can possibly give you.*

When little Moises reached the number fifty, he stopped counting. Today, he was more interested in the spoon with the emblem of an eagle sitting atop a crown. "That's *my* spoon," he declared.

"I used to feed you with it when you were a baby. But you're a big boy now."

The child nodded, not certain he liked that answer. Then he pleaded, "Tell me, Mommy. Tell me the story of the spoon and the mean people. And my grandfather."

Hinda took a deep breath, then intoned, "Once upon a time, I lived in a faraway land where very wicked people ruled. One day, for no good reason, they imprisoned me in a camp."

"Were you scared, Mommy?"

"I was petrified. It was not a nice place. It had mean Gestapo guards dressed in stiff uniforms. They gave me this spoon to eat with, but then they only served thin watery soup."

"I don't like watery soup," little Moises exclaimed, his face scrunched into an expression of disgust. "I like soup you cook. It's thick. Mommy, tell about being hungry."

"Given crumbs to eat, I was so hungry that my stomach hurt terribly, even at night when I was trying to sleep." With little effort, Hinda conjured a pained expression, as if she were reliving it. "These mean people mistreated millions of others who were like me and my family, people who went to synagogue to worship God. One day, the bad guys attacked your grandfather, my tatae, Salomon Mondlak. He was a devout and wonderful man, like your tatae is. Before your grandfather died, he made a promise to me. He said, "Hinda, I *know* for sure that *you will live* through this unjust persecution, and *you will tell*."

"Tell what?"

"Someday, when you're older, my sweet son, I'll tell you the full story of how I suffered but survived, just as Grandfather Salomon said that I would."

"Why?"

Placing the spoon back on the tray, Hinda explained, "First, I want you to know, my sweet boy, that there are tons more good people in the world than there are mean, bad ones. When good people hear stories like mine, they then want to do their part to stop such badness from ever happening again. That's why I want to fulfill the promise my tatae made and tell the world what awful things happened to me, my family, and millions of other innocent people."

Little Moises turned to his abacus. Sliding the colorful balls across the wire, he said, "When I'm bigger, Mommy, I will help you."

Baby Sara clapped her hands together, her sign for *more*. Gripping the spoon, Hinda heaped thick pureed green peas onto it and fed her little daughter. Before Hinda could take her hand away, Sara reached for her mother's ring, grabbing at it. The diamond sparkled brightly in the sunlight from the nearby row of windows, which overlooked a common's area where hot-pink bougainvillea bloomed.

At the moment that Sara grabbed at the diamond, the family's newly adopted cat brushed against Hinda's leg, which sparked a memory of another diamond and another cat. Transported back to Auschwitz, specifically the warehouse named Canada, Hinda felt the weight of the large diamond in her pocket as she sought out a guard amenable to trading it for food. Shifting in her chair, Hinda remembered how the grass had tickled her legs as Rachel and she sat in the field licking the bones of the animal they had just eaten, meat protein that was not rabbit. Rachel, her dear sister, her best friend and soul mate, still did not know what they had eaten that day. And not just ate, but devoured, because they had been reduced to behaving like animals, ravenous, starving ones.

Returning to the present, Hinda's eyes fastened onto the face of her son, then her daughter—beautiful, healthy children she feared she could never have. She thought of Wolf, her devoted and wonderful husband, forever her lover and protector. Breathing in gratitude, her hand fluttered to her bosom where it felt as if her heart, with its every beat, cascaded rose petals, pumping love through her veins. Her neck swiveled; her eyes roved around the fully furnished room, so unlike the empty, old mill in the Mława ghetto, and so unlike the pest-ridden, miserable bunk at Auschwitz. She took in the abundance, the comfort, the health, the beauty, and the peace—all the goodness that surrounded her now.

Fingering the underside of the spoon's handle, Hinda traced the eagle and crown, the symbol of the Third Reich. She whispered, "Though I will never forget, *I have triumphed.*"

A victorious feeling surged, reverberating through her. The triumphant sensation coaxed her lips into a jubilant smile. Hinda laughed, softly at first. Then an uncontrollable laughter burst forth from her depths, from her very soul. Little Moises jumped up from the floor, giggling and dancing around his mother. Baby Sara clapped her hands, squealing with delight.

Hinda laughed and laughed, so merrily that her russet tresses jiggled, and joyful tears flooded her eyes of azure.

Sunbeams

December 1952 | Mexico City, Mexico

Saturday's sun shone brightly as the Goldman family approached the entry to their local synagogue. Wolf carried little Moises. Hinda cradled baby Sara who slept.

The sun's rays glinted against the temple's roofline in such a way that the radiating beams appeared as flames. Hinda gasped. She halted. Transported back to Zieluń, Poland, she stood alongside her father watching fiery fingers spiking high into the sky, reaching heavenward, even though the fire had been ignited by evil. Fear shook her soul. The ground trembled under her feet moments before the roof and walls of her family's synagogue crashed downward, crumbling with loud cracks that echoed in her ears.

Hinda felt an arm come around her shoulder, hugging her close. It was not her father's arm, which had held her when she was eighteen years old and had watched her shtetl's temple turn to rubble. Hinda's eyes moved upward to the face of her husband, who gazed at her with deep concern. Wolf's arm around her shoulder, plus his powerful hand gripping her upper arm, had transported her back to the present, where she was thirty-one years old and was safe and at peace, living in Mexico City.

Awestruck, Hinda blinked repetitively as she stared with wonder. The sunbeams no longer appeared as flames. They flickered on the synagogue's roof as if they were rays of glory.

The Afterword

The Afterword — The Family

Hinda Mondlak Goldman

A devoted wife and mother, Hinda fiercely loved her family. Her two children —Moises and Sara—were the lights of her life, along with Wolf and her sister, Rachel. Hinda and Wolf were married thirty-nine years, until her death on May 5, 1985. She and Rachel maintained their extraordinary bond, their homes mere streets apart. They even vacationed together. Hinda was active in social circles of their Jewish community and the Israeli embassy.

The day following her sixty-fourth birthday, Hinda died of cancer in the arms of her son, Moises. In the months before she passed away, she recorded eleven audio tapes—speaking primarily in Spanish and Yiddish—telling of her father's prophetic letter, her torture at the hands of the Nazis, her escape from Auschwitz, and her subsequent survival. This book is based on those tapes, which were transcribed by her son, Moises. In the final recording, Hinda mentioned her love and appreciation for Mexico, the land where she found her peace.

In 1961, the Israeli embassy in Mexico City, where Hinda volunteered her services, proposed that Hinda give testimony against Adolph Eichmann, a top official in the Third Reich, and cite all that she endured and witnessed at Auschwitz. Her husband, Wolf, objected, pleading that Hinda not suffer the stress of being deposed or testifying. Although Hinda yearned to be part of condemning such malevolence, in the end, she decided to preserve her peace and her family's happiness. A year later, it was a great relief to her to learn of Eichmann's conviction and subsequent execution.

According to the Auschwitz-Birkenau archives, there were less than two hundred (200) documented, successful "prisoner escapes" from Auschwitz-Birkenau. *Successful* escape was defined as prisoners who went on to be free, not being recaptured or killed. Most of that number were men. Hinda and Rachel's victorious escape was truly remarkable.

All who knew Hinda were inspired by her beauty, her acute instincts, and her bold and courageous spirit.

Wolf Yoskowitz / Samuel Goldman

A talented businessman, Wolf built two extraordinarily successful companies in Mexico City, a clothing manufacturing business and a construction company —his dream to own and operate a business doubly fulfilled. In the clothing business, Wolf had accounts such as Sears & Roebucks; he manufactured garments for their catalogues and retail stores. Two of Hinda's brothers, Shio and Leon, owned a major textile company, and Wolf purchased fabrics from them. Another brother, Zalel, was one of the suppliers for buttons and zippers.

Only Wolf's family and close friends called him by the name of Wolf. His employees, customers, and the general public knew him strictly as Samuel Goldman.

Wolf made frequent trips to Israel to see his brother, Joseph, and his sister, Erna. He helped maintain both of them financially throughout the remainder of their lives.

In the early years after the war, Wolf was adamant about not speaking about his time at Buchenwald and the heinous horrors that he endured. It was only after Hinda passed away that he began to open up to his daughter, Sara, about the monstrous abuse he had suffered.

Wolf vehemently declined all reparation money offered by the German government to Holocaust survivors. And he refused to purchase *any* German-made goods, not a car or even a pen.

Wolf continued his daily strengthening exercises, never forgetting the time he was incapacitated. His favorite exercise was swimming. Whenever possible, he swam in the strong tides of the ocean, which he loved.

Just as Wolf promised Hinda when he proposed to her in 1946, he took incredible care of her, seeing to it that she had everything she needed, and then beyond—what she wanted. Hinda was his queen to her last breath.

A devoted husband and father, Wolf was also devout in the practice of his Jewish faith. He died on December 27, 2003. His tombstone was inscribed with the name, *Wolf Goldman*. Underneath, written in Hebrew, was the name *Zev Ben Moshe Yoskowitz*. Zev is Hebrew for Wolf. Moshe was Wolf's father's first name, and normally, the Hebrew phrase *Zev Ben Moshe* (Wolf, Son of Moshe) would have been inscribed. Wolf insisted upon adding his birth surname of Yoskowitz.

Moises Julian Goldman

At the age of seventeen, Moises left home to attend university in the United States. And that he did—three different higher-learning institutions, located from coast to coast. Moises' father, Wolf, desperately wanted his son to join him in the operations of the garment manufacturing and construction businesses, but Moises' passion to study engineering could not be quelled. He began at the University of Houston, where he received two degrees, a BS in Electrical Engineering in 1971 and a Master of Electrical Engineering in 1973. Moises was then awarded a scholarship to pursue a doctorate from NATO AGARD (Advisory Group for Aerospace Research and Development). In 1976, he received a PhD in Systems Engineering and Inertial Navigation Systems (Aeronautics) from UCLA, (the University of California, Los Angeles).

Moises held executive positions in aerospace leaders, Lockheed and Rockwell. During that time, he studied at MIT (Massachusetts Institute of Technology), where he earned an MBA in 1984. An executive in diverse industries, Moises was a board member of MIT Engineering Systems Division for nine years and an advisory board member of MIT Institute of Data, Systems, and Society.

Moises and his beautiful wife, Terry, reside in Austin, Texas, and his son, Josh, lives in a nearby metropolis. Moises is a member of Congregation Agudas Achim, a synagogue in Austin.

To this day, Moises wears his mother's fourteen-karat white gold wedding ring on a chain around his neck along with a Star of David. With the publication of this book, Moises has fulfilled his mother's dying wish, coming full circle to the promise Hinda's father made to her: You will live, and you will tell.

Sara Goldman

A registered nurse, Sara worked in the health care industry for numerous years. Later, she was the primary caregiver for her mother and her father through their becoming ill to their respective deaths. Sara's father, Wolf, begged her to work with him in the garment manufacturing business after Moises, her brother, was advancing his career as an aerospace scientist in the United States. Sara contributed significantly to the success of that company, much to her father's delight. Sara has one son, Jonathan, and three grandchildren who reside in California. Sara's oldest grandchild, Ayala (Hebrew for Hinda), is named after her great-grandmother. Currently, Sara maintains homes in Mexico City and California.

Jack Mondlak

A political journalist and prolific writer, Jack spoke multiple languages and traveled in high-profile and sophisticated circles. The father of two children— Liora and Drori—Jack passed away in 2013 at the age of ninety-six. All of Hinda's brothers, who immigrated from Poland in 1933 and did not suffer the brutalities of the Holocaust, lived to old ages. Fanny, who immigrated to New York at the same time as her brothers went to Mexico City, lived past one hundred years old. In contrast, Hinda died at sixty-four years, and Rachel at fifty-one.

Aizik Shatz

While attending the University of London, Aizik met a lovely woman, whom he married. After earning his master's degree, Aizik and his wife made their home in London where he worked for an international company. Aizik could not sire offspring, due to Dr. Josef Mengele mutilating his genitals when he was at Auschwitz. Yet he enjoyed being the father of two adopted children. Hinda's second cousin on her maternal side, Aizik stayed in touch with Hinda and Rachel and celebrated their success. In her tapes, Hinda never mentioned Aizik's last name, and her family cannot verify it. The surname of *Shatz* was used fictitiously.

Rachel Mondlak Sochazewski

The mother of two boys—Salomon and Jaime—Rachel became an acclaimed artist. Her paintings, with titles such as *Birds on Fire*, often reflected the torment she endured during World War II. Rachel and David's oldest son, Salomon, was born with cerebral palsy. The doctors speculated that the boy's condition was due to a difficult birth, plus the toxic effects of chemicals that Rachel was exposed to at Auschwitz, along with her suffering years of life-threatening malnutrition. Rachel and David were married thirty years, until Rachel passed away in February of 1978. At the age of fifty-one, Rachel died from liver cancer. She predeceased her older sister, Hinda, by seven years.

The Spoon

In December of 1942, a spoon was issued to Hinda at Auschwitz. She kept it through all her travails and travels. Unbeknownst to Wolf, Hinda fed both of their children with it when they were babies. For her, it was healing to use the spoon to scoop up thick, nutritious food for Moises and Sara, who she prayed would never starve or be under the dominion of cruel, hateful people. The spoon's underside handle is stamped with the official motif of the German government under Hitler's reign, the Nazi eagle sitting atop a crown. Manufactured by the German company, Kriegsmarine, the spoon sported multiple markings, such as the letters ROSTFREI, which indicated it was made from an alloy, of steel and chromium, that resisted rust. Hinda's daughter, Sara Goldman, is still in possession of *the spoon* today.

The Afterword — The Nazi Regime

Otto Adolph Eichmann

One of the major organizers of the Holocaust, Otto Adolph Eichmann was responsible for facilitating and managing the logistics for moving millions of innocent European Jews from their homes into ghettos and concentration camps. In 1941, the Nazi party's Jewish policy changed from one of "deportation" to one of "extermination." This engendered the document, *The Final Solution*, which meant that Eichmann then organized and facilitated mass murders. He coordinated logistics for the gas chambers and the crematoriums for all camps.

One of Eichmann's deputies, Dieter Wisliceny, testified at the Nuremberg trials that Eichmann told him he would "leap laughing into the grave because the feeling of having five million people on his conscience was for him a source of extraordinary satisfaction."

Upon Germany's defeat in 1945, Eichmann was captured by US forces but later escaped. In disguise, he moved about varying locations around Germany. In 1950, Eichmann moved to Argentina using false papers obtained through an organization directed by Catholic Bishop Alois Hudal. In 1960, a team of agents from Israel's Intelligence Agency, the Mossad, and Israel's Security Agency, Shin Bet, captured Eichmann and brought him to stand trial in Israel. He was indicted on fifteen criminal charges that included war crimes, crimes against the Jewish people, and crimes against humanity. Eichmann did not deny the Holocaust or his role in it. He was found guilty on all charges and executed by hanging on June 1, 1962.

Heinrich Himmler

The main architect of the Holocaust, Heinrich Himmler was one of the most powerful men in all of Nazi Germany. Known as Adolph Hitler's right-hand man, Himmler was initially responsible for the building of the concentration camps and then the extermination facilities. While overseeing the genocidal programs, Himmler was responsible for staggering numbers of murders: some six million Jews, hundreds of thousands of Romanis, known as Gypsies (some reports claim as many as 500,000), and thousands of other victims, such as the mentally ill, homosexuals, Jehovah's Witnesses, and political objectors.

Realizing Germany was losing the war, Himmler attempted to open peace talks with the Allied forces without first informing or seeking permission from

Hitler. When Hitler discovered Himmler's betrayal, Hitler ordered him arrested in early April of 1945. Himmler escaped but was then captured by British Forces. While in British custody, Himmler committed suicide on May 23, 1945.

Adolph Hitler

The evil dictator and mastermind of the Holocaust, Adolph Hitler took his own life by gunshot on April 30, 1945 when the Soviets closed in on the bunker where he was hiding.

Rudolph Höss

Auschwitz camp commandment, Rudolph Höss, was discovered in hiding in northern Germany and arrested by the British in March of 1946. He was taken to Nuremberg to testify for the defense in the trial of another top Third Reich official. Höss was forthcoming about his role in the mass murders, saying he was following orders of Heinrich Himmler. Höss' trial, held before the Supreme National Tribunal in Warsaw, opened in March of 1947. He was sentenced to death on April 2 and then hanged two weeks later, on April 16, in Auschwitz, near the crematorium.

On the day of his execution, Höss wrote a letter to his children, saying: "*The biggest mistake of my life was to believe everything faithfully which came from the top, and I didn't dare to have the least bit of doubt about the truth of that which was presented to me.*"

The original affidavit of Höss' handwritten and signed confession is displayed in the Holocaust Memorial Museum in Washington, DC.

Dr. Josef Mengele

Known as the Angel of Death, Mengele has been dubbed as one of the most villainous and notorious Nazis. His heinous human experiments were performed in the name of eradicating inferior genes and creating an Aryan-German super-race. Mengele was never captured or brought to trial. He left Auschwitz mid-January 1945, shortly before the Red Army invaded and freed the camp. He then lived in disguise as a farmhand in an area near his native Günzburg until 1949. At that time, he fled to Argentina and later moved to Brazil. In 1979, Mengele purportedly drowned in a lake accident. In 1995, using evolved DNA technology, the remains buried in Brazil proved to be those of the monstrous doctor.

Hermann Pister

The second commandant of Buchenwald concentration camp, Pister was known as one of the most sadistic commanders. He replaced Karl Otto Koch in January 1942. He remained at Buchenwald until he was captured and arrested by American forces in 1945. Famous for his brutality to prisoners, Pister designed games, such as *The Singing Horses,* to further torture innocent slave laborers, such as Wolf and Joseph Yoskowitz.

In 1947, Pister was brought to trial by the American Military Tribunal in Dachau. He was tried for committing war crimes and violations of the Laws and Usages of War set by the Hague Convention in 1907, as well as violation of the Third Geneva Convention of 1929. Pister was found guilty on all counts and was sentenced to death by hanging. He died from an acute heart attack in his prison cell in September of 1948, days prior to the fulfillment of his execution orders.

Other Auschwitz References

Richard Baer

The third commandant of Auschwitz, Baer died of a heart attack while in detention before he went to trial.

Victor Capesius

The head pharmacist at Auschwitz, who worked closely with Dr. Mengele, was captured and released numerous times. At one point, using the gold he had stolen from Auschwitz (inmates' teeth and confiscated jewelry), he opened a pharmacy and a beauty parlor. Finally, in 1959, Capesius was arrested and held in custody without bail or bond. In 1965, he was indicted in the Frankfurt Auschwitz Trials and was sentenced to nine years in prison. Adept at refuting evidence and lying about his role in the mass murders, he served only two and one-half years.

Franz Hössler

The Auschwitz women's camp director was hanged for war crimes.

Arthur Liebehenschel

The second commander of Auschwitz (following Rudolph Hoss) Liebehenschel was tried before the Supreme National Tribunal in Warsaw. He was convicted and sentenced to death.

Maria Mandel

The Auschwitz women's camp supervisor was tried and sentenced to death at the Supreme National Tribunal in Warsaw.

Dr. Hans Munch

A doctor at Auschwitz, he was the only principal staff member to be acquitted.

Tesch & Stabenow

The owners of this Zyklon B manufacturing company were both executed for knowingly supplying the toxic chemical for use on humans.

Dr. Eduard Wirths

The Auschwitz chief camp physician was captured by the Allies in 1945. Wirths committed suicide, days before his upcoming trial.

Nazi-Regime Statistics

Six million Jews were murdered in the Holocaust. That reflects the number of those accounted for and does not include the millions who were persecuted and displaced.

When the United States Holocaust Memorial Museum first began to document the Nazi camps across Europe, researchers expected to find approximately seven thousand. Instead, they found evidence of 42,500 Nazi camps and ghettos existing between the years of 1933 and 1945. Included in this number are 1,150 Jewish ghettos; 980 concentration camps; 30,000 slave labor camps; 1,000 prisoner-of-war camps; 500 brothels filled with sex slaves; thousands of other camps used for slaughtering the ill and the elderly and as killing centers for mass murders; and hundreds more as training camps to indoctrinate camp staff, instilling hatred for Jews and others deemed undesirable.

In Poland—Hinda, Rachel, and Wolf's homeland—it is estimated that three million Polish Jews were killed, which equals a whopping ninety percent of the country's prewar Jewish population.

The estimated total killed by the Nazi regime nears *fourteen million people.*

Ongoing Effects upon
Hinda, Wolf, Rachel, and David

Immensely grateful for their survival, for their very lives, and their freedom, Hinda, Wolf, Rachel, and David enjoyed success and joyous moments after settling in Mexico City. Yet the fear of being unjustly targeted and persecuted again, merely because they were Jews, never left them. Except for occasional events, both couples maintained low profiles, living, working, and socializing within the bounds of the large Jewish community in Mexico City.

Each one of these four lived with deep, psychological scars from the inhumane, debasing atrocities they suffered while subsisting under the reign of villainous Nazis.

Facts and Fiction

Sources for Facts

- Audio tapes recorded by Hinda Mondlak Goldman
- Auschwitz Archives *Auschwitzarchives.org*
- Buchenwald Memorial Archives, *Documents from the SS administration of the concentration camp; Public Papers buchenwald.de/en/*
- Eisenhower Presidential Library *eisenhowerlibrary.gov*
- Encyclopedia Britannica *britannica.com*
- Günzburg City Hall *Historical Data, Visitor Information*
- NARA (The National Archives and Records Administration) *archives.gov/research/holocaust*
- United States Holocaust Memorial Museum *encyclopedia.ushmm.org*
- Yad Vashem, The World Holocaust Remembrance Center in Israel *yadvashem.org*

Auschwitz Commanders, Directors, and Supervisors

Names used for all commanders, directors, and supervisors are factual. Dialogue associated with these characters is a re-creation. *Fact:* **Rudolph Höss** served as commander of Auschwitz Concentration Camp from May 4, 1940 to November 1943. *Fact:* **Franz Hössler**, Nazi SS officer served as women's camp director, at times, and also worked other commands. *Fact:* **Arthur Liebehenschel** served as commander of Auschwitz from November 1943 to May 1944. *Fact:* **SS Major Richard Baer** served as commander from mid-May 1944 to January 1945. *Fact:* **Maria Mandel** served as Auschwitz women's camp supervisor. She created the women's orchestra to fullfill Hitler's request for a propaganda film from the women's camp.

Auschwitz Doctors and Pharmacists

Names used for doctors and pharmacists are factual with the exception of the surname, Zeilhofen. Dialogue associated with these characters is a re-creation. *Fact:* **Victor Capesius** served as head pharmacist at Auschwitz from December 1943 to January 1945. *Fact:* **Dr. Josef Mengele**, a Nazi Schutzstaffel (SS) officer, began his official duties at Auschwitz on May 30, 1943, and he was there until mid-January of 1945. He intentionally fled before the Soviets arrived late January

1945. *Fact:* **Dr. Eduard Wirths**, a Nazi SS officer, served at Auschwitz as chief camp physician from 1942 to 1945. *Fact:* **Dr. Walter Zeilhofen**, a German doctor at Auschwitz, treated Hinda for malaria, saving her life. He gave her curative medications, which defied policy. In Hinda's tapes, she indicates that Dr. Walter fell in love with her; she describes the encouraging notes he sent to her. After Hinda's escape from Auschwitz, she was informed, by an eyewitness, that Dr. Walter had been hanged for treason. Hinda does not mention Walter's last name. The surname of Zeilhofen was selected at random.

Auschwitz Orchestra and Choir

Names used for orchestra directors are factual. The name for the choir director was fictional, but the character was factual. Dialogue associated with these characters is a re-creation. *Fact:* **Zofia Czajkowska**, Polish musician and political prisoner at Auschwitz, served as the first conductor of the women's orchestra, and she later assisted conductor Alma Rosé. *Fact:* **Elisa Gaensel** is a fictional name for the Jewish choir director at Auschwitz. According to archived records, the informal choir did perform with the orchestra, at times. The choir director was identified as a young woman in her twenties, which matches the information in Hinda's tapes. Hinda reported that she was forced to go to the square late at night to view the mutilated body of the director after Dr. Josef Mengele had performed experiments and an autopsy on her. *Fact:* **Alma Rosé**, a Jewish Austrian violinist and conductor, served as conductor of the women's orchestra at Auschwitz from August 1943 to April 1944, when she suddenly died.

Auschwitz and Buchenwald Guards and Wardens

Fact: Guards and wardens were required to undergo Nazi indoctrination programs where they were incited to hate Jews, anyone considered a societal misfit or genetically inferior, and political resistors to the Nazi regime. **Fact:** Commander Rudolph Höss visited a penitentiary near Munich and selected one hundred felons, all robust German women, to work at Auschwitz as guards and wardens.

Buchenwald Concentration Camp

Dialogue associated with these characters is a re-creation. *Fact:* **General Dwight D. Eisenhower**, an American general who served as Supreme Commander of the Allied Expeditionary Force in Europe during World War II, was instrumental in freeing Buchenwald prisoners, including Wolf and Joseph

Yoskowitz. On April 12, 1945, one day after the US Sixth Armored Division, from the American Third Army, invaded Buchenwald Concentration Camp, General Eisenhower visited the camp, along with General George Patton and army officer Omar Bradley. After touring the camp, General Eisenhower's words in this story regarding the inhumane brutality he witnessed at Buchenwald are paraphrased, with the meaning retained, from a speech he gave the following week. Later, General Eisenhower wrote this about Buchenwald: "Nothing has ever shocked me as much as that sight." *Fact:* **Hermann Pister** served as commander of Buchenwald Concentration Camp from January 1942 to April 1945, the years that Wolf and Joseph Yoskowitz were interred there.

Hinda, Rachel, and the Mondlak Family

Dialogue associated with these characters is often a direct quote from Hinda's tapes and, at times, is a re-creation. *Fact:* The Mondlak family's valuables were confiscated—packed, crated, and moved from their home—by Nazi soldiers on orders from the Third Reich. *Fact:* Joel was arrested by the soldiers on the day the home in Zieluń was raided. Two years later, he showed up at the mill, a broken man. He made the journey to Auschwitz with Hinda, Rachel, and Sara. After the Selection process, Joel was never seen again. *Fact:* In September of 1939, the Mondlak family and all Polish Jews were commanded to publicly wear a white armband with a blue, six-pointed star affixed to it. Identifying them as Jews, the compulsory armband limited where they could go and what they could buy. At Auschwitz, Hinda and Rachel wore uniforms with a badge consisting of an inverted red triangle (political prisoner designation) overlapped by a yellow triangle (Jew designation) which together created a six-pointed star. *Fact:* At gunpoint, the Mondlak family was coerced from their rightful home in Zieluń and hauled to the Mława ghetto, where they lived in an abandoned mill with no kitchen and no furniture. *Fact:* The Third Reich government issued a *ration card* to Mława ghetto residents that entitled families to obtain provisions (bread, potatoes, and one other vegetable daily), up to three hundred calories a day, per family member. *Fact:* Hinda sneaked through the ghetto gates, seeking work to obtain extra food for her family. In exchange for food, she worked for a Polish woman, five days a week for nine months, before she was caught and sent to jail. *Fact:* Hinda was imprisoned in the Mława jail for six months, from April 1941 to September 1941. *Fact:* Hinda sneaked through the ghetto gates and traded her best sweater for three cans of sardines at the Mława train station, which was heavily guarded by Gestapo. *Fact:* Amidst chaos during the Selection process at Auschwitz, Hinda seized opportunity and boldly moved Rachel into her line. *Fact:* Hinda and Rachel endured numerous, life-threatening beatings while at Auschwitz. *Fact:* The sisters labored at multiple Auschwitz workstations, including Budy vegetable fields, Canada, the Sola River, the guards' laundry, the SS' laundry, the guard's kitchen, and the corpse warehouse. *Fact:* Hinda traded a diamond for food when working in the warehouse named Canada. The guard agreed to bring a cooked rabbit. Due to the animal's body shape, Hinda believed that he brought a cooked cat instead. *Fact:* Sara was extremely ill prior to going to Auschwitz. Still coughing, she was assigned to the outermost line during the Selection process. Typically, the elderly, the ill, the disabled, and children too young to work were placed in that line and then sent directly to the gas chambers. *Fact:* The sisters' experiences described throughout this story are factual according to Hinda's tapes. This includes, but is not limited to, Hinda suffering malaria, other serious conditions, and diseases (likely hepatitis); Rachel's desire to throw herself on the fence; the details of their escape from Auschwitz; their various living quarters after escape; life at the Jewish compound in Wrocław; the telegrams; Hinda's love for Walter and her grief upon learning of his death; Hinda and Wolf's wedding; Hinda's miscarriage; their travels with Jack Mondlak.

Miscellaneous

Annie–Fact: In her tapes, Hinda spoke about Annie, who was her childhood friend from Zieluń. A violinist, Annie played in the Austrian Symphony Orchestra before the war, and then in the orchestra at Auschwitz.

Auschwitz Main Gate–Fact: On Third Reich orders, the gate was made by Polish prisoners from one of the first transports. The German words, *ARBEIT MACHT FREI* (Work Will Set You Free), were forged by prisoners in the metalworkers' labor detail. It is believed that the imprisoned workers deliberately turned the letter *B* upside down in the word *ARBEIT* as a camouflaged act of disobedience. Later, the upside down *B* was replaced with an upright one. The Auschwitz Museum has since restored the gates to include the upside down *B*.

Buchenwald Zoo–Fact: The zoo was intentionally placed near the prisoner roll call area by Ilse Koch (wife of the first commandant of Buchenwald). Her intent was to taunt the abused and starved prisoners with the abundance and quality of the animals' food and the tenderness in which the staff cared for the animals.

Bromide–Fact and Fiction: Many Holocaust survivors believed that bromide was used in the concentration camps to halt women's menses and to reduce sexual urges in men. Although it was widely rumored to be true, in the end, no "conclusive" evidence was documented during the Nuremberg trials. Medical experts claim that the starvation and severe malnutrition the internees suffered would have had the same effects.

Burning of Books and Synagogues–Fact: Decrees to burn Jewish books and synagogues in German-occupied Poland were issued by Hitler between 1939 and 1942. In her tapes, Hinda spoke of the horror of watching her family's synagogue burn. In addition, she discussed the torment of seeing her father's personal library desecrated, along with the sacred texts from the yeshiva that Salomon had tried to save. According to Hinda's tapes, Gestapo forced her father, at gunpoint, to pour gasoline onto the books and to personally ignite the fire.

Bus to Siberia–Fact: In her tapes, Hinda said the Soviets accused Rachel and her of being German spies. The sisters were arrested at the Olmoses' home and incarcerated by the Soviets for three days, and then ordered to board a bus to Siberia. Hinda boldly asked to speak to the highest officer in command. Her request granted, Hinda was interrogated for hours by a Russian commander before he released Rachel and her. They narrowly escaped a *life-long* sentence in a Siberian labor camp.

Church of Our Lady–Fact: Located in Günzburg, Germany, the historic rococo-style Church of Our Lady was designed and built by German architect and stuccoist, Dominikus Zimmermann during the years of 1735 to 1740.

Document–The Final Solution: The Questions of the Jews–Fact: The Nazi regime, under the direction of Himmler, created a written document (entitled exactly as above) that explicitly mapped out mass genocide of European Jews. Their broader intention was to execute this plan on a global basis, invading other countries and exterminating Jews, worldwide.

Dutka Family–Fact and Fiction: Based on the fact that the Yoskowitz family owned and operated a flour mill that delivered flour to bakeries in Gliwice, the

Dutka family served as a fictitious tool to support Wolf's survival before he was captured and sent to Buchenwald. It was a fact that Wolf worked in the mill and delivered flour to bakeries and other customers as early as ten years of age; yet, little was known of exactly how Wolf survived the in-between years. It's true that part of Wolf's family, including Joseph, hid in the woods for months. And it is factual that both Wolf and Joseph were interned at Buchenwald concentration camp.

Another key role the Dutka characters fulfilled was to shed light on the fact that, after the German occupation of Poland, the Third Reich government confiscated farm property from even non-Jewish families. The government then moved in German families, all in the name of instilling the German culture in Poland.

Elderly Couple–Fact: After being forced from the Olmoses' home, Hinda and Rachel stayed with an elderly couple in a small house located in a rural area. Details in the story about the couple and what happened to the sisters there, including members of the German army and the International Red Cross unexpectedly showing up and working from that home, are factual according to Hinda's tapes.

Eleonore Hodys–Fact: A political prisoner at Auschwitz, Hodys became pregnant while having an affair with Commander Rudolph Höss. According to Hodys' testimony in the Nuremburg trials, she underwent a forced, late-term abortion, performed in the officer's hospital, immediately upon release from her arrest in the standing cell. She stated that she narrowly escaped the gas chambers.

Esther's Death–Fact: Esther died in the Mława ghetto hospital after fainting in the street when looking for Hinda. According to Hinda's tapes, Esther fell upon a rock and cracked her sternum. This transpired on the day that Hinda was jailed. Later, Hinda went back to Mława to find her mother's grave and only found a wheat field. She carried immense guilt, believing she caused her mother's death.

Gerda–Fact: A warden at Auschwitz, Gerda told Hinda that she was a convicted felon who was released from a penitentiary in Munich to work as a policewoman at Auschwitz. Hinda mentions Gerda in her tapes and admits that she readily lied to her about being trained in cosmetology and massage therapy. Gerda transferred the sisters to work in the kitchen, and Hinda and Rachel gave Gerda massages and mock facials.

Golda of the Sosnowiec Refugee Center–Fact: Golda was a resident and employee of the Refugee Center located in Sosnowiec. She readily accepted Hinda and Rachel into her living quarters and treated them both with exceptional kindness. In the tapes, Hinda called Golda their real-life, red-haired angel.

Haim (Uncle Haim)–Fact and Fiction: In Hinda's tapes, she spoke about the Jewish compound in Wrocław where Rachel and she found a safe home. Hinda described the man who headed the compound as incredibly generous and kind. Working for the Soviet Secret Police, he employed young Jewish men who also lived at the compound. The name Haim is fictitious.

Hangings of Mali and Gelden–Fact: In her recordings, Hinda relayed how it affected her emotionally to watch Auschwitz prisoners, Mali and Gelden, die after their attempt to escape. Gelden hanged; Mali died by self-inflicted knife wounds. Hinda said that, surprisingly and ironically, when watching their deaths, her instincts spoke to her, creating a strong desire within her to attempt escape.

Helga–Fact: Hinda met Helga at Auschwitz; they were Block mates and became close friends. Fully aware that Helga was a professional ballerina, Josef Mengele removed three of Helga's toes. Her foot became infected, and Mengele sent her to the gas chambers. Hinda was devastated by Helga's mutilation and death.

Meliks–Fact: After their escape, Hinda and Rachel stayed in the attic of the Melik home, where they slept on seed sacks. Hinda presumed that to ensure the sisters departed at the one-week mark, Mr. Melik turned them in to Gestapo Officer Olmos.

Mengele and the Viking Division–Fact and Fiction: Josef Mengele served in the SS's Viking Division from mid-June of 1940 to January of 1943. Some sources state that he served the term without interruption. Others state that he was in and out multiple times. This book embraced the latter and compressed time to have him return in October of 1942 instead of January of 1943.

Mława Ghetto–Fact: Polish Jews were interned in the Mława Ghetto from 1939-1942. The information in Hinda's tapes of her family being forced to live in squalor there corresponds with historical data.

Olmoses–Fact: According to Hinda's tapes, Officer Olmos and his wife harbored Hinda and Rachel in their home for seven weeks. The sisters stayed in the room where the Olmoses' son kept white doves. Hinda witnessed Mrs. Olmos being raped by Russian soldiers. As Hinda reports it, it's true that Officer Olmos appeared semi-catatonic at that time, constantly repeating Heil Hitler salutes. Hinda and Rachel never learned what happened to the couple. For the second time, the sisters stayed in the Olmoses' house, and they were there until the Soviets arrested them for allegedly being German spies.

Song–Fact: *"Westerwaldlied,"* the German Marching Song – Lyrics: Willi Münker; music: Joseph Neuhäuser; released 1937.

Soviet Officer from Czechoslovakia–**Fact:** Hinda spoke about this Jewish officer in her tapes and how he broke down and cried when she said the first verse of the Shema. He saved the sisters from suffering more brutality at that particular Soviet camp site.

Synagogue in Wrocław–Fact: According to the descriptions rendered in Hinda's tapes of the synagogue the sisters found in Wrocław when they first arrived there, it was war-riddled, but it had not been burned despite the decree from the Third Reich government. It is highly probable that it was the historic "White Stork Synagogue" dating back to the 1800s, which is documented to have eluded Nazi torches because of the dense development around it. The Jewish compound where Aizik, Hinda, and Rachel resided was attached to a synagogue, which points to the area's density.

Tatae's Letter–Fact: On the day that he was murdered by the Gestapo, Salomon Mondlak wrote a profound and prophetic letter to his daughter, Hinda. The Jewish Council of Mława intercepted the letter and kept it in their files. If not for a capo, a young man from Hinda's native village of Zieluń, Hinda would never have known about the letter. She did get to read it (as described in the story). Her father's words, *I know for certain, you will live, and you will tell,* were forever emblazoned on her heart and mind, fueling her will to live.

Acknowledgements

It is with a heart overflowing with gratitude that I thank Moises J. Goldman for trusting me to write his mother's astounding story. In addition, I sincerely appreciate Terry Goldman, Moises' wife, who was an enthusiastic cheerleader and an avid beta reader throughout this project.

Our deepest appreciation and most sincere thanks for the historical guidance of world-renowned Dr. Michael Berenbaum, a globally acknowledged expert on the Holocaust. Michael was the Director of the Holocaust Research Institute at the U.S. Holocaust Memorial Museum, as well as President and CEO of the Survivors of the Shoah Visual History Foundation. Michael is author and editor of twenty-four books, as well as Executive Editor of the Second Edition of the *Encyclopedia Judaica*. His work in film has won Academy Awards and Emmy Awards.

Thank you to my amazing husband, Stephen Maysonave, for being my sounding board and main support through this four-year process. He held my hand when I had nightmares and wept over the heinous atrocities and grievous losses that Hinda, Rachel and Wolf suffered. A diligent beta reader, Stephen was enormously helpful with the book's compendious research.

Multiple beta readers have added tremendous value. Shout-outs and hearty thanks to Lois Reiswig and Carla Meaux.

Heartfelt thanks to our publisher, Gordon McClellan, founder of DartFrog Books, and his exceptional team, especially Suanne Laqueur. And thank you to our expert editors, Lee Cart, DartFrog Books, and Stacey Miller, S. J. Miller Communications.

A huge thank you to Larry Jolly of Jolly Designs for creating the extraordinary book cover. Larry photographed Hinda's Auschwitz spoon to form the Star of David. This artful design represents a powerful and meaningful symbol of Hinda's faith and amazing triumph. For the book's beautiful interior design, we thank Rebecca Finkel, F + P Graph Design.

Thank you to Ted Wozniak who gave me an old-world Polish cookbook (his heritage) that was so helpful when writing about Polish food. We thank Ted for his service in the Thirtieth Infantry Division in the United States Army during World War II. Ted received the President's Award for extraordinary heroism when defending France against Germany in August of 1944.

Lastly, a sincere thank you to Sara Goldman, who provided superb details, especially regarding her father, Wolf, his life, and tribulations.

Writing this daunting and inspiring story has been an enriching experience. I heard Hinda whispering in my ear, felt Rachel perched on my shoulder, and sensed Wolf standing by my side.

Blessings to all who have contributed to this profound book,
Sherry Maysonave

Aspirations of Authors

Sherry Maysonave and Moises J. Goldman, PhD

Our ongoing prayer is for all people to be informed of the gross injustices that transpired during the Holocaust, and for all people to be fully aware of the panoptic perils of hate, of anti-Semitism, of racism, of genocide, and of apathy toward humankind.

Our deepest hope is that people, around the world, enjoy freedom and be willing to do their part to disallow mass injustices from ever happening again to any group of human beings.

Sherry Maysonave, who brought Hinda's story to life on the written page, is an award-winning author and acclaimed motivational speaker. Sherry has been interviewed by over two hundred television, radio, and print publications across the U.S., Canada, and Europe. This includes multiple appearances on NBC's *Today,* ABC, CBS, Fox, and NPR radio. Sherry has been featured in *USA Today, The Financial Times, The Wall Street Journal, The New Yorker, InStyle,* and *BusinessWeek.*

Hinda's son, **Moises J. Goldman, PhD,** translated and transcribed his mother's eleven audio tapes that were recorded in Yiddish and Spanish. Moises is an accomplished aerospace scientist, executive, and entrepreneur. He has served on boards at MIT and the Illinois Institute of Technology, Knapp Center for Entrepreneurship. He was a founding member of the Talent Program at the Illinois Math and Science Academy (I.M.S.A.).

For the Table of Contents and Book Club tools, go to TataesPromise.com

Hinda Mondlak Goldman

May 4, 1921 – May 5, 1985

Made in the USA
Columbia, SC
02 October 2023

23747488R00300